PREFACE

This volume is a comprehensive treatment in the technical and industrial field of woodworking. Wood is a material which has always been used extensively in the manufacturing, construction, transportation, and service industries. It offers outstanding opportunities in the ever-widening horizons of management and research.

Wood and the numerous by-products continue to gain prominence in the industrial area as a result of the many technological advances and recent concepts in its use. The material in this book is the result of an exhaustive survey of city and state educational courses of study and teaching plans, research in technical industrial materials, and conferences with technical personnel in the wood producing industries.

The contents are designed for use in high school industrial arts and vocational classes, post-high school technical courses, and college courses pertaining to wood processes and technology. Home craftsmen will also find extensive use of informative material.

The text is written in a vocabulary based on the reading level of high school students. Sentence and paragraph structure is designed to increase understanding and stimulate interest. New terms are explained, defined, and illustrated when first used.

A second color is used to accent illustrations, to indicate direction and action, and to emphasize significant points. Over 1500 photographs and line drawings show dynamically and realistically the vital activities and materials of industry. This is the most profusely illustrated, informative, and challenging text of its type in the field.

CHRIS H. GRONEMAN

EVERETT R. GLAZENER

ACKNOWLEDGMENTS

Sincere thanks is extended to the Adjustable Clamp Co.; Baker Furniture Company; The Black Brothers Co., Inc.; The Cleveland Twist Drill Company; DeWalt, Incorporated; dry Clime Lamp Corporation; The Franklin Glue Company; Greenlee Bros. & Co.; Heli-Coil Corporation; Minnesota Mining & Manufacturing Company; Porter-Cable Division, Rockwell Manufacturing Company; United States Department of Agriculture, Forest Service; and the United States Department of Agriculture for booklet No. 73, *Wood-Frame House Construction*.

Specific recognition of the many photographs, sketches, charts, and diagrams used in the sections dealing with hand and machine tools, finishing, and upholstery has not been cited for purposes of unity, continuity, simplicity, and clarity. In all other units, individual line courtesies have been given.

Special appreciation is due the following individuals who assisted directly in producing this volume: E. J. Auer, Clark Foam Products Company, special upholstery products and processes; Mrs. Betty Fisk Baily, Publicity Director, Drexel Furniture Company; Howard Berry, Director, Photographic and Visual Aids Laboratory, Texas A&M University; J. H. Bramley, Esq., Managing Director, Educational Productions Limited, Yorkshire, England, for material adapted from Paxton Lumber Company; Richard Campbell, Promotional Assistant, Millers Falls Company, for hand-tool photographs; Robert Campbell, Educational Director, Stanley Tools, for hand-tool photographs and building construction information; Franklyn E. Doan, Publications Director, The Seng Company, special photographs, diagrams, and charts; J. C. Glidewell, Bryan, Texas, photographer; Jay Helsel, California Pennsylvania State College, draftsman and illustrator for projects; officials of the Rockwell Manufacturing Company, P. F. Maxwell and E. L. Tabat, Vice Presidents; Dan Irvin, Director of Education, and John Greguric, Editor, of the Delta Power Tool Division for information and illustrative processes; W. F. Liggon, Sales Manager, Ozan Lumber Company, for automated lumbering photographs and processes; and Dean F. Sherman, Editor, *Forest Industries*, for special information on automated lumbering. Appreciative mention is also given Jeane Glazener and Virginia Groneman.

CONTENTS

SECTION
1

TECHNOLOGY OF WOODS

Unit 1 The Importance of Wood

Wood has always been one of man's most important resources. Directly and indirectly, in fact, it has been one of his basic necessities. For example, primitive man used wood to make fires and to make the clubs with which he could protect himself and hunt. His wooden hunting weapon brought meat to his fire and fur clothing for his body. Besides clothing himself with skins, he used them—again with wood—to make crude shelters. Those shelters that he did not make from wood and skins he made by weaving tree branches together.

But it was not until thousands of years later that he learned to make wooden houses. During these years he used wood for his tool handles and for his first machines, the lever and the wheel. Wood also provided his first means of transportation when he learned to make carts, wagons, canoes, and ships.

Throughout history, man has perfected ways to bend, carve, smooth, polish, stain, and paint wood, as well as to change its size, shape, and appearance to suit his needs and his ideas of beauty.

Forests as an Economic Necessity

Forests are a valuable world resource. They are the only natural resource capable of renewing themselves in a relatively short time. They prevent soil erosion caused by dust storms and water runoff from rains and melting snows. In addition, they furnish

1

1-1. Forests are sources of wood products.

(American Hardboard Association)

(American Forest Products Industries)

1-2. Wood is a principal export item.

shelter and protection for wildlife and provide recreation areas. They also beautify our country.

Forests also give the raw material for thousands of products (Fig. 1-1). Forest-products industries account for 10 percent of all manufacturing employment in the United States. They produce over $23 billion worth of goods annually.

Lumber production is one of our largest industries, and lumber is one of the United States principal exports (Fig. 1-2). An estimated 3,000 billion board feet of lumber have been processed since the year 1776.

Sawmills were in operation in America as early as 1610. From 1700 to 1892 the center of the lumber industry was in the eastern regions. From 1892 to 1909 the industry was most active in the Michigan-Wisconsin area. The period from 1909 to 1920 found the center of lumbering in an area from eastern Texas to the Atlantic Ocean. Since 1920 it has been in the northwestern states.

Millions of board feet of lumber are produced annually. There is sufficient sawtimber standing in the nation's forests to build a six-room house for every person in the United States, with lum-

ber left over. Lumber for modern homes (Figs. 1-3 and 1-4), other types of construction (Figs. 1-5, 1-6, and 1-7), and pulpwood for paper make life both more comfortable and more interesting. Wood helps insulate walls and makes them more pleasing to the eye, and it is the base product for many products that make life more pleasant.

Forest Products in Colonial America

The early explorers of North America saw the value of the vast forests. Timber was harvested and sent to Europe to be used for fuel, ships, furniture, and buildings. The first-known specific export item, other than timber, was a cargo of sassafras bark, gathered along the coasts of Maine and Massachusetts around the year 1603. Soon after, the best white pine logs were selected and sent to be used as ship masts. Companies were formed in England to send colonists to America. They were sent to harvest forest products and ship these cargoes to England.

Tar, pitch, and turpentine were produced from pines for shipbuilding and repair. Other products were clapboard

1-3. Lumber and wood constitute the principal materials for modern homes.

(National Homes)

2

lumber and wainscoting for outside walls and inside paneling of homes. Wood was burned to yield potash, used in making soap and glass.

Forests gave the early colonists, including those at Jamestown (1607 onward), the source of raw materials that were transformed into homes and useful furnishings. Figure 1-8 shows some typical hand tools used by the colonists. The Pilgrims at Plymouth, during the bitterly cold winters, used many layers of bark to make their huts or homes. Wooden boats were used for transportation and exploration. Indians

(California Redwood Association)

1-5. Oriental influence is shown in a uniquely constructed resort-area modern hotel.

1-6. U-arched laminated timbers make an interesting food-market structure.

(Unit Structures, Koppers Company, Inc)

(Weyerhaeuser Company)

1-7. Laminated wood arches spanning 208 feet will form the dome-shaped roof of an athletic fieldhouse.

1-8. Eighteenth- and nineteenth-century wooden hand tools.

(The L. V. Hawkins collection)

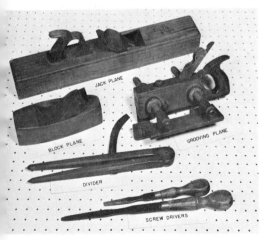

1-11. Fabricated wooden arches and beams form a modern structure.

(Southern Pine Association)

4

taught the Pilgrims how to make sugar and syrup from maple sap. They told them which nuts, fruits, berries, and greens were edible and how to make medicine from certain trees and shrubs.

Hemlock bark was used in tanning animal hides into leather. Colonial beverages included sassafras root bark tea, willow leaf tea, spruce beer, and elderberry wine. Spruce and pine gum were gathered to chew. Some bark and leaves provided dye for homemade clothing, food seasoning, ink (from galls on oak leaves), and a form of tobacco.

Until the twentieth century, most forest products were those from either the wood itself or its natural by-products. As we shall see, the technological developments in changing the form of wood have been significant in recent years.

Wood in the Twentieth Century

Wood resources are readily available. For this reason, man has used them into the twentieth century without considering their value and potential for forms other than their natural ones.

The chemical industry first used petroleum and coal deposits for basic sources of raw materials. It is now supplementing these by using forests as sources of supply for nitrocellulose, which is used in making such products

(Rayonier, Inc.)

1-9. Imitation leather products and decorative laminates are chemical creations from wood substances.

1-10. Cellophane and other food packaging materials are the result of chemical research in wood.

as dynamite, rayon, and phonograph records. Chemists are now experimenting with the composition and structure of wood and are developing new uses and products. Some typical by-products of this experimentation are imitation leather and plastic goods (Fig. 1-9), food packaging materials (Fig. 1-10), food flavoring, and cosmetics.

Before the middle of the twentieth century, many people thought that wood had reached its peak usefulness. However, research and technology are developing numerous fabrication techniques (Figs. 1-11 and 1-12), treatments, and means of breaking down the wood structure, revealing new uses for wood and its substances.

At least half of the wood harvested today goes into construction. Home building, paneling (Fig. 1-13), furniture (Fig. 1-14), shipping crates, newsprint paper, and other paper products are familiar uses.

Wood is also the basic material for many hobbies. Furniture construction (Figs. 1-15 and 1-16) done in the home workshop is useful and provides many hours of leisure-time pleasure. Recreational equipment made of wood enables us to enjoy many activities. Physical recreation includes the use of boats, baseball bats (Fig. 1-17), bows and arrows, and rifles (Fig. 1-18).

The remaining units in this section give additional information about forests and wood products.

(California Redwood Association)

1-13. **Redwood paneling and exposed beams beautify a home.**

1-14. **Modern wooden furniture adds warmth to home decoration. Note the Southern pine paneling.**

(Southern Pine Association)

1-12. **Laminated fir runners accentuate the curved stairway in a modern motel.**

(National Lumber Manufacturers Association)

(Howard Berry, Texas A&M University)

1-15. A cherry-wood tea wagon designed, adapted, and built by a home craftsman.

1-16. A specially adapted cherry-wood hutch cabinet.

(Howard Berry)

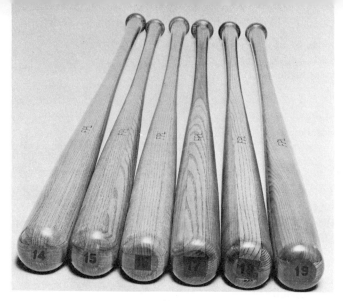

(American Forest Products Industries)

1-17. Laminated baseball bats made of a hickory core faced with ash.

1-18. Home craftsmen often make their own beautifully grained gunstocks.

(Forest Products Laboratory)

Unit 2 American Forests

There are over 775 million acres of forest land in the United States. This is about one-third the total land area. Almost 70 percent of these forests are commercial (approximately 535 million acres). National forests cover about 180 million acres of the total forest lands, with 95 million acres within them considered accessible and profitably usable. These are called **commercial.** The national forests are properly managed for timber production, recreation, watershed protection, and habitat (natural homes) for wildlife. For these reasons they are called **multiple-use forests.**

The remaining 240 million acres of the total forests, including some national ones, are called **noncommercial.** This acreage includes parks, rough mountains, wilderness areas that are not easily accessible, and swamps. The slow-growing interior forests of Alaska and the scattered areas of pinion pine and juniper in the Southwest are also noncommercial stands of timber.

American Continental Forests

The 50 states have 10 different forest regions (Fig. 2-1). Climate and elevation partially determine these areas. Continental forests are divided into 6 general areas: (1) West Coast, (2) Western, (3) Northern, (4) Central Hardwood, (5) Southern, and (6) Tropical. Trees do not grow in abundance in the grasslands and desert regions of the central great plains or in the arid basins of the West.

The **West Coast Forest** (Fig. 2-2) is on the Pacific Coast and the western slopes of the Cascade Mountains. This

2-1.   Ten forest regions of the United States.   (American Forest Products Industries)

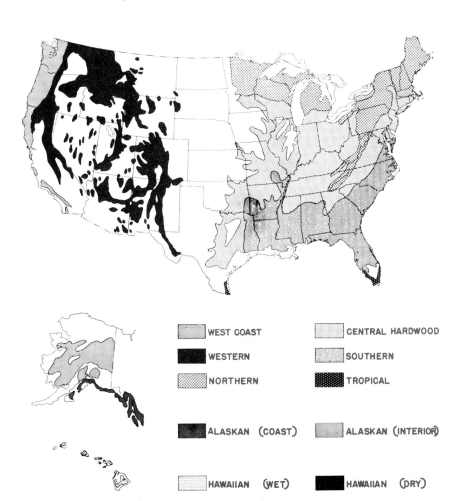

WEST COAST
WESTERN
NORTHERN
CENTRAL HARDWOOD
SOUTHERN
TROPICAL
ALASKAN (COAST)
ALASKAN (INTERIOR)
HAWAIIAN (WET)
HAWAIIAN (DRY)

2-2.   A stand of old-growth Douglas fir in the West Coast Forest.

(American Forest Products Industries)

7

area is in the states of Washington, Oregon, and northern California. The most famous trees in this forest are the giant redwoods, which grow in a narrow belt 10 to 30 miles wide along the northwest coast of California.

The West Coast Forest region contains most of the Douglas fir. It produces almost one-third of the lumber in the United States, about one-fifth of the pulpwood, and nearly all the fir plywood.

Other woods that are characteristic of the area are sugar and lodgepole pines, incense and Port Orford cedar, true firs, western hemlock, western red cedar, and Sitka spruce. Bigleaf maple and red alder are common hardwoods that grow in the West Coast Forest region.

The **Western Forest** (Fig. 2-3) contains 89 million acres of timber and produces nearly one-fourth of the United States lumber. It lies in 12 states from Canada to western Texas and Mexico. The general boundaries

are from the eastern slopes of the Rocky Mountains to within 50 miles of the Pacific Ocean.

The area is known as the **Western Pine Region** because pine species predominate, especially the famous ponderosa, Idaho white, and sugar pines. Other important timber trees are Douglas fir, Engelmann spruce, western larch, incense and western red cedar, true firs, and lodgepole pine. Aspen is the predominant hardwood.

The **Northern Forest** (Fig. 2-4) extends from Wisconsin to Maine. This forest follows a long, narrow, mountainous ridge from Maine to parts of North Carolina, Tennessee, and northern Georgia. The area includes about 115 million acres and produces about one-tenth of the United States lumber and almost one-fifth of its pulpwood.

Softwoods (conifers) found in this region are red (or Norway) and jack pine, and they grow in almost pure stands. Others are white and red spruce, eastern hemlock, white cedar,

tamarack, white pine, and balsam fir. Hardwood (broadleaf) species are black, yellow, and paper birch; maple; oak; black cherry; black gum; basswood; and aspen.

The **Central Hardwood Forest** (Fig. 2-5) has the largest forest area; it contains 131 million acres. The thin strip of Northern Forest on the Appalachian Mountain range is excluded.

The Central Hardwood Forest extends from the central prairies to the Atlantic coastal states and almost to the Gulf of Mexico. Parts of it are in northern Arkansas, western Oklahoma, and eastern and central Texas. This area is the source of about one-twentieth of the lumber and almost one-tenth of the pulpwood for the nation.

Among the many hardwood species in this forest are sweet or red gum, black gum, tulip or yellow poplar, oak, beech, red maple, hickory, elm, ash, sycamore, cottonwood, and walnut. Conifers are the shortleaf and Virginia pines and the red cedar.

2-3. Idaho pine region of the Western Forest.

(American Forest Products Industries)

2-4. A New Hampshire tree farm located in the Northern Forest region.

(American Forest Products Industries)

2-5. A virgin stand of hardwoods in the Central Hardwood Forest.

(American Forest Products Industries)

The **Southern Forest** (Fig. 2-6) produces about three-fifths of the United States' pulpwood and nearly one-third of the lumber. It covers 12.3 million acres in a belt along the Atlantic and Gulf Coasts from New Jersey to eastern Texas. Shortleaf, longleaf, loblolly, and slash pines, and swampland bald cypress, are predominant conifers. Leading hardwoods are red gum, black gum (tupelo); red, white, water, live, and pin oak; coast white cedar; willow; cottonwood; ash; and pecan.

The **Tropical Forest** (Fig. 2-7) is essentially noncommercial. It is the smallest region of the forest lands, lying in the extreme tips of southern Texas and southern Florida. Broadleaf trees found in this area are bay, mangrove, eucalyptus, and mahogany.

Alaskan Forests

The **Alaskan Coast Forest** (Fig. 2-8) furnishes pulpwood and lumber from its 5 million commercial acres. Most of the production is from four major conifers: western hemlock, Sitka spruce, western red cedar, and Alaska yellow cedar.

The **Alaskan Interior Forest** is not especially useful at the present time because it is so remote. Its 40 million acres of potential commercial forest cover most of the heartland of this new state. White and black spruce are the conifers in the area. White birch, aspen, and other poplars are the common broadleaf trees here.

Hawaiian Forests

Except for fuelwood and fence posts, the **Dry Forest** of Hawaii is relatively noncommercial. Algaroba, koa, haole, wiliwili, and monkeypod grow here.

The **Wet Forest** (Fig. 2-9) contains a million acres of commercially valuable trees. Production is mostly for furniture, lumber, and souvenirs. These are made from ohia, koa, tree fern, kukui, mamani, tropical ash, and eucalyptus.

(American Forest Products Industries)

2-8. The Alaskan Coast Forest contains timber stands like this.

2-6. **Pulpwood and sawlog area of the Southern Forest.**

(American Forest Products Industries)

2-7. **A large eucalyptus tree in the Tropical Forest area.**

(American Forest Products Industries)

2-9. **Stilt roots of an ohia tree in the Hawaiian Wet Forest.**

(American Forest Products Industries)

Unit 3 Classification and Characteristics of Trees

The classification and characteristics of trees should be understood to appreciate the technology of woodworking. Knowledge of specific species, their locations, and their uses is also of major importance and interest.

Classification of Trees

Trees are a division of seed plants termed by botanists as **spermatophytes.** Two general designations are (1) **endogens** (monocotyledons) and (2) **exogens** (dicotyledons). Endogenous (inward-growing) trees have no commercial value. Most of their growth takes place inwardly in a hollow trunk, as in bamboo, yucca, and palm trees.

Exogenous trees are outward growing. Layers of growth (annual rings) form the trunk and branches and indicate the age of the tree. In moderate climates, one ring is added each year. When food and water are abundant, the tree grows more and the rings are wide. The rings are narrow when there are adverse conditions of drought and lack of food. The light band of an annual ring is spring growth; the dark one is formed in the summer.

The valuable, lumber-producing exogens are divided into two classes, **angiosperms** and **gymnosperms** (Figs. 3-1 and 3-2). Angiosperms are called **hardwoods,** or **deciduous woods** (meaning "leaf losing"). They are often fruit and nut bearing, are broad leaved, and have covered seeds. **Hardwood** is a common term, but it is not always precise in relation to softness or texture. For example, basswood, balsa, butternut, and poplar are softer than southern yellow pine and yew, which are classified as softwoods. Although most hardwoods shed their leaves annually, such trees as holly, live oak, and magnolia in tropical and subtropical regions keep theirs.

The more important hardwoods are ash, basswood, beech, birch, cherry, elm, and gum. Also in this category are hickory, mahogany, maple, magnolia, oak, Osage orange, poplar, and walnut.

Gymnosperms are classified as softwoods, evergreens, or conifers (meaning "cone bearing"). They have needlelike or scalelike leaves. The name was derived from the Greek word *gymnos* meaning "naked," as the seeds are. **Softwood** and **evergreen** are common names for conifers, but they are somewhat misleading. It was mentioned that some softwoods are harder in texture than some hardwoods. Likewise, some evergreens, such as larch and bald cypress, shed their foliage annually.

Most lumber for building construction is cut from the softwoods. Included in this group are cedar, bald cypress,

3-1. Angiosperm hardwood example and classification.

(Paxton Lumber Company)

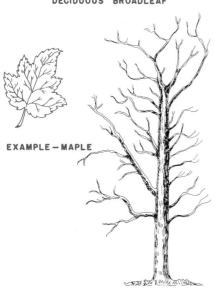

ANGIOSPERM HARDWOOD
DECIDUOUS BROADLEAF

EXAMPLE—MAPLE

3-2. Gymnosperm softwood example and classification.

(Paxton Lumber Company)

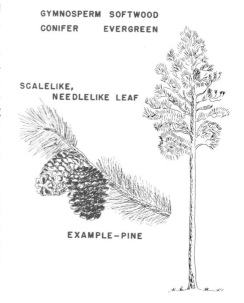

GYMNOSPERM SOFTWOOD
CONIFER   EVERGREEN

SCALELIKE,
NEEDLELIKE LEAF

EXAMPLE—PINE

fir, hemlock, larch, pine, spruce, and redwood.

Outer Tree Structure

The three main parts of a tree are the **roots,** the **trunk,** and the **crown.** Figure 3-3 shows clearly the total tree structure and the major function of each part.

In the **root structure,** the taproot grows deepest. This growth begins as a seed sprouts. It continues to develop through the seedling and the sapling stages (Fig. 3-4) to maturity. Countless surface roots, containing many root hairs, serve to support and anchor the tree. The root hairs, which are living cells, absorb water from the earth and dissolve the minerals and nitrogen necessary to make food. Roots also help to hold soil against erosion. A layer of growth cells at the root tips makes new root tissue during the growing season.

The **trunk,** or main stem of a tree, is the part that is of greatest commercial value. It supports the crown and produces the most useful wood. Figures 3-5, 3-6, and 3-7 show cross sections of a tree. The outer bark of the trunk protects the tree from injuries. The inner bark **(phloem)** carries food made in the leaves down to the branches, trunk, and roots.

The **crown** of the tree is formed by the branches and leaves. Leaves have been called the most important chemical factories in the world. Millions of green microscopic bodies called **chloroplasts** manufacture sugar inside each leaf. The green pigment in leaves is **chlorophyll.** Power is generated by combining radiant energy from sunlight with water from the earth and roots and carbon dioxide from the air. See Fig. 3-3 (crown insert).

Oxygen is a by-product; it is released through the leaves. Water vapor is discharged from living plants through pores **(stomates)** on the undersides of leaves. Air passes in and out. This breathing process is called **transpira-**

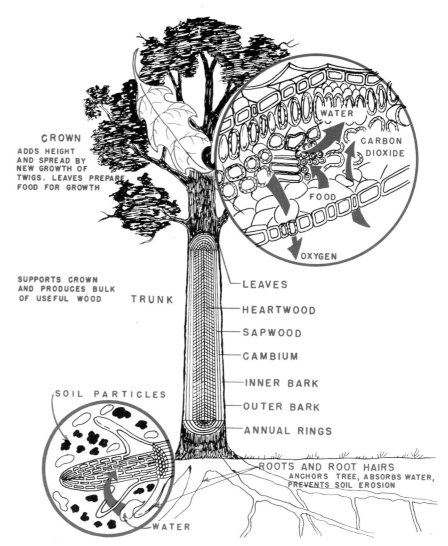

CROWN
ADDS HEIGHT AND SPREAD BY NEW GROWTH OF TWIGS. LEAVES PREPARE FOOD FOR GROWTH

SUPPORTS CROWN AND PRODUCES BULK OF USEFUL WOOD

TRUNK

WATER

CARBON DIOXIDE

FOOD

OXYGEN

LEAVES

HEARTWOOD

SAPWOOD

CAMBIUM

INNER BARK

OUTER BARK

ANNUAL RINGS

SOIL PARTICLES

WATER

ROOTS AND ROOT HAIRS
ANCHORS TREE, ABSORBS WATER, PREVENTS SOIL EROSION

3-3. The total tree structure.

(American Forest Products Industries)

tion. The manufacturing process of storing energy and making sugar is termed **photosynthesis.** Each year trees increase in height and spread of branches. New growth comes from young cells in buds at the ends of twigs. See Fig. 3-4 (insert).

Every living cell from roots to crown produces new products with the aid of chemical substances called **enzymes.** In general, enzymes break down the sugar which is combined with minerals and nitrogen to form various substances. Some of the sugar is used

directly for energy in the growing buds, cambium layer (see page 12), and root tips.

Cell-wall substances such as cellulose, lignin, and suberin utilize sugar to make wood and bark. Enzymes change some sugar into the starches, fats, oils, and proteins which help to form seeds, fruits, and nuts. Other sugar is converted into products of special use to industry. These include resin and turpentine from southern pines and syrup from maple trees. Other products are chewing gum, made from chicle gum taken from sapodilla trees and spruces, and tannin, made from oaks, hemlocks, and chestnuts.

Inner Tree Structure

A thin layer of cells between the bark and the wood is the **cambium.** This layer is where growth in diameter occurs. The cells are capable of dividing and forming new ones in the part toward the sapwood (xylem) and bast cells (phloem) in the part toward the inner bark.

Sapwood contains food cells (parenchyma) which store and conduct food vertically. Sap is carried from the roots to the leaves through tiny openings, or cells, called **vessels.** Heartwood was once sapwood; it matured and became inactive. It is composed of strong fibers which give the tree strength. Fiber length, we should mention, is another means of differentiating between hardwoods and softwoods. On an average, softwood fiber length is two to four times greater than that of hardwood. Sap in softwoods is conducted through fibers. They have no open-end cell structure so are **nonporous** (Fig. 3-8).

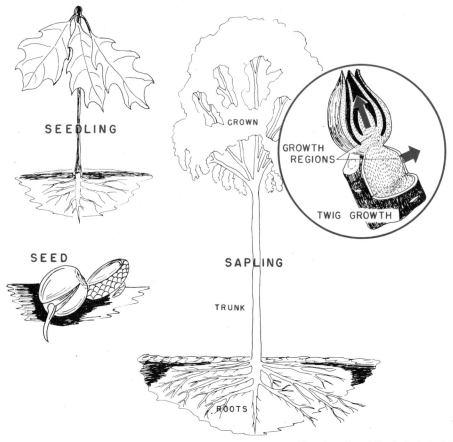

(American Forest Products Industries)

3-4.   The growth cycle of a tree from seed to maturity.

3-6.   The structure of a log.   (Paxton Lumber Company)

3-5.   A cross section of a tree trunk.

(Paxton Lumber Company)

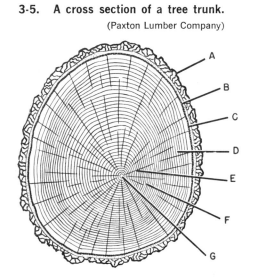

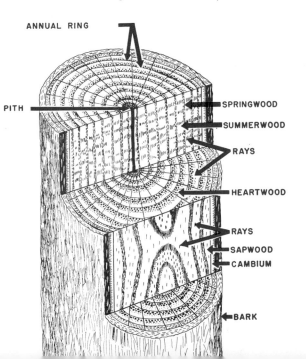

Hardwoods are **porous** (Fig. 3-9), having open-end cells. Comparison of cell structure is one of the best methods of wood classification. Some cells are larger than others. In relation to porosity, hardwoods are called **open-** and **close-grain** woods. Walnut, oak, and mahogany, for example, have larger open-end cells than maple or cherry. These cells are "arteries" through which sap travels to all parts of the tree. Hardwood and softwood cells are compared in Fig. 3-10.

Air-in the cells of dry wood allows most wood to float when placed in water. The dry weight of different woods varies because of these hollow cells. Balsa is exceptionally light, weighing approximately 7 pounds per cubic foot. Oak weighs about 40 pounds per cubic foot, and lignum vitae, 70. Lignum vitae, rosewood, and ebony are almost solid woods. They sink in water because there are only a relatively few air-filled cell cavities.

The size, shape, and function of wood cells vary. Cells store food, conduct sap, and give strength to wood. The lines, or rays, running from the **pith** to the bark in all exogenous trees are called **medullary rays**. See Figs. 3-6

and 3-7. These rays store and conduct food horizontally. They are very noticeable in plain oak, beech, and sycamore and are easily seen as flakes in quartersawed lumber. Medullary rays add beauty to some woods and are important when drying lumber. The larger the rays, the more they tend to affect the process of drying lumber by shrinking and checking (cracking). This accounts for the difficulty in drying many hardwoods, as compared to the softwoods.

The cell structure of some woods makes them more valuable as building materials. Nails and screws hold better in such soft-textured woods as pine, redwood, cypress, mahogany, and basswood. Paint does not usually scale off wood, as it does from metal. A natural insulator, wood protects against heat, cold, and sound. The size and arrangement of cells, along with color pigments, add to the beauty of the wood by enhancing the figure, or grain.

Most of the characteristics mentioned are means of identifying and classifying woods of various kinds and species. Color and additional qualities and properties of many common woods are given in Table 3-1.

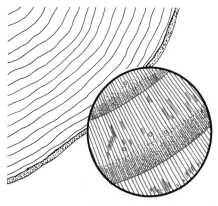

(Paxton Lumber Company)

3-8. Cross section of nonporous end cells of softwood.

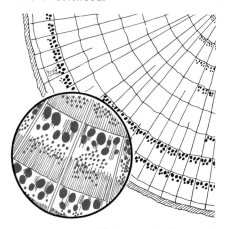

(Paxton Lumber Company)

3-9. Cross section of porous end cells in hardwood.

3-10. Enlarged cell structures: (A) hardwood, (B) softwood.

(Forest Products Laboratory)

3-7. A cross-section detail of a log.

(Paxton Lumber Company)

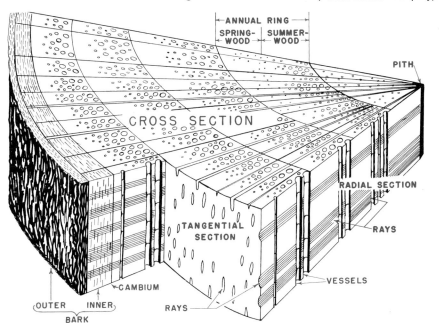

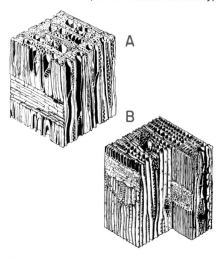

Table 3-1 CHARACTERISTICS OF MANY COMMON WOODS

Species	Comparative weights[1]	Color[2]	Hand-tool working	Nail-ability[3]	Relative density	General strength[4]	Resistance to decay[5]	Wood finishing[6]	Cost[7]
Hardwoods[8]									
Apitong	Heavy	Reddish brown	Hard	Poor	Medium	Good	High	Poor	Medium high
Ash, brown	Medium	Light brown	Medium	Medium	Hard	Medium	Low	Medium	Medium
Ash, tough white	Heavy	Off-white	Hard	Poor	Hard	Good	Low	Medium	Medium
Ash, soft white	Medium	Off-white	Medium	Medium	Medium	Low	Low	Medium	Medium low
Avodire	Medium	Golden blond	Medium	Medium	Medium	Low	Low	Medium	High
Balsawood	Light	Cream white	Easy	Good	Soft	Low	Low	Poor	Medium
Basswood	Light	Cream white	Easy	Good	Soft	Low	Low	Medium	Medium
Beech	Heavy	Light brown	Hard	Poor	Hard	Good	Low	Easy	Medium
Birch	Heavy	Light brown	Hard	Poor	Hard	Good	Low	Easy	High
Butternut	Light	Light brown	Easy	Good	Soft	Low	Medium	Medium	Medium
Cherry, black	Medium	Medium reddish brown	Hard	Poor	Hard	Good	Medium	Easy	High
Chestnut	Light	Light brown	Medium	Medium	Medium	Medium	High	Poor	Medium
Cottonwood	Light	Grayish white	Medium	Good	Soft	Low	Low	Poor	Low
Elm, soft, northern	Medium	Cream tan	Hard	Good	Medium	Medium	Medium	Medium	Medium low
Gum, red	Medium	Reddish brown	Medium	Medium	Medium	Medium	Medium	Medium	Medium high
Hickory, true	Heavy	Reddish tan	Hard	Poor	Hard	Good	Low	Medium	Low
Holly	Medium	White to gray	Medium	Medium	Hard	Medium	Low	Easy	Medium
Limba	Medium	Pale golden	Medium	Good	Medium	Medium	Low	Medium	High
Magnolia	Medium	Yellowish brown	Medium	Medium	Medium	Medium	Low	Easy	Medium
Mahogany, Honduras	Medium	Golden brown	Easy	Good	Medium	Medium	High	Medium	High
Mahogany, Philippine	Medium	Medium red	Easy	Good	Medium	Medium	High	Medium	Medium high
Maple, hard	Heavy	Reddish cream	Hard	Poor	Hard	Good	Low	Easy	Medium high
Maple, soft	Medium	Reddish brown	Hard	Poor	Hard	Good	Low	Easy	Medium low
Oak, red (average)	Heavy	Flesh brown	Hard	Medium	Hard	Good	Low	Medium	Medium
Oak, white (average)	Heavy	Grayish brown	Hard	Medium	Hard	Good	High	Medium	Medium high
Poplar, yellow	Medium	Light to dark yellow	Easy	Good	Soft	Low	Low	Easy	Medium
Primavera	Medium	Straw tan	Medium	Medium	Medium	Medium	Medium	Medium	High
Sycamore	Medium	Flesh brown	Hard	Good	Medium	Medium	Low	Easy	Medium low
Walnut, black	Heavy	Dark brown	Medium	Medium	Hard	Good	High	Medium	High
Willow, black	Light	Medium brown	Easy	Good	Soft	Low	Low	Medium	Medium low
Softwoods[9]									
Cedar, Tennessee red	Medium	Red	Medium	Poor	Medium	Medium	High	Easy	Medium
Cypress	Medium	Yellow to reddish brown	Medium	Good	Soft	Medium	High	Poor	Medium high
Fir, Douglas	Medium	Orange-brown	Medium	Poor	Soft	Medium	Medium	Poor	Medium
Fir, white	Light	Nearly white	Medium	Poor	Soft	Low	Low	Poor	Low
Pine, yellow longleaf	Medium	Orange to reddish brown	Hard	Poor	Medium	Good	Medium	Medium	Medium
Pine, eastern white (*Pinus strobus*)	Light	Cream to reddish brown	Easy	Good	Soft	Low	Medium	Medium	Medium high
Pine, ponderosa	Light	Orange to reddish brown	Easy	Good	Soft	Low	Low	Medium	Medium
Pine, sugar	Light	Creamy brown	Easy	Good	Soft	Low	Medium	Poor	Medium high
Redwood	Light	Deep reddish brown	Easy	Good	Soft	Medium	High	Poor	Medium
Spruces (average)	Light	Nearly white	Medium	Medium	Soft	Low	Low	Medium	Medium

[1] Kiln-dried weight.
[2] Heartwood. Sap is whitish.
[3] Comparative splitting tendencies.
[4] Combined bending and compressive strength.
[5] No wood will decay unless exposed to moisture. Resistance-to-decay estimate refers only to heartwood.
[6] Ease of finishing with clear finishes.
[7] Prices for best grade.
[8] Leaf-bearing tree.
[9] Cone- and needle-bearing trees.

14

Unit 4 Species of Wood

Variations in climate and geography influence the development and growth of the many different kinds of trees found in the United States. Over 1,000 species have been identified. About 100 are suitable for manufacturing into lumber, paper, and other commercially valuable products. Approximately 60 percent of the commercial species of trees are hardwoods; the remainder are softwoods.

Color and Grain Patterns

Color plates between pp. 18 and 19 show some of the American species most often used in forest-products industries, school industrial laboratories, and retail lumber markets. There are **14** hardwoods and **10** softwoods shown.

Color and grain of surfaces are of help in identifying woods. The manner in which lumber is sawed from the log will show the flat- or edge-grained pattern of annual growth rings.

Flat-grained and **edge-grained** are terms used in reference to softwoods. **Plainsawed** and **quartersawed** generally refer to hardwoods. In each color illustration a cross section, or end grain, is shown at the top. The middle section shows edge-grained, or quartersawed, lumber. The lower section displays flat-grained, or plainsawed, surfaces.

Common Hardwoods (Broad Leaves)

Oak is the most important commercial hardwood. Other valuable species are cherry, walnut, maple, ash, and yellow poplar. In addition, there are red (sweet) gum, black gum (tupelo), beech, birch, cottonwood, basswood, aspen, hickory, sycamore, magnolia, willow, and pecan.

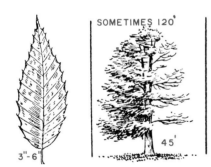

4-1.　American beech.

4-2.　American sycamore.

4-3.　American elm.

4-4.　Black walnut.

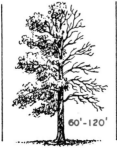

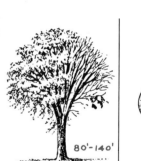

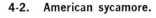

The paragraphs that follow contain descriptions of some of the outstanding species of, first, hardwoods, then softwoods. Listed are the common and Latin names, density, characteristic hardness, properties, uses, and general color and appearance of the wood. Figures 4-1 through 4-19 show a leaf or needle; the fruit, cone, or nut; and the summer and winter silhouette.

American beech (*Fagus grandifolia*). Figure 4-1. Heavy (45 pounds per cubic foot). Hard. Extensive shrinkage when dried; high strength and shock resistance; readily bent when steamed. Lumber, veneer, cooperage (for example, curved pieces, or staves, for barrels), food containers, boxes, cabinetwork, pulpwood, and novelties. Heartwood white with reddish tinge to reddish brown. Tiny pores not visible; conspicuous rays.

American sycamore (*Platanus occidentalis*). Figure 4-2. Medium heavy (34 pounds per cubic foot). Medium hard. Close texture; interlocking grain; large shrinkage; difficult to season;

warps easily. Inexpensive furniture, boxes, baskets, cooperage, veneer. Heartwood reddish to flesh brown. Very small pores not visible to the naked eye; rays visible on all surfaces.

Rock elm (*Ulmus thomasi*). Heavy (44 pounds per cubic foot). Hard. More shock resistant than other American hardwoods except hickory and dogwood; extensive shrinkage; excellent bending qualities. Containers and furniture requiring high shock resistance and bending. Heartwood is from brown to dark brown and shades of red. Summerwood pores are in concentric, wavy lines and are easily visible upon magnification.

American elm (*Ulmus americana*). Figure 4-3. Medium heavy (35 pounds per cubic foot). Medium hard and stiff. Good shock resistance; extensive shrinkage; easily glued. Barrels, kegs, other containers, and bent parts of furniture. Heartwood is from brown to dark brown and shades of red. Summerwood pores not visible; springwood pores large and easily visible.

Black walnut (*Juglans nigra*): Figure 4-4. Heavy (38 pounds per cubic foot). Hard, strong, stiff. Good shock resistance; one of the most durable woods; easily worked; finishes beautifully. Outstanding for solid and veneer furniture, gunstocks, interior woodwork. Chocolate to dark brown and purplish. Easily identified. Pores hard to see on end grain; otherwise easily distinguished.

Black cherry (*Prunus serotina*). See color plate. Medium heavy (35 pounds per cubic foot). Medium hard, strong, stiff. High shock resistance; medium-large shrinkage; little warpage after seasoning. High bending strength; glues satisfactorily with care; finishes beautifully. Furniture, backing blocks for electrotype plates in printing, woodenware, patterns and flasks for foundry in metalworking, and interior finish. Distinct light to dark reddish-brown heartwood. End-grain rays just visible; quartersawed, unusual flake pattern.

Hickory (*Carya ovata*). Figure 4-5. Very heavy (42–52 pounds per cubic foot). Very hard, strong, stiff. Very high

5 LEAFLETS RARELY 7
8"–20"

60'–140'

1" – 2½"

4"–10"

SOME-TIMES 130'

⅓" – ½"

4-5. Hickory.

4-7. American basswood.

4-6. White ash.

4-8. Sweet gum.

5-11 LEAFLETS LEAF 8"–15"

50'-75'
SOMETIMES 120'

1"   2"

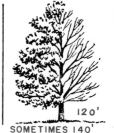

3"–5"
RARELY 7 POINTS

120'
SOMETIMES 140'

1"-1½"

grain surfaces between springwood and summerwood. No normal resin canals.

White fir (*Abies concolor*). See color plate. Light (26–28 pounds per cubic foot). Medium soft, stiff; low in shock resistance. Difficult to season; low decay resistance; gluing properties satisfactory. Lumber and pulpwood, building construction, planing-mill work. Nearly white to red-brown heartwood. Lacks normal resin canals; more contrasting rings than eastern balsam fir.

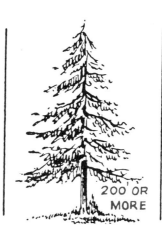

$\frac{1}{2}$" OR LONGER

200' OR MORE

$\frac{3}{4}$ – 1"

4-19.   Western hemlock.

Unit 5   Trees from Forest to Millsite

One who studies the technology of woods is interested in learning something about the occupations, processes, and working conditions involved in getting trees from the forests to a shop or retail lumberyard. Technological advancements in mechanical equipment used in the forest and in millwork are helping to develop the industry and speed production of lumber. Some of the numerous methods of harvesting, processing, and grading lumber are explained below.

Logging Surveys

A detailed study is first made of a suitable area and source of marketable timber and lumber (Figs. 5-1 through 5-5). Facilities for operations, the

5-1.   Commercial stands of redwood are an excellent source of lumber.

(Georgia-Pacific Corporation)

5-2.   Southern pine forests provide marketable building timber.

(Georgia-Pacific Corporation)

5-3.   The northwest Douglas fir area furnishes construction timber.

(Georgia-Pacific Corporation)

Incense cedar (*Libocedrus decurrens*). Light (26 pounds per cubic foot). Limber, medium soft, medium weak. Low shock resistance; small shrinkage. One of the most decay resistant. Easy to work with tools; holds paint well. Lumber, fence posts, cross ties, pencils, venetian blinds. Heartwood reddish to dull brown, with occasional lavender tinge; shavings give burning sensation to taste. Growth rings prominent on flat-grained surfaces; straight grain. Hard to tell from western red cedar except with a microscope.

Western red cedar (*Thuja plicata*). See color plate. Light (23 pounds per cubic foot). Medium soft, limber. Low shock resistance. Weak when used as beams. Easy to kiln-dry; little tendency to warp; easily glued; holds paint well; good weather resistance. Shingles, lumber, poles, posts, piling, exterior uses, interior finish, doors, ships, boats. Reddish- or pinkish-brown to dull brown heartwood; cedar odor; no sensation to taste as in incense cedar; confused with redwood except for odor.

Ponderosa pine (*Pinus ponderosa*). Figure 4-16. Medium light (28 pounds per cubic foot). Variable properties; outer portion of sawtimber has medium weakness, shock resistance, softness. Lumber (principally), piling, posts, mine timbers, veneer, hewn ties, high-grade millwork, boxes, crates, knotty interior finish. Heartwood yellowish to light-reddish brown or orange. Abundant resin canals.

Sitka spruce (*Picea sitchensis*). Figure 4-17. Medium light (28 pounds per cubic foot). Medium soft, stiff, shock resistant. Weak in bonding and compression strength. High strength properties on basis of weight; medium-large shrinkage; works easily; not difficult to kiln-dry. Straight grain, few hidden defects; woolly or fuzzy grain under planer knife action; long fibers. Lumber, cooperage, paper pulp, boxes, crates, some furniture, planing-mill products such as sashes and doors. Piano sounding boards. Pinkish-yellow to pale-brown heartwood. Color and more prominent resin canals distinguish it from other spruces.

Engelmann spruce (*Picea engelmanni*). Light (24 pounds per cubic foot). Soft; weak as beams; medium limber; low shock resistance. Readily air-dried; little tendency to warp; low in decay resistance; glues easily. Lumber, boxes, subflooring, sheathing, studding, some paper pulp. Heartwood not distinct from sapwood; almost white to pale yellow-brown. Appearance similar to most other spruces microscopically (except the Sitka).

Sugar pine (*Pinus lambertiana*). See color plate. Lightweight (25 pounds per cubic foot). Medium softness and weakness; low shock resistance; easily worked with tools. Used almost entirely for lumber in building, foundry patterns, general millwork. Heartwood from light brown to pale reddish brown. Abundant resin canals; springwood and summerwood have gradual transition.

Western white pine (*Pinus monticola*). Figure 4-18. Medium light (27 pounds per cubic foot). Weak, medium softness and stiffness; medium low shock resistance; easily glued and worked. About three-fourths of production used as building construction lumber, matched planks, exterior and interior trim, paneling. Cream-colored to light- or reddish-brown heartwood. Resin canals large and abundant.

Western larch (*Larix occidentalis*). Heavy (38 pounds per cubic foot). Medium hard, stiff, strong; medium high shock resistance. About three-fourths of production used in building construction as rough dimension, small timbers, planks, and boards. Heartwood russet brown. Abrupt transition from springwood to summerwood. Very small resin canals.

Douglas fir (*Pseudotsuga menziesii*). See color plate. Medium weight (33 pounds per cubic foot). Medium strength, hardness, shock resistance. Very stiff. Lumber, timbers, piling; plywood in wide use for sheathing, concrete forms, prefabrication of house panels, millwork, ships and boats, other structural forms. Orange-red to red or yellowish heartwood. Distinctive odor. Resin canals more abundant than in larch, less than in southern pines.

Western hemlock (*Tsuga heterophylla*). Figure 4-19. Medium light (29 pounds per cubic foot). Medium hard, weak, fairly low shock resistance; satisfactory gluing and working properties; easy to season. Pulp and most construction purposes, plywood core wood, mine timbers. Light reddish-brown heartwood; little color contrast on end-

4-17. Sitka spruce.

FLAT   POINTED
$\frac{3}{16}$" $\frac{1}{2}$"   180'–200'   2"–4"

4-18. Western white pine.

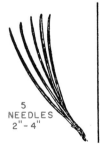

5 NEEDLES
2"–4"   90'–100'   6"–10"

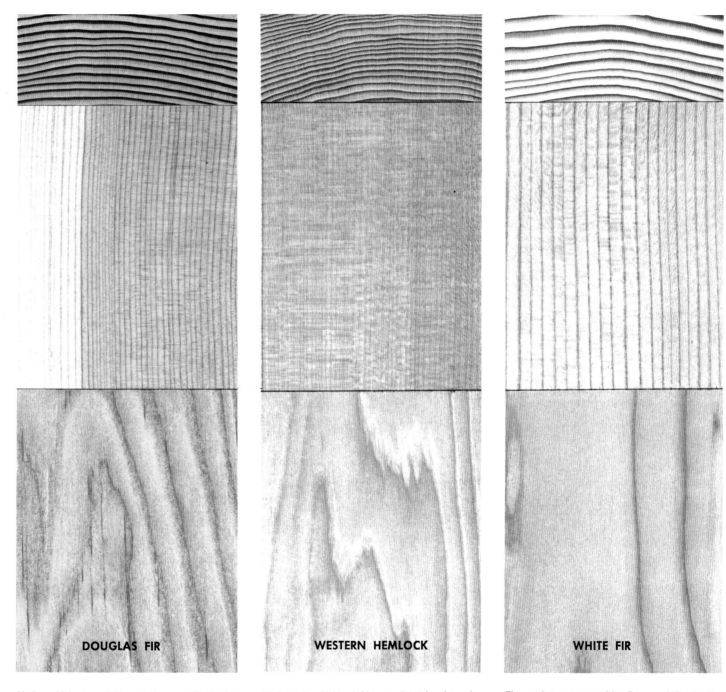

DOUGLAS FIR

WESTERN HEMLOCK

WHITE FIR

Varies widely in weight and strength. Most old-growth wood is moderately heavy, strong, hard, and shock resistant. Very stiff and difficult to work, but holds nails well. Moderate decay resistance. Heartwood: orange-red to red or yellowish. Distinctive odor. Average weight 33 lb to cu ft.

Moderately lightweight, moderately low in strength. Fairly hard, stiff. Heartwood low in decay resistance; easy to work. Heartwood: light reddish-brown, often with purplish cast, especially in summerwood bands. Wood lacks normal resin canals. Average weight 39 lb to cu ft.

Fir species names—white fir, grand fir, Pacific silver fir, California red fir, noble fir. Light in weight, moderately soft and weak, low in nail-holding power and decay resistance. Heartwood: nearly white to pale reddish-brown. Wood lacks normal resin canals. Average weight 27 lb to cu ft.

SITKA SPRUCE

SUGAR PINE

WESTERN WHITE PINE

Grain straight; fine, uniform texture; fairly strong; works easily; holds nails well; decay resistance low; often produces fuzzy grain under planer knives. Heartwood: pinkish-yellow to pale brown. Springwood-summerwood change slow; flat-grain surface rings faint. Average weight 28 lb to cu ft.

Straight grain, fairly uniform texture; easy to work; holds nails well. Lightweight; strength moderately low; not stiff. Fairly decay resistant, soft. Heartwood: pale reddish-brown. Resin canals abundant and commonly stain the wood surface. Average weight 25 lb to cu ft.

Straight grained, easy to work; kiln-dries easily and stays in place well after seasoning. Lightweight, moderately soft and stiff. Low to moderate in decay resistance. Heartwood is cream colored to light brown or reddish-brown. Resin canals abundant. Average weight 27 lb to cu ft.

method of logging, and timber available for selective harvesting must then be determined before an operation is begun.

The approximate volume (amount) of timber is determined from aerial photographs or by men called **cruisers.** These men go through an area and make careful estimates of the timber by volume, size, and species. After establishing the cutting area, they **blaze** (mark) the trees chosen for cutting. They spray white or yellow marking material on the lower part of the tree trunk, where it can easily be seen (Fig. 5-6). Cruisers may also plan logging and transportation routes. They often suggest camp sites when the logging operation is to extend over a long period of time. (Several industrial cities developed from early logging camps. These include Saginaw, Bay City, and Muskegan, Michigan, and some cities in the South and West.)

Men, equipment, and supplies must be brought into an area to build the necessary roads, railroads, power lines, buildings, and other facilities. When these services are nearly complete, the actual cutting of the trees and the logs begins.

Felling Trees

Trees are felled by men called **sawyers,** or **fallers.** These men use axes, crosscut saws, power chain saws (Fig. 5-7), and other power units. When the tree is exceptionally tall, it is usually **topped** (Fig. 5-8) before felling to prevent damage to itself and other trees.

To fell a tree, a V notch, or **undercut** (Fig. 5-9), is made on one side of the tree. This cut helps control the direction the tree falls and prevents **slabbing** (splitting) and damaging the log. A saw cut is started on the side opposite this notch and slightly above it. On large trees, a wedge is driven into the saw **kerf** (cut) to prevent **binding** (sticking) of the saw blade. The wedge also aids in forcing the tree to fall. Workers must be skillful and alert to avoid injury and to fell trees in the proper direction. An incorrectly felled tree can be damaged, and it can lodge itself against or damage other trees.

After trees are felled (Fig. 5-10) the branches are trimmed from the trunks by men called **swampers,** or **limbers.** A worker called a **log bucker** (Fig. 5-11) cuts the trunk into standard lengths for logging and transporting.

(American Forest Products Industries)

5-6. A cruiser marks trees with a spray gun so that loggers will know they are to be cut. Selective cutting improves a forest stand, giving younger trees more sunlight and room to grow.

5-4. White pine trees of the northern Idaho region are the chief source of matchwood in the United States.

(American Forest Products Industries)

5-5. The western section of the United States is a prime source of timber.

(United States Forest Products Laboratory)

5-7. Felling timber with a large power chain saw.

(West Coast Lumbermen's Association)

(Weyerhaeuser Company)

5-8. Topping an exceptionally tall tree.

5-9. Fallers making an undercut on the side of the tree facing the direction it is to fall. Loggers do this with a power saw. It takes from 7 to 10 minutes to fell a big Douglas fir.

(Weyerhaeuser Company)

(Atkins Saw Company)

5-10. One man, using a power chain saw, can fell a small tree.

Logging and Transporting

Logs are **skidded** (pulled) from forests to central points of collection (Fig. 5-12). Two-wheeled, wagonlike trucks, log slides or chutes, and flumes (water skids) have been used. Spar trees and cableways are still used in areas where they are needed (Fig. 5-13). Horses and oxen are still sometimes used to drag logs from the forest (Fig. 5-14). The modern method of logging, however, is to use tractors and special power equipment (Fig. 5-15). Pulpwood is cut to length in the forest and often skidded with slides and a tractor (Fig. 5-16).

5-11. A log bucker cuts trees into the standard lengths needed for logging and transporting.

(West Coast Lumbermen's Association)

5-12. Skidding logs from the woods to a landing, using a crawler tractor with a logging arch.

5-15. The most common method of skidding logs is with tractors.

5-13. Spar trees and a cableway are used to skid several logs.

5-14. Horses are sometimes used to skid logs out of the forest.

23

(Caterpillar Tractor Company)

5-16. Pulpwood, cut to suitable lengths, is often skidded on a slide with a tractor.

(Weyerhaeuser Company)

5-18. A truck being loaded with heavy timbers to be hauled to the millsite. In the background is a portable spar tree mounted on a truck body to furnish leverage for lifting the logs.

Logs are lifted with a fork lift (Fig. 5-17) and loaded on trucks (Fig. 5-18) or on railroad cars (Fig. 5-19) for shipment. They are also floated down rivers and streams to the mills. River transportation is often the most economical, but log jams and inadequate supplies of water are problems.

Logs that have arrived at the mill are placed on land decks (platforms) if they are to be used immediately. At this time they are often scaled (measured) to determine the volume of board feet contained in each (Fig. 5-20). If they are to be used later, they are kept wet by sprinklers or in the millpond (Fig. 5-21). Sprinkling or floating in the millpond keeps the reserve logs from drying and cracking. If mixed species of wood are being processed, the logs are sorted and graded before they are sawed. Different species may be sawed for different uses, require different drying conditions, or pose different problems in sawing. If these were sawed as mixed logs, more time would be required for separating the lumber.

5-17. Seventy-five-foot-long poles are loaded on trucks with a fork lift.

(Caterpillar Tractor Company)

5-19. A trainload of big pine logs being transported to a lumber mill.

(American Forest Products Industries)

(American Forest Products Industries)

5-20. A scaler measuring logs to determine the board-foot volume.

5-21. Logs are often kept in a millpond to prevent drying and cracking.

Unit 6 Automated Lumber Production

6-1. A small open-shed sawmill.

(Caterpillar Tractor Company)

Logs are processed at mills ranging in size from small, open-shed ones (Fig. 6-1) to the newest, most automated type (Fig. 6-2). The small mill is often portable. It is operated by only a few men, but it supplies both lumber and employment for people in a locality. Most of the operations are done by hand. Board-foot output per 8-hour day is often less than that produced in an automated mill in 1 hour.

The automated mill features automatic metal detectors, pushbutton riderless carriage control, complete conveyor systems, gang sawing, unique drop-sorting devices, and high-speed stackers. (These terms are all explained in this unit.) The mill can be designed for the production of lumber from both soft- and hardwoods.

In all types of mills the processing of logs is similar, but the manpower needs and board-foot lumber output are very different. One large automated lumber mill with dry kiln, grading sheds, planing mill, and storage and shipping areas employs only 150 persons. It cuts 10,000 to 12,000 board feet per hour. This is an expenditure of 10 to 12 man-hours per thousand board feet (MBF). The other mills in that area spent an average of 22 man-hours per MBF of the same type of lumber.

Modern industrial methods and technology are developing rapidly, and because of this the operations in an automated plant have been chosen for description. An explanatory and pictorial trip through an automated mill will help you better to understand modern lumber production.

Processing Logs for Sawing

Inside the automated plant is an efficient network of catwalks, stairs, and stiles (steps which go up, over, and down the opposite side of an object). See Fig. 6-3. This network allows for swift foot traffic and provides an excellent vantage point for foremen. Automatic sprinklers protect the entire mill from fire. Large fans in the ceiling pull

6-2. This automated lumber mill contains a sawmill, kiln, grading sheds, planing mill, burner, power plant, and shipping area.

6-3. Catwalks, stairs, and stiles give good movement and visibility.

in fresh air and circulate it throughout the building. Corrugated plastic panels set in the roof filter in daylight.

Logs are unloaded by a railroad-type crane (Fig. 6-4) onto decks (platforms). They are fed onto a conveyor, which moves them into the scaling shed. A man operating a semiautomatic log turner controls the direction of logs so that the small end always enters the scaling shed first for more accurate and uniform scaling. A **scaler** can measure and quickly calculate the board feet in each log without moving. The

logs continue along on the conveyor and enter the **debarker**.

Different types of debarkers handle logs of different sizes. The mechanical debarker (Fig. 6-5) handles logs from 6 to 26 inches in diameter at the rate of 47 to 94 linear feet per minute. Logs over 26 inches across are rejected and are routed by conveyor to a semiautomatic debarker, then conveyed to the mill. The mechanical debarker has metal rollers with rough "fingers" to remove bark from the log. In some mills a stream of water under extremely high pressure is used for debarking (Fig. 6-6). Sometimes large logs are debarked in the forest (Fig. 6-7) to reduce transportation weight and to eliminate the necessity of disposing of waste bark at the mill.

Just outside the debarker building is an automatic metal detector. Logs which have nails, spikes, metal bands and markings, or other metal objects are "kicked" onto a runaround conveyor to an area where the metal is removed. They go back through the detector for another check before proceeding to the saws, which they can no longer damage.

6-4. Unloading logs on decks with a crane.

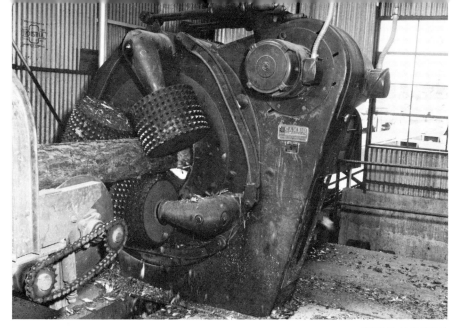

6-5. A mechanical debarker for handling logs 6 to 26 inches in diameter.

6-6. Debarking a log under extremely high water pressure.

The scaler, who can work on either the ground or on the second-story mill floor, operates a pushbutton-controlled side lift (Fig. 6-8). It takes debarked logs into the mill. He also marks the small end of the log to aid the person called a **block setter** in placing the log properly on the carriage to go into the saw. The large end of the log moves into the saw first so that it can be sawed flat on its sides more easily. The large end provides a clear view of the log to the sawyer so that the least waste of log wood results.

Sawing Logs into Lumber

The block setter works at a push-button control panel (Fig. 6-9) to position (set) each log on a riderless carriage (Fig. 6-10). Air-operated setworks (holders) handle logs up to 20 feet

6-8. A push-button-controlled lift.

6-7. Debarking a large log in the forest.

6-9.   Positioning logs on a riderless carriage.

(Forest Industries)

6-10.   The riderless carriage takes a log to the band mill or headsaw.

(Forest Industries)

long. The carriage takes the log past the **band mill** (band saw) or **headsaw** (Fig. 6-11), which cuts it into a **cant**. A cant is a log that has been slabbed (sawed flat) on two or four sides (Fig. 6-12). The band in this mill travels at 10,500 feet per minute and can be braked to a stop in 50 seconds.

The **offbearer**, or **tail sawyer**, operates a series of control buttons and levers. The tail sawyer shunts (turns or pushes) cants toward the horizontal resaws or to one of several gang saws (Fig. 6-13). Pushbutton panels shown in Fig. 6-14 control different sizes of gang saws. A cant is processed in the horizontal resaw (Fig. 6-15) as many times as needed to cut all available lumber from it. The waste material remaining is sent automatically to the chipper (see discussion below). The lumber is sent to edger saws.

Edger saws are located on the production line directly behind the resaws. Edger saws cut off rough edges. A special overhead light casts shadows which assist the operator to determine (without measuring) the maximum width which can be cut from each rough board. Special rolls automatically dispose of waste strips. These are conveyed to the chipper.

A conveyor chain (Fig. 6-16) picks up lumber from the horizontal resaws, the gang saws, and the edgers. It moves the board to **trimmer saws** located in a hall-like structure between the mill and the sorting building. The trimmers, operated by remote control, square the ends, remove defects, and cut the final lumber to desired lengths. Usable waste is conveyed to the chipper.

Waste utilization is an integral part of any modern mill. Waste wood from each operation in the entire plant is sent to the **chipper** unit to be reduced to uniform chips. These are screened (Fig. 6-17) and conveyed by blower or gravity to waiting boxcars. Several rail carloads per day are sent to paper mills, hardboard, or particle board plants. Unsuitable chips, sawdust, and

6-11. Sawing cants with a large headsaw or band saw. (Weyerhaeuser Company)

(Forest Industries)

6-12. Cants on a conveyor waiting resawing or gang sawing.

6-13. Push-button panels control the operation of 26-inch gang saws, set to produce 1-inch lumber.

(Wood and Wood Products)

6-14. Overhead shadow lights direct cants into proper sizes of gang saws. Separators behind the gangs guide boards on the belt conveyor to the edger.

(Wood and Wood Products)

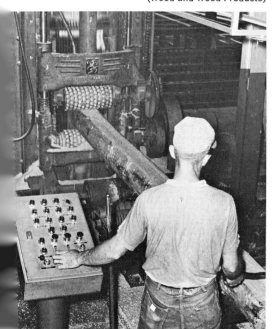

(Weyerhaeuser Company)

6-15. A battery of saws resaw cants into preset thicknesses and widths.

(Wood and Wood Products)

6-16. A conveyor chain picks up lumber from gang saw, horizontal resaws, and edgers and moves it toward the trimmer.

6-17. A screen separates usable ¾-inch-long chips from sawdust, bark, and unsuitable chips.

(Wood and Wood Products)

bark which cannot be used commercially are consumed as fuel, producing steam power. Excess waste is disposed of in a specially constructed outside burner.

After trimming, the boards are carried down troughlike conveyors which run the length of the sorting building. As the lumber travels at high speed, a series of electrical switches operates electronic devices to measure the length of each piece. Gates are activated (opened) to shunt (turn) the lumber to drop into one of 24 bays (sorting compartments or areas). See Fig. 6-18. Each bay holds about 1¼ kiln-car loads of lumber. These bays retain lumber ranging from 6 to 16 feet in length. When full, boards continue to move on a chain conveyor toward the stacker.

The lumber is placed in layers on railroadlike **kiln cars** by a semiautomatic **chain-arm stacker** (Fig. 6-19). Men place sticks about 2 feet apart between layers to help prevent any type of crooking, such as wind (twisting). As each stack is completed, it is pulled out on rails to the **dry kilns** (Fig. 6-20). After proper drying, the lumber is ready for storage or shipment. It goes to flooring mills, planing mills, construction companies, furniture plants, and other industries which manufacture wood products.

6-18. Automated lumber sorting. The boards ride on edge on a high-speed conveyor system and are automatically separated into 24 storage bays.
(*Wood and Wood Products*)

6-19. Stacking lumber for drying in a kiln.
(*Wood and Wood Products*)

6-20. A battery of dry kilns.
(Weyerhaeuser Company)

Unit 7 Sawing, Drying, Grading, and Purchasing Lumber

The exact date of the first sawmill in America is not known, but sawmills were in operation around the year 1610. One of the earliest methods of sawing lumber during colonial American times was **pit sawing.** Figure 7-1 shows **whipsawing,** which was a modification of this earlier procedure.

Methods of Sawing Lumber

The two general methods of sawing lumber are **plainsawing,** often also called **common, flat,** or **slash** sawing (see Fig. 7-2), and **quartersawing,** of which there are four methods (see Fig. 7-3).

A slab (Fig. 7-2A) is the first cut in plainsawing. The log is slabbed on either two or four sides to form a cant, from which other plainsawed lumber is cut. Plainsawed lumber has several advantages over quartersawed: (1) more lumber is produced when grain and figure are not considered, (2) it is cheaper to cut, and (3) under similar conditions it dries more rapidly.

Quartersawing can be done by any one of four methods: (1) radial (Fig. 7-3A), (2) tangential (Fig. 7-3B), (3) combined radial and tangential (Fig. 7-3C), and (4) quarter-tangential (Fig. 7-3D). The log is quartered (thus the name) and then cut radially from the bark to the center. This is perpendicular to the annual rings and parallel to the medullary rays. A few pieces of plainsawed lumber, however, fall in the quartersawed category (Fig. 7-2B).

Quartersawing has the following advantages over plainsawing: (1) the wood does not twist (wind), and it warps less; (2) there is less shrinkage in width (lumber shrinks very little in length); (3) the wood lasts longer and wears more evenly when used for such purposes as flooring; and (4) it does not surface check (crack) as easily during seasoning (drying).

Seasoning, or Drying, Lumber

Seasoning lumber is the removal of moisture (water) from the wood until a

7-1.   Whipsawing is a method of cutting timber used by American colonists.
(United States Forest Products Laboratory)

7-2.   Common, flat, or slash sawing: (A) slab, and (B) plainsawing.

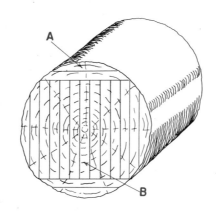

7-3.   Four methods of quartersawing: (A) radial, (B) tangential, (C) combined radial and tangential, and (D) quarter-tangential.

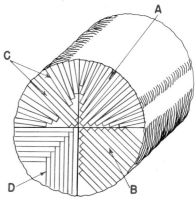

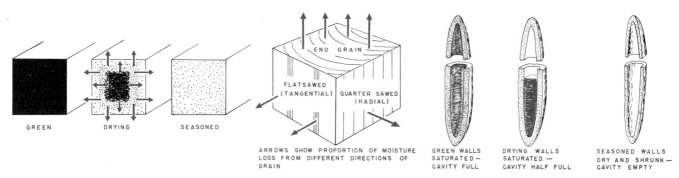

GREEN   DRYING   SEASONED

END GRAIN

FLATSAWED (TANGENTIAL)   QUARTER SAWED (RADIAL)

ARROWS SHOW PROPORTION OF MOISTURE LOSS FROM DIFFERENT DIRECTIONS OF GRAIN

GREEN WALLS SATURATED — CAVITY FULL

DRYING WALLS SATURATED — CAVITY HALF FULL

SEASONED WALLS DRY AND SHRUNK — CAVITY EMPTY

7-4. **How wood loses moisture.** The three illustrations on the right help to explain how moisture is lost in the three stages of seasoning illustrated on the left.

specified dryness is obtained. Correctly seasoned wood has more strength, is more stable in use, and is more resistant to decay than unseasoned stock. In seasoning, the moisture content (MC) is expressed as a percentage. For example, lumber under 20 percent MC is immune to decay. The lower the percentage figure, the drier the wood.

Wood has an equilibrium moisture content (EMC) when the moisture in the wood equals the humidity (moisture) in the surrounding air so that it neither gains nor loses moisture. When wood is dried to the correct EMC it is more stable (shrinks or swells less).

Damp wood in dry air shrinks; dry wood in damp air swells. The MC is only slightly affected by temperature, but it is considerably influenced by humidity. The EMC varies under different weather conditions. As an example, if lumber is too dry, doors and drawers of chests swell and fit too tightly.

Methods of Drying

Lumber may be **air-dried** (AD), **kiln-dried** (KD), or both. Several days or weeks of kiln drying equal several years of air drying. The method of drying, the loss of moisture, and the time required for drying affect shrinkage of a particular wood during seasoning (Figs. 7-4 and 7-5). Softwoods can usually be dried faster than hardwoods, by either method.

7-6. **The proper method of stacking lumber for air drying, or seasoning.**

(Paxton Lumber Company)

7-5. **Shrinkage during seasoning:** (A) shrinkage is greatest in the direction of growth rings; (B) about half as much radially; (C) least in length; (D) effect of shrinkage on outer boards; (E) shrinkage in board B is about half as much as in board A; and (F) splits caused by excessive shrinkage.

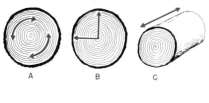

A   B   C

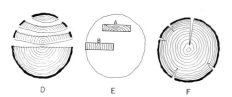

D   E   F

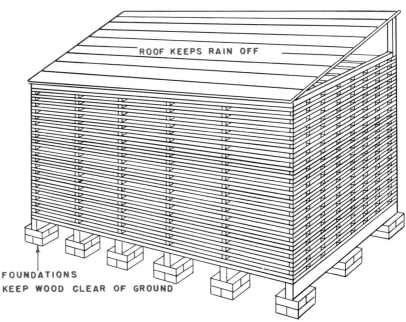

ROOF KEEPS RAIN OFF

FOUNDATIONS KEEP WOOD CLEAR OF GROUND

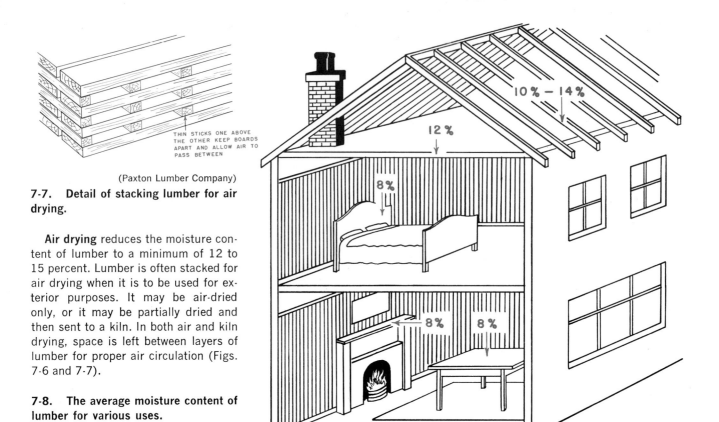

(Paxton Lumber Company)

7-7. Detail of stacking lumber for air drying.

Air drying reduces the moisture content of lumber to a minimum of 12 to 15 percent. Lumber is often stacked for air drying when it is to be used for exterior purposes. It may be air-dried only, or it may be partially dried and then sent to a kiln. In both air and kiln drying, space is left between layers of lumber for proper air circulation (Figs. 7-6 and 7-7).

7-8. The average moisture content of lumber for various uses.

(Paxton Lumber Company)

7-9. The relative humidity and equilibrium moisture content of some manufactured wood products.

(Paxton Lumber Company)

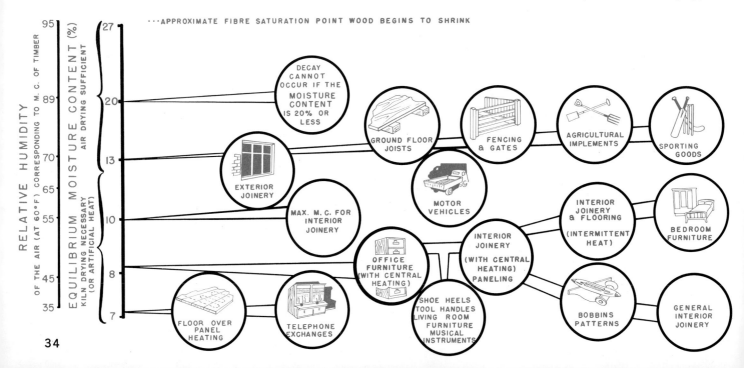

34

7-10. Stacks of lumber in a dry kiln.

(Weyerhaeuser Company)

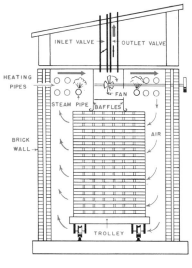

(Paxton Lumber Company)

7-11. Cross section of a dry kiln.

A good rule to apply is the following: the drier the climate, the drier the wood preferred. About 6 or 7 percent MC is adequate for most dry climates.

Lumber used in humid areas for furniture, construction, and other industrial products can contain a higher moisture content than that used in dry regions. Most lumber is kiln-dried to about 12 percent MC or less for ordinary uses (Figs. 7-8 and 7-9).

Dry kilns are of two types, compartment and progressive. After lumber is sawed, it is usually seasoned (dried) in kilns. It is stacked and enters the **compartment kiln** (Fig. 7-10). In this type of kiln it usually remains in one location until it is dry.

A **progressive kiln** is similar to an assembly line. A carload of lumber enters the kiln and goes through each of several drying compartments, or stages of drying.

The most modern kilns scientifically control heat, moisture, and air circulation, using special instruments. At the beginning of the process, the air is exceptionally moist and cool (Fig. 7-11). As the drying procedure continues, this condition is gradually reversed. Moisture is decreased and the heat is increased until the correct moisture content of the lumber is secured. The lumber is allowed to cool before removal to the area where it is stored until it is shipped.

Determining Moisture Content

Moisture content of lumber can be determined by using an electric moisture-content meter (Fig. 7-12). Perform an MC experiment by observing Fig. 7-13 and following the procedure given below.

1. Select a board from the lumber to be tested. About 2 feet from the end of the board, saw off a piece ¼ to ¾ inch long.

2. Weigh the sample as accurately as possible, and record the weight.

3. Place the sample in an electric oven. Set the heat at approximately 215 degrees Fahrenheit (215°F). Bake about 30 minutes.

7-12. Determining the moisture content of lumber with an electrical moisture-content meter.

(Paxton Lumber Company)

7-13. Pictorial formula and procedure for determining the moisture content of lumber.

(Paxton Lumber Company)

WEIGH SAMPLE ("WET" WEIGHT)

DRY IT UNTIL NO FURTHER WEIGHT LOSS

WEIGH SAMPLE ("DRY" WEIGHT)

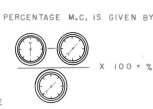

(Weyerhaeuser Company)

7-14.   Grading and sorting lumber for thickness, width, and grade.

7-15.   Moving lumber with a fork-lift truck.

(Forest Industries)

4. Weigh the sample, record its weight, and return it to the oven for approximately 15 minutes.

5. Continue weighing the sample periodically until the weight is constant.

6. The moisture content can be computed by using the following formula:

$$MC = \frac{W - D}{D} \times 100 = \%$$

where MC = percentage of moisture
(moisture content)
W = "wet," or beginning, weight
D = "dry" weight

Grading Lumber

Grading rules and standards are used by the leading lumber associations. Some of these are the National Hardwood Association, the California Redwood Association, and the Western and Southern Pine Associations. A detailed description of the various grading rules is found in the bulletin *Wood Handbook*, which can be obtained from the Forest Products Laboratory, Madison, Wisconsin.

Lumber is often graded (Fig. 7-14) both before and after it is taken to the kiln or storage yard. It is moved about the yard by a fork lift (Fig. 7-15) or by some other type of modern carrier (Fig. 7-16).

Softwoods are graded on the basis of the use of the whole board. A uniform standard has been established to simplify the grading rules for common thicknesses, widths, and lengths. Most softwood lumbering associations apply

7-16.   A modern lumber carrier.

(Forest Industries)

these rules and divide lumber into three groups: (1) **yard lumber,** (2) **factory and shop lumber,** and (3) **timbers** for structural purposes.

Yard lumber in softwoods is graded (1) **Select,** or **Finish,** A, B, C, and D; (2) **Common Boards,** Nos. 1, 2, 3, and sometimes 4 and 5; and (3) **Dimension,** Nos. 1, 2, and 3. The select, or finish, grades are used in visible construction. Common boards are used for sheathing, general utility, and construction purposes. Dimension grades are used for framing where strength and stiffness are needed. They are usually 2 to 5 inches thick.

The factory and shop lumber group is for special uses, such as window sashes and doors. The boards are 1¼ inches or greater in thickness.

Timbers are mostly for structural purposes and are left round or sawed to size and shape. They are graded on the basis of strength, and they are used where working stresses are required. Sawed timbers are either rough or finished. They serve as beams, posts, and joists. Common sizes are 4 inches square or larger, in either thickness or width. Round timbers are sometimes used in framing structures, but they are more frequently employed as poles and piling.

Hardwood lumber is graded on the basis of the amount of usable lumber cut clear (free) of blemishes from one piece. One face must be **clear** (flawless), the other one **sound** (perhaps knotted but without holes), to rate a high grade. Boards are sawed to standard thicknesses. The widths and lengths are cut so as to obtain the greatest amount of usable lumber.

The two highest grades of hardwood are **Firsts and Seconds** (FAS), which are usually combined into one category. The third grade is **Selects.** Lesser grades are No. 1 Common, No. 2 Common, No. 3 Common, Sound Wormy, No. 3A Common, and No. 3B Common.

Grades and grading rules help establish a standard for designating prices according to kind, quality, and use of lumber. The number, type, and condition and location of blemishes or defects (Fig. 7-17) help establish the grade. Defects are classified as heart shake, wind shake, starshake, knots, checks, and splits.

Heart shake is a rot beginning with a hole in the center of the tree from which cracks extend outward. This is common in older trees.

Wind shake is a separation of the fibers or the annual rings.

Starshake is similar to heart shake, but it has solid wood along the cracks with no rot.

Knots are caused as limbs form on a tree. The fibers arrange themselves around this point and form the knot. Solid knots can make the wood more beautiful and more valuable, or they can decrease the value if the knots are soft or cause holes.

Checks and **splits** in logs and timbers result when the outer surfaces of a log shrink faster than the inner portion.

Study the *Wood Handbook* discussion of defects, blemishes, and grades of lumber. The knowledge you will gain will assist you in becoming a wiser purchaser and consumer.

Purchasing Lumber

After drying and grading, most softwoods are sent to the planing mill for surfacing and cutting into special or standard sizes. Most softwoods are purchased in standard thicknesses, widths, and lengths.

Standard 1-inch pine stock is actually only $^{25}/_{32}$ inch thick; 2-inch stock is only 1⅝ inches thick.

The 4-inch widths are 3⅝ inches wide. The 6-inch widths are 5⅝ inches wide. The 8-, 10-, and 12-inch-wide boards lose ½ inch in width.

Standard lengths range from 8 to 20 feet in 2-foot intervals.

Hardwood lumber is usually left in rough condition. It is purchased in random widths and lengths (RWL) and in thicknesses of ¼-inch intervals. One-

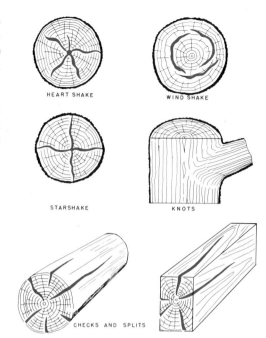

7-17. Blemishes and defects of logs and timbers.

inch lumber is called **four-quarter** (4/4), and so on [1¼-inch, five-quarter (5/4); 1½-inch, six-quarter (6/4); and 2-inch, eight-quarter (8/4)].

Lumber is left **rough** (RGH) when it is unplaned, and it is **dressed** when it is surfaced or planed. Common designations of surfaced lumber are (1) surfaced on one side (S1S), (2) surfaced two sides (S2S), (3) surfaced one side and one edge (S1S1E), and (4) surfaced four sides (S4S).

Consider the following points when ordering a bill of lumber: (1) use, (2) species desired, (3) grade, (4) size, (5) quantity, (6) type of drying, and (7) surfacing requirements. An example of a common order would be:

3 MBF, 1″ black walnut,
FAS, KD, RGH, RWL

This means: Three (3) thousand (M) board feet (BF) of one inch thick (1″) black walnut, firsts and seconds (FAS), kiln-dried (KD), rough (RGH), random widths and lengths (RWL).

Unit 8 Products of Forests and Research

Wood products are important in our everyday lives. Man first used wood for basic necessities, but today he uses over 5,000 wood products. These are made *of* wood in its natural form or *from* wood which has had its form changed through scientific research and development.

8-1. Products from saw mills and specialty mills.

(American Forest Products Industries)

SAWMILLS
SPECIALTY MILLS

SAWLOGS

PRODUCTS   USES

TIMBERS
Barges, bridges, building foundations, churches, dams, derricks, docks, factory and warehouse buildings, mine timbers, schools, ships, stringers, trailers, trucks, tugs

CONSTRUCTION LUMBER
Beams, boards, boat hulls and parts, dimensioned lumber, factory flooring, form lumber, heavy framing, joists, light framing, planks, posts, rafters, sheathing, sills, studs, subfloors, walls

FINISHED LUMBER
Baseboard, battens, casing, ceiling, flooring, lath, paneling, pickets, scaffolding, ship decking, siding, stepping

RE-MANUFACTURED LUMBER
Airplane parts, agricultural implements, athletic equipment (baseball bats, skis, tennis racquets, etc.), balusters, bowling alleys and pins, bobbins, boxes, burial boxes, butchers' blocks, cabinets (for radios, television, sewing machines, etc.), car construction and repair, caskets, clothespins, conduits, crates, crossarms, displays, door jambs and frames, doors, dowels, floors, fixtures, furniture, glued laminated structural members, grain doors, gunstocks, gutters, handles, house trailers, ladders, lattice, laundry appliances, machinery, matches, medical supplies, millwork, moldings, musical instruments, novelties, pallets, panels, patterns, pencils, penholders, phonographs, playground equipment, plumbers' woodwork, professional instruments, printing material, pumps, radios, refrigerators, rollers for shades and maps, scientific instruments, ship and boat building (including aircraft carrier flight decks), shiplap, shoe heels and lasts, shuttles, signs, skewers, spools, sporting equipment, stage scenery, surgical supplies, tanks, toothpicks, toys, trim, trunks, valises, vehicles, venetian blinds, wedges, window frames, wood pipe, wooden shoes, woodenware

TIES
Railroad cross ties, mine ties, switch ties

COOPERAGE (STAVES)
Barrels, buckets, cooling towers, kegs, pipes, silos, tanks, tubs

MISCELLANEOUS
Acid washers, benches, corncribs, dunnage, elevators, fence pickets, grain bins, insulator pins, planks, reels, shingles, stakes, trestles, tunnel and mine props, wood chips for making wood pulp, wood turnings (for buttons, jewelry, etc.)

RESIDUES
Fuel, planer shavings for compressed fuel logs and briquettes, poultry litter, raw material for hardboard and particle board, and other bark, pulp, and sawdust products (such as sawdust soil conditioner)

All construction lumber, furniture woods, and plywood are, of course, examples of products composed of wood. This book, though it does not look or feel like wood, is made of paper, which is made from this natural resource. This unit discusses things made directly of wood, or coming directly from trees. Unit 13, "Miscellaneous Wood Products," deals with items made from wood.

Products of the Forests

There are many products made of wood (Figs. 8-1 and 8-2). These include such varied items as cooperage products (e.g., staves), poles, posts, veneers, and cordwood. Gum, turpentine from pines, maple syrup and sugar, fruits, berries, and nuts are a few natural products from trees (Fig. 8-3). Some newer uses of wood are special tanks (Fig. 8-4), duct systems (Fig. 8-5), and chemically treated woods and plywoods.

Wood can be bonded together in layers and pieces to produce exceptional laminated beams, arches, and forms used in construction (Fig. 8-6). A laminated beam or arch is compressed to remove 60 to 70 percent of the air spaces of the natural wood. Resin-impregnated wood (Fig. 8-7) will not burn, shrink, swell, warp, or rot.

Research in Wood

The Forest Products Laboratory (Fig. 8-8) is a public service institution, the world's first devoted to scientific research in wood utilization. Located at Madison, Wisconsin, it was established in 1910 as a part of the Forest Service of the U.S. Department of Agriculture. The research activity yields information that increases the value and usefulness of forests, aids in developing new products and improving old ones, and reduces wood waste. Research in this laboratory benefits producers, processors, handlers, and consumers of wood products. Many of the efficient, eco-

nomical, long-lasting products used today, though seemingly unrelated to wood, have had their origin here.

Raw materials from forests are being processed to open a new era in the space age. Over 1½ million tests have been made at the Laboratory to evaluate specifically the mechanical properties of wood and materials derived from it. One test may involve one stroke of a machine and last only a short time. Another may take years, requiring the specimen to be subjected to millions of repeated stresses. Through scientific research, wood and its by-products are showing unlimited possibilities.

8-2.   Products of plywood and veneer mills.   (American Forest Products Industries)

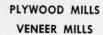 

PLYWOOD MILLS
VENEER MILLS

PRODUCTS   USES

VENEER LOGS AND BOLTS

CONSTRUCTION PLYWOOD
Boxcar lining, boxes, cabinets, concrete forms, crates, door panels, finish, prefabricated houses, roofing, sheathing, siding, signboards, subflooring, truck floors and trailer panels, wainscoting, wall panels

MARINE PLYWOOD
Canoes, motorboats, naval craft, racing shells, sailboats

COMPREGNATED PLYWOOD
Airplane propellers, bearings, die stock, table tops, tubing, utensil handles, patterns

PACKAGE VENEER
Baskets, crates, hampers, matchboxes, wirebound boxes

FACE VENEER
Furniture, Pullman car lining, show windows, store fixtures, wainscoting, wall paneling, wallpaper

MISCELLANEOUS VENEERS
Applicators, balloon sticks, book covers, candy and ice cream sticks, cigar boxes and wrappers, floral sticks, ice cream spoons, luggage, mustard paddles, novelties, square stick matches, surgical items, toothpicks, tongue depressors

RESIDUES
Fuel, raw material for other bark and pulp products, paper roll plugs, particle board

Utilizing Wood Waste

Some of the newest products are made of wood left over from other manufacturing processes. Small pieces, slabs, chips, bark, and sawdust were once discarded or used as fuel. The use of 40 percent of a tree was considered efficient; modern operations utilize over 70 percent. Unit 10, "Production and Uses of Hardboard," and Unit 11, "The Manufacture of Particle Board," describe important products made from wood chips, particles, and flakes.

Logging and milling leftovers once remained in the forest areas or were burned. They now provide about 50 percent of the pulpwood for papermaking (see Unit 12, "The Paper Industry").

Bark is used to make insulation, mulch, and fertilizer. Sawdust and shavings are compressed into fuel logs and briquettes, and serve as ingredients in sweeping compounds and as bedding for animals. Stumps are made into beautiful veneers (see Unit 9, "Veneer and Plywood Manufacture") and are the material for smoking pipes and other products (see Unit 13, "Miscellaneous Wood Products").

Improvements in mechanical equipment have made it possible to harvest more usable wood. Power saws make it easier to cut trees closer to the ground, leaving less stump. In the mill, thinner gauge (thickness) saws reduce the size of the kerf (saw cut). These saws save more board feet and reduce the amount of sawdust. Knotholes and defects in a board are filled and repaired by machines to make more useful footage.

8-3. Miscellaneous wood products.

(American Forest Products Industries)

MISCELLANEOUS PRODUCTS

PRODUCTS	USES
 POLES, POSTS, PILINGS	Antennae, arbors, bridges, channel markers, dams, docks, pole frame buildings, fence posts, flagpoles, foundations, guard rails, jetties, levees, revetments, signposts, tank traps, telephone poles, weirs, wharves
FUELWOOD	Fireplace, stove, steam boilers
SAP AND GUM	Balsam, birch beer, butternut syrup, gumthus, heptane, larch (Venetian turpentine), maple sugar, mesquite gum, rosin, spruce gum, storax, turpentine
 BARK	Adhesives, birch (flavoring) oil, cascara (drug), clothing (wood wool), drilling mud dispersants (oil industry), dye (osage orange and black oak), insulating wool, slippery elm (drug), soil building, tannins (hemlock, chestnut, and tanbark oak)
EDIBLE FRUITS	Butternuts, chinquapins, hickory nuts, pawpaws, pecans, piñon nuts, serviceberries, walnuts, wild plums
NEEDLES	Pine and cedar needle oil
SAWDUST	Absorbent for explosives, artificial leather, artificial wood, body for paint, butcher shops, camouflage, clay products, composition flooring, curing concrete, filler for linoleum, filter for oil and gas, fireworks, glues, hand soaps, ice storage, insulating, insulating brick, livestock bedding, meat smoking, mild abrasives for cleaners, moth deterrent, nursery mulch, packing, plastics, soil conditioners, and wood flour for billiard balls, bowling balls, explosives, molded products
 ROOFING FELTS	Roll roofing, shingles
CHRISTMAS TREES	Decorations

8-4. A resin-impregnated acid-drip tank.

(Koppers Company, Inc.)

8-5. A resin-impregnated plywood duct system.

(Koppers Company, Inc.)

8-6. Laminated-beam construction provides a footing for an ultramodern home.

(Douglas Fir Plywood Association)

8-7. Resin-impregnated compressed-wood items. These are, from top to bottom, left to right: a picker stick used in the textile industry, an aircraft antenna, an aircraft propeller, a mallet, a gavel, a nut and bolt, a portion of a clarinet, a textile shuttle, a gear, knife handles, and a compreg block.

Unit 9 Veneer and Plywood Manufacture

The production and use of veneers can be traced back to the earliest days of civilization. From the time of the pharaohs, 1500 years before Christ, the art of veneering has been advanced by the Babylonians, Assyrians, Romans, and Egyptians. In the modern world, the improvement in the appearance and quality of veneers has been a result of three developments: (1) machinery for cutting has been improved; (2) new adhesives for bonding have been developed; and (3) more kinds of woods are being used for additional cuts, colors, and decorative designs.

Wood for Veneers and Plywood

Wood for veneers comes from many places in the world besides the United States. Mahogany and woods which substitute for mahogany veneers come from Mexico, Honduras, South America, Africa, and the Philippines. Rosewood comes from Brazil; zebrawood, from Africa; primavera, from Central America; and satinwood, from India, Ceylon, and the East Indies. Walnut,

oak, myrtle burl, red gum, maple, birch, and fir are common United States woods used in veneers.

The American southern pine is now being processed into plywood after many years of research and experimentation (Fig. 9-1). The brittleness and other characteristics of the wood formerly made it difficult to find an efficient, economical way of cutting veneer from logs. Flitches (logs) from sycamore, gum, and poplar are also used as center layers of plywood.

Flitches for Veneer

A **flitch** is a log or part of a tree which has been prepared for a veneer cutting knife or saw. They come from four parts of a tree (Fig. 9-2): **stumpwood, longwood** (flat, rotary, and quartered), **crotch,** and **burl.** Stumpwood comes from the stump after the tree is cut. Longwood comes from the main trunk. Crotch is obtained from a section just below the point where the crown forks from the trunk. Burl is believed to result from early tree injury.

(Forest Products Laboratory)

9-1. Hot-pressing southern pine veneers in recent plywood experiments.

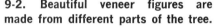

9-2. Beautiful veneer figures are made from different parts of the tree.

The finest flitches are sent to **face-veneer mills.** Logs chosen for strength and sturdiness, but not particularly for beauty, are sent to **commercial veneer plants.** They are made into boxes and other rough materials, such as sub-floors for underlayment in building construction.

Some logs at mills are first debarked and placed in the log storage pond, where they are sorted according to size, species, and grade. They are later removed and cut into sections for further processing (Fig. 9-3). Other logs are cut into flitches or lathe-size **peeler logs** and are put into the storage pond before debarking (Fig. 9-4). Peeler logs are removed from the pond and put in steam vats for **conditioning** (softening). After conditioning, they are placed in a barker machine (Fig. 9-5). Bark is removed by steel claws as the log rotates on a giant turning lathe.

Methods of Cutting Veneer

Beautiful figures in decorative veneers are determined by six factors: (1) the part of the tree from which the veneer is cut, (2) the pattern of annual

9-3. Some logs are debarked and cut into peeler blocks before they are placed in the storage pond.

(Weyerhaeuser Company)

(Douglas Fir Plywood Association)

9-4. Peeler logs (flitches) are often cut to lathe size and placed in the log pond with the bark still attached.

rings, (3) the medullary rays, (4) the color distribution, (5) the irregularity of grain structure, and (6) the method of cutting. An expert craftsman decides which one of three methods will be used to cut the log: (1) rotary cutting, (2) sawing, and (3) slicing (Fig. 9-6).

Rotary cutting (Fig. 9-6A) is the most economical. The flitch is prepared and swung into place on a huge lathe or is mounted into position by a chain (Fig. 9-7). It is turned against a sharp steel knife. This produces a continuous sheet of veneer somewhat like unwinding a roll of paper (Fig. 9-8).

Sawing is the oldest method, but produces only a small percentage of veneer stock. Band saws and special circular saws cut plain- or quartersawed veneers. This method is used on oak to reveal its flake pattern. It is also used when veneers are comparatively thick and on extremely hard woods, such as ebony. Hard-textured woods are difficult to make into veneer by slicing or by rotary cutting because they split easily.

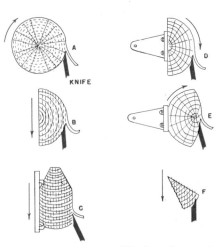

(The Seng Company)

9-6. Various methods are used to cut veneer to obtain beautiful grain effects and patterns: (A) rotary cutting, (B) flat slicing, (C) quarter slicing, (D) half-round slicing, (E) back slicing, and (F) rift slicing.

9-5. Debarking a peeler log on a giant lathe in preparation for cutting veneer.

(American Forest Products Industries, and Douglas Fir Plywood Association)

9-7. A chain lift moves pine logs into position for rotary veneer cutting.

(Georgia-Pacific Corporation)

Slicing is used to obtain special grain effects, particularly for face veneers. There are five ways of slicing: (1) flat, (2) quarter, (3) half round, (4) back, and (5) rift (see Fig. 9-6). Numerous patterns and figure variations of wood-grain structure are obtained by slicing. Some of these are **swirl, fiddleback, stripe, feather, rope, mottle, mixed,** and **patterned grain** (Fig. 9-9).

In slicing, the flitch is mounted in a movable frame and brought straight down or rolled against a stationary knife. This cuts the veneer to the desired thickness. It varies from $\frac{1}{100}$ to $\frac{1}{20}$ inch. The standard American thickness for face veneer is $\frac{1}{28}$ inch; for commercial veneer, $\frac{1}{20}$ inch; and thicker for general use.

Flat slicing (Fig. 9-6B) directly through the heart, or half section, of a log produces a combination of straight grain and heart figures. This method is the most common, and it is used in particular for cutting walnut veneers.

Quarter slicing (Fig. 9-6C) produces a striped effect. Small segments (quarters, sixths, and eighths) are cut at right angles to the annual growth rings.

Half-round slicing (Fig. 9-6D) is accomplished by mounting the heart of a flitch on an eccentric (off-center) holder and cutting off center. Adjacent sheets yield a matching symmetrical veneer pattern with a broader grain pattern than would be obtained by quarter slicing.

Back slicing (Fig. 9-6E) is the opposite of half-round slicing. It produces sheets which come from the center of the log first. The log is mounted to the stay log (holder) on the bark side.

Rift slicing (Fig. 9-6F) is the method used to obtain the combed grain, rift oak, striped effect. The knife cuts at a 45-degree angle to both the medullary rays and the annual rings.

Plywood Manufacture from Rotary-cut Veneer

From the veneers comes plywood. The name is used to designate wood panels of 3, 5, and 7 layers of cross-

9-8. An 8-foot pine log is rotary-cut into veneer on a huge lathe.

(Georgia-Pacific Corporation)

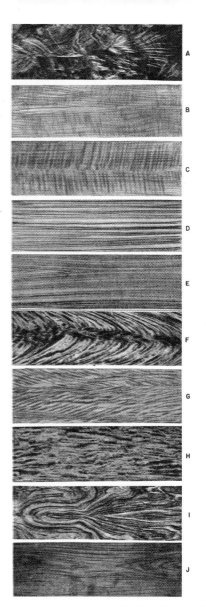

(The Seng Company)

9-9. Many beautiful grain patterns in veneer are cut from American and imported woods: (A) swirl figure in mahogany; (B) and (C) fiddleback figure in quartered hardwood and matched teak panels; (D and E) stripes characteristic of quartered tigerwood and zebrawood (zebrano), and (F) feather figure in African mahogany crotch wood; (G) rope figure in avondire wood; (H) mottle figure in African mahogany; and (I and J) mixed- and patterned-grain figures in rosewood and walnut.

(Douglas Fir Plywood Association)

9-10. Plywood is made from an odd number of veneer layers with the grain at right angles in adjacent layers. Pound for pound, plywood is stronger than steel.

banded wood (Fig. 9-10). The center layer of plywood is sometimes thicker than other layers; it is called the **core** (Fig. 9-11).

Cross bands are glued to the core with the grain of adjacent bands running at right angles to each other. This gives the plywood maximum strength and rigidity with the least weight.

(Georgia-Pacific Corporation)

9-12. Pine veneer is clipped into proper sheet sizes for plywood.

Pound for pound, plywood is considered stronger than steel.

Most veneer for plywood is rotary cut. Mastering the complicated machinery involved in these various procedures requires craftsmen of good judgment and long training.

After peeling (cutting), the veneer is clipped (Fig. 9-12). It is cut into sheets and graded (Fig. 9-13) while it is on its way to the dryer. Clipping is done electronically. An inspector marks defective areas with special electrolytic fluid

(Fig. 9-14). The fluid sets the clipper knives into motion a few seconds afterward to remove the defects.

On the semiautomated assembly line, the veneer is fed slowly into the dryer (Fig. 9-15). As sheets come out of the dryer (Fig. 9-16), and before further grading, they pass under an electronic **moisture sentry** for a dryness check.

9-13. After peeling (cutting), some factories clip veneer sheets to size semiautomatically. The veneer is graded at the same time to three different quality levels as it progresses to the dryers.

9-11. Face veneers and cross bands are glued to a core of veneer or thin lumber. The core may be a different kind of wood than the face veneers.

(Paxton Lumber Company)

(United States Plywood Corporation)

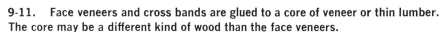

VENEER CONSTRUCTION

LUMBER CORE CONSTRUCTION

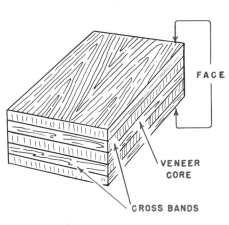

FACE

VENEER CORE

CROSS BANDS

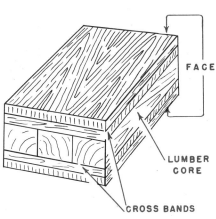

FACE

LUMBER CORE

CROSS BANDS

9-14. Electrolytic fluid is applied to defective areas. It activates electronic knives which automatically cut out defects.

9-16. Sheets of veneer emerge from a carefully controlled dryer.

The backs of plywood panels are made by using solid veneer sheets. Pieces of the same veneer wood as the face can be tape spliced to form the back (Fig. 9-17). In hardwood plywood manufacture, back-panel pieces can be made of a less expensive wood that has characteristics similar to the face veneer. The tape used in the splicing operation is sanded off the back after pressing. Tapeless splicing (Fig. 9-18) is used to form face-veneer panels from several pieces. The backs and faces are glued to the cross bands and the core.

The edges of the core are planed on the jointer. The core stock is edge glued and cut to panel size by a clipper machine (Fig. 9-19). All the plies are then ready to be glued into a sheet.

9-17. Panel back pieces are joined by paper tape. The machine pulls the veneer together and applies thin tape. This tape is sanded off the back of the finished panel after pressing.

9-15. Veneer is fed slowly into the dryer for proper drying before it is used in plywood.

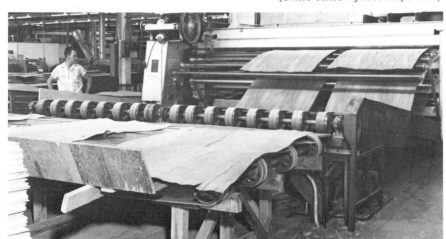

9-18. Pieces of face veneer are spliced without using tape.

9-19. Edge-glued stock being cut to panel size by clipper machine.

Glue is applied to the sheets of veneer as they go through large rollers (Fig. 9-20). The veneer layers are crossbanded as the plies are built up.

After the glue is applied to the crossbanded layers, core, face, and back panels, the press-gluing operation begins. The use of the giant hot press (Fig. 9-21) is one of the crucial steps in the manufacture of plywood. Extreme pressure and controlled heat are used to cure (set) the adhesive. The bond between the plies becomes stronger than the wood itself. After heating and pressing, skinner and trim saws cut the panel edges and stack the panels in one automatic operation (Fig. 9-22).

The panels are sanded by a large drum sander (Fig. 9-23) in preparation for further grading. After that, the sheets of plywood are packed and shipped to distributors and consumers, including lumberyards, building contractors, and school suppliers.

Types and Grades of Veneer in Plywood

Fir plywood is manufactured in two types: exterior and interior. The type depends upon the bonding agent and the grade of the veneer.

Exterior plywood is manufactured with a completely waterproof glue. No veneer used is less than grade C. **Interior plywood** is made with either waterproof or highly water-resistant glue. The inner plies and back veneers can be of lower grades than the faces. Faces are graded by their appearance, quality, and defects.

The six grades are designated **N, A, B, C, C plugged,** and **D.** Grade N is a grade for special order, a "natural finish" veneer, select, all heartwood, and free of open defects. Grade A is the best standard veneer. It is smooth, with more than one piece joined, and neatly made repairs are permitted. Grade B is a solid-surface veneer, with tight knots

9-20. Glue is applied to the veneer by feeding the sheets through large rollers covered with glue.

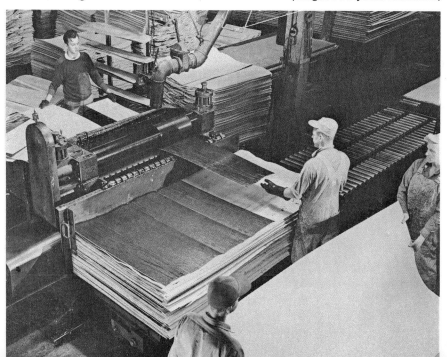

(Georgia-Pacific Corporation)

9-21. Giant high-speed, electronically controlled hot presses produce durable plywood.

(United States Plywood Corporation)

9-22. A skinner and trim saw trims panel edges and stacks them in one automatic operation after hot-pressing.

and circular repair plugs permitted. Grade C is the lowest-grade veneer permitted in exterior plywoods. Knotholes up to 1 inch in diameter, splits, plugs, and other minor blemishes are accepted. The C-plugged grade is an improved grade C veneer. Grade D is used only in interior-type veneers for inner plies and backs, where specified.

Typical fir plywood stamps (Figs. 9-24 and 9-25) are used to mark the panel grade. Exterior-type edge marks are also used. Some panels are marked on the face, the back, and the edges.

Decorating Surfaces with Wood and Veneers

Decorating the surface of wood is an ancient art which is still practiced. Careful inspection of some modern wood decoration reveals imitation veneering made by painted patterns and transfers imitating true wood grain.

Five types of surface decoration are **marquetry** (overlaying), **inlaying, intarsia, mosaic,** and **plastic laminates.** The first three are discussed briefly. Plastic laminates are discussed in Unit 164, "The Production and Use of Plastic Laminates."

Marquetry consists of cutting thin wood veneers into desired shapes, tap-

9-23. Panels of plywood are sanded in large drum sanders.

(United States Plywood Corporation)

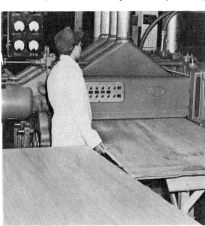

9-24. A typical back stamp for designating the grade of plywood.

(Douglas Fir Plywood Association)

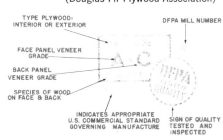

9-25. Typical exterior edge marks used in grading plywood.

(Douglas Fir Plywood Association)

EXT-DFPA·A-B **(1)***

EXT-DFPA·PLYFORM **(3)***

EXT-DFPA·A-A **(1)***

EXT-DFPA·A-C **(2)***

EXT-DFPA·B-C **(2)***

EXT-DFPA·C-C·PLUGGED **(3)***

EXT-DFPA·C-C **(3)***

TEXTURE I-II·EXT-DFPA **(2)***

℥·MARINE·EXT-DFPA·𝓛 **(1)***

EXT-DFPA Overlaid panels also carry this symbol branded on edge.

*Numbers in brackets above indicate where to look for DFPA grade-trademarks on plywood—see explanation below.

(1) Marked on panel edge only.

(2) Stamped on back and, in addition, may also be marked on edge.

(3) Stamped either face or back and, in addition, may be also marked on edge.

(Weyerhaeuser Company)

9-26. Marquetry design on a table. Other items are produced from hard-, particle, flake-, and chipboards.

9-27. An example of intarsia decoration.

ing them together, and gluing them to a plywood surface (Fig. 9-26). The results depend on the difficulty of the design, the amount of time put into the work, and the number of pieces of veneer used. Many designs require 20 to 25 pieces of veneer to be cut at one time for commercial marquetry. Complicated works of art may contain many hundred individual pieces. Approximately the same procedure is used in both simple and complex designs.

Inlaying is the process of inserting a design into a solid surface. See Unit 85, "Routing, Inlaying, and Shaping." Common inlay materials are ivory, metal, and wood. These inserts, as designs or segments, are fitted closely together or are set into tiny grooves cut out to fit them. Borders and flowers are frequently used decorations.

Intarsia is decoration that is similar to inlay and marquetry. It is of Italian origin. A contrasting color of wood is usually used as a background, and colored segments are sunk into the darker wood (Fig. 9-27). Sometimes entire scenes are created. A surface area is routed out to receive the decoration or scene, as in common inlaying.

9-28. Radial arches from 140 to 150 feet long form the span for a university gymnasium.

(Weyerhaeuser Company)

50

Laminating and Molding Veneers and Wood

Laminated and molded wood have almost unlimited possibilities. Using laminated arches and beams (Fig. 9-28), architects and engineers can design such large structures as a sports arena (Fig. 9-29) with no posts or other obstructions. Beautiful church construction and interior furnishing (Fig. 9-30) and interesting designs for furniture (Fig. 9-31) are made possible by laminated and molded wood.

Laminated wood is stronger and does not expand and contract as much as one piece of solid wood. Designers have a wide choice in designing pieces which are curved or unusual in shape.

In furniture manufacture, veneers are coated with special adhesives and placed in a mold for laminating. See Fig. 9-32. They are held in place as the press moves into position (Fig. 9-32). After 30 seconds in the laminating press, the mold is opened. In Fig. 9-33, a curved table apron has been formed, and is removed from the press. The pieces are ready to be sent to other process stations.

(Unit Structures, Koppers Company, Inc.)

9-30. Laminated beams and interior furnishings are used in many modern churches.

9-29. An unobstructed floor space is provided when laminated arches and beams are used for a large structure, such as this sports arena.

(Forest Products Laboratory)

(Drexel Furniture Company)

9-31. Unique furniture shapes are made possible by laminating and molding the original forms.

(Drexel Furniture Company)

9-32. A workman holds the veneers in place as the press moves into position for forming.

9-33. A shaped, laminated table apron is removed from the press.

(Drexel Furniture Company)

Similar manufacturing operations laminate various large and small products. Steps in the manufacture of golf club heads (Fig. 9-34) are excellent examples.

Uses of Veneers and Plywood

Fir and hardwood plywood are used for many products. Some of these, in addition to those discussed earlier in this unit, are house siding, main floors and subfloors, sides and ends of railroad boxcars, shelving, loading and stacking pallets, and beam construction.

Many hardwood plywood products are used in the home and in the office. If you look, you will see many of them.

9-34. Basic steps in laminating and forming a golf club head: (*A*) veneer layers stacked in special pattern, (*B* and *C*) forming angles for head and neck, (*D*) pattern mark on a block of bonded layers, (*E*) shape after turning on the lathe, (*F*) finished club head, and (*G*) test for retention of shape.

(Wilson Sporting Goods Company)

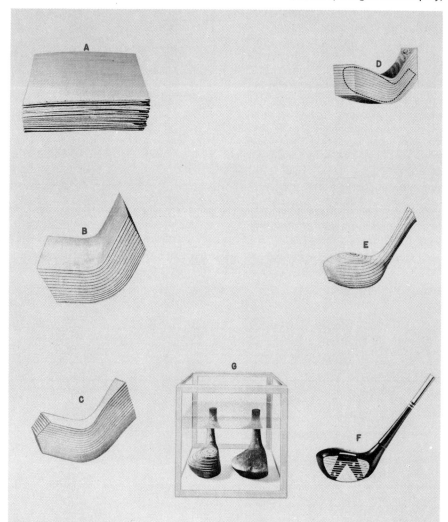

Some examples are kitchen cabinets and paneling (Fig. 9-35), furniture and wall panels (Fig. 9-36), musical instruments (Fig. 9-37), desks (Fig. 9-38), and veneer for use in the home workshop (Fig. 9-39).

Plywood can be impregnated (saturated) with chemicals and compressed to develop **impreg** and **compreg**. Special products from this denser, harder plywood include foundry patterns, knife and tool handles, and propellers.

Veneers and plywood for sports equipment have practically unlimited uses. Tennis rackets, bowling pins (Fig. 9-40), snow and water skis, hockey sticks, boats (Fig. 9-41), and hunting bows illustrate a very few of the thousands of items made of hardwood plywood (Fig. 9-42).

9-35. Hardwood plywood used for kitchen cabinets and paneling.

(Hardwood Plywood Institute)

9-36. Modern cabinets and paneled room divider of hardwood veneers.

(Hardwood Plywood Institute)

(Hardwood Plywood Institute)

9-37. Beautiful veneers are used in the manufacture of musical instruments, such as this electric organ.

9-38. Luxury veneers of Brazilian rosewood add rich color to desk and office panels. Rosewood is so heavy that it cannot be floated, and it creates a harvesting problem when cut in interior forests and virgin jungles.

(Hardwood Plywood Institute)

(National Association of Furniture Manufacturers)

9-39. Veneers are also cut and matched by hand by the home craftsman.

(Hardwood Plywood Institute)

9-40. This bowling pin of laminated white, hard maple demonstrates the versatility of plywood.

(Hardwood Plywood Institute)

9-41. Boats are made from marine plywood.

9-42. The wood for this beautiful bow is laminated maple. Mercury vials are built into the rosewood handle to cushion the shock when the bowstring is released.

(Ben Pearson, Inc.)

Unit 10 Production and Uses of Hardboard

Hardboard is a board, panel, or sheet manufactured from tiny wood fibers, whereas timber, lumber, and plywood are wood in its natural state. Hardboard fibers have been rearranged during manufacture to form hard panels. Only hardboard uses natural lignin to hold the fibers together. Other types of wood sheets use various synthetic binders to hold the chips or the thin wood sheets together.

Wood from trees has certain defects which are eliminated in hardboard. For example, there are no knots or natural grain structure to allow splitting.

American manufacturers (Fig. 10-1) produce about one-half the world's hardboard supply. This amounts to over 2 billion square feet per year. The hardboard industry is a relatively young one, but it is steadily growing and expanding. Skilled engineers and technicians are needed.

Discovery of Hardboard

An unforseen accident made possible the discovery of hardboard in 1924 at Laurel, Mississippi, by William H. Mason, an early associate of Thomas A. Edison. Mason found that small wood chips could be "exploded," or fiberized. The process was somewhat like that used in papermaking; chips were

(Kroehler Manufacturing Company)

10-1. An aerial view of a hardboard plant that covers 30 acres of land, with 4 acres of manufacturing area under one roof.

(Masonite Corporation)

10-2. The steam-heated press which produced hardboard by accident.

cooked with high-pressure heat and steam. He was attempting to make a strong, tough paper or an efficient insulating board. The fibers were too tough and strong to make satisfactory paper by his process. Baking the fibers in an oven after they were pressed into a flat board also proved unsuccessful.

He obtained a small press with steam-heated platens, or plates (Fig. 10-2), from a paper mill. He placed a wet lap (layer) of fibers between the platens. As a safety precaution, Mason turned off the steam when he went to lunch. However, one day a faulty valve allowed steam to continue to heat the press. By the time he returned, the lap had been pressed into a sheet of grainless, dry, ironlike board unlike any board previously produced. From this accident the extensive hardboard industry developed. The first plant was established in 1926; the first piece of Masonite **Presdwood** (hardboard) was made.

Raw Materials

Practically any form of wood can be the raw material for hardboard manufacture. Straight logs, sound material from oddly shaped trees and limbs, and

10-3. A diagram of the hardboard manufacturing process.

(Masonite Corporation)

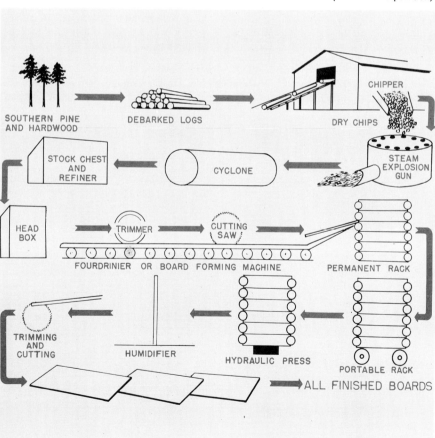

SOUTHERN PINE AND HARDWOOD — DEBARKED LOGS — CHIPPER — DRY CHIPS — STEAM EXPLOSION GUN — CYCLONE — STOCK CHEST AND REFINER — HEAD BOX — FOURDRINIER OR BOARD FORMING MACHINE — TRIMMER — CUTTING SAW — PERMANENT RACK — PORTABLE RACK — HYDRAULIC PRESS — HUMIDIFIER — TRIMMING AND CUTTING — ALL FINISHED BOARDS

plywood and lumber-mill residues are often used.

In the eastern and southern United States, plants chiefly use wood from pine, gum, tupelo, magnolia, cottonwood, willow, aspen, and oak trees. In the West, the major tree species used are Douglas and white fir, redwood, and lodgepole pine.

Manufacture of Hardboard

In addition to the use of residue materials, trees are selected, felled, peeled, and cut into 5-foot lengths. These dry for a brief period and are then delivered to the mill. Figure 10-3 is a diagram of the manufacturing process.

Materials are run through **chippers,** which cut the wood diagonally across the grain into ¾-inch lengths. The chips are **screened,** and the wood dust is removed for fuel. Large pieces are re-chipped and re-screened.

Either of two **defiberizing** processes is used. In the first, chips are sent to fibering machines. These machines tear the chips apart and reduce them to fiber. They are stored in large tanks (Fig. 10-4) for later use. In the second process, the chips are defiberized by steam pressure and are exploded through a large gun. The chips are poured into vertically mounted thick steel gun barrels. Valves at the top of the barrels are closed, and extremely hot steam enters at the bottom. This creates great pressure. The chips dissolve and explode with tremendous speed from the guns into catching chambers called **cyclones.** Actually the chips are no longer chips; the explosion leaves a fine, fluffy, brown mass of fibers covered with a film of lignin. This covering, a major component of wood, makes it stick together naturally.

Refiner machines take fiber masses and reduce them to individual fibers. From this machine, fibers are formed into **mats** one of two ways. In the **water-suspension** method, fibers are mixed in a tank of water and fed to a screen to form a mat. In the **air-sus-**

(Kroehler Manufacturing Company)

10-5. Mats of loose fibers being transported on a conveyor to the steam press.

pension method, they are blown into a large metal cone, where they settle like snowflakes, forming a mat. Depending on the amount of moisture used, the various processes are called **air-, dry-, semidry-,** or **wet-suspension** processes.

Mats are thick blankets of loose fibers about the size of the final panel. They are trimmed approximately to size as they travel toward the press (Fig. 10-5). Up to 20 mats are hauled and placed in a **hot press** (Fig. 10-6) which develops pressure up to 310 pounds per square inch on the board surface at a temperature of 330°. The thin, dry board emerges (Fig. 10-7).

Because the hardboard is so dry, the sheets are placed in a **humidification chamber,** where a small amount of moisture is added. The boards remain here for several hours for conditioning. This process helps eliminate any tendency to warp.

10-4. Wood fibers stored in gigantic tanks.   (Kroehler Manufacturing Company)

Boards are carefully inspected, and samples are tested for defects. Several high-speed saws trim them to one of the standard sizes. They are stacked and transported to storage (Fig. 10-8) for later shipment to consumers.

Classifications, Textures, and Sizes

Standard, tempered, and **service** are basic commercial classifications of hardboard. Special-purpose boards are produced by some manufacturers. All must meet the standards of the hardboard industry.

Standard hardboard is in substantially the same form as it is when it comes from the steam press except for trimming and humidifying. It is strong, water resistant, easy to machine and finish, and popular in the manufacture of furniture and cabinet work. It can be worked easily with hand tools (Figs. 10-9 and 10-10) as well as with power machines.

10-6. Hot presses dry the mats under hundreds of pounds of pressure per square inch.

(Masonite Corporation)

(Forest Fiber Products Company)

10-7. Thin, dry hardboard emerges from the hot press.

(Masonite Corporation)

10-9. Hardboard can be sawed like wood panels.

10-8. Hardboard is stacked and transported to storage to await shipment to consumers.

(Masonite Corporation)

(Masonite Corporation)

10-10. Hardboard is easily worked with ordinary hand tools.

Tempered hardboard has certain chemicals added to it, and then it is sent through a heat-treating process. It is often prefinished with colored plastic film, which makes it very serviceable. This product is superior to standard hardboard. It is stiffer, harder, finishes better, and has greater resistance to abrasion (cuts and scratches) and moisture. This makes it better for use as exterior siding (Fig. 10-11), wearing surfaces, and storage bins.

Service hardboard is suitable for general use, but its properties are moderate in relation to standard hardboard. Its lower weight is an advantage that makes it a typical board for interior paneling (Fig. 10-12).

The surface texture of hardboard may be smooth on one surface (S1S) or on both (S2S). Specialty surface patterns include types such as **perforated,** striated (ridged), **grooved, tiled,** and **embossed.** Perforated panels are particularly useful in the kitchen (Fig. 10-13) and in the home workshop (Fig. 10-14). It can be obtained prime coated, prefinished, in wood-grain patterns, and in colors ranging from blond to dark brown.

Standard panel dimensions range up to 5 feet in width and 16 feet in length. Thicknesses are $\frac{1}{12}$, $\frac{1}{10}$, $\frac{1}{8}$, $\frac{3}{16}$, and $\frac{1}{4}$, etc., to $\frac{3}{4}$ inch. Special thicknesses, widths, and lengths are available.

Uses

The large size of hardboard panels makes them particularly useful for both exterior and interior construction. A few such uses are listed here; many others are easy to think of.

10-12. Hardboard wall panels with a wood-grain finish produce the effect of any wood grain or color.

(Masonite Corporation)

10-11. Tempered hardboard is heat-treated and prefinished for exterior siding.

(Masonite Corporation)

10-13. Perforated panels are useful in the kitchen.

Exterior uses include those for concrete forms, siding, fences, shutters, boats, trailers, signs, and small houses (Fig. 10-15). **Interior** sheets are used for storage cabinets and shelves (Fig. 10-16), drawers (Fig. 10-17), ceilings, merchandise racks, wall panels (Fig. 10-18), and sliding doors (Fig. 10-19).

10-14. Pegboard panels accommodate home workshop tools.

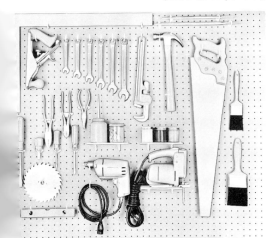

10-15. A summer home can use hardboard panels for exterior as well as interior construction.

10-16. A modern arrangement of hardboard storage cabinets and shelves.

(Masonite Corporation)

10-17. A special tempered hardboard is ideal material for building drawers with splinter-free dividers.

(Masonite Corporation)

10-18. This attractive marble-tone effect is achieved with a hardboard wall-paneling finish.

(Masonite Corporation)

10-19. Quarter-inch hardboard panels make excellent sliding doors in cabinets.

Unit 11 Manufacture of Particle Board

Particle board is an engineered (man-made) board, panel, or sheet that is made in various shapes and sizes from wood particles. These particles include flakes (Fig. 11-1), splinters (Fig. 11-2), and chips and shavings (Fig. 11-3). Called furnish, they are bonded together with various synthetic resins.

The first commercial particle board using a phenolic-resin binder was made in Bremen, Germany, in the early 1940s. This fast-growing industry developed here during the 1950s.

Chipboard and flakeboard are other common names for particle board. Typical brand names include Cedawood, Chipcore, Customwood, Duraflake, Flakewood, Laneboard, Novoply, Resincore, Timblend, and Versaboard.

Materials

All commercial species of hardwoods and softwoods can be used in making the many types of particle boards. Materials are obtained from such sources

11-1. Particle board made from aspen flakes.

(American Forest Products Industries)

11-2. Particle board made from mixed hardwood splinters.

(American Forest Products Industries)

11-3. Wood chips and shavings mixed with a resin binder form an attractive panel material.

11-4. A 50-inch continuous chipboard extrusion press.

as specially prepared logs, shavings, or chips, or slabs from lumber, plywood, and planing mills. Common softwoods used are hemlock, fir, pine, cedar, and redwood. Hardwoods processed are willow, aspen, walnut, gum, and oak.

Production Processes

There can be no all-purpose wood panel. Various characteristics of wood species affect the production and final selection of a panel for a given use. Physical properties and uses are affected by such factors as (1) the process, (2) the type and amount of binder, (3) the kind of particles, (4) the amount of compression, and (5) the type of finish.

There are two types of particle board: **platen pressed** and **extruded.** Several basic highly automated processes are used in the platen-type mat-forming particle board plants in America. In the extrusion type, the particles are forced through an opening of specified size and shape. The board can be continuous, and special machines (Fig. 11-4) are designed for it. Molded items in different shapes are produced by closely related operations of compression and extrusion.

Manufacture of Particle Board

Wood arrives at the particle board plant as waste and residue particles from other wood-products mills or in the form of 5-foot logs (Fig. 11-5). The logs range in size from 4 to 16 inches in diameter.

From the storage area a crane feeds logs to a conveyor belt into the **debarker.** Debarked logs are carried by a conveyor to **slasher saws,** which cut

11-5. Moving pine logs to an automated particle board plant.

them into **billets** (short logs). Billets, lumber residue, and slabs are converted into particles in a **flaker machine** (Fig. 11-6).

Particles from the other sources and regular supply stock are stored in bins and sheds (Fig. 11-7) and are sent to **beater mills** (Fig. 11-8). The mills break the wood into flakes of the specified size. The green (unprocessed) flakes are then stored in a green-flake holder, or bunker (Fig. 11-9).

11-6. Wood slabs being fed into a flaker cutting head.

11-7. Storage of raw materials, including chips and shavings.

11-9. Green flakes stored in bunkers waiting transfer to dryers.

11-11. The belt balance and blending machine, where synthetic-resin adhesive and emulsified wax are sprayed on flakes.

The flakes leave the bunker to go through **dryers,** which reduce the moisture content to the desired level. From the dryers, the particles go to separators, or **sorting screens** (Fig. 11-10), and into **surge bins** (for storing). These screens separate the correct sizes from the oversize (**overs**) and undersize (**fines**) particles. The overs return to the hammer mill (beater) for reprocessing. Fines can be used as fuel or as additional wood products, such as wood flour in some glue and in filler, used to fill wood pores before finishing.

Acceptable flakes flow from surge bins to a mixer, or **blending machine** (Fig. 11-11). The flakes are continuously weighed as they pass over a belt balance or scale. (See the top of the photograph, Fig. 11-11.) Their weight regulates the flow of synthetic resin adhesive and emulsified (thoroughly mixed) wax. These materials are blended and sprayed on the particles to ensure even coverage on all flakes.

Forming machines (Fig. 11-12) accept the coated flakes and spread an even, continuous mat on moving **cauls**

(plates). Cauls are placed end to end and are bridged at their joints. For a ¾-inch finished board, the mat is about 4 inches thick. The continuous mat is separated into individual ones by sawing (Fig. 11-13). The flakes are examined before the mats proceed to assure a properly finished board.

Each mat proceeds on its caul to a **weight controller** (Fig. 11-14) before it is conveyed to a cold **prepress.** Mats of incorrect weight are automatically rejected because they do not meet manufacturing specifications. They are re-

11-8. Chips are pulverized in a hammer mill.

11-10. Sorting screens sort the correct size, from oversize to fine particles.

11-12. The blending, forming, and prepress section of an automated particle board production line.

(Duraflake Company)

11-13. Sawing individual mats and inspecting flakes.

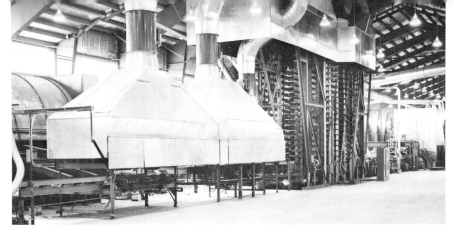

(Collins Pine Company)

11-15. A steam-heated hot press binds the materials into particle board.

turned for reuse as properly made mats. The prepress compresses the mat to about one-half its original thickness. One operator at a pushbutton panel controls the operations from the surge bins through the blender, forming machines, weight controller, and prepress.

The mats pass through **trim saws**, which trim the edges and recover the trim for reuse. About 20 or fewer trimmed mats are automatically loaded into the steam-heated **hot press** (Fig. 11-15). The time, temperature, and

pressure used in pressing vary in accordance with the thickness and grade of particle board required. Caul and mats are removed from the hot press automatically and sent to a cooling unit. Automatic **feeders** and **stackers** (Fig. 11-16) prepare the panels for the **sizing saws** (Fig. 11-17).

During the various operations, particle board is constantly tested for quality, durability, and grade. Thickness is checked by **electronic monitors** that automatically signal any variation from required thickness (Fig. 11-18).

Particle boards are stored where they are conditioned (cured) several days before they are cut to final size and sanded to exact thickness (Fig. 11-19). Fork-lift trucks (Fig. 11-20) move the finished sheets to the main storage areas (Fig. 11-21). There the sheets are held for shipment throughout the United States and abroad.

Sizes, Types, and Uses

Standard panel sizes of particle board range up to 5 feet in width and

11-14. The weight of the mat is checked with a scale before it is sent to the cold prepress.

(Duraflake Company)

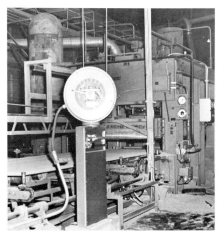

11-16. Automatic feeders and stackers prepare the panels for the sizing saws.

(Weyerhaeuser Company)

(Weyerhaeuser Company)

11-17. Sizing saws automatically cut panels to size.

(Duraflake Company)

11-20. Lift trucks move the sanded sheets to storage.

(Duraflake Company)

11-21. Panels in storage ready for shipment.

(United States Plywood Corporation)

11-18. Sensitive electronic monitors check panel thickness.

16 feet in length. Thicknesses range from 1/8 inch to 1 1/2 inches.

Some panels have a uniform flake, shaving, or particle appearance on all surfaces. These are called **homogenous** (one-kind) particle boards. Others are manufactured with various sizes of particles to create a type of "plyboard." Coarse particles are sandwiched between faces of fines which provide smoother surfaces.

Panels can be cut to size and banded with solid wood strips. Glue is applied to these pieces (Fig. 11-22), and hardwood face veneer is attached

for use as furniture panels (Fig. 11-23). Particle board sheets make excellent core stock for plastic laminates (Fig. 11-24), vanity table tops covered with tile (Fig. 11-25), and cabinet parts covered with plastic or wood veneer (Fig. 11-26). Panels are grain printed, embossed, or treated with insect repellents and fire retardants at the factory.

The main uses of particle board are for furniture core stock and subfloors. The largest volume is used in home construction and where smooth surfaces are required.

11-22. Applying glue to banded particle board cores.

(Weyerhaeuser Company)

11-19. Both faces of panels are sanded simultaneously at speeds up to 150 feet per minute.

(United States Plywood Corporation)

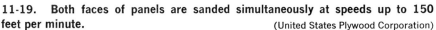

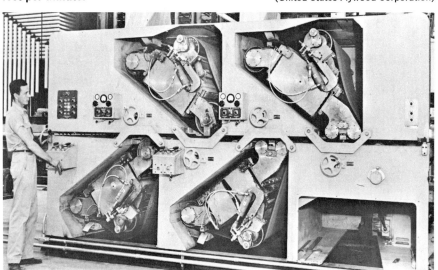

(Weyerhaeuser Company)

11-23. Particle board forms cores of hardwood veneer furniture panels.

Panels can be machined (bored, routed, shaped, or grooved) to form tight joints used in the construction of numerous products. Some of these are counter fronts and display shelves (Fig. 11-27), doors of all kinds, tables of all kinds, serving trays, and lamp bases. School laboratory cabinets, desks, and drawing boards are familiar objects made for the school from particle board. This material is also used to make all types of furniture cabinets, metal spinning molds, traffic signs, and children's furniture and toys.

11-24. Placing plastic laminate on a preformed particle board core.

(Weyerhaeuser Company)

(Duraflake Company)

11-25. Particle board vanity underlay for tile and plastic-coated bathroom cabinet.

11-26. A wood veneer over particle board cabinet doors, shelves, side, and top.

(Weyerhaeuser Company)

11-27. Display shelves being made with particle board.

(Weyerhaeuser Company)

Unit 12 The Paper Industry

Paper was invented by the Chinese about 1,000 years ago. Until the nineteenth century, one sheet at a time was generally made, by hand, from straw, rags, or hemp. It was scarce and expensive. Chemical methods and the wood pulp, paper, and paperboard industry are about 100 years old. Today, paper is one of the least expensive items in daily use. Each person in the United States uses about 500 pounds of it annually.

Approximately 97 percent of the paper consumed annually comes from wood. Almost any tree species can be used. About four-fifths of the pulp for paper mills comes from pine, spruce,

hemlock, and fir trees. Most pulp mills use regular pulp logs. Others operate almost exclusively on chipped wood left over from veneer and sawmills. These leftovers, or waste, formerly burned or used as fuel, account for about 6 percent of the pulpwood used in the industry. Some paper products are made from flax, cotton fiber, and bagasse (sugar cane pulp) instead of wood pulp. However, similar methods are used in the manufacture of all paper.

Wood Pulping Methods

Five principal methods are used for making pulp: the **mechanical** process,

12-1. Flow chart of pulp and papermaking.

(American Paper and Pulp Association)

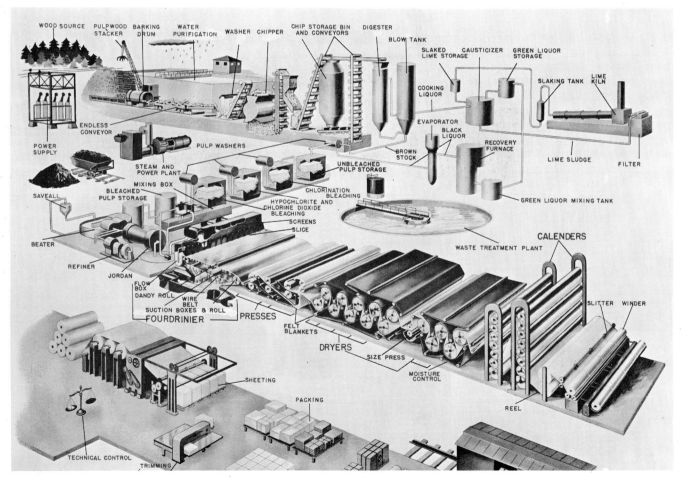

three **chemical** processes (soda, sulfite, and sulfate), and the neutral **semichemical** process. Study a chemistry book for a full description of the chemicals used in papermaking.

The mechanical process makes ground-wood pulp by using huge, rough-faced grinding stones to reduce the wood to fibers. The lignin is not removed. Low-grade papers which do not need unusual strength and are intended for short-time use are made by this method. Newsprint paper is a typical product.

The chemical processes involving soda, sulfate, and sulfite separate lignin for other uses by cooking the wood chips in chemical solutions and steam under heat and pressure. Each process results in cellulose fiber, a second major part of wood. The differences are primarily in the types of chemicals used in the cooking and in the wood species being used as pulp.

The soda process makes paper that is noted for its fine texture and printing qualities. Sulfate and sulfite pulps are used in the manufacture of cellophane, explosives, plastics, and rayon.

The sulfate process uses primarily Douglas fir and pine. Alkaline compounds, caustic soda, and sodium sulfate are added to the chips. The mixture is **bathed** (cooked) with steam and high pressure in a **digester** (cooker). This bath is cooked several hours until the cellulose fibers are separated from the lignin, wood sugars, and unusable substances in the wood.

The fibers are blown into a storage tank and eventually are made into paper. The cooking liquor and other residues (leftovers) are fed into a special furnace which recovers the chemicals for reuse. The sulfate process is especially adaptable for kraft (brown) papers, which must be **strong**. Improved bleaching process**es** have expanded the usefulness of this pulp in making bright, white grades.

Sulfite pulp is made in much the same way as sulfate pulp, but the usual tree species used are hemlock,

(American Paper and Pulp Association)

12-2. Kraft pulp, paper, and board mills are often in one location.

spruce, alder, and white fir. The chemical solution is an acid bisulfite salt of an alkali. Magnesium oxide (MgO) has been introduced as a primary chemical in the sulfite process. This permits recovery of over 85 percent of the pulping chemicals. It is also highly effective in keeping streams, harbors, and air free of polution.

The semichemical (neutral sulfite) process is a combination of the chemical and the mechanical methods. It is particularly adaptable for making pulp from alder and native western hardwoods. Alder was once regarded as a "weed" tree, or one having little value. In this process, a neutral solution of sodium sulfite plus sodium carbonate is added to the digester. Final fiberizing is done by mechanical means. The difference between the regular chemical processes and the semichemical process is in the wood species, chemicals, and fiberizing methods that are used.

Chemical Pulp and Papermaking

A pictorial flow chart (Fig. 12-1) tells the story of pulp and papermaking from the forest to the finished paper product. Pulp, paper, and board mills are frequently found in one location (Fig. 12-2).

Pulpwood for paper is cut in the forest, loaded onto trucks (Fig. 12-3), hauled to the paper mill, and dumped (Fig. 12-4) for storage. It is also shipped by water or railway. Actual papermaking begins after the pulpwood is in the woodyard. The 4-foot lengths of pulpwood are often piled high and cover many acres (Fig. 12-5). Large cranes pick up loads of wood from the pile and place them on a conveyor belt for transfer to the mill.

Removal of the bark is the first step in the manufacturing process. The sticks (pulpwood logs) are tumbled together in a **barking drum.** Steel bars running the length of the drum catch the

(American Paper and Pulp Association)

12-3. Mechanical loading of hardwood pulp.

(American Paper and Pulp Association)

12-4. Dumping a load of pulpwood at the mill.

12-5. Wood for pulp stored in huge stacks.

(Caterpillar Tractor Company)

logs and carry them up, then drop them over and over until they are free of bark. In some mills, high-pressure jets of water blast away the bark.

The logs are washed and fed into a high-speed **chipper machine.** They are sliced by rotating knives into chips about ⅛ inch thick and ½ to ⅝ inch long. Smaller pieces of logs are cut in a pulpwood **grinder** (Fig. 12-6) to prepare ground-wood and chemiground-wood pulp used in research at the Forest Products Laboratory.

Chips pour out of the chipper in a continuous stream and pass across **shaker screens.** The screens sort larger pieces for further chipping and undersize pieces for use as fuel. Most of the chips, however, are the correct uniform size. They flow on a conveyor belt (Fig. 12-7) to storage silos (bins) and large "pressure cookers," or **digesters.**

Wood chips and chemicals are cooked under high pressure and steam heat from 3 to 4 hours. This process dissolves the gluelike lignin and frees the long, flexible cellulose fiber pulp from which paper is made. After cooking, the pulp is again passed over screens, which sort out any knots and uncooked chips. It is then bleached with chlorine, hypochlorite, and chlorine dioxide solutions.

If the pulp is to be stored for later use it is washed in a large revolving drum of wire mesh. Suction draws out the chemicals, and clean hot water washes the pulp. A **lap machine** takes the liquid pulp, spreads it over a wire-mesh cylinder, and draws the water out by suction. The damp pulp is picked up on a felt blanket, becomes a dry blanket itself, and is stored in **laps** (folded layers) (Fig. 12-8).

If pulp is to be used immediately, it is bleached and goes to a deep tub or bowl with an agitator (beater) in the bottom. For fine papers it is beaten again in the **hollander** (beater). See Fig. 12-9. It passes under a roller in the bottom of the tub that grinds it into a fiber of the proper length for specialized grades of paper. The ends and sides of the fiber are slightly frayed so that they will mat together properly on the papermaking machine. During the beating, necessary dye and sizing (stiffener) are added. White pulp is blended with artificially colored pulp to obtain the desired shade.

Pulp then goes to the **jordan.** In this machine two cones with steel bars are nested within each other. The cones rub and cut the fibers still more, providing pulp for the particular grade of paper being made.

12-6. A grinder used in preparing ground-wood and chemigroundwood pulp at the Forest Products Laboratory.

(American Paper and Pulp Association)

12-7. Pulpwood chips screened to uniform size are conveyed to large pressure vessels called *digesters.*

(American Paper and Pulp Association)

As the pulp flows on its journey, it is again washed, and more water is added. The saturated material enters the "wet end" of a **Fourdrinier machine** (Fig. 12-10). It is poured smoothly from a headbox (reservoir) through a slice (slit) onto a moving wire screen to make a uniformly thick layer. Some of these machines are as long as a city block.

Pulp fibers flow on the fast-moving screen like logs moving downstream. They line up with the direction of flow. The screen shakes from side to side, causing the fibers to tangle and cross. This is the secret of papermaking.

On the screen, the continuous sheet is about 90 percent water and 10 percent fiber. The sheet of "paper" moves along the various rolls at a speed of about 30 miles per hour (approximately 2,600 feet per minute). Suction boxes at the end of the screen remove some water. Felt sheets pick up the "paper" and carry it through a series of press rolls. Each of the rolls removes more water.

The longest part of the machine is the drying section. Steam-heated rolls turn at different speeds to allow for shrinkage as the sheet dries and to prevent breaking the web of new paper. At the "dry end" of the machine the paper is ironed dry as it passes through **calender stacks** (vertical rolls). As the dry paper comes from the drying stacks, it forms huge rolls (Fig. 12-11).

The large rolls of paper are cut into required lengths. It is rewound (Fig. 12-12) at speeds up to 3,000 feet per minute into rolls which may be 60 inches or more in diameter. Before it is shipped to other paper-product manufacturers, it is given many bursting-strength (Fig. 12-13) and tear-strength (Fig. 12-14) tests to determine that the paper will meet their needs.

Pulp and Paper Products

Hundreds of pulp and paper products are manufactured (Fig. 12-16). Paper for magazines, books, and catalogs; business and wrapping papers; newsprint; and facial (Fig. 12-15) and other personal tissues are some of the products. An impregnated kraft paper (Fig. 12-17) can also be made. These papers are made on machines of varying sizes and modifications.

Laminated paper (paper put together in layers) has greater strength and becomes paperboard, boxes, and shipping containers. For moistureproof containers, wax, asphalt, polyethylene, and

(American Paper and Pulp Association)

12-9. The hollander, or beater, refines pulp by beating and mixes colors uniformly.

starch are used. A large amount of paper is molded into such products as plates, trays, and egg cartons.

High-grade printing papers are further ironed, or calendered, and coated

12-8. Dry pulp folded into laps and hauled to storage for shipment or use in making paper.

(American Paper and Pulp Association)

12-10. The "wet end" of a Fourdrinier paper machine.

(American Paper and Pulp Association)

12-11. Paper wound in huge rolls at the "dry end" of the Fourdrinier machine.

12-14. A technician testing paper for tear strength.

12-12. Rewinding rolls of specially cut lengths of paper.

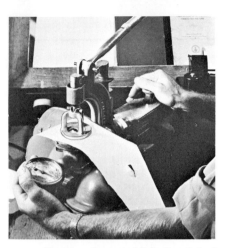

12-13. Paper being tested for bursting strength.

12-15. Facial tissues are made by a process like that used for newsprint.

to produce flat, shiny surfaces. Some paper is run through printing presses, where designs (such as for wallpaper) are imprinted (Fig. 12-18).

The chemical industry is producing many new lignin and cellulose chemical products from **spent liquors** left over from the pulping processes. See Unit 13, "Miscellaneous Wood Products," for a more complete discussion of products made from, rather than of, wood.

12-16.   Numerous paper products and uses.

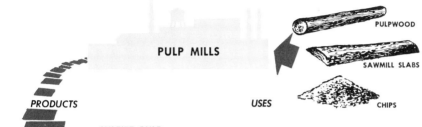

PRODUCTS   USES

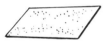

SULFITE PULP
Paper and paperboard for bags, blotters, printing papers, boxes, bristol board, envelopes, folding boxboard, fruit wrappers, greaseproof packaging, insulation, labels, paper napkins, patent coated boards, photo processing paper, sanitary tissues, stationery, stencils, tag board, wallpaper, waterproof packaging, wrapping
Dissolving pulps for cellophane, explosives, lacquers, plastics, photo film, rayon

SULFATE PULP
Paper and paperboard for bags, printing papers, bond paper, boxes, bristol board, chart paper, coating raw stock, condenser tissues, corrugated boxboard, envelopes, food containers, folding boxboard, insulation, ledger paper, liner board, offset paper, onionskin, parchment, sheathing paper, stationery, tag stock, towels, twisted cord and rope, waxed paper

SODA PULP
Paper and paperboard for blotters, printing papers, bristol board, corrugated paper, filters, insulating and wallboards, labels, liners for coated boards, stationery, testliners

SEMI
Corrugated paper, egg cartons, insulating board, testliners, wallboard, printing papers, glassine paper

GROUNDWOOD PULP
Absorbent papers, bags, boards, building and insulating papers, newsprint, printing papers, wallboard, wood cement boards and blocks, wrapping paper, writing papers

RESIDUES (Liquor containing leftover cellulose and lignin not used in paper manufacture)
Sulfite liquors used in making adhesives, building briquettes, core binder, cymene, dyes, emulsifiers, ethyl alcohol, fatty acids, feeding yeast, fertilizers, fuel briquettes, linoleum cement, mordants, paint and varnish remover, plastics, road binder, tannins, vanillin
Sulfate liquors used in making acetic acid, acetone, dimethyl-sulfide, fatty acids, furfural, methyl alcohol, oxalic acid, pine oil, rosin soap, rosin acids, tall oil, turpentine, ore flotation, pharmaceutical chemicals
Soda liquors used in making acetic acid, acetone, calcium carbonate, methyl alcohol, oxalic acid, plastics

12-17.   Impregnated kraft paper overlaid on low-grade lumber improves appearance and paintability and hides surface blemishes.

12-18.   Rolls of paper are run through a printing press, where designs are imprinted.

71

Unit 13 Miscellaneous Wood Products

Many products have been created from wood substances as a result of chemical analysis and experimentation. The form of wood is changed when it is broken into the basic units of **cellulose** and **lignin.** All parts of the tree contribute raw materials for products made from wood. Some of these are manufactured in distillation and hydrolysis plants (Figs. 13-1 and 13-2).

13-1. Wood products derived from wood distillation plants.

(American Forest Products Industries)

WOOD DISTILLATION PLANTS

BOLTS
· LIMBS
STUMPS
EDGINGS

HARDWOOD DISTILLATION PRODUCTS

PRODUCTS	USES

ACETIC ACID
Acetate solvents, cellulose acetate for rayon, photo film, lacquers, and plastics; coagulant for latex, perfumes, and textile dyeing; manufacturing inorganic acetates, white lead pigments

ACETONE
Acetylene, explosives (cordite), solvent

CHARCOAL
Activated carbon, black powder explosives, chemical manufacture, fuel, livestock and poultry foods, manufacturing charcoal iron, medicines, metacase hardening compounds, producer gas, water purification

METHANOL
Antifreeze, dry-cleaning agents, formaldehyde, manufacturing chemical compounds, paints, pyroxylins, shellac, textile finishing agents, varnishes

PITCH
Insulation in electric transformers, rubber filler

TAR OIL
Flotation oils, gasoline (inhibitor oil), paints and stains, preservatives, solvent oils, wood creosote

SOFTWOOD DISTILLATION PRODUCTS

PRODUCTS	USES

CEDAR OILS
Furniture polish

CHARCOAL
Activated carbon, black powder explosives, chemical manufacture, fuel, livestock and poultry foods, manufacturing charcoal iron, medicines, metacase hardening compounds, water filtration

CREOSOTE OILS
Cattle and sheep dips, disinfectants, medicines

DIPENTINE
Solvent for reclaiming old rubber

LACQUER SOLVENT
Lacquers, paints, varnish

PINE OIL
Disinfectants, fabric dyeing, flotation oil, paints

PINE TAR
Coating and binding materials, disinfectants, manufacturing cordage, medicines, oakum, soaps

ROSIN
Paper sizing, varnish, soap, greases, waterproofing, linoleum

TAR OIL SOLVENTS
Disinfectants, flotation oils, paints, soaps, stains

WOOD TURPENTINE
Paint and varnish manufacture, synthetic camphor for celluloid manufacture

Cellulose Products

Two-thirds of the wood in a tree is cellulose. This substance is the woody, tubelike fiber of the wood. It can be treated by chemical and mechanical processes. Cellulose is divided into two product groups: **fiber** and **chemical.**

Fiber products are further divided into two parts: **fiberboard** and **paper.** Fiberboard products include boxboard, hardboard (see Unit 10, "Production and Uses of Hardboard"), insulation board (Fig. 13-3), and wallboard (Fig. 13-4). Paper products were discussed in Unit 12, "The Paper Industry."

(Insulation Board Institute)

13-3. Insulation board is made from the cellulose fiber products group.

13-2. Commercial products from wood hydrolysis plants.

(American Forest Products Industries)

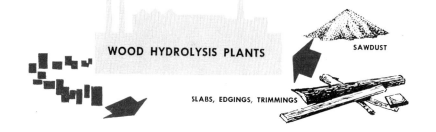

PROCESS	PRODUCTS	USES
WOOD HYDROLYSIS	ACETIC ACID	Textile manufacture, white lead pigment, cellulose acetate, perfume
	BAKING YEAST	Bakery products
	BUTADIENE	Synthetic rubber
	CARBONIC ACID	Industrial chemicals
	ETHYL ALCOHOL	Solvents
	ANIMAL FOOD	Cattle feed, chicken feed
	FURFURAL	Resins, plastics
	GLYCERINE	Medicines, industrial chemicals
	LIGNIN POWDER	Plastic and laminates
	SUGARS	Stock feed, ethanol
WOOD CONDENSATION	FURFURAL	Resins, plastics
	SOIL CONDITIONER	To make soils more porous
ALKALINE FUSION	OXALIC ACID	Bleaching, industrial chemicals
	PYROGALLOL	Stains
	RESINS	Plastics

13-4. Chemical technology is producing the ever-popular wallboard.

(Insulation Board Institute)

13-5. Photographic film is a wood product.

The cellulose chemical group includes hundreds of items. None of these products has the appearance of wood, but they are made *from* wood. Explosives such as dynamite and gunpowder are in this group. Glycerine, alcohol, and a solid-fuel rocket propellant are products made from wood pulp, nitrocellulose (chemically a nitrate of cellulose). Other items in this category are photographic film (Fig.

13-6. Synthetic textiles made from wood cellulose are colorful and serviceable. (Forest Products Laboratory)

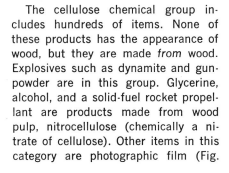

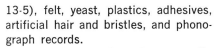

13-7. Rayon upholstery fabrics and carpeting are results of wood technology.

13-5), felt, yeast, plastics, adhesives, artificial hair and bristles, and phonograph records.

Many other wood products contribute to modern living. Synthetic textiles (Fig. 13-6) and rayon are used in clothing, home furnishings, and carpeting (Fig. 13-7). Carboxymethyl cellulose (CMC) acts as a suspension agent in powdered detergents (Fig. 13-8) and as a controlling additive in oil-well drill-

13-8. Household detergents include carboxymethylcellulose as a suspension agent. (Rayonier, Inc.)

13-9. A conveyor belt made from industrial rayon-rubber reinforcing cord.

ing needs. Viscose reinforcing cord used in belts (Fig. 13-9) and tires (Fig. 13-10) is a product made from wood. An ingredient for water-base latex paints (Fig. 13-11) is hydroxyethyl cellulose (HEC). New interior acrylic paints and lacquers used in furniture and automobile finishes are also made from cellulose fibers. Additional products include coatings for welding rods and acetate sheeting (Fig. 13-12).

13-10. Tyrex rayon tire cord is a viscose product made from wood.

(Rayonier, Inc)

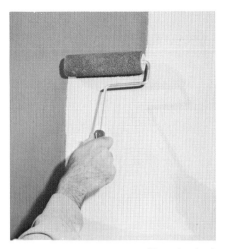

13-11. An ingredient for water-base latex paints is a product made from wood called *hydroxyethylcellulose.*

13-12. Acetate sheeting for boxes is a product made from wood.

Lignin Products

One-third of wood is composed of lignin and wood sugar. The exact composition of this substance remains a mystery to chemists, but progress is being made in research efforts to analyze it. Lignin is used in mixing concrete for road-building and other purposes, tanning leather, and as a water softener and purifier.

Lignin is also used as a base in fertilizers and as an ingredient in perfumes, cosmetics, food preservatives, drugs, and plastics. These plastics are used in telephones, radio and television cabinets, electrical equipment, combs, toys, dishes, and jewelry.

Vanillin was the first item to be produced successfully from lignin on a commercial basis. From this product comes vanilla food flavoring, vanillic acid, and fibers similar to Dacron.

Women's hose can be derived from wood, since xylose is a wood sugar which can be converted into **furfural,** a base for nylon.

Unit 14 Forest Conservation

The Federal government makes periodic surveys of the nation's forest resources. Forests are growing from one-fourth to one-third more wood than is cut for use or lost to destructive forces. Both private and national forests bring the most security to wildlife and prosperity to mankind when they are kept in good condition. This can be accomplished by good forest management, through conservation, and through proper protection from destruction.

Millions of acres of timberland are destroyed each year by insects (Fig. 14-1), disease (Fig. 14-2), severe weather (Fig. 14-3), improper grazing (Fig. 14-4), and man-made fires. See Fig. 14-5. Some fires are caused by careless campers, smokers, and hunters. Others are purposely set. Nine out of every ten forest fires are *caused by man* and therefore *preventable.*

Types of Forest Fires

There are three types of forest fires: **surface, ground,** and **crown.** The surface fire burns young trees and seeds and often becomes more serious (Fig. 14-5). The ground fire may smolder for long periods, burning deeply into the humus and soil. A crown (treetop) fire

75

(American Forest Products Industries)

14-1. Insects have ruined this once-proud ponderosa pine forest. The western pine beetle destroys millions of board feet of timber annually.

(Weyerhaeuser Company)

14-3. Cyclonic winds have virtually destroyed this once magnificent stand of timber.

(American Forest Products Industries)

14-5. Fires destroy over 8 million acres of forest annually.

is the most destructive. It occurs especially in high winds among cone-bearing trees. The gums, resins, and highly flammable branches permit the fire to burn rapidly in the crowns of trees. Total destruction (Figs. 14-6 and 14-7) can result.

Timber Losses

Approximately 140,000 fires destroy over 8 million acres of forest yearly. This total is decreasing as the American people come to realize the necessity to "Keep America Green."

Insects and disease are not as spectacular as fire, but together they kill more timber than fire does and damage ten times as much. Most losses occur in virgin timber stands. Cutting is the only cure for diseased, overmature trees (Fig. 14-8).

14-6. The young trees in the background were killed by a fire and then removed in the salvage operation. It will require at least 100 years before profitable tree crops can be taken from this tree-farm acreage.

(American Forest Products Industries)

14-2. A forester points to a tree which has been infected with white pine blister rust. Diseased trees must be cut out of the forest.

(American Forest Products Industries)

14-4. Cattle grazing can do real damage to a timber stand.

(American Forest Products Industries)

14-7. This photograph shows the aftermath of a fire that completely destroyed a 1,600-acre tree farm.

14-9. This stand of Douglas fir is being seeded from the air. Much aerial seeding is being done to start new timber growth.

As diseased timber is cut, aerial seeding (Fig. 14-9) can be done to start new growth. New seedlings are also planted by hand (Fig. 14-10) or with mechanical planters (Fig. 14-11). From these seedlings come the greatest growth, which results in more wood growth than is harvested yearly. Much restoration of our forests has been accomplished by these means.

14-8. A fire-scarred, overmature tree marked for removal to make way for the vigorous young trees now pushing up around it.

All types of losses are being reduced by application of chemicals after quick discovery of insects. Helicopters are of great use in discharging chemicals to put out fires.

Education in Forestry

The first school of forestry was founded in the year 1898. More

schools were established, and there are now over 17,000 trained foresters (Fig. 14-12). They help in land management, timber production, marketing, and utilization of wood.

Scientifically managed forests require personnel with special training in forestry education. Forestry has to do with the development, conservation (Fig. 14-13), and perpetuation of the

14-11. Mechanical planting of pine seedlings.

14-10. Hand-planting fir seedlings.

(American Forest Products Industries)

14-12. A professionally trained forester taking a boring in a mature poplar tree. This tree proved to be 51 years old.

(American Forest Products Industries)

14-14. Soil erosion happens quickly when trees are removed. One year before this picture was taken, this area was wooded.

forests. Foresters are interested in preventing soil erosion (Fig. 14-14), regulating the water supply for irrigation, and controlling the flow of streams for power and other uses. They also create outdoor recreational facilities (Fig.

14-15. Scientifically managed forest areas provide outdoor recreational sites. (Weyerhaeuser Company)

14-15) and havens for wildlife. Conservation of the forests helps provide more of these benefits.

Tree Farming

One of the most dynamic developments in forest conservation is **tree farming** (Fig. 14-16). There are over 10,000 tree farms of more than 40 acres per farm in the United States. This scientific management system is rapidly growing. It is organized and supervised by representatives of forest industries, government associations, and state forestry associations. These farms range in size from about 3 acres to nearly 1 million acres each. Some are small woodlots; others are large commercial and investment properties. Standards are high, and foresters inspect them often to advise the owner on profitable practices and to check that the high standards are maintained.

14-13. Clear cutting opens blocks or patches to provide new forest areas. These spaces reseed naturally from the surrounding timber.

(American Forest Products Industries)

14-16. A timber stand in a certified tree farm.

(American Forest Products Industries)

DISCUSSION TOPICS

1. What were some of the early American methods of transportation which were almost entirely dependent on wood?
2. Other than to supply lumber and wood products, what major functions do the forests fulfill?
3. Approximately how many million acres of forest lands are there in the United States?
4. What are the six general forest areas of continental United States? What are the other United States forest areas?
5. Where is the majority of the pulpwood in the United States produced?
6. Into what two general classifications can all trees be divided?
7. Classify the kinds of trees growing in your state and in your specific locality.
8. Discuss the methods by which we can differentiate between softwoods and hardwoods.
9. Discuss the qualities and characteristics of such woods as walnut, maple, cherry, and oak.
10. What species of woods are especially useful for handles, athletic equipment, and similar uses?
11. What woods have properties which make them adaptable for bending?
12. What is meant by the term **cooperage,** and which woods are used in this industry?
13. Define or explain the terms **flat-grained, edge-grained, plainsawed,** and **quartersawed.**
14. What is noticeably different about the growth rings of elm and gum compared to most other woods?
15. Approximately how many species of woods have been identified? How many are suitable for manufacturing lumber and other commercial products? What percentage of these are hardwoods?
16. What is meant by the expression **to blaze a tree?**
17. What is the function of an undercut?
18. Name several methods of skidding logs.
19. How do mills prevent stored logs from cracking?
20. Organize the class and plan a group project to locate pictures in newspapers and magazines to make a pictorial flow chart of lumber production from the forest to the consumer.
21. Discuss the advantages of each method of sawing lumber.
22. Name the two kinds of kilns used for drying lumber.
23. Select several pieces of lumber and perform an experiment: determine the moisture content of the various samples cut from the pieces.
24. Relative to lumber, explain the meaning of these abbreviations: (a) S2S, (b) AD, (c) KD, (d) S4S, (e) FAS, and (f) No. 1 Common.
25. What are some of the defects and their causes which affect the grade of a particular piece of lumber?
26. Discuss the major functions of the Forest Products Laboratory.
27. What are briquettes?
28. What are some uses of stump wood?
29. What are some natural products obtained from trees?
30. Explain the differences between veneers and plywood.
31. What special parts of a tree are used to produce beautiful grain designs in veneers?
32. From what parts of the world do the various mahoganies and mahogany substitutes come?
33. What are the methods used to cut veneer?
34. Name five patterns, or figures, produced in cutting veneers.
35. What do **G1S** and **A-D** mean in relation to plywood?
36. What are five sports which use hardwood laminated-plywood equipment?
37. Organize, or enter into, a class project to make either a pictorial or a miniature flow chart for plywood manufacturing.
38. What are the differences among marquetry, inlay, and intarsia?
39. What is the major difference between hardboard and particle board?
40. What woods are chiefly used in hardboard?
41. Name several surface patterns available on hardboard.
42. Give six trade, or manufacturing, names of particle board.
43. What are the two types of particle board?
44. Explain or define the words **extrusion, caul, platen, conveyor,** and **billet.**
45. What are the sizes of particle board sheets available?
46. What are the principal methods of making pulpwood for paper?
47. Enter into a class project and make a large flow chart of pictures showing the orderly procedure of making paper.
48. Name three products used for paper besides wood pulp.
49. Why are the high-grade papers calendered, or ironed, more than lower quality grades?
50. What becomes of the liquids left over from the paper pulping processes?
51. What are the two products or divisions of wood cellulose? Name some products made from each.
52. Name 10 products made from lignin.
53. How can you prevent forest fires?
54. What are the types of forest fires?
55. With what does the subject of forestry deal?
56. What is the greatest destroyer of our forests?
57. What percentage of forest fires are caused by man?

SECTION 2

DESIGN PRINCIPLES, READING DRAWINGS, AND PLANNING THE WORK

Unit 15 Basic Design Principles

Designing is planning a direct and simple solution to the problems involved in creating a product. Although primitive man did not have the word "design" in his vocabulary, the tools and implements he made by hand were simple and functional. He was able to measure, cut, drill, bore, scrape, chop, saw, and burnish.

Man's needs became wider as civilization developed. Craft guilds and specialization began to flourish. These guilds produced craftsmen who took pride in the things they designed and produced. Special-purpose tools and power machines were designed and constructed as the need arose and knowledge permitted. It is clear that hand tools and machines have aided in both material and cultural progress. They have helped produce items created through imagination, design, and proper planning, and they will always do so.

LEG STYLES

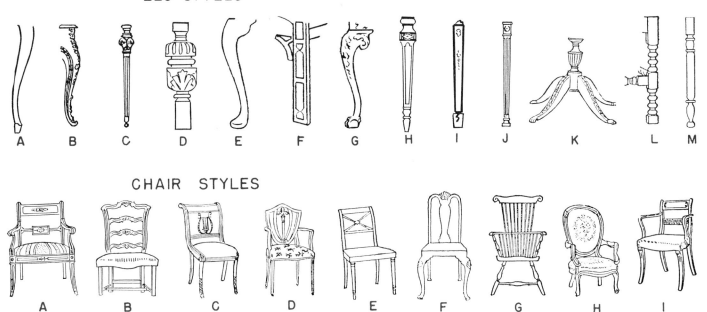

CHAIR STYLES

15-1. Legs and chair shapes of furniture styles. Legs: (A) French Provincial, (B) Louis XIV, (C) Louis XV, (D) Tudor, (E) Queen Anne, (F) Chinese Chippendale, (G) Chippendale, (H) Sheraton, (I) Hepplewhite, (J) Adam Brothers, (K) Duncan Phyfe, (L) Jacobean, and (M) Colonial. Chairs: (A) Adam Brothers, (B) Chippendale, (C) Duncan Phyfe, (D) Hepplewhite, (E) Sheraton, (F) Queen Anne, (G) Colonial, (H) Victorian, and (I) Regency.

15-2. Queen Anne style characteristics, 1702–1714. (A) Lower edge of seat frame often shaped; (B) chair splat (center back); (C) highboys and tall cabinets have "broken" parts with shaped finials at outer edges and center; (D, E, and F) cabriole leg; (G) vase-shaped splat; (H) plain brass ball handles or pierced handles; (I) flat tops in early models; (J) escalloped shell decoration; and (K) fiddle-shaped splat.

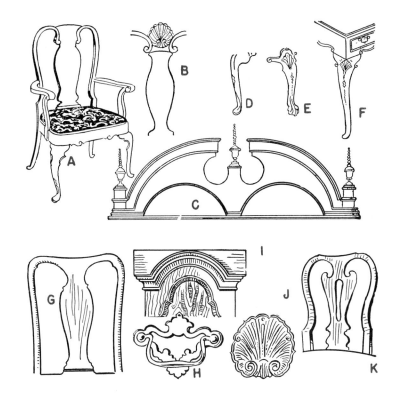

Originality in changing an old design or in creating a new idea is an individual challenge. Two people are not likely to have the same ideas, likes, or dislikes for a particular design. Experimentation with different ideas and numerous wood products also helps to develop the talent for good design in woodworking.

81

(National Association of Furniture Manufacturers)

15-3.   Twentieth-century adaptation of Queen Anne furniture.

(Mount Airy Furniture Company)

15-4.   Modern use of Louis XIV style, 1643–1715.

Furniture Styles

The word "style" in furniture design refers to, and identifies, work done by a famous designer or a group of designers. Leg and chair shapes (Fig. 15-1) are the easiest to recognize in style designs. Distinctive furniture is divided into three overall categories: (1) traditional, (2) provincial, and (3) contemporary.

Traditional (formal) styles were usually named after either the designer or reigning monarchs. The following figures illustrate with line drawings, and some representative photographs, modern adaptations of famous styles. Listed in chronological order, they are **Louis XIV** (Fig. 15-4), **Queen Anne** (Figs. 15-2 and 15-3), **Louis XV** (Figs. 15-5 and 15-6), **Chippendale** (Fig. 15-7), **Adam Brothers** (Fig. 15-8), **Hepplewhite** (Fig. 15-9), **Sheraton** (Fig. 15-10), and **Victorian** (Fig. 15-11).

Provincial (informal) styles were influenced by the traditional. Different skills, cruder tools, and application of

15-5.   Louis XV furniture features, 1723–1774. (A, E, H, and I) Carved decoration; (B) carved knees; (C) carved rails; (D) scroll feet; (F and G) curved legs, and (J) elaborate carving for ornamentation.

(The Seng Company)

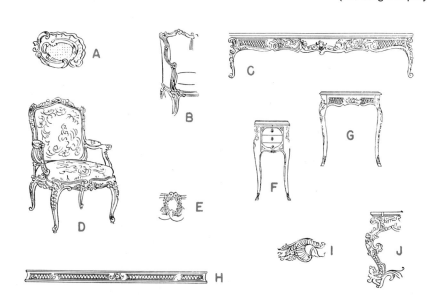

(Drexel Furniture Company)

15-6.   Modern Louis XV furniture.

personal, plain ornamentation helped to make provincial furniture different from previous basic designs. Names for these styles came either from the people who produced them or from the geographical area of their origin. Some examples of this group are the Early American Colonial (Fig. 15-12), French Provincial (Figs. 15-13 and 15-14),

15-7. Chippendale styles, 1740–1779. (*A*) Claw and ball foot; (*B*) curves more pronounced on legs than in Louis XV style—later pieces had straight legs; (*C*) ladder back; (*D*) legs more slender in form than in Queen Anne chairs; (*E* and *G*) extensively carved splats in backs; (*F*) carved cabriole leg; (*H* and *J*) "broken" pediments on large pieces; (*I, K,* and *N*) ribband (ribbon) back and straight front legs; (*L*) carved decorations; (*M*) carved leaf design; (*O*) scroll design; and (*P*) Chippendale settee.

(The Seng Company)

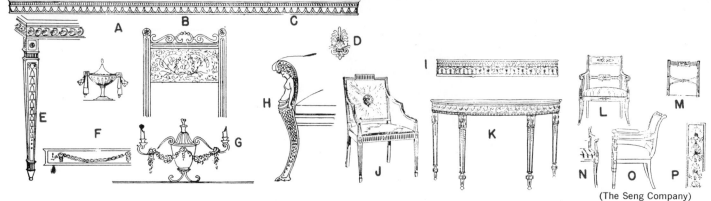

(The Seng Company)

15-8.   Adam Brothers designs, 1760–1792. (A) Classic urn was most commonly used feature; (B) backs frequently were solid panels or caned; (F, C, I, and P) daintily carved moldings; (D and G) floral swags and pendants; (E, N, and O) slim, tapered round or square legs; (H) use of human figures; (J) upholstered seat and back; (K) decorative moldings on tables; (L) arms supported by extension of front legs; and (M) square or curved open splats.

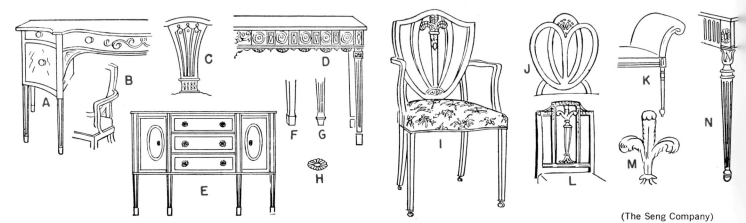

(The Seng Company)

15-9.   Hepplewhite identification, 1770–1786. (A) Concave corner construction; (B) arms short or concave; (C) hoop design splat; (D, G, and N) slender fluted legs; (E and F) tapered feet; (H) rosette decoration; (I) shield splat; (J) heart-shaped splat; (K) curved wings on arms; (L) vase-shaped splat; and (M) Prince of Wales feather decoration.

15-10.   Distinctive Sheraton patterns, 1780–1806. (A and D) Tapered reeded legs; (B and J) shaped pediments on bookcases or doors; (C) light, slender legs on sofas; (E) urn-shaped splat; (F and I) rounded legs splay outward; (G) fretwork panels; (H) turned posts for splats; (K) central panel rises above top; and (L) shield splat.

(The Seng Company)

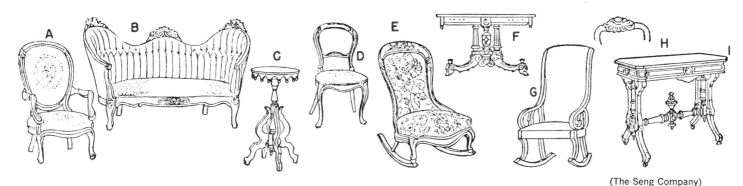

(The Seng Company)

15-11. Victorian furniture, 1830–1890. (A) Oval back and rounded seat; (B) carved ornaments on top rail of curved sofa backs; (C) round or oval occasional table; (D) horseshoe-shaped back; (E) low, rounded seat and high back on rockers; (F) turned columns for central pedestals for early tables; (G) arms low and curved, joining seat rail near back; (H) carved flower motif; and (I) oblong marble table tops.

15-12. Early American Colonial identifications, 1620–1670. (A) Composite furniture with woven rush seats; (B) dropleaf table imported from England by colonists; (C) high chest; (D) ladder-back rocker; (E) cupboard; (F) New England version of Jacobean and Puritan styles; and (G) trestle-type tables.

(The Seng Company)

15-13. French Provincial types, 1650–1900. (A) Shaped tops and aprons; (B, C, D, G, and H) cabriole legs on later pieces; (E) upholstered chair with turned straight legs; (F and J) curved and turned stretchers; (I) curved-front chests and buffets; (K) straight legs on early pieces; and (L) high posts and canopies on beds.

(The Seng Company)

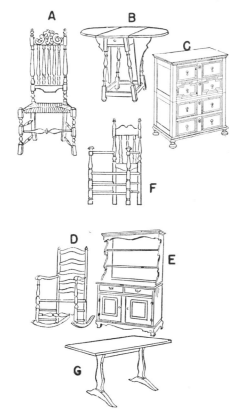

85

(National Association of Furniture Manufacturers)

15-14. French Provincial furniture of modern design.

(The Seng Company)

15-16. Late American Colonial types, 1700—1790. (*A through G*) Late Colonial copies of Queen Anne, Chippendale, French, and English styles; (*H*) hoop-back chair; (*I*) barrel-back chair; (*J*) braced-back chair; (*K*) comb-back chair; (*L*) bow-back rocker; and (*M*) fan-back chair.

15-15. Pennsylvania Dutch traits, 1680—1850. (*A*) Cupboard; (*B and G*) round legs; (*C*) bride's dower chest; (*D*) chest-on-chest cupboard; (*E*) chest; and (*F*) square legs.

(The Seng Company)

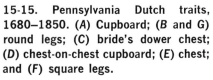

Pennsylvania Dutch (Fig. 15-15), Late American Colonial (Fig. 15-16), Italian Provincial (Fig. 15-17), Duncan Phyfe (Fig. 15-18), and American Frontier, or Primitive (Fig. 15-19).

Contemporary (modern) styles are products of the twentieth century, but designs may reflect earlier tastes. The current Early American design (Figs. 15-20 and 15-21) is a revision of the

15-17. Italian Provincial lines, 1700—1850. (*A*) Smooth curves on dining chairs; (*B*) desk; (*C*) occasional chair; (*D*) molding follows outline of drawer or door; (*E*) sideboard; (*F*) straight, square tapered legs; and (*G*) a chest.

(The Seng Company)

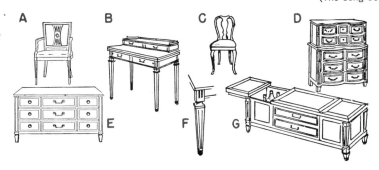

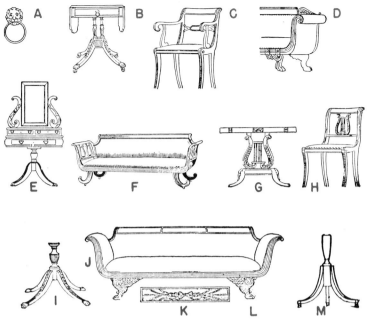

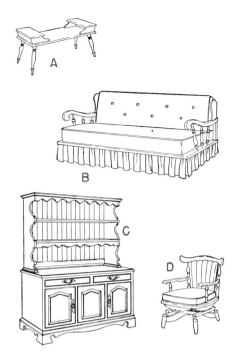

(The Seng Company)

15-18. Duncan Phyfe design, 1790—1830. (*A*) Lion's-head drawer pull; (*B, I,* and *M*) column pedestals and three or four curled feet; (*C*) plain splayed legs; (*D*) rolled-over top rails; (*E*) dressing table; (*F*) carved molding on side rails; (*G*) distinct Duncan Phyfe lyre; (*H*) lyre-back and carved splayed legs; (*J*) "sleigh-front" arms; (*K*) wheat motif; and (*L*) carved feet.

(The Seng Company)

15-20. Early American Contemporary pieces (current). (*A*) Ornately turned legs; (*B*) sofa bed; (*C*) scrolled hutch; and (*D*) revolving chair.

American Colonial. Swedish Modern is an adaptation of classic period forms.

Characteristics and lines of furniture in the modern era are constantly changing. Mass-production methods, new techniques and materials, comfort, and American likes and dislikes influence selections and uses of the various patterns. Some of these functional designs are Modern (Figs. 15-22 and 15-23), Oriental (Fig. 15-24), Ranch Style (Fig. 15-25), and Scandinavian (Swedish and Danish) Modern (Figs. 15-26 and 15-27).

Dual-purpose furniture (Fig. 15-28) has been much in demand, and it meets a real need in small homes and apartments. Special molded designs in plywood and plastic (Figs. 15-29 and 15-30) are changes from the solid-wood furniture of the past.

Furniture Periods

The word "period" refers to a particular time in history, a cultural era, when different peoples preferred furniture of similar design. It is almost impossible to determine when one period

15-19. American Frontier (Primitive), 1790—1890. Wagon-seat twin chairs are characteristic of those used by early Midwest settlers.

(The Seng Company)

15-21. Upholstered Early American reclining chair.

(The Seng Company)

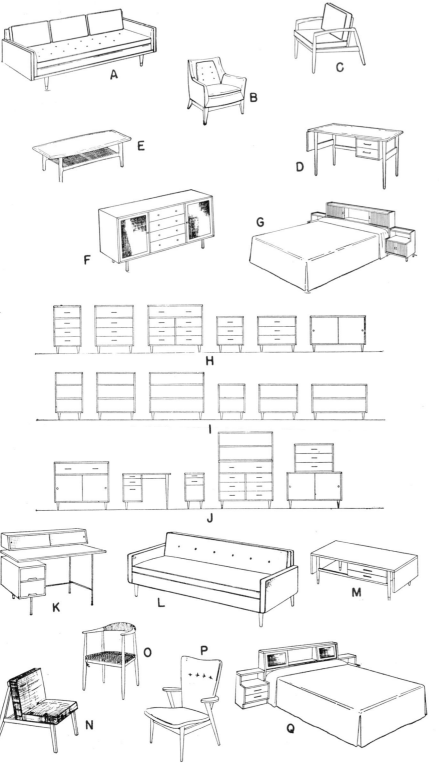

15-22. Modern: a period still in transition. (*A* through *D*) Square and round tapered legs; (*E*) coffee table; (*F*) cabinet, (*G* and *Q*) bookcase and cabinet headboard; (*H* through *J*) modern "sectional assembly" designs; (*K*) desk; (*L*) sofa bed; (*M*) drop-leaf coffee table; and (*N* through *O*) upholstered and woven-seat chairs.

(The Seng Company)

15-23. A bachelor's armoire (chest) in modern design.

(National Association of Furniture Manufacturers)

(The Seng Company)

(The Seng Company)

15-24. Oriental influences (current). (A and D) Ends of legs; the geometric treatment of upholstery and frames (B and C) still show the influence of early Chinese and Japanese styles.

15-25. Ranch-style details (current American). (A) rope drawer pulls; (B, C, E, and K) no attempt to hide juncture of joined pieces; (D and F) cushions often used on wood seats; (G and I) legs usually square cornered and tapered; (D, F, H, and J) use of interlaced leather, plastic, or rawhide cords to maintain ranch, or western, atmosphere.

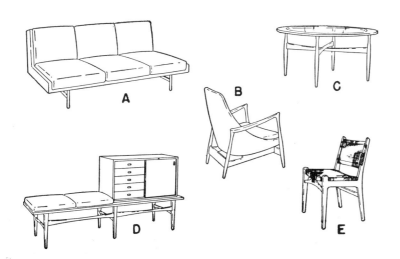

15-26. Scandinavian Modern influence (Swedish and Danish Modern). (A and B) Modern plastic or fabrics evident in upholstery treatment; (C and D) Legs square and round tapered; and (E) woven fiber widely used in chair seats.

(The Seng Company)

(Georg Jensen, Inc.)

15-27. A typical Scandinavian chair.

15-29. Wood and plastic utility chair.

(Burke Division, Brunswick Corporation)

15-30. Plastic and wood chairside table.

(Burke Division, Brunswick Corporation)

Design Principles

ends and another begins. Styles overlap periods. There were five general periods: (1) Gothic, (2) Sixteenth-century Renaissance, (3) Seventeenth and Eighteenth Century, (4) Nineteenth Century, and (5) Modern.

Study of the chronology in Table 15-1 gives a quick reference to the relationships between styles and periods.

Design is either **formal** or **informal.** When a craftsman plans, sketches ideas, makes necessary detailed drawings, determines materials and processes to be used, and constructs a product, it is called **complete formal design.** Construction without the aid of all or part of these steps is **informal.**

Whether formally or informally designed, a functional product created for the modern era should reflect certain principles. These include simplicity of line, economy of materials, usefulness, strength, durability, and originality. Replicas (copies) of past eras should still reflect many of these principles when placed in modern settings.

There are three major aspects of design: (1) the creative aspect; (2) the construction, or technical, aspect; and (3) the beauty, or aesthetic, aspect. The three are equally important.

The **creative** aspect of design involves the application of ideas to the form and shape of an object. Some of the problems are those of simplicity, balance, and proportion.

Simple designs are usually more pleasing to the eye. They are easier to construct, more functional, and more economical.

The two kinds of balance are **axial** and **radial.** Axial balance can be either formal or informal. In formal axial (symmetrical) balance, all shapes and parts on each side of a balance point, or center line, are equal. Examples are turned fruit bowls, tidbit trays (Fig. 15-31), candle holders, bud vases, lamps, smoking stands, and posts of

15-28. A multiple- or dual-purpose upholstered sofa-sleeper.

(The Seng Company)

No furniture material can replace wood for warmth. Woods also lend themselves to interesting design and detail. They can be readily fabricated and finished to suit individual tastes. (Basic-Witz.)

Living rooms use wooden beams to create interest and add color to ceilings. This method of construction is also economical since it combines rafter and roof strength with ceilings.

(Western Wood Products Association.)

Giant logs of this type are unwound to make exquisite veneers and core stock for plywood fabrication.

(American Plywood Association.)

Veneer for beautiful plywood is being unwound as the log spins in a rotary cutting production lathe. Veneer provides interesting possibilities for figure grains and designs on plywood.

(American Plywood Association.)

Precision and intricate carving are performed by this craftsman who is carving thirty mirror frames at one time on the thirty-spindle master carver machine in a Drexel Furniture Company plant. Production and beauty are combined in making uniform pieces from expensive furniture woods.

Redwood was the long-lasting, serviceable wood used to make this curved redwood screen. The screen is constructed of a series of straight sections tangential to an arc. The bench is formed by curved redwood set on edge.

(California Redwood Association.)

Western red cedar is one of the more attractive woods to be used as vertical siding on this Pacific Coast suburban home. Framing and millwork are of Douglas fir. The roof, with its interesting fluid roofline, is made of hemlock.
(Western Wood Products Association.)

Ceiling beams and other preformed structural features are radiated and made functional through the use of wood. Heavy structures such as joists, trusses, plates, or supporting beams are often used with flair and style. Timbers of this type give beauty, strength, and excitement to contemporary design.
(Western Wood Products Association.)

Contemporary architecture is the result of blending function with topographic site. This original home combines the ideas of an imaginative architect and the materials of an ingenious builder. Wood products give warmth to such a home.

(Minnesota Mining and Manufacturing Company.)

Tudor arches permit great freedom in design. These laminated wooden forms offer warmth, friendliness, and the appearance of fine wood—plus economy. They are individually designed and prefabricated to fit the architectural plan. They bring remarkable strength and rigidity to the basic design concept.

(Weyerhauser Company, Rico Laminated Wood Products Division.)

The use of dark-toned matching woods in cabinets, chests, tables, and chairs provides a theme of consistency, warmth, and continuity to the decor of this living area.

(Basic Witz.)

Walnut paneling, with its deep rich hues, imparts a dignity to accent walls. This setting will welcome traditional and period furnishings.

(Weyerhauser Company.)

Table 15-1. CHRONOLOGICAL TABLE OF FURNITURE PERIODS AND STYLES*   (The Seng Company)

Time	England	France	America	Other countries
Early styles	Gothic (1100–1500)	Gothic (1100–1500)	. . .	Gothic (1100–1500) in Spain, Germany, Italy, etc.
Sixteenth century	Renaissance Tudor (1509–1558) Elizabethan (1558–1603)	Renaissance (1500–1610)	. . .	Early Renaissance (1500–1600) in Italy, Spain, Holland, Germany
Seventeenth century	Jacobean (1603–1649) Commonwealth (1649–1660) Carolean (1660–1688) William & Mary (1689–1702)	Louis XIII (1610–1643) Louis XIV (1643–1715) Early French Provincial (1650–1700)	Early Colonial (1620–1700)	Late Renaissance (1600–1700) in Italy, Spain, Holland, Germany
Eighteenth century	Queen Anne (1702–1714) Early Georgian (1714–1754) Late Georgian (1754–1795), including: Chippendale (1740–1779) Hepplewhite (1770–1786) Sheraton (1780–1806) Adam Bros. (1760–1792)	French Regency (1715–1723) Louis XV (1723–1774) Louis XVI (1774–1893) Directoire (1795–1804) Early French Provincial (1700–1800)	Late Colonial (1700–1790) Copies of English, French, Dutch styles. Duncan Phyfe (1790–1830)	European furniture of this time greatly influenced by French, Dutch, English craftsmen
Nineteenth century	English Regency (1793–1830) Victorian (1830–1890) Eastlake (1879–1895)	French Empire (1804–1815) Late French Provincial (1800–1900)	Federal (1795–1830) (also Duncan Phyfe) Victorian (1830–1900)	Biedermeier (1800–1850) in Germany
Twentieth century	Arts & Crafts (1900–1920) Modern Utility (1939–1947)	L'Art Nouveau (1890–1905) Arte Moderne (1926) Modern	Mission (1895–1910) Modern	Swedish Modern in Sweden Modern in other countries

* NOTE: It is virtually impossible to determine the exact date when one period ends and another begins, since furniture styles have a tendency to overlap. The above dates, however, are approximately correct, and they delineate the years of maximum popularity for each style. This table will serve as a quick reference to determine the leading styles in each century. It also shows the interrelation of styles in the various countries given.

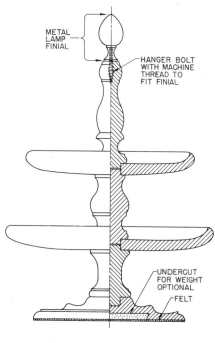

METAL LAMP FINIAL

HANGER BOLT WITH MACHINE THREAD TO FIT FINIAL

UNDERCUT FOR WEIGHT OPTIONAL

FELT

beds. In informal axial (asymmetrical, or not symmetrical) balance, areas of shapes and parts are not the same on both sides of the balance point. To achieve this balance, a large area near the center line is balanced with a small area at a greater distance from the center line. Radial balance is best characterized by a central point of rotation. The faces of modern electric clocks (Fig. 15-32) best illustrate this kind of balance.

15-31. The tidbit tray is an example of formal axial (symmetrical) balance.
(Delta Power Tool Division, Rockwell Manufacturing Company)

15-32. Radial balance is illustrated by a modern clock face.
(Delta Power Tool Division, Rockwell Manufacturing Company)

Proportion is the ratio of one part to another. The ratio of lines, different areas of color, and different areas of space must be balanced to secure an appealing and useful product. Common ratios of size are 2 to 3, 3 to 5, and 5 to 8. The ancient Greeks developed what they called the **Golden Mean,** or **Golden Rectangle.** It was considered the ideal proportion. If the short side of the rectangle measures 2 units, the long side should measure approxi-

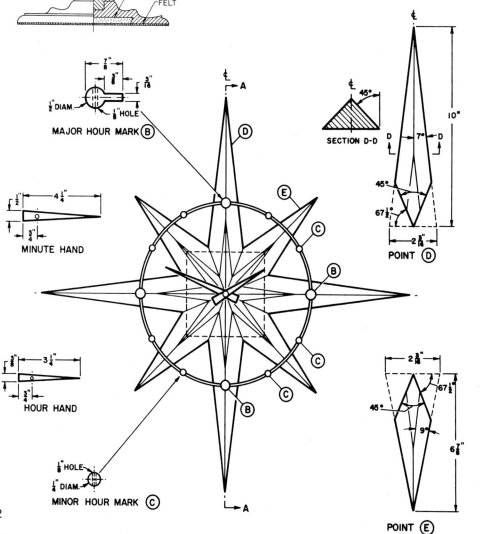

MAJOR HOUR MARK B

MINUTE HAND

HOUR HAND

MINOR HOUR MARK C

SECTION D-D

POINT D

POINT E

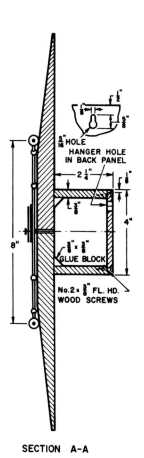

SECTION A-A

mately 3¼ units. This proportion is still in use.

The **construction,** or **technical,** aspect of design involves (1) making detailed drawings of the object and its parts so that craftsmen can read and follow the notes and measurements for construction, and (2) studying and planning the orderly procedure of the processes and operations. These include planing, jointing, sawing, turning, drilling, assembling, and finishing. Knowledge of this part of design is absolutely necessary before a person can read, plan, or make drawings, or follow directions for doing the work.

Beauty, or the **aesthetic** aspect, requires answers to these questions: Are the lines pleasing to the eye? Does the project look the way it is supposed to look? Is it graceful? Will the color harmonize with the setting in which it will be placed? At least three problems are encountered in developing beauty: (1) rhythm, (2) harmony, and (3) color and texture.

Rhythm is orderly repetition and symmetry of straight lines, curves, angles, spaces, and color. It is often seen in modern architectural structures, and it is almost always present in early masterpieces. Architecture has been called "frozen music" because of this quality.

Harmony groups similar spaces, shapes, and colors to achieve a feeling of complete agreement. A circular object, for example, should be decorated with a similarly shaped design, if decoration is used.

Color and texture are brought together in colors of woods, grain, structure, and patterns. A beautiful surface texture and finish and a pleasing color contribute to the beauty of the final product.

Color Harmony in Design

Proper color combinations make a home, office, or any other area more beautiful and more enjoyable. The colors used in furniture should harmonize

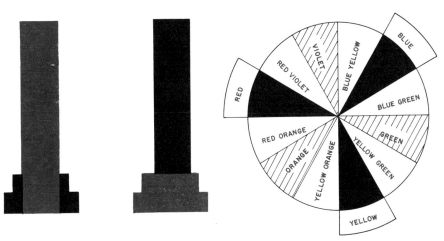

15-33. Unbroken color dimension makes an object seem taller.

15-34. The color wheel is a guide for selecting color combinations.

with those in the room where the furniture is to be used. Scientists have discovered that colors influence and affect people. They can inspire, stimulate, soothe, or relax one. Improperly used, color can bring about nervousness or fatigue.

Color makes an object or area seem larger or smaller than it really is. Light colors enlarge; dark ones diminish. Yellow can usually be seen at a greater distance than many other colors; it has a longer "wave length" than darker colors and therefore projects. An unbroken length of color (color dimension) makes an object appear taller than it does if the color dimension is broken (Fig. 15-33).

The color wheel (Fig. 15-34) is a guide to the selection of harmonious color combinations. The color sequence of the chart is based on the three primary colors: **red, yellow,** and **blue.** When these are mixed, secondary colors are obtained. These are **orange, green,** and **violet** (purple). All other color mixtures are called **tertiary** (third order). Four basic harmonies are used to derive many pleasing color plans from the primary ones: analogous, triadic, complementary, and split complementary.

Analogous, or **related,** color harmony is obtained by using any three adjoining colors on the color wheel (Fig. 15-35). For example, orange, yellow-orange, and yellow give a north room sunny brightness.

Triadic color harmony (Fig. 15-36) results when the three colors used are spaced equal distances from each other on the color wheel. The three primary colors illustrate this principle.

15-35. Analogous color harmony is obtained by using three adjoining colors on the color wheel.

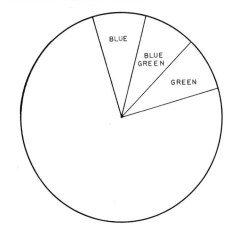

93

Complementary, or **opposite,** color harmony (Fig. 15-37) uses two colors which are opposite each other on the color wheel. This gives dramatic effects: e.g., red-orange and blue-green.

Split-complementary color harmony (Fig. 15-38) is a variation of complementary harmony. Two hues just next to the true complementary color are used. Violet (purple) is the true com-

plement to yellow, and red-violet and blue-violet are the adjacent ones. Two violet tones are in monochromatic (single) harmony; the yellow provides vivid contrast.

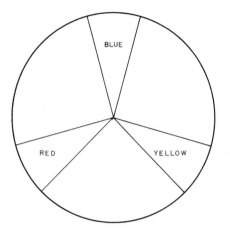

15-36. Triadic color harmony is obtained by using three colors equally spaced on the color wheel.

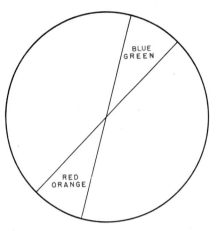

15-37. Complementary color harmony is formed by using two colors opposite each other on the wheel.

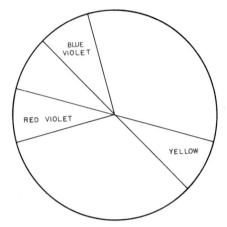

15-38. Split-complementary color is a variation of complementary color harmony.

Unit 16 Understanding Working Drawings

Drafting is a universal language with a special alphabet of lines, letters, and symbols. Working drawings and plans are often made and read in planning, experimentation, and construction activities.

A drawing is a pictorial description. It shows the sizes of all the parts of an object and how they are fitted and joined together. Sizes, materials, and fitted positions of parts are often complicated. Words alone cannot be used to describe aircraft, missiles, or interplanetary space vehicles. A drawing is needed even for much simpler objects, such as chairs, chests, and cabinets, which do not have as many parts.

A neat sketch or drawing should be made of each project before construction is started. The material needed, the procedure of operations, and the tools and machines necessary for com-

pleting the project can be determined by reading the basic drawing. One must know the different kinds of drawings and the meanings of the various lines, letters, numbers, dimensions, and symbols. It must be learned well to read and interpret the language of drawings quickly and easily.

Alphabet of Drafting Lines

Lines are the alphabet of the language of drafting. They indicate certain parts or functions of parts. Each one should be recognized quickly for its use in drawing an object (Figs. 16-1 and 16-2). At least 11 kinds of permanent lines are used: (1) border, (2) object, (3) hidden, (4) extension, (5) dimension, (6) center, (7) cutting plane, (8) section, (9) ditto, (10) break, and (11) adjacent position.

A **border line** (Fig. 16-2A) is the widest, or heaviest. It is used to frame, or border, the drawing sheet.

An **object line** (Fig. 16-2B) is a solid heavy line and one of the most important. It outlines the visible edges and surfaces of the object being drawn.

Hidden lines (Fig. 16-2C) are used to show the invisible edges and surfaces of an object. They are medium heavy and are dashes about 1/8 inch long with about 1/16 inch space between the dashes.

Extension lines (Fig. 16-2D) are used in connection with dimension lines. They are thin and dark and begin about 1/16 inch away from an object line and extend about 1/8 inch beyond the last dimension-line arrowhead.

The **dimension line** (Fig. 16-2E) shows the size of an object, or of some part of it. This line is usually placed between two extension lines. It should be as narrow as extension and center lines and broken near the middle for the insertion of the measurement. Arrowheads should be on each end touching the extension lines. In small spaces, the number may be placed between extension lines with the dimension lines outside. Dimension lines should not cross main lines on a drawing. They may cross center lines which have breaks where the dimension line crosses.

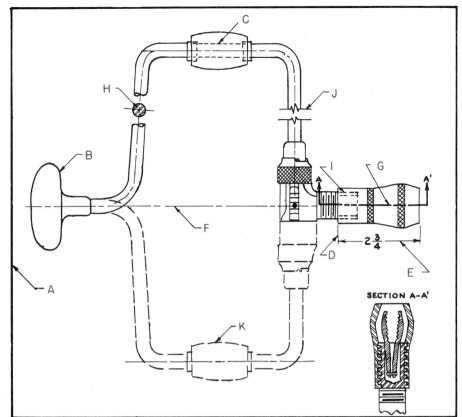

16-2. Application of lines on a drawing.

16-1. An alphabet of drafting lines.

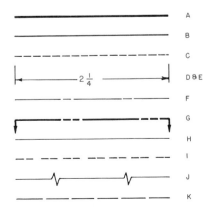

A **center line** (Fig. 16-2F) is particularly important in showing the center of any arc, circle, or cylindrical object. It is as narrow as an extension line and is made of alternately long and short dashes. Short dashes should cross at the centers of arcs and circles.

The **cutting-plane line** (Fig. 16-2G) suggests that an object has been cut to remove a part to show its internal construction. It is made by one dash about 3/4 inch long and two short dashes, each about 1/8 inch long. About 1/16 inch of space is left between dashes. The width of this line is between that of the object and that of the border lines.

Section lines (Fig. 16-2H) are often called **crosshatch** lines. They are narrow ones, similar to extension lines. Solid and dashed lines are used to indicate the part of the object "cut" by

the cutting plane. Various lines designate the type of material (Fig. 16-3).

Ditto lines (Fig. 16-2I) are short, evenly spaced double dashes. They are drawn to show that some part of the drawing is repeated in another place. These eliminate drawing a part in detail more than once.

A **break line** (Fig. 16-2J) is frequently used to eliminate the repetition of, or to shorten, a long part and to draw it in less space. It is also used when sectioning a solid part. This line may be made either mechanically or freehand. It is about the width of an object line.

The **adjacent-position line** (Fig. 16-2K) is used to show that some part, such as a handle, moves to another position. Even dashes about 1/2 to 3/4 inch in length are used with a slight break between them.

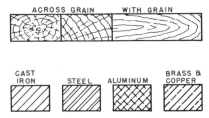

16-3. **Section lines for building materials.**

16-5. **Properly spaced letters.**

The **construction guideline** is not shown. It is a trial line so light in color that it should not have to be erased. It is used to outline the shape of parts and to act as a guide in making proper letters and numerals.

Letters

Well-made letters improve the appearance of a drawing and make it easy to read. Guide (construction) lines assist the draftsman to make uniform sizes of letters for notes and other information. These include the kind of material, part names, and numerical sizes of parts. Skill in this aspect of planning and drafting for woodwork will be of much value. The ability to letter is of special value if a person chooses a profession, such as engineering, architecture, industrial technology, industrial education, or related technical activities.

The single-stroke Gothic capital letter is most widely used. Some draftsmen use special lettering devices to form letters. Practice making letters and numbers (Fig. 16-4).

Some letters differ in width. For example, the I is a single line, and the J is slightly narrower than others. The M and the W are slightly wider. All other letters can be made approximately the same width. Practice spacing letters properly; because they do not take up the same space, they look odd if equally spaced (Fig. 16-5). Letters for notes (special directions) and whole numbers should be about ⅛ inch high on most drawings.

Numbers

Dimension numerals (whole numbers and fractions) show the exact size of a space, hole, curve, or other part of the object. The total height of a fractional dimension should be about twice as high as that of a whole number (Fig. 16-6). Whole numbers are about ⅛ to 3/16 inch high. Numbers for the numerator and the denominator of a fraction are each about 3/32 to ⅛ inch high. The division line is drawn in the space between them. It is always aligned with the dimension line unless unidirectional dimensioning is used. See Fig. 16-11. The sizes of parts are easy to locate when numerals are placed along this line. An arrowhead is drawn at one or both ends of the dimension line, as needed.

Arrowheads

Arrowheads are made freehand on the ends of dimension lines. The head is about ⅛ inch long, or three times as long as it is wide (Fig. 16-7). Arrowheads, numbers, and letters assist the worker in locating measurements.

16-4. **Single-stroke vertical Gothic letters and numbers.**

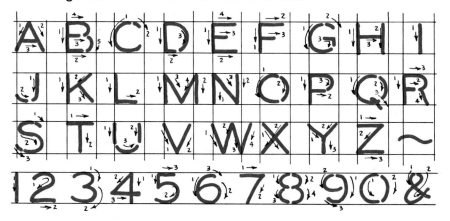

16-6. **Proportions of fractions and whole numbers.**

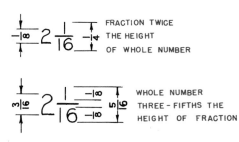

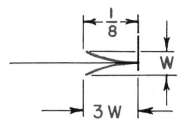

16-7. Proportion of arrowheads.

Reading and Making Measurements

Reading a rule, or scale, and making measurements with the various squares and measuring devices are discussed in SECTION 3, "Basic Hand-tool Processes." Accurate measuring for drawing or in constructing a project is one of the first requirements of good craftsmanship.

Measurements in woodworking are usually expressed in sixteenths ($\frac{1}{16}$) of an inch (see Fig. 16-8). The scales, squares, and rules used are divided into these units.

Dimensions

Well-placed dimensions on a drawing give the exact sizes of the various parts of a project. Size and location dimensions are of three types: (1) position, (2) detail, and (3) overall (Fig. 16-9).

16-8. Measurements given in sixteenths ($\frac{1}{16}$) of an inch.

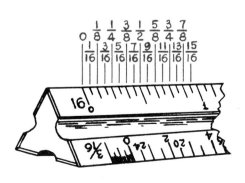

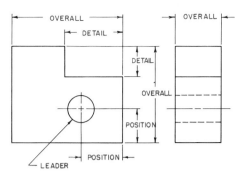

16-9. Overall, position, and detail dimensions.

Position dimension shows where a hole or other detail is located. A **detail dimension** gives the correct length, width, height, or depth of some specific detailed part. **Overall dimension** shows the total length, width, and height of an object.

The following rules and procedures for dimensioning are helpful:

1. Dimensions should be outside, between, and to the right of the views whenever possible. Other dimensions are placed on and around the views as needed (see Fig. 16-10).

2. The first line of dimensions around views should begin about $\frac{1}{4}$ to $\frac{3}{8}$ inch away from the nearest object line. Overall dimensions are farthest from the object.

3. Some drawings have dimensions which all read from the bottom of the

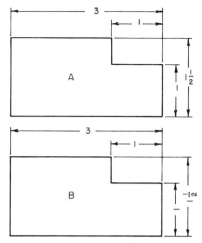

16-11. Unidirectional (A) and aligned dimensions (B).

sheet. This is called **unidirectional** dimensioning. In woodworking, most dimensions are placed to read from both the bottom and the right of the sheet. This is **aligned** dimensioning. Both methods are shown in Fig. 16-11.

4. The dimension of a particular part is usually given only on the one view where the part is most clearly shown.

5. Sizes of very small spaces are usually placed outside the area dimensioned (Fig. 16-12).

6. Large arcs and circles, or holes, are usually dimensioned on the view where they appear in true form (Fig.

16-10. The correct placement of dimensions on views of an object.

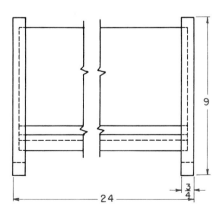

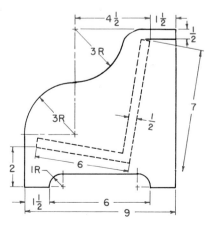

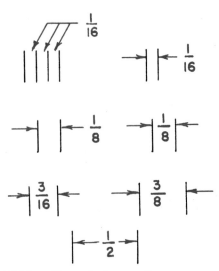

16-12. Dimensioning small spaces.

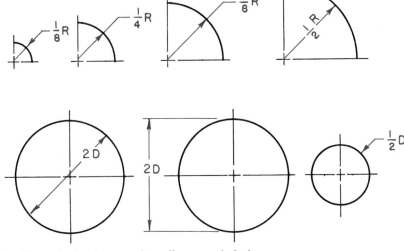

16-13. Dimensioning large and small arcs and circles.

16-13). The letter **R** or **D** follows the size numeral to indicate either **radius** or **diameter.**

7. One leader, dimension, and note are sometimes used to dimension several holes. This is done when the holes are equally spaced on the same center line and are the same size (Fig. 16-14).

8. Precision measurements are shown as whole numbers and decimals.

9. Very small arcs and internal and external corners of a project are called **fillets** and **rounds.** Their size is designated by a note and a dimension (Fig. 16-15). This is common practice on patternmaking drawings.

10. Angles are dimensioned either in degrees or linear measurements or in a combination of both (Fig. 16-16).

Symbols

Symbols tell much on sight that would be difficult to explain by words or dimensions. A system of conventional standard symbols is accepted for general use on all types of drafting. Those that follow are of value in reading or making drawings:

1. Threads on bolts and screws (Fig. 16-17).

2. Construction symbols used in cabinet and architectural drawings (Fig. 16-18).

3. Electrical drawings are called **schematic** and are made by using lines and symbols. They are seen on electrical circuit diagrams for products such as radios, meters, and television sets. Electrical plans for architectural construction contain some of these same symbols, as well as many others (Fig. 16-19).

Pictorial Drawings

When one looks at an object, he receives a picture impression. A photograph presents a similar picture. When drawings are made to resemble these impressions, the results are called **pictorial drawings.** These are valuable to give general ideas of how an object will appear when it is completed.

There are three major kinds of pictorial drawings: (1) isometric, (2)

16-14. Dimensioning equally spaced holes of the same size.

16-15. Fillets and rounds on patternmaking drawings.

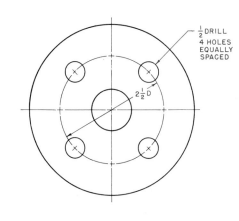

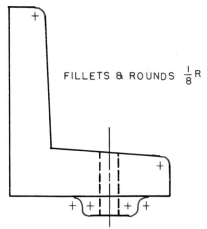

FILLETS & ROUNDS $\frac{1}{8}$R

98

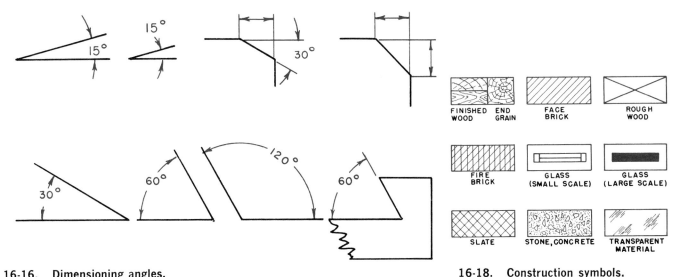

16-16. Dimensioning angles.

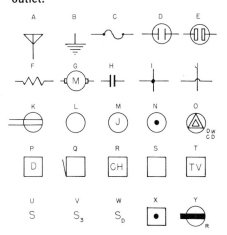

16-18. Construction symbols.

oblique, and (3) perspective (Fig. 16-20). A knowledge of perspective drawing is helpful but not absolutely necessary for construction in woodworking. Isometric and oblique drawings and their variations are most frequently used. Receding lines in pictorial drawing may slant to the left or to the right, as desired.

Isometric drawing is similar to perspective drawing. Several sides of an object are shown in one view. It is most

16-17. Simplified thread symbols.

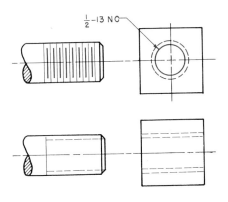

valuable in sketching the view of a rectangular object.

Three axes are used in isometric rendering. They may be placed in different positions to show an object (Fig. 16-21). One axis is vertical and represents the corner of the object nearest the viewer. The other two axes recede at 30 degrees from the horizontal, making the axes 120 degrees apart. In drawing the object, measurements for total height, width, and length of an object are made along these axes. Hidden lines are shown on pictorial drawings only when they are absolutely necessary.

Several basic steps are used in laying out and making a simple straight-line isometric sketch or drawing (Fig. 16-22). A different procedure is followed when constructing circles which appear as ellipses (Fig. 16-23).

An isometric drawing that shows all parts of an object separated is an **exploded assembly drawing** (Fig. 16-24). It is valuable to show the relationship between the various parts of an entire object and how they fit together. It is also useful to sketch how joints and other parts fit together for a small section of the project.

16-19. Some common electrical symbols. (A) Antenna, **(B)** ground, **(C)** fuse, **(D)** power plug, **(E)** power receptacle, **(F)** resistor, **(G)** motor, **(H)** condenser, **(I)** wires connected, **(J)** wires not connected, **(K)** duplex convenience outlet, **(L)** lighting outlet, **(M)** junction box, **(N)** floor outlet, **(O)** dishwasher and clothes drier, **(P)** electric door opener; **(Q)** buzzer, **(R)** chime, **(S)** interconnection box, **(T)** television outlet, **(U)** switch, **(V)** three-way switch, **(W)** automatic door switch, **(X)** pushbutton, and **(Y)** stove or range outlet.

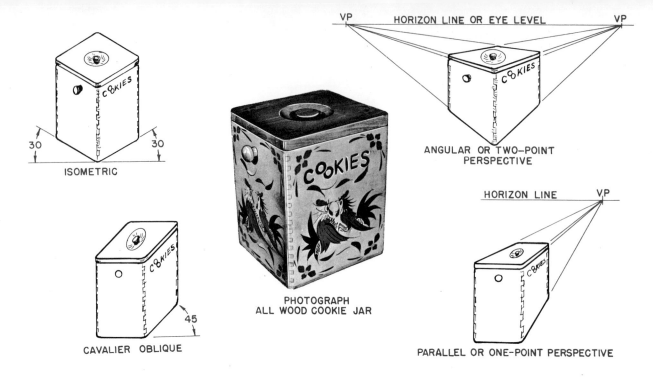

16-20. Common pictorial drawings and their relation to a photograph.

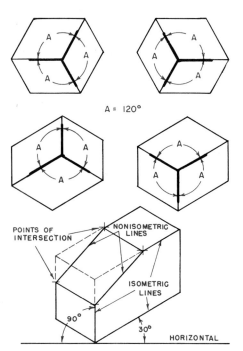

16-21. Different positions of iso-metric axes and nonisometric lines.

There are two kinds of **oblique draw-ing:** (1) cavalier and (2) cabinet (Fig. 16-25). Oblique drawing is sometimes the best drawing method because the front side (the one nearest the viewer) is drawn in true shape. The axes repre-senting the top and the side surfaces recede at 30-, 45-, or 60-degree angles (Fig. 16-26). Axes usually recede at 45 degrees. If measurements along the re-ceding (slant) lines are made full scale (size), the drawing is called **cavalier oblique** (Fig. 16-25A). The object ap-pears out of proportion and distorted. To eliminate this appearance, the depth measurements are made one-half their true length (Fig. 16-25B). The result-ing drawing is **cabinet oblique.** Al-though these slant lines are drawn half size, measurements placed on the drawing give full size.

In oblique drawing, circles on the front side of an object appear in their true shape. On the top and sides, they appear as ellipses.

16-22. Basic steps in making an iso-metric drawing.

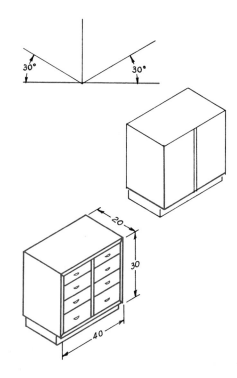

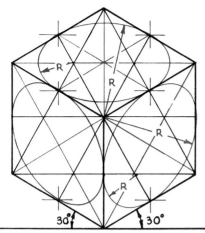

16-23. Circles appear as ellipses in isometric rendering.

Pictorial drawings occasionally include dimensions (Fig. 16-27). Intricate parts are best shown in detailed, multiview drawing (Fig. 16-28). The multiview drawing is the one used most in actual construction; it is known as a **working drawing.**

Multiview (Working) Drawings

Multiview drawing is one form of **orthographic,** or straight-line, projection. Every object has six sides: (1) front, (2) back, (3) top, (4) bottom, (5) right side, and (6) left side (Fig. 16-29). These are called **views.** Exact sizes and shapes can be drawn in detail when the views are used in their proper position. It is not necessary to use them all to show most objects.

Cylindrical objects and some rectangular ones often require only two views (Figs. 16-30 and 16-31). Most objects

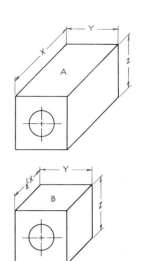

16-25. Cavalier (A) and cabinet (B) oblique drawings.

16-24. An exploded assembly drawing shows the relationship of all parts.

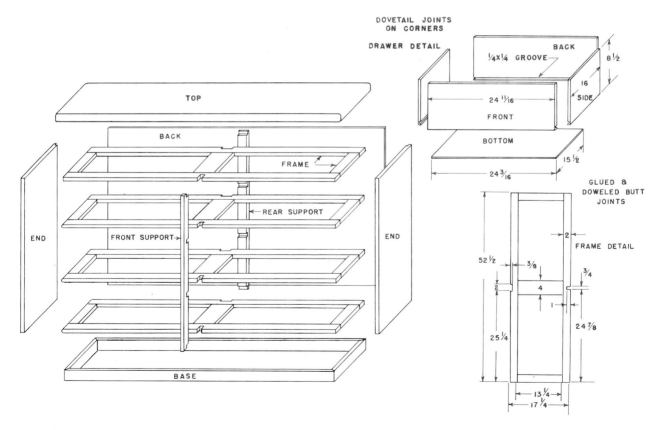

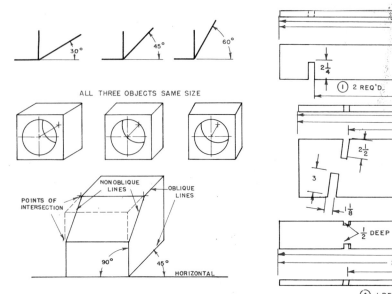

ALL THREE OBJECTS SAME SIZE

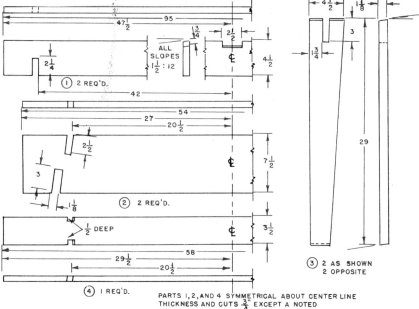

16-26. Oblique axes recede at 30, 45, and 60 degrees.

can be properly drawn with three views placed in accurate relationship (Fig. 16-32). The views are drawn as they are seen from the position of viewing (Fig. 16-33). In multiview drawing, all details are shown. These include all parts, notes, symbols, dimensions, and hidden lines.

16-27. Dimensions on a pictorial drawing of a ping-pong table.

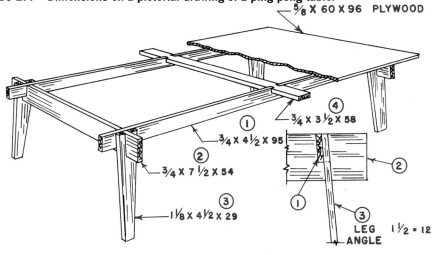

16-28. Dimensions on a multiview drawing of the ping-pong table.

The front view shows the most important details of the object. It usually depicts the greatest length or width and height of the subject. The right-side view is immediately to the right of the front view. The top view is drawn directly above the front one. The correct location of lines and parts on these views is projected from one view to another. Adequate space for dimensions and notes is allowed between views.

Only the views necessary to "describe" the object completely are used. For example, a croquet ball requires only one view. A croquet mallet head requires two. Complicated objects must have three or more views, and sometimes a section as well, to show detailed parts.

Sections

Part, full, or **half sections** are used to show the inside of an object, especially irregular and complicated shapes. Drawings of these sections are made directly on the part of the object to be shown. They can be offset and enlarged to show the part in detail (Fig. 16-34). On some drawings, section lines show what part is cut by the cutting plane.

Enlarging or Reducing Designs

Patterns, or templates, for irregular parts of an object are enlarged or re-

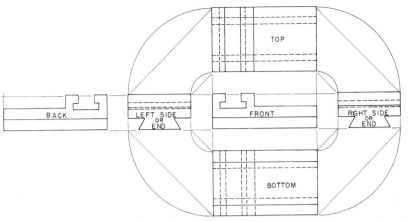

16-29. Six views of an object placed in their proper position on a drawing.

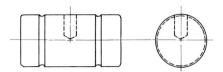

16-31. Two views required on some cylindrical objects.

16-32. Three views placed in proper position show most objects.

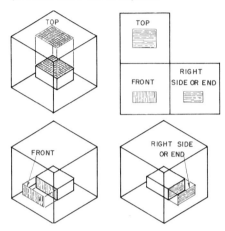

duced from drawings. One method is to use a machine or piece of equipment called a **pantograph.** The method used most in woodworking is called the **co-ordinate** method. It is effective for either isometric or parallel line drawing (Figs. 16-35 and 16-36).

The following procedure will assist you: steps 1, 2, and 3 can be eliminated if the design already has cross-hatch lines on it (Fig. 16-37).

1. Tape or otherwise fasten a piece of tracing or other transparent paper over the scaled drawing.

2. Draw vertical and horizontal lines to form squares over the entire area of the irregular design. The squares should be small (1/8 to 1/4 inch) on small designs and larger (1/2 to 1 inch) on large ones.

3. Trace lightly the shape of the object or design.

4. Lay out lightly the *same* number of *larger* squares on another piece of paper.

5. Where each line of the irregular shape crosses a vertical or horizontal line in the tracing, place a point (dot)

16-30. Two views describe some large objects.

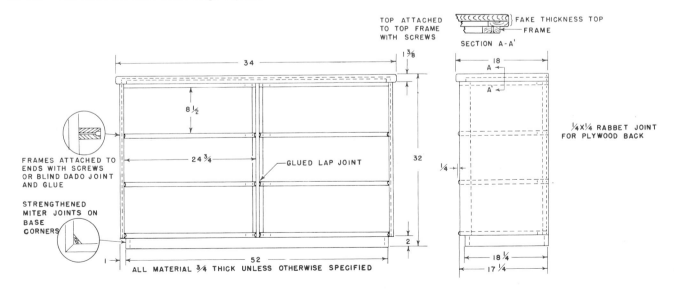

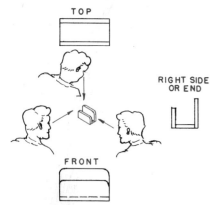

16-33. Observing an object from the proper positions.

on the corresponding line of the larger (or smaller) squares drawn in step 4.

6. Connect the points with a light line.

7. Check the two drawings for likeness in shape. When they are similar, darken the lines of the pattern.

8. Cut out the template, and trace around it to make the correct design on the wood.

Layout Problems

Various layout problems involve both mathematics and accurate drawing. Types shown in Figs. 16-38, 16-39, and 16-40 are encountered in performing woodworking operations. In each figure, the letters **C.C.** refer to the **circumscribing** (outside) **circle.** The letters **I.C.** designate the inscribing (inside) **circle.**

The tools and procedures for laying out the common hexagon, the octagon, and the ellipse (pin and string method) are listed in Unit 21, "Laying Out Geometric Figures and Irregular Curves."

Laying Out a Pentagon

To lay out a pentagon, or star, see Fig. 16-40A, and use this procedure:

16-34. Sectioning parts and enlarging details.

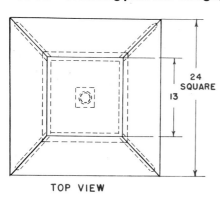

TOP VIEW

REVERSIBLE-TOP
GAME TABLE

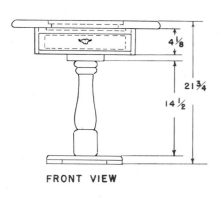

FRONT VIEW

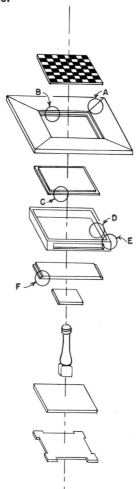

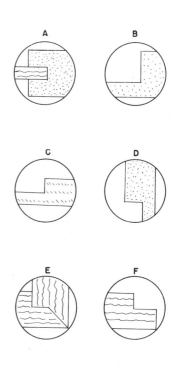

JOINT DETAILS

A - SPLINED MITER
B, C, D, & F - RABBET
E - STEPPED MITER

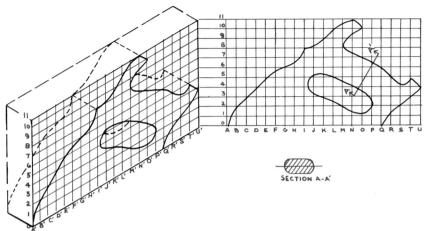

16-35. Making a pattern of an irregular object, drawn in isometric rendering by the coordinate method.

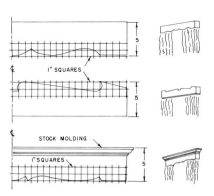

16-36. Valance patterns drawn in parallel-line rendering.

1. Divide radius *OB* at *D* (two equal parts).

2. With *D* as center and radius *DC*, draw arc *CE*. Point *C* will be one point of the pentagon.

3. With center *C* and radius *CE*, draw arc *EF*.

4. Line *FC* will be the side of the pentagon and will locate the second point of the star.

5. Continue marking the distance *FC* around the circle to locate points *G*, *H*, and *I*.

Constructing Any Polygon

A polygon is a geometric figure having many angles and sides. The length of the side must be given. The procedure given is for a polygon of seven sides with line *AB* the length of the given side (Fig. 16-40*B*):

1. With the side *AB* as a radius and *A* as a center, draw a semicircle.

2. Divide the semicircle into seven equal parts by trial and error.

3. Through the second division from the left, draw the radial line *A2*.

4. Extend radial lines through points 3, 4, 5, and 6.

5. With *AB* as a radius and *B* as a center, draw an arc to cross line *A6* at *C*.

6. With the same radius *AB*, and with *C* as a center, drawn an arc to cross line *A5* at *D*.

7. Continue until points are located at *E* and *F* to form the heptagon (seven-sided figure).

Drawing an Ellipse by the Trammel Method

To draw an ellipse, the major and minor axes must be known:

1. Draw the major and minor axes on a piece of paper or on the wood to be cut. See Fig. 16-40*C*.

2. On a piece of cardboard, mark distance *LN* equal to one-half the major axis and *LM* equal to one-half the minor axis.

3. Place the cardboard on the axes drawn in step 1, with points *M* and *N* on the major and minor axes.

4. Move the strip, keeping *N* on the minor axis and *M* on the major axis.

5. As the position of the strip is changed, point *L* will locate the points of the required ellipse.

16-37. An irregular design, free-form coffee table is enlarged by using coordinate lines.

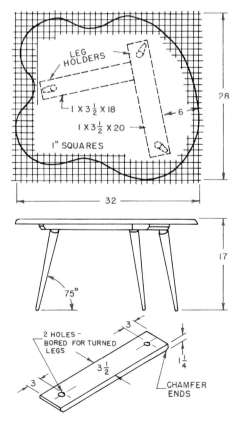

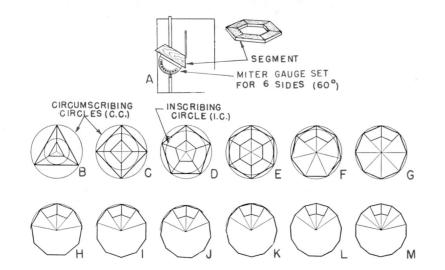

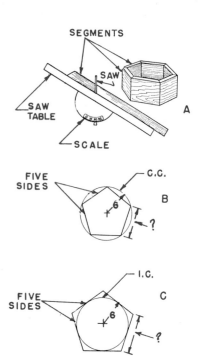

16-38. Mitered segments are cut with the use of a miter gauge. Angle settings are made according to the information given below as required for the shape to be cut:

Layout for cutting segments of a hexagon (six-sided figure). See A above.

	Sides	Name	Miter	Bevel	Circumference circle (C.C.), in.	Inscribing circle (I.C.), in.
B	3	triangle	30°	cannot be cut	1.732	.289
C	4	square	45°	45°	1.414	.5
D	5	pentagon	54°	36°	1.176	.688
E	6	hexagon	60°	30°	1.000	.866
F	7	heptagon	64.17°	25.83°	.868	1.038
G	8	octagon	67.5°	22.5°	.765	1.207
H	9	nonagon	70°	20°	.684	1.374
I	10	decagon	72°	18°	.681	1.538
J	11	undecagon	73.38°	16.62°	.563	1.702
K	12	dodecagon	75°	15°	.518	1.866
L	13	sides	76.31°	13.69°	.479	2.028
M	14	sides	77.14°	12.86°	.445	2.189

16-39. Cutting beveled segments.

A Beveled segments are cut by tilting the saw or saw table to the required angle.

B Given: Radius of circumscribing circle (C.C.) and number of sides
Find: Length of side
Rule: Multiply radius of C.C. circle by C.C. factor
Example: 5 sides, 6-inch radius

$1.176 \times 6'' = 7.056''$, $7.056'' = 7\frac{1}{16}''$ length of side

C Given: Radius of inscribing circle (I.C.) and number of sides
Find: Length of side
Rule: Divide the radius of the inscribing circle by the I.C. factor
Example: 5 sides, 6-inch radius

$6 \div .688'' = 8.72''$ length of side

16-40. Laying out a pentagon, a polygon (any number of sides) and an ellipse by the trammel method.

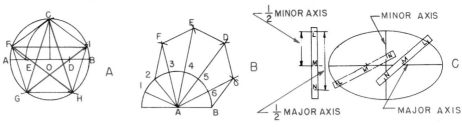

Unit 17 Selecting an Activity Project

Skill is as necessary to choose a project as to construct it. Deciding on a sound idea for an original piece of work and then planning it completely are basic to a successful outcome.

Planning

Thorough planning eliminates many mistakes and results in a finished product of superior quality. Complete plans should be made whether the final product is a piece of furniture, a boat, a vacation cabin, or a home.

Planning may begin with looking at pictures in your text, other books, magazines, furniture catalogs, and elsewhere. If the project is to be a piece of furniture, visit a furniture store to obtain ideas. As your ideas develop, make rough sketches (Fig. 17-1) of the better ones. After the design becomes completely clear, these ideas are organized into a finished drawing of the project.

Choice of an Activity Project

When one designs a project, there are several factors he should consider:

1. Will the project be an interesting one? Is there a real need and use for it?

2. Is the project well designed? Will it harmonize with its surroundings? Will it be pleasing to the sight? Is it satisfactory as to balance, proportion, color, rhythm, and general appearance?

3. Is it strong enough to withstand the use for which it is intended? If it is to be moved often, will it be too heavy?

4. Is there a reasonable amount of time to plan and make the project? Is it too difficult to construct in the time remaining after proper instruction has been given?

5. Are suitable materials available? Are the plans drawn so that the project is economical in its use of the materials? Is the cost reasonable?

6. Are tools, machines, and other equipment available to perform the necessary operations?

7. Is the project designed, drawn, and constructed in such a way that many processes of industry will be learned? Will the work involved be valuable in the future for use in a hobby, leisure-time activity, or occupation?

17-1. Rough sketches of project ideas and designs.

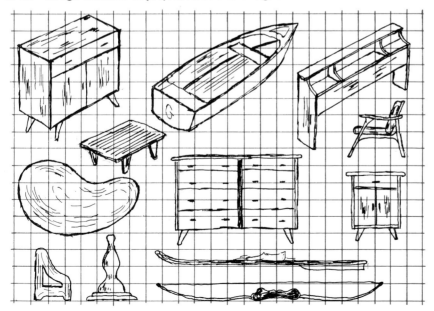

107

Unit 18   Project Specifications

Creative ideas, sketching, and designing are the necessary steps when a project is planned, before it is constructed and finished. The complete drawings are the bases which help to develop and fill in the project plan sheet. Drawings and plan sheets represent some of the same planning steps that are taken in industry to produce a well-designed, functional product.

Cost, time requirements, quality, and quantity of production are essential economic factors in industrial production. Proper selections of wood, hardware, finishes, and construction processes help increase production quality and quantity.

Estimate as closely as possible the cost and amount of materials needed to construct a project. Keep an exact record, and compare the final figures with the original estimates. These estimates are made from information given on the multiview, or working, drawing.

Working Drawing

A detailed **working drawing** gives the information needed to determine sizes and quantities of wood and other materials. It is necessary for complete planning. It saves time and money and helps to eliminate mistakes in construction. Therefore, proper planning includes a multiview drawing of the whole project, one or more pictorial drawings, and sections of parts. Planning may also include making special drawings of parts and developing patterns preliminary to making final plans.

The working drawing shows all necessary joints, all plans for construction, and assembly. Refer to SECTION 19, "Hardware and Assembly."

Selecting the Correct Wood

Careful selection of wood to be used is very important. A review of the questions in the preceding section will assist in making a wise choice. Also study the information available in SECTION 1, "Technology of Woods." Do this before filling in a project plan sheet like the one on page 109.

Project Plan Sheets

Most project plan sheets include space for a complete bill of materials, a procedure for doing the operations, and a list of the tools and machines to be used. A suggested project plan sheet is shown in Fig. 18-1. Parts of this unit will help in preparing most of the plan sheet. Unit costs of various materials, either available or to be ordered, are obtained from the instructor and from supply catalogs.

Determining Linear, Square, and Board Feet

The quantity of ash, or other wood, necessary to make water skis is simple to determine. However, estimating amounts and figuring costs become more difficult when larger quantities of wood in different shapes and sizes are to be used. The rough sizes of each piece of lumber, plywood, molding, or other wood products are determined from the working drawing.

Molding is sold by the **linear** (running) **foot.** For example, a certain molding costs 7 cents per linear foot. If 4 feet are needed, the total cost (4 × .07) is 28 cents. All information about quantity, size, shape, length, unit cost, and total cost should be recorded on the project plan sheet.

Plywood is sold by the **square foot** (sq ft) or as a standard sheet. A standard sheet size is 4 by 8 feet, or 32 square feet. The cost of a square foot or a sheet depends upon such factors as thickness, grade, type of face veneer, kind of wood, and the bonding agent. The thickness (*T*) is a preset factor used by the manufacturer to

PROJECT PLAN SHEET

Name_____ Course & Period_____

Name of Project_____ Date Begun_____

Date Completed_____ Estimated Time_____Hrs._____Min.

Actual Time Required_____ Actual Time ÷ Estimated Time = _____% Efficiency

Source of the idea & drawing _____

BILL OF MATERIAL

No. of Pieces	Part Name	All Specifications T × W × L Material	Board Feet	Unit Cost	Total Cost
				Total Cost	

STEPS OF PROCEDURE	TOOLS & MACHINES REQUIRED
1.	
2.	
3.	
4.	
5.	
6.	
7.	
8.	
9.	
10.	
11.	
12.	
13.	
14.	
15.	

I. Make detailed working drawing and attach to this plan sheet.

II. Use back for (1) additional steps of construction procedure, (2) finishing procedure, (3) pictorial sketch of project.

18.1.   A suggested project plan sheet.   Approved By_____

determine the unit cost per square foot or sheet. It is not used in the formula to figure cost. The formula is

$$\frac{\text{\# Pcs} \times L'' \times W''}{12 \times 12} = \text{sq ft}$$

where: # Pcs = number of pieces
L″ = length in inches
W″ = width in inches

Example:

$$\frac{\cancel{3} \times \cancel{8}'' \times \cancel{15}''}{\cancel{12} \times \cancel{12}} = \frac{5}{2} \text{ or } 2\frac{1}{2} \text{ sq ft}$$

Most solid **lumber** is sold by the **board foot** (bd ft). A board foot is a piece of material 1 inch thick, 12 inches wide, and 12 inches long, or 144 cubic inches. Lumber that is less than 1 inch thick is usually sold as 1-inch lumber. A piece which was once 1-inch rough stock is usually surfaced to about ¾ inch thickness. In the formula for figuring board feet, lumber over 1 inch thick is listed by its true thickness in quarters of an inch.

Several tables have been developed to assist in determining board feet. It is best, however, to learn first to compute board measure using one of the formulas given. Thickness (T) and width (W) should always be given in inches (″). Decimal sizes are used sometimes instead of fractions.

When the length is given in feet (′), use the following formula:

$$\frac{\text{\# Pcs} \times T'' \times W'' \times L'}{12}$$

where: # Pcs = number of pieces
T″ = thickness in inches
W″ = width in inches
L′ = length in feet

Example 1:

$$\frac{\cancel{3} \times 1'' \times \cancel{4}'' \times 2'}{\cancel{12}} = 2 \text{ bd ft}$$

Example 2:

$$\frac{6 \times 2'' \times 3\frac{1}{2}'' \times 3'}{12}$$

(Change 3½ to 3.5)

$$\frac{\cancel{6} \times \cancel{2}'' \times 3.5'' \times 3'}{\cancel{12}}$$

$$= 10.5, \text{ or } 10\frac{1}{2} \text{ bd ft}$$

Example 3:

$$\frac{3 \times 1\frac{1}{4}'' \times 4'' \times 2'}{12}$$

(Use true size of thickness over 1″)

$$\frac{\cancel{3} \times 1.25'' \times \cancel{4}'' \times 2'}{\cancel{12}}$$

$$= 2.50, \text{ or } 2\frac{1}{2} \text{ bd ft}$$

When the length is given in inches (″), use the following formula:

$$\frac{\text{\# Pcs} \times T'' \times W'' \times L''}{12 \times 12}$$

where: # Pcs = number of pieces
T″ = thickness in inches
W″ = width in inches
L″ = length in inches

Example:

$$\frac{4 \times \frac{3}{4}'' \times 3'' \times 30''}{12 \times 12}$$

(Remember: use 1″ as thickness on lumber under 1 inch in size.)

$$\frac{\cancel{4} \times 1'' \times \cancel{3}'' \times \cancel{30}''}{\cancel{12} \times \cancel{12}}$$

$$= \frac{5}{2}, \text{ or } 2\frac{1}{2}, \text{ or } 2.5 \text{ bd ft}$$

The total cost of one kind of lumber is determined by adding the exact board-foot amounts and multiplying by the cost per board foot. The kind of lumber and its grade, thickness, and other factors influence the cost. Lumber prices are most frequently quoted as the price per 100 (C) or 1,000 (M) board feet.

Example 1: 1,000 bd ft of lumber costs $350.00

$$\frac{\$350}{1,000} = .350, \text{ or } 35 \text{ cents per bd ft}$$

Example 2: 100 bd ft costs $35.00

$$\frac{\$35}{100} = .35, \text{ or } 35 \text{ cents per bd ft}$$

Example 3: 1,000 bd ft costs $355.00

$$\frac{\$355}{1,000} = .355, \text{ or } 35\frac{1}{2} \text{ cents per bd ft}$$

Finishing Costs

Finishing costs can be estimated in several ways. The price for finishing supplies (including thinner, polishing compound, and wax) is often estimated at 20 to 25 percent of the cost of the lumber. If this method is used, one-fifth to one-fourth of the total lumber cost should be added to the plan sheet.

Finishes are sold in bulk quantities. Common amounts are one-half pint (1 cup), pint, quart (4 cups), and gallon (4 quarts). The amount needed to finish a project is estimated in these units, or in cups.

A third method is also used: the square footage of surface to be finished is computed, and a specific cost per square foot is assigned.

Procedure

The various operations in the work procedure should be listed in numerical order on the plan sheet. The basic processes can be partially determined from the working drawing. Opposite each operation, list the tools and machines for doing the particular job.

DISCUSSION TOPICS

1. What is the difference between "style" and "period" in furniture design?
2. Name and discuss the relationships among time periods in furniture design.
3. What are the three major fundamentals of modern design?
4. What are the two categories of design?
5. Discuss and explain the necessity of planning and the factors involved in choosing a project.
6. List some professions in which advance planning and design knowledge are absolutely necessary.
7. Identify the primary, secondary, and tertiary colors.
8. Explain the terms **analogous** and **monochromatic.**
9. What are complementary colors?
10. What are the various types of lines found on project drawings?
11. What type of freehand work is done on mechanical drawings?
12. Explain the purposes of the three types of dimensions on drawings.
13. What are the types of common pictorial drawings?
14. Name and explain the kinds of oblique drawings.
15. Name the principal drawing views.
16. How many sixteenths ($1/16$) are in $1\,3/8$ inches?
17. What is the common method of enlarging and reducing drawings of irregularly shaped objects?
18. Prepare a rough sketch of a project you are interested in constructing.
19. How can the internal parts of an object be best represented when they are shown in detail?
20. Why is it necessary to plan and make a drawing of a project before beginning work?
21. Name some sources of project ideas.
22. Why is time important (1) in building a house and (2) in commercial production of furniture and other wood products?
23. Give some examples of how choice of materials affects cost and construction of various products.
24. Discuss briefly how each of the seven questions asked affects the choice of a project.
25. In what units of measure are lumber, plywood, and molding sold?
26. Discuss the factors which are essential to industry when workers begin to plan, design, estimate, and select materials for a product.
27. Prepare a sample bill of material of lumber and plywood for a project, giving all necessary information.

SECTION 3

BASIC HAND-TOOL PROCESSES

Unit 19 Safety with Hand Tools

The safety suggestions given here refer generally to the use of hand tools. Safe practices for using power tools and machinery are included in each section involving such processes. "An ounce of prevention is worth a pound of cure" is an adage which applies to safety in school industrial laboratories or shops and home workshops.

Studies made by the National Safety Council indicate that more school shop accidents occur in the forenoon around ten o'clock than any other time of the day. There are also more accidents on Wednesday than on any other day of the week except the working day just before or after a vacation. The most

dangerous laboratory or shop activity is woodworking. The wood chisel has caused more injuries than all other hand tools. Fewer accidents occur with sharp tools than with dull ones. These are just a few safety facts gathered from studies and surveys. They indicate that hand tools must be used wisely.

Physical Safety

■ **Lifting.** Use your leg and arm muscles to lift heavy objects. Never depend on your back muscles.
■ **Sharpness.** Test the sharpness of cutting tools on paper, not on your hand.

- **Hand protection.** Be careful when you use your thumb as a guide during crosscutting and ripping.
- **Knives.** Always direct the cutting action of knives away from your body.

Clothing Safety

- **Clothes protection.** Wear a laboratory or shop apron when you work with wood.
- **Ties and sleeves.** Tuck your tie into your shirt. Roll up your sleeves or button them.
- **Rings.** It is desirable to remove your ring. It could catch under a splinter or on a moving piece of machinery.

Tool Safety

- **Tool placement.** Place tools in an orderly arrangement on the bench top.

Point the cutting edges away from you. Do not let them rub against each other.
- **Screw-driver tips.** Keep screw drivers properly shaped to prevent injuries to hands or to the wood fiber.
- **Handles.** Keep handles firmly fastened on planes, hammers, mallets, chisels, and files.
- **Correct use of tools.** Use all tools properly and only for their intended purpose. **Example:** Do not pry with a file, screw driver, or wood chisel.

Materials Safety

- **Fastening materials.** Always fasten or hold wood properly in a vise, use clamps, or hold firmly on sawhorses.
- **Waste lumber.** Put waste and short pieces of lumber in a storage rack. Do not throw them on the floor where they may cause an accident.

- **Waste rags.** Keep oily or finishing rags in closed metal containers.

Laboratory and Shop Courtesy

- **Accidents.** Report any type of accident immediately so that first aid can be given.
- **Carrying stock.** Warn others to move out of your way when you are handling long pieces of lumber.
- **Walking.** Walk carefully. Do not run in the industrial laboratory, shop, or home workshop.
- **Carrying tools.** Carry only a few tools at a time.
- **Accident prevention.** Cooperate with fellow workers to help prevent accidents. Be aware of the movement of others. Think ahead. Accident prevention must become a full-time task of all workers in the shop.

Unit 20 Measuring and Laying Out Lumber

You must learn to measure accurately when working with wood. The inch ('') and the foot (') are measurements used in school shops, laboratories, and the wood-products industries throughout the United States. Most measuring tools used in woodworking are divided into sixteenths ($\frac{1}{16}$), eighths ($\frac{1}{8}$), quarters ($\frac{1}{4}$), and halves ($\frac{1}{2}$). See Fig. 20-1.

Tools

The tools most commonly used for measuring and laying out are the **wooden** or **steel bench rule** (Figs. 20-2 and 20-3), **try square** (Fig. 20-4), **steel framing square** (Fig. 20-5), **combination** or **carpenter's square** (Fig. 20-6), **extension folding zigzag rule** (Fig. 20-7), **flexible steel tape** (Fig. 20-8),

20-1. The fractional divisions of an inch.

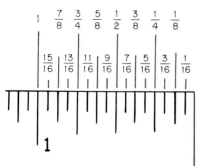

20-2. A wooden bench rule, available in 12- and 24-inch lengths.

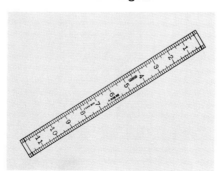

20-3. A steel bench rule, available in 6-, 12-, 18-, and 24-inch lengths.

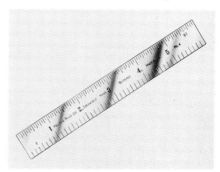

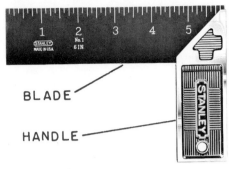

20-4. A try square.

20-8. A flexible steel tape.

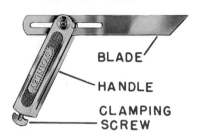

20-10. A T bevel.

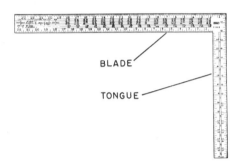

20-5. A steel framing square.

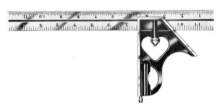

20-6. A combination, or carpenter's, square. It is equipped with a spring-held scriber and a double hairline level.

20-7. An extension folding, or zigzag, rule. The brass slide extends 6 inches for use on inside measurements or as a depth gauge.

steel measuring tape (Fig. 20-9), **T bevel** (Fig. 20-10), **marking gauge** (Fig. 20-11), **marking** or **utility knife** (Fig. 29-12), **level** (Fig. 20-13), and **plumb bob** (Fig. 20-14).

Laying Out Length

1. Select the board with the fewest checks, cracks, or blemishes (Fig. 20-15).

2. Square a line across the face (first surface) of the board (Fig. 20-16). Use a pencil or a knife.

3. Lay out and mark the desired length (Figs. 20-17 and 20-18).

4. Square this line across the board, as in step 2.

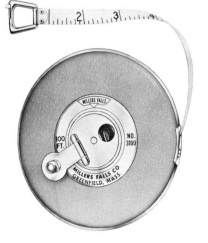

20-9. A steel measuring tape, available from 25- to 100-foot lengths.

Laying Out Width and Thickness

1. Measure and mark the desired width (Figs. 20-19, 20-20, and 20-21).

2. Divide the board into any number of equal parts. Lay the rule on its edge across the board in a diagonal (slanting) direction and mark the divisions (Fig. 20-22).

Laying Out an Edge

Extend a line across the edge of the board (Fig. 20-23) by continuing the face line. See Fig. 20-16.

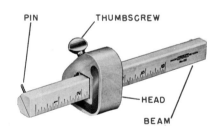

20-11. A marking gauge.

20-12. A marking, or utility, knife.

20-13. A level used to test horizontal and vertical trueness in carpentry.

20-17. Measuring and marking with a wooden bench rule placed on its edge.

20-20. A rule and pencil used for gauging width.

20-14. A plumb bob ensures accuracy in plumbing and leveling.

Laying Out an Angle

1. Adjust the T bevel to the angle desired (Figs. 20-24 and 20-25).

2. Hold the handle of the T bevel against the face, or edge, of the board. Mark along the bevel blade.

20-21. Scribing a width line with a marking gauge.

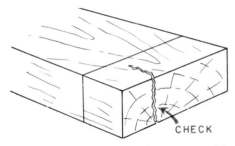

20-15. A board marked to avoid checks.

20-18. Measuring and marking with a flexible rule.

20-19. Measuring for width with a rule.

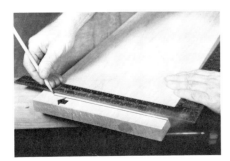

20-16. Squaring a line across the face of a board.

20-22. Dividing a board into equal parts.

20-23. Extending a line across an edge.

20-24. Adjusting a T bevel to the desired angle against a square.

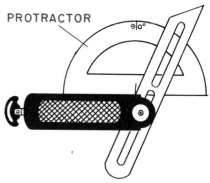

20-25. Adjusting a T bevel to the desired angle with a protractor.

Unit 21 Laying Out Geometric Figures and Irregular Curves

It is frequently necessary to draw arcs and circles, to enlarge patterns, and to trace around a template. Parts of projects often have hexagonal (six-sided), octagonal (eight-sided), and elliptical (oval) shapes. Additional shapes and forms are shown and described in Unit 16, "Understanding Working Drawings."

Tools

The **dividers** (Fig. 21-1) is a layout tool used by both wood- and metalworkers.

Trammel points (Fig. 21-2) are used for laying out arcs and circles which are too large for the dividers or compass.

21-1. Two types of dividers, one with a pencil and one with metal legs.

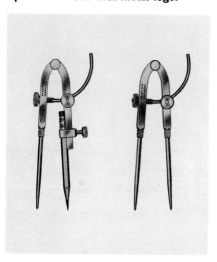

21-2. Trammel points.

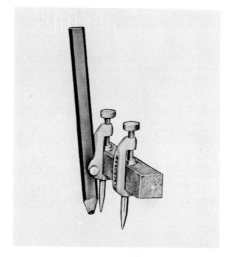

21-3. Setting the dividers to a radius on the rule.

Laying Out Curves, Arcs, and Circles

1. Set the dividers or trammel points to the desired radius (Fig. 21-3).
2. Scribe (mark) the arc, curve, or circle (Figs. 21-4 and 21-5).

Laying Out a Hexagon

1. Set the dividers or compass to the length you want for one side of the hexagon.
2. Draw a circle, using the radius set in step 1.
3. Mark off distances on the circumference with the dividers set to the radius length (Fig. 21-6).
4. Connect the intersecting (crossing) points on the circumference with straight lines (Fig. 21-7). This forms the hexagon.

Laying Out an Octagon

1. Draw a square the size of the octagon.
2. Draw diagonal lines AD and BC. See Fig. 21-8.
3. Set the dividers to the distance of A to O. Scribe arcs intersecting the

21-5. Scribing a circle with trammel points.

sides of the square. Use the corners as centers (Fig. 21-8).
4. Connect the intersecting points of the square with straight lines (Fig. 21-8). This is an octagon.

Laying Out an Ellipse

1. Draw a rectangle with the sides representing the width and length of the desired ellipse (oval). See Fig. 21-9.

21-6. Marking off radius lengths on the circumference for a hexagon.

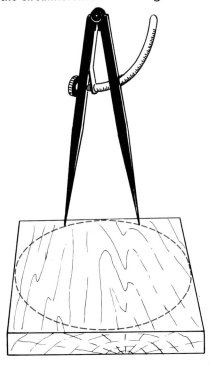

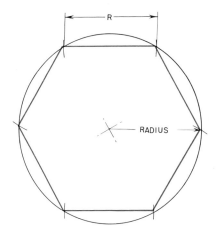

21-7. Hexagon (R = radius).

2. Divide the rectangle with a horizontal line AB and a vertical line CD. See Fig. 21-9.
3. Use C and D as centers. Draw arcs with the dividers set for a radius of XB. The arcs will intersect line AB at E and F. See Fig. 21-9.
4. Fasten a string at points E and F so that it will reach to C. This will form triangle CEF.
5. Place a pencil against the string, starting at point C. Draw half the ellipse ACB. Repeat this for the other half.

Tracing Around a Template

Designs are often transferred by using cardboard or wooden **templates** (patterns). Figure 21-10 shows how to trace a design onto wood by using a template.

21-4. Scribing an arc with dividers. Note the cardboard under one point so that the wood grain will not be dented.

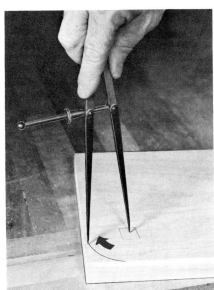

21-8. Octagon.

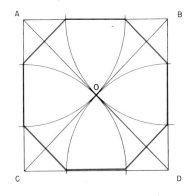

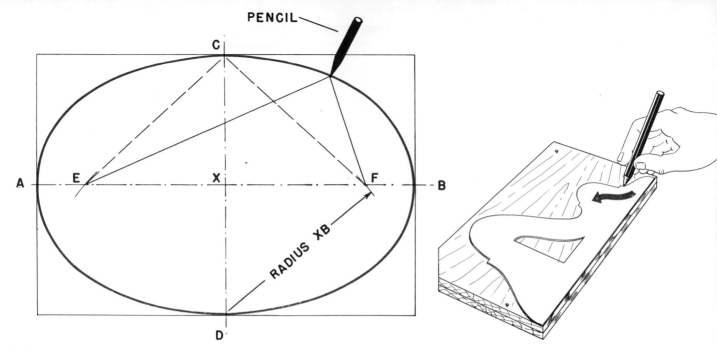

21-9.   Ellipse.

21-10.   Tracing around a template.

Unit 22   Crosscutting and Ripping

Handsaws are generally classified as either crosscut or rip, according to the cutting action of the teeth. The crosscut is designed to cut *across* the grain (fiber direction) of the wood. The ripsaw cuts *with* the grain. Backsaws, coping saws, and keyhole saws get their names from either their construction or the purpose for which they are intended. These are described in Unit 25, "Cutting and Forming Irregular Pieces and Curves." Basically they are also either crosscut or rip.

Tools

The **handsaw** (Fig. 22-1) and the **backsaw** (Fig. 22-2) are among the most popular hand tools for the woodworker. Figures 22-3 and 22-4 illustrate and explain the difference between crosscut and ripsaw teeth. Figure 22-5 shows how points per inch are counted on handsaw blades. The number of points per inch is usually stamped on the blade near the handle of the saw.

22-1.   A handsaw.

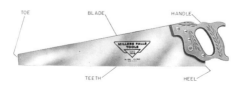

22-2.   A backsaw.

POINTS PER INCH ON CROSSCUT SAW

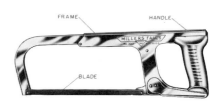

POINTS PER INCH ON RIPSAW

22-3. A view of crosscut saw teeth (top) and their cutting action (bottom).

22-5. Points per inch on a crosscut and a ripsaw.

The **miter box** and the **stiff-backed saw** (Fig. 22-6) make a tool for accurate angle sawing.

The **hacksaw** is frequently used by woodworkers and carpenters to cut through nails and metal (Fig. 22-7).

A **carpenter's vise** (Fig. 22-8) is convenient for builders because it is portable.

Crosscutting

1. Lay out and mark the board using a sharp pencil and a straightedge.

2. Fasten the board in a bench vise, or lay it across sawhorses.

3. Crosscut on the *waste* side of the marked line (Figs. 22-9, 22-10, and 22-11).

22-7. A hacksaw.

22-4. A view of ripsaw teeth (*top*) and their cutting action (*bottom*).

22-6. A miter box and a stiff-backed saw.

22-8. A carpenter's vise.

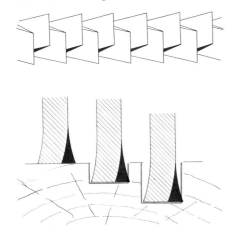

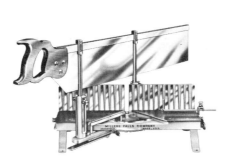

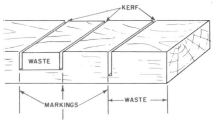

22-9. Waste portions of a board.

22-10. Testing the angle of cross-cutting, using a try square.

Ripping

1. Mark the board to be cut.
2. Fasten the board in a bench vise, or lay it on sawhorses.
3. Cut the board by ripping on the waste side of the mark (Figs. 22-12 and 22-9).

Cabinet Sawing

1. Lay out and mark the board.
2. Fasten it in a bench vise, or hold it on a bench hook.
3. Saw on the waste side, using a backsaw (Fig. 22-13).

22-11. Crosscutting a board held in a bench vise.

22-12. Ripping a board on a sawhorse. The cutting angle should be 60 degrees with the face of the board.

22-13. Crosscutting a board in a vise, using a backsaw.

Unit 23 Planing Lumber

Planing a board requires knowledge of all the types of planes and how they are used. The basic skill of hand planing can be learned in squaring stock (lumber). A board has been "squared" when all its surfaces, edges, and ends are at 90-degree angles to each other. Pieces will fit correctly if each part has been squared to the dimensions given in a drawing for the project. Figure 23-15 shows by number a sequence

(order) of steps in squaring a board. This method is used by many.

Planes

Planes are some of the most frequently used hand woodworking tools. There are many types of planes, but most are assembled, adjusted, and handled the same way. The main parts of a plane are shown in Fig. 23-1.

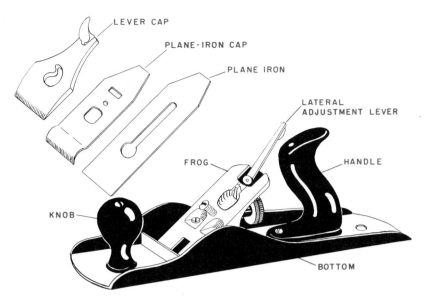

LEVER CAP

PLANE-IRON CAP

PLANE IRON

LATERAL
ADJUSTMENT LEVER

FROG

HANDLE

KNOB

BOTTOM

23-1.   The parts of a plane.

23-5.   A block plane.

23-2.   A jack plane.

23-6.   A bullnose rabbet plane.

23-3.   A smoothing and bench plane.

The illustrations and the brief descriptions of planes which follow will help you to select the best type for a particular job.

The **jack plane** (Fig. 23-2) is the most useful because of size. It will do the work of the smoothing, jointer, and block planes (mentioned below). The most common jack plane has a bed, or bottom, that is 14 inches long.

The **smoothing**, or **bench, plane** (Fig. 23-3) is like the jack plane, but the bed is only about 9 inches long.

The **jointer**, or **fore, plane** (Fig. 23-4) is also like the jack except that the bottom is 22 to 30 inches long.

The **block plane** (Fig. 23-5) is approximately 6 inches long. It is ideal for planing end grain, and it is easy to handle.

23-4.   A jointer and fore plane.

23-7.   A rabbet and fillister plane.

23-8.   A hand router plane.

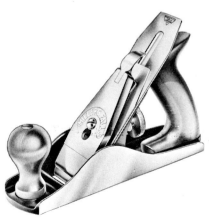

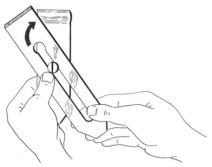

23-9. Assembling the plane-iron cap to the plane iron.

23-10. Aligning the cap and the plane iron.

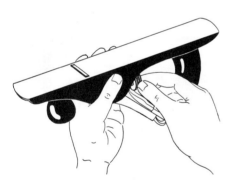

23-11. Adjusting for cutting depth.

23-12. Planing a surface.

The **bullnose rabbet plane** (Fig. 23-6) has a bed about 4 inches long. It is ideal for working in close quarters and in corners. Figure 23-7 shows a **rabbet,** or **fillister, plane.** The adjustable fence makes it possible to plane a rabbet (groove).

A **hand router plane** (Fig. 23-8) can also be used for cutting out rabbets and grooves.

Assembling and Adjusting

Planes are assembled as follows:

1. Hone (sharpen) the cutting edge of the plane iron. Refer to Unit 169, "Maintaining Basic Hand Tools."

2. Place the plane-iron cap against the flat side of the plane iron with the screw in the slot (Fig. 23-9).

3. Slide the cap to within $\frac{1}{16}$ inch of the cutting edge of the blade (Fig. 23-10). Tighten the cap with a screw driver.

4. Place this assembly in the plane with the bevel side of the blade on the frog. See Fig. 23-1.

5. Lay the lever cap over the plane-iron assembly; tighten the cap.

Adjust a plane as follows:

1. Adjust (move) the cutting edge with the lateral lever parallel with the slot in the bottom of the plane.

2. Turn the knurled adjustment nut carefully and precisely right or left to regulate the depth of the cutting edge (Fig. 23-11).

23-13. Testing across the board for flatness.

23-14. Testing the board diagonally for a wind.

Planing a Face Surface

1. Fasten the board on the workbench between the vise dog and a bench stop. Place it so that you can plane in the direction of the fibers.

2. Adjust the cutting edge of the plane iron to cut evenly and not too deep. See Fig. 23-11.

3. Plane the surface until it is smooth (Figs. 23-12, 23-13, and 23-14). Figure 23-15 presents a set of basic steps in squaring stock. You might wish to follow these if you are going to hand-plane all faces, edges, and ends of a board.

Planing an Edge

1. Fasten the board in a vise with the best edge up. The direction of the grain should be away from you.

23-15. Basic steps in planing and squaring a board.

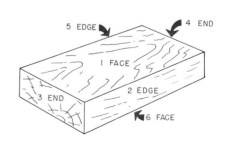

23-16.   Planing an edge.

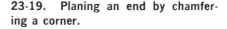

23-18.   Testing an edge for straightness.

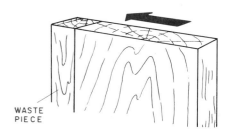

23-20.   Adding a piece of scrap stock to keep the edge from splintering.

2. Plane the edge until it is square with the planed surface (Figs. 23-16, 23-17, and 23-18).

Planing an End

1. Fasten the board in a vise with the best end up.

2. Plane the end. Use one of the three methods suggested in Figs. 23-19, 23-20, and 23-21.

3. Test the end for squareness to the planed surface (face). See Fig. 23-22. Test it for squareness to the planed edge (Fig. 23-23).

Planing the Opposite End

1. Measure, mark, and cut the board to the desired length. Allow 1/16 inch for sawing and planing to the line.

2. Plane the end to the marked line, square with the planed face and the planed edge.

Planing the Opposite Edge

1. Measure, mark, and rip the board to the desired width. Allow 1/16 inch for planing to the line.

2. Plane this edge to the line so that it will be square with the planed face and with both ends.

Planing the Last Surface

1. Mark the board for thickness, using a marking gauge.

2. Plane the last surface (face) to the gauge line. Test it for squareness. To be sure the last surface is parallel to the first surface, measure the thickness of the edges at several points.

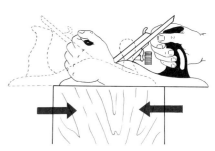

23-21.   Planing end grain from both directions.

23-22.   Testing an end for squareness to the face.

23-17.   Testing an edge for squareness.

23-19.   Planing an end by chamfering a corner.

23-23.   Testing an end for squareness against the edge.

Unit 24   Planing a Chamfer and a Bevel

A chamfer and a bevel look similar (Fig. 24-1). A chamfer is an edge decoration; a bevel can be either an edge decoration or a way to fit two boards together at an angle. The chamfer is usually planed to a 45-degree angle; the bevel can be made at any angle.

Laying Out a Chamfer or a Bevel

1. Mark light guide lines for the chamfer or bevel. Use a pencil or a marking gauge (Fig. 24-2).

Planing and Testing

1. Fasten the board in a vise. Plane the chamfer or bevel to the marked line (Figs. 24-3 and 24-4).

2. Test the angle of the chamfer (Fig. 24-5) or bevel with a sliding T bevel (Fig. 24-6).

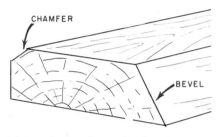

24-1.   A chamfer and a bevel.

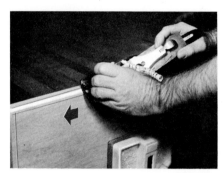

24-3.   Planing a chamfer to a marked line.

24-5.   Testing the angle of a chamfer with a sliding T bevel.

24-2.   Gauging a line with a pencil will not damage the grain of the wood.

24-4.   Planing a chamfer on a small block. Note the piece of wood is held in the vise with a hand clamp.

24-6.   Testing the angle of a bevel.

Unit 25 Cutting and Forming Irregular Pieces and Curves

There are several excellent woodworking tools for sawing, cutting, shaping, and forming irregular parts of projects. Those listed and illustrated are especially suitable for these processes.

Tools

The **coping saw** (Fig. 25-1) is especially useful for cutting thin boards and plywood.

The **compass saw** (Fig. 25-2) cuts inside curves after a hole has been bored near the line to be sawed.

The **spokeshave** (Fig. 25-3) is used mostly for forming concave (inside-curve) and convex (outside-curve) edges.

A **drawknife** (Fig. 25-4) cuts away waste stock quickly.

Wood, or **cabinet, files** (Figs. 25-5, 25-6, 25-7, and 25-8) have various shapes. Their lengths vary from 4 to 14 inches. They are used to smooth edges. Figure 25-9 shows the patterns of teeth on single- and double-cut files.

Edge-forming tools (Figs. 25-10, 25-11, and 25-12) can be used for

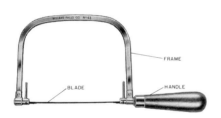

25-1.   A coping saw.

25-2.   A compass saw.

25-3.   A spokeshave.

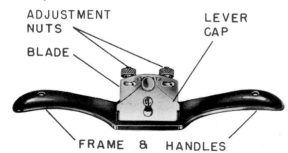

ADJUSTMENT NUTS

LEVER CAP

BLADE

FRAME & HANDLES

25-4.   A drawknife.

125

25-5. A half-round wood file.

25-6. A flat wood file.

25-7. A triangular wood file.

25-8. A round wood file.

25-9. Patterns of file teeth: (*A*) single-cut, and (*B*) double-cut.

25-10. The flat, file-type edge-forming tool.

planing, filing, shaping, and smoothing. The replaceable steel blades are inexpensive.

The **file card** (Fig. 25-13) has steel bristles which clean the teeth of a file.

Cutting with a Coping Saw

1. Lay out the design directly on the stock, or trace it around a template. See Fig. 21-10.

2. Hold the stock on a V block, or fasten it in a vise. Cut with the coping saw (Figs. 25-14 and 25-15).

Cutting with a Compass Saw

1. Transfer or draw the design on the wood.

2. Bore a hole in the waste part of the wood. Start the cut.

3. Saw to within $\frac{1}{16}$ inch of the line (Fig. 25-16).

Shaping with a Drawknife

1. Fasten the stock in a bench vise so that you will cut in the direction of the grain.

25-11. The plane-type edge-forming tool.

25-12. The round-type edge-forming tool.

25-13. A file card.

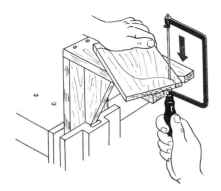

25-14. Sawing on a **V** block.

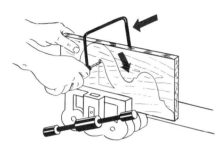

25-15. Cutting with a coping saw.

2. Carefully cut away the waste portion of the wood. Use short strokes pulled toward your body (Fig. 25-17). Proceed carefully.

Forming with the Spokeshave

1. Fasten the board securely in a bench vise.
2. Pull or push the spokeshave. Smooth the curved edge to the pattern line (Fig. 25-18).

Forming with a File and the Surface-forming Tool

1. Fasten the board in the bench vise.
2. Push the file or the surface-forming tool over the edge of the wood (Figs. 25-19 and 25-20). Clean the file frequently with a file card (Fig. 25-21).

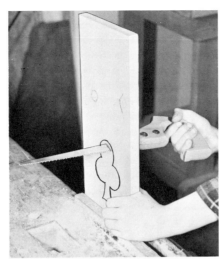

25-16. Internal cutting with a compass saw.

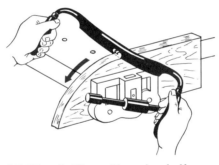

25-17. Cutting with a drawknife.

25-18. Smoothing a curved edge with the spokeshave.

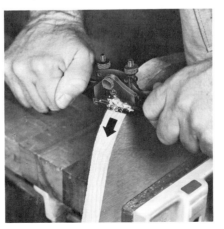

25-19. Filing a curved edge.

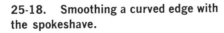

25-20. Dressing a straight edge with a plane-type forming tool.

25-21. Cleaning a file with a file card.

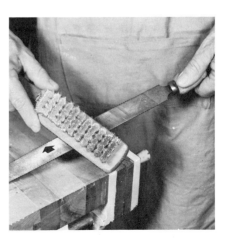

Unit 26 Trimming with a Wood Chisel

The wood chisel is used for cutting, trimming, fitting, and shaping. This tool must have a sharp cutting edge with the correct bevel (slant).

Tools

Wood chisels are classified as **socket** or **tang,** depending on how the handle is fastened to the blade (Fig. 26-1). The width of the blade determines sizes, which range from 1/8 to 1 inch by eighths and from 1 to 2 inches by fourths.

Inside- and outside-bevel **gouges** (Figs. 26-2 and 26-3) are most often used for grooving, shaping, and model making. They vary from 1/4 to 2 inches in width.

A wood or fiber **mallet** (Fig. 26-4) is used to exert additional pressure in chiseling.

Horizontal and Vertical Chiseling

Push the chisel with your right hand. Guide the blade with your left (Figs. 26-5 and 26-6).

Curved Chiseling and Trimming

1. Push the chisel with a shearing motion when you cut a round corner (Fig. 26-7). Keep the beveled side up.
2. Trim a concave (inside) edge by holding the beveled side of the chisel against the wood (Fig. 26-8). Always cut in the direction of the grain.

Grooving

Grooves can be cut in boards with a gouge (Fig. 26-9). Inside carving or cutting can also be done with the inside- or outside-bevel gouge.

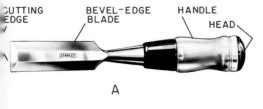

CUTTING EDGE   BEVEL-EDGE BLADE   HANDLE   HEAD

A

B

26-1. Wood chisels: (A) tang butt, and (B) socket firmer.

26-2. Inside-bevel socket firmer gouge.

26-3. Outside-bevel socket firmer gouge.

26-4. A wood mallet.

26-5. Horizontal chiseling. Note the sequence of steps shown in the inserts for through chiseling.

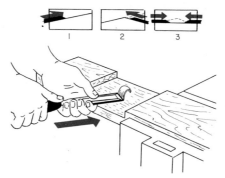

26-6. Vertical chiseling a mortise.

26-7. Trimming an outside curve with a chisel

26-8. Trimming an inside curve with a chisel.

26-9. Cutting a groove with a gouge.

Unit 27 Smoothing a Board by Scraping

Scrapers are used to remove irregularities and blemishes from surfaces and edges. They smooth with a turned, or **burred,** edge (Fig. 27-1).

Tools

The two shapes of **hand scrapers** are the **rectangular** (Fig. 27-2) and the **swan neck** (Fig. 27-3). Properly sharpened blades make thin shavings. Some scrapers are pulled; others are pushed. Other types are the **cabinet scraper** (Fig. 27-4), which must be pushed; the **pull, box,** or **floor scraper** (Fig. 27-5), which is pulled; and the **wood scraper** (Fig. 27-6).

A scraper plane looks like a smoothing plane except that the blade is held forward to scrape rather than cut.

Hand Scraping

Grasp the scraper blade firmly between the thumb and fingers. Spring it to a slight curve. The blade is pushed or pulled (Figs. 27-7 and 27-8).

Smoothing with Cabinet and Pull Scrapers

Scrape the surface of the wood, using long, even strokes. Work with the grain (Figs. 27-9 and 27-10).

27-1. A burred edge and angle for scraping.

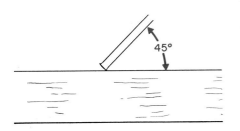

27-2. A straight-edge scraper blade.

27-3. A swan-neck scraper blade.

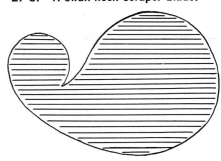

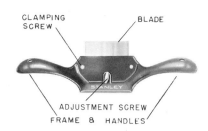

27-4. A cabinet scraper.

27-5. A pull, box, or floor scraper.

27-6. A wood scraper. Each blade has four scraping edges.

27-7. Pushing a scraper blade to smooth a surface.

27-8. Pulling a scraper blade to smooth a surface.

27-9. Smoothing with a cabinet scraper.

27-10. Smoothing with a pull scraper.

Unit 28 Boring and Drilling Holes

Holes must be bored or drilled in wood for screws, bolts, dowels, internal sawing, and ornamentation. Some of the tools for performing these processes are described below.

Tools

The **ratchet brace** (Fig. 28-1) holds bits which have a square **tang** (shank).

The **right-angle brace** (Fig. 28-2) is used to bore holes in close quarters.

A **hand drill** (Fig. 28-3) is usually used for drilling holes ¼ inch or less in diameter. A straight-shank drill should be used with this tool.

The **automatic drill** (Fig. 28-4) is sometimes used instead of the hand drill.

Standard **auger bits** (Figs. 28-5, 28-6, and 28-7) vary in length from 7 to 10 inches. Dowel auger bits are only 5½ inches long. Auger bits are sized by sixteenths (¹⁄₁₆) of an inch from ³⁄₁₆ to 1 inch. The number stamped on the square tang shows the bit size in sixteenths. The bit illustrated in Fig. 28-7 is designed to be used with either the hand ratchet brace (Figs. 28-1 and 28-9) or the portable electric drill. See also Fig. 88-3 in Unit 88, "Chucks and Drill Bits."

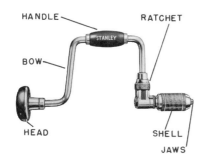

28-1. A ratchet brace.

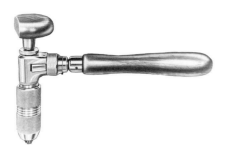

28-2. A right-angle brace.

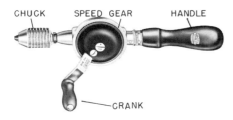

28-3. A hand drill.

28-4. An automatic drill.

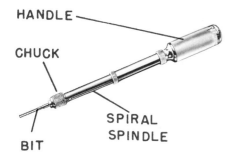

HANDLE

CHUCK

SPIRAL
SPINDLE

BIT

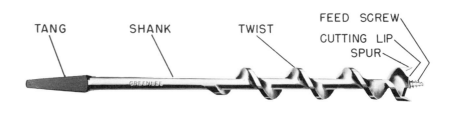

28-5. A single-twist auger bit.

28-6. A double-twist auger bit.

28-7. The dual-purpose shank unispur auger bit.

28-8. The wood-boring brace drill.

28-9. The shank of a dual-purpose auger bit fitted into the chuck jaws of the ratchet brace.

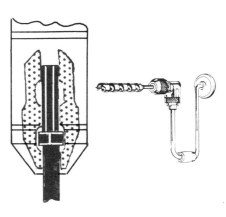

The **wood-boring brace drill** (Fig. 28-8) makes holes for screws, nails, and bolts. It must be used with the brace.

The **expansive bit** (Fig. 28-10) bores holes from ½ inch to 3 inches in diameter. It has a movable spur, or cutter. Cutters are available to bore holes up to 5 inches in diameter.

A **Foerstner bit** (Fig. 28-11) will bore a flat-bottom hole because it has no lead screw. Single- and double-twist auger bits have lead screws. See Figs. 28-5 and 28-6.

The **straight-shank drill** (Fig. 28-12) is used with a hand drill. Fractional

28-10. The expansive bit.

28-11. The Foerstner bit. This particular one has a round tang for drilling. A square-tang bit is also available.

28-12. A straight-shank drill.

28-16. A doweling jig.

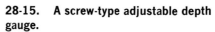

28-17. An awl.

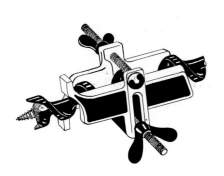

28-13. An assortment of automatic drill bits.

28-14. The adjustable depth gauge.

28-15. A screw-type adjustable depth gauge.

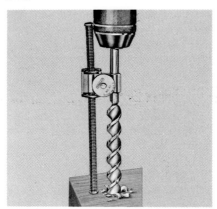

drill sizes are marked in sixty-fourths ($\frac{1}{64}$) of an inch.

Automatic-drill bits (Fig. 28-13) fit into the automatic drill (Fig. 28-4). They drill small holes.

Two types of **depth gauges** are shown in Figs. 28-14 and 28-15. They control the depth of boring by stopping the drill at the desired level.

The **doweling jig** (Fig. 28-16) is often used to guide and direct a bit for boring holes in dowel joining. It may be adjusted to practically any position to bore holes at any angle.

An **awl** (Fig. 28-17) is used for marking the location for boring and drilling holes.

Boring a Hole

1. Fasten a suitable bit of the correct size in the chuck of the brace (Fig. 28-18).

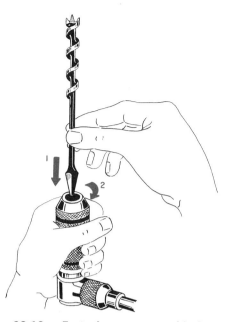

28-18. Fastening an auger bit in a ratchet-brace chuck.

28-19. Using an awl to start a hole for boring.

28-21. Boring a hole horizontally. Note the scrap wood on the back to keep the piece from splintering.

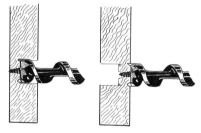

28-22. A two-step procedure for boring a hole through a piece of wood.

2. Mark and locate the center to be bored or drilled, using an awl (Fig. 28-19).

3. Bore the hole carefully. See Figs. 28-20, 28-21, and 28-22.

4. There are two ways to bore a hole through a board. Fasten a piece of scrap wood on the back, as shown in Fig. 28-21, or follow the two-step procedure shown in Fig. 28-22.

5. Figure 28-23 illustrates the use of a depth gauge for boring a dowel hole to a specified depth. Figure 28-24 shows a hole being bored with the aid of a doweling jig.

Drilling a Hole

1. Use a straight-shank or automatic drill. Fasten the bit in the chuck.

2. Place the bit on the place marked as the center of the hole. Drill the hole carefully (Figs. 28-25 and 28-26).

28-20. Boring a hole vertically.

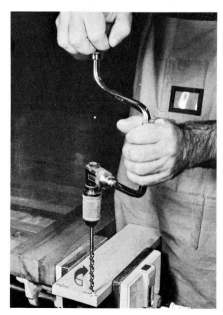

28-23. Boring, with a depth gauge and a self-centering jig.

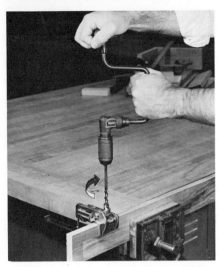

28-24. Boring a hole with a doweling jig.

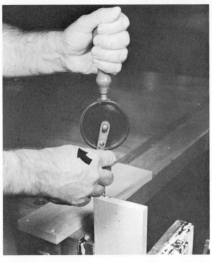

28-25. Drilling a hole with a hand drill.

28-26. Drilling a hole with the automatic drill.

Unit 29 Sanding by Hand

A completed wood project must be thoroughly sanded before the finish is applied. Sanding is done with any of several abrasive materials.

Abrasives

Sandpaper is the abrasive most often used on wood. It gets its name from its grit surface, which resembles sand. It is, however, crushed flint or quartz, and it is sometimes called **flint paper.**

Garnet paper is more durable than flint paper. It is a reddish color.

Emery cloth (or paper) is a tough, black paper. It is usually used for polishing metal.

29-1. Melting stick shellac to fill a knothole.

29-2. Pressing in wood plastic to fill a defect.

29-3. Tearing sandpaper against a metal edge.

29-4. Sanding a surface with the grain.

Table 29-1 ABRASIVE MATERIALS

Abrasive material	Grit classification	Number classification
Sandpaper (flint or quartz, 9″ × 10″ sheets)	Extra coarse	2½–3
	Coarse	1½–2
	Medium	½–1
	Fine	2/0–1/0
	Extra fine	3/0–4/0
Garnet paper (9″ × 11″ sheets)	Coarse (rough sanding)	½–1½
	Medium (intermediate sanding)	1/0–2/0
	Fine (finish sanding)	3/0–6/0
Emery cloth (9″ × 11″ sheets)	Extra coarse	2½–3
	Coarse	1½–2
	Medium	½–1
	Fine	2/0–1/0

29-5. Sanding a rounded edge.

Abrasive papers and cloth are graded from **coarse** to **fine**. Table 29-1 lists the grit and number classifications of these three types of abrasive.

Preparing a Surface for Sanding

1. Use a scraper to remove all planer marks and traces of glue.
2. Raise the dents in the wood by moistening the immediate area.
3. Fill small knots, holes, checks, and cracks by melting in colored stick shellac (Fig. 29-1). Colored wood plastic or dough (Fig. 29-2) can be pressed into the defect.

Sanding

1. Tear a piece of sandpaper or other abrasive into four equal parts (Fig. 29-3).
2. Fold the sandpaper around a block of wood, and sand all flat surfaces and edges *with the grain*. Use an even pressure (Fig. 29-4). Sand irregular, concave, or shaped edges as shown in Fig. 29-5.

Start sanding with coarse abrasive paper. Use a medium grade next, and finish with a fine grit. Inspect all surfaces to ensure proper sanding before applying the finish.

DISCUSSION TOPICS

1. List 10 safety rules which apply to hand-tool woodworking.
2. How many sixteenths (1/16) are there in ¼, ⅜, ½, ¾, ⅞, 1, 1⅜, and 1½?
3. Define and draw each of the following: (a) hexagon, (b) octagon, and (c) elipse.
4. What are trammel points used for?
5. At what hour of the day, and on what day of the week, do most accidents happen in school industrial laboratories or shops? Why?
6. Illustrate the difference between ripsaw and crosscut saw teeth. Explain and describe the cutting action of each.
7. Name and describe five types of hand planes.
8. What is meant by a "squared" board?
9. List the six general steps sometimes used for squaring a board.
10. Illustrate the difference between a chamfer and a bevel.
11. List and describe the functions of six tools used in cutting and forming irregular pieces and curves.
12. List the two classifications of wood chisels.
13. Name three kinds of scraper frames.
14. Give the names of six kinds of drills and bits. Cite a specific use for each.
15. What are the sizes of auger bits which have these numbers stamped on the tang: 4, 7, 9, 11, 13, and 16?
16. Name three natural abrasive materials used in sanding. Which is the most commonly used?
17. List the grades of grit for: (a) sandpaper, (b) garnet paper, and (c) emery cloth.

SECTION 4

SAWING, SHAPING, AND MOLDING ON THE CIRCULAR SAW

Unit 30 General Information About the Circular Saw

The circular, or table, saw is one of the oldest known power machines used in woodworking. The modern one (Fig. 30-1) performs many processes. The kind of circular saw most common for the school shop or laboratory and home craft use has one arbor (shaft) and one blade. The universal production models often have a double arbor with two saw blades. Either blade can be raised and put into use without changing blades on the arbor. These are usually ripsaw and crosscut blades. The picture above shows an industrial production roll-feed gang ripsaw in operation.

Sizes and Types

The size of a circular (variety) saw is measured by the largest-diameter saw blade it will accommodate. For school use, the size varies from a 10- to a 14-inch-diameter blade. The 10-inch blade runs at a speed of about 3,100 rpm (revolutions per minute). The cutting speed is approximately 8,100 sfm (surface feet per minute). The maximum sfm is about 9,000.

To cut bevels, chamfers, and certain types of miters, either the arbor or the table top must tilt. The most common solution is to use a tilting arbor; the table top remains stationary. On some circular saws the table top tilts. This type of saw is difficult to use because lumber has a tendency to slide off the table. The saw shown in Fig. 30-1 is the tilting-arbor type.

Saw Parts and Uses

The main parts of the circular saw are the arbor, frame, table, rip fence, saw-tilt hand wheel, miter gauge, cut-off guide, blade-raising wheel, safety guard, splitter, and electric motor.

- **Arbor.** The arbor has a shaft that holds the blade, dado head, or molding head.
- **Frame.** The frame includes the base and the housing for the internal operating mechanisms and the motor.
- **Table.** The table supports the rip fence, cut-off guide, safety guard, and the wood stock being cut.
- **Rip fence.** The rip fence is used as a guide for ripping. It often has a vernier (sensitive or fractional) adjustment for fine calibrations.
- **Miter-gauge cut-off guide.** The miter-gauge cut-off guide is used as a guide for crosscutting.
- **Saw-tilt hand wheel.** This is a hand wheel for tilting the saw blade or the table, depending upon the type of machine.

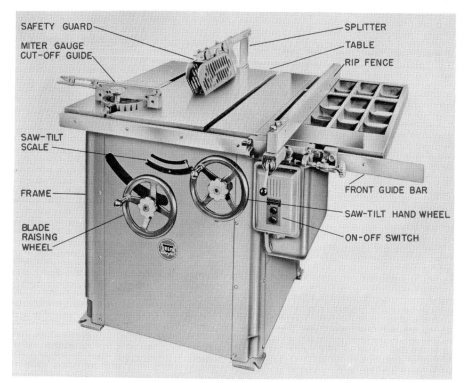

30-1.   A 12-inch circular, table, or variety, saw.

- **Blade-raising wheel.** This is a hand wheel that regulates the cutting height of the saw blade.
- **Safety guard.** The safety guard protects the operator from the saw. It is detachable, but it should be used whenever possible.

- **Splitter.** The splitter is used to prevent the stock from binding against the saw blade while the cut is being made. Sometimes this is a separate piece, but it is often part of the guard.
- **Electric motor.** The electric motor drives the circular saw.

Unit 31 Circular Saw Blades and Accessories

The two general types of circular saw blades are the **spring set** and the **hollow ground.** Crosscut and ripsaw blades are usually spring set. Combination and carbide-tip blades are hollow ground. Within these two general groups of blades are the crosscut, rip, combination, and carbide-tip blades. A number of accessories and attachments are also available, among which are the dado head and the molding head.

Saw Blades

The **circular crosscut,** or **cut-off, blade** (Fig. 31-1) is used for cutting *across* the grain of the wood. Figure 31-5 shows in detail how the teeth are filed. On the spring-set blade, the teeth are set alternately right and left so that a cut (kerf) is made that is wider than the thickness of the blade. The hollow-ground blade does not require setting because it is tapered from the edge to

137

31-1. A circular crosscut saw blade.

31-2. A circular ripsaw blade.

31-3. A circular combination, or planer, saw blade.

the center for clearance. That is, the blade is thicker at the teeth than it is at the center.

The **circular ripsaw blade** (Fig. 31-2) is used for cutting or ripping a board lengthwise (*with* the grain). Some manufacturers produce a combination saw blade whose teeth resemble rip teeth. The teeth are ground without quite so much hook as the rip teeth. Also, the teeth are beveled to cut across the grain of the wood.

The **circular combination saw blade** (Fig. 31-3) has both crosscut and rip teeth. It can be used for either crosscutting or ripping.

The **planer saw blade** is hollow ground, but it looks like the combination blade. It does a smooth job of crosscutting, ripping, and mitering.

Carbide-tip saw blades (Fig. 31-4) are available in several tooth patterns, depending upon the manufacturer's preference. The ones shown are typical. This type of blade can be used for all cutting operations. The carbide tips do not dull easily and therefore seldom need sharpening.

Blades vary from 8 to 16 inches in diameter. The 8- and 9-inch sizes are usual for home workshops. The 10- to 16-inch blades are used in many schools and industries.

Figure 31-5 shows in detail how saw teeth are filed.

Dado Head

The dado head is a combination of two outside saws and several inside cutters, which come in various thicknesses (Fig. 31-7). Various combinations of saws and cutters can be used to cut grooves from $\frac{1}{8}$ to $\frac{13}{16}$ inches. The outside cutters are swaged (that is, the tips are wedged); they must be arranged in the assembly of the dado head so that this portion falls in the gullets (between the teeth) of the outside saws, as shown in Fig. 31-6.

Figure 31-8 shows how the saw blade and the cutter overlap: (A) is the outside saw blade, (B) is an inside cutter, and (C) is a paper washer or washers, which are sometimes needed to control the exact width of the groove. The outside saw blades are $\frac{1}{8}$ inch thick; hence, two blades fitted together will cut a groove $\frac{1}{4}$ inch thick. The teeth should fit together as shown in Fig. 31-9.

To use the dado head, the throat (opening) plate on the saw table must be replaced. The throat of the plate must be wide enough for the dado

31-4a. A circular carbide-tip saw blade.

31-4b. A taper-thin design carbide-tip saw blade.

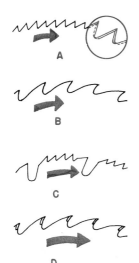

A

B

C

D

31-5. Detail of circular-saw blade teeth: (A) crosscut, (B) rip, (C) combination, or planer, and (D) carbide-tip.

31-6. Arrangement or placement of chipper blades or inside cutters with outside blade.

head to come up through it. Compare the throat plates in Figs. 32-1 and 32-2.

Molding Head

Straight molding or shaping can be done on the circular saw. Either the saw blade or the dado head is replaced with a molding head, which includes sets of formed knife or cutter shapes (Fig. 31-10). The four shown are standard molding-head cutters. The molding head consists of a cutter head with

31-7. Parts for the dado head: two ⅛-inch outside blades, four ⅛-inch thick chipper blades, and one 1/16-inch chipper blade. This combination will cut grooves and dadoes from ⅛ to 13/16 inch wide.

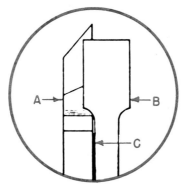

A → ← B

← C

31-8. Placement and overlapping of inside cutter with the outside saw blade.

31-9. Arrangement of outside dado head saw blades for cutting ¼-inch dado or groove.

31-10. A molding head with four standard knife or cutter shapes. Also note the wide-opening throat plate for one type of circular saw table.

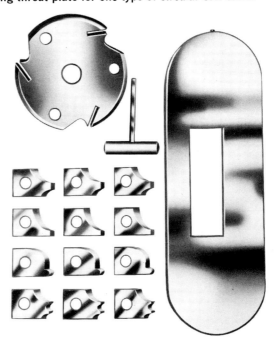

various shapes of matched steel knives fastened to it (Fig. 31-11).

Many manufacturers make assortments of knife or cutter shapes that fit molding heads. These shapes offer almost unlimited possibilities for making molding shapes on the circular saw.

A special rip fence is required. It has a cut-out in the center that gives clearance to the cutter head when the knives are at their highest cutting point. A cut-out wood facing can also be clamped or screwed to a standard rip fence. Remove the throat plate from the saw table, and replace it with a throat having an opening sufficiently large to accommodate the molding cutters. See Fig. 31-10.

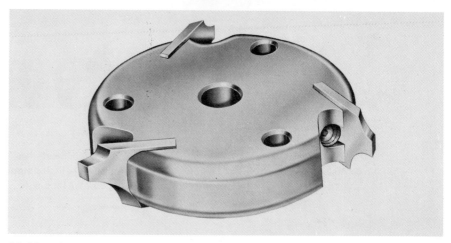

31-11. A cutter head complete with matched steel knives. The key (wrench) shown in Fig. 31-10 is used to fasten the knives on the head.

Unit 32 Operating Adjustments

The circular saw makes accurate cuts if care is taken to check a few adjustments before using it. Manufacturers make data sheets and operating manuals available for their machines. Study them to learn any particular adjustment specifications. The operating techniques described in this unit, however, are basic to most circular saws.

Always make sure that the bearings and other working parts of the machine are properly lubricated according to the operation manual.

Installing Saw Blades, Dado Heads, and Molding Heads

This procedure is for removing a saw blade and installing the dado-head assembly on the arbor. The saw blade and the molding cutter head are placed on the arbor in the same way the dado head is.

1. Remove the throat plate. See Fig. 32-1.

2. Raise the saw blade as high as it will go, using the hand wheel.

3. Loosen and remove the nut, the outer flange, and the saw blade (Fig.

32-1). As you stand on the working side of the saw table, hold a piece of wood in the throat opening against the teeth while loosening the nut (Fig. 32-1).

32-1. A safe way to loosen the nut which holds the saw blade on the arbor.

32-2. The dado head assembly fastened on the saw arbor. A throat plate with a wider opening is ready to be put in place.

32-4. Saw blade flanges and other parts of a saw arbor assembly.

4. Place the parts of the dado head on the arbor to get the desired thickness. First, one outside blade; next, the chipper blades needed; and last, the opposite outside blade. See Fig. 32-2.

5. Put the flange back on the arbor, and screw on the nut by hand.

6. Adjust the assembly of blades and chippers as shown in Figs. 31-7 and 31-8 or 31-9.

7. Tighten the nut with the wrench.

8. Place the throat plate with the wider opening in position (Fig. 32-2).

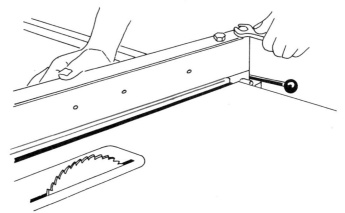

32-5. Aligning the fence parallel with the table groove.

32-3. The saw fence-control assembly.

32-6. Adjusting the pointer to zero on the front bar of the rip fence.

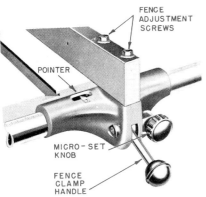

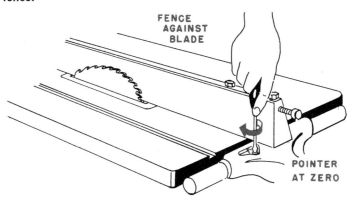

Figure 32-4 shows a saw blade, flanges, and other parts of a typical arbor assembly on a 10-inch variety saw.

Adjusting the Rip Fence

The typical rip fence has adjustment screws to maintain its parallel alignment with the circular saw blade (Fig. 32-3). The easiest way to check this is to adjust the fence parallel to the table groove and to make the necessary proper positioning (Fig. 32-5). The distance indicator or pointer can be checked by moving the fence against the blade (Fig. 32-6).

Adjusting the Miter Gauge Cut-off Guide

The miter gauge or index on the cut-off guide occasionally gets out of align-

32-7.   Checking squareness of the cut-off guide with the saw blade.

ment. A simple way to check this is with a square, as shown in Fig. 32-7. The blade, when raised, should be at right angles (90 degrees) to the table top for a square cut. Adjust the pointer when blade is square with the table.

Unit 33 Safety for the Circular Saw

■ **Permission.** Request permission from the instructor before you start to operate the saw.

■ **Clothing.** Do not wear loose clothing or hanging neckties. Button or roll up your sleeves.

■ **Jewelry.** If you wear a ring, take it off. It could catch in splinters and cause injury to your hand, or it can simply annoy you while you work.

■ **Stance.** Stand to one side of the saw. If the board binds and kicks back, it will not hit you. Always stand firmly on the floor.

■ **Blade sharpness.** Keep the saw blades sharp.

■ **Teeth and cutter direction.** Be sure the saw, dado head, or molding head teeth and cutters point toward you as you stand on the operator's side of the saw.

■ **Safety guard.** Make certain that the safety guard is properly in place and ready to use.

■ **Hand protection.** Keep your hands away from moving parts of the saw. Use the proper guard to protect them. Remove your ring if you wear one.

■ **Use of guard.** Always use a safety guard if the saw teeth extend above the stock being cut.

■ **Saw teeth extension.** When using the saw blade, set it to extend approximately ⅛ inch above the stock to be cut.

■ **Adjustments.** Make no adjustments while the blade, dado head, or molding head is in motion.

■ **Reaching.** Never reach behind a saw blade to pull stock through.

■ **Freehand sawing.** Always use the rip fence or the cut-off guide. Because of the danger involved, *never* saw freehand.

■ **Rip fence.** Remove the rip fence when you crosscut.

■ **Splitter attachment.** Whenever possible, especially in ripping, use the splitter attachment. It is fitted with antikickback fingers.

■ **Push stick.** Use a push stick when you rip narrow stock.

■ **Stopping saw.** Shut off the power. Don't leave until blade stops completely.

Unit 34 Crosscutting on the Circular Saw

Crosscutting is the process of sawing a board *across* the grain (fiber). It is called **square crosscutting** because the board is placed against the cut-off guide and is pushed through the circular saw. Crosscutting short pieces is slightly different from cutting long ones. They are easier to handle, but there is always the danger of trying to cut a piece which is too short. A good practice is to remember that any piece shorter than 8 inches must be handled with extreme care.

To handle long pieces of wood, get assistance from someone or use a support to hold the end up, especially the loose end which is cut off. Do not try to crosscut freehand (without a cut-off guide or fence). Always hold the supported piece very securely against the cut-off guide.

Crosscutting

1. Place the cut-off guide in the slot, or groove, on the table. Usually the left groove is more convenient for crosscutting.

2. Check the cut-off guide to see that it is set at the correct angle of 90 degrees for a right angle.

3. Make certain that the saw blade is set to cut at 90 degrees from the table edges.

4. Mark the board where it is to be cut off.

5. Hold the board firmly against the cut-off guide. See Fig. 34-1. Place the board so that you saw on the waste side of the marked line.

6. Start the saw, and let it come to full speed.

7. Push the cut-off guide and the board forward (Fig. 34-1), holding the board firmly against the guide. The saw blade should extend above the board approximately ¼ inch.

8. Pull back the board and the cut-off guide at the end of the cut.

9. When several short pieces are to be cut to the same length, clamp a block on the rip fence as shown in Fig. 34-2. This gives sufficient clearance between the saw blade and the rip fence to keep the piece from binding (sticking) between the blade and the fence.

10. Another method of cutting several short pieces to the same length is shown in Fig. 34-3.

34-1. Crosscutting on a circular saw. Hold the board firmly against the cut-off guide.

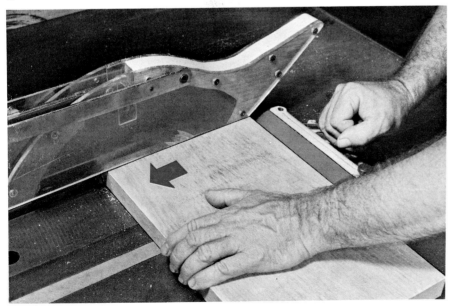

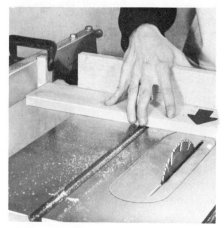

34-2. Crosscutting short pieces to the same length. Note the block clamped on the rip fence.

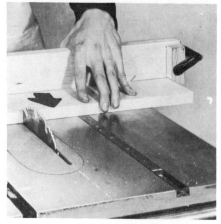

34-4. Crosscutting duplicate longer pieces. A wooden fence is fastened to the cut-off guide with a block.

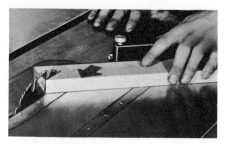

34-6. Making a miter cut in the open position.

When crosscutting duplicate long boards, it is easier to fasten a longer wooden facing onto the cut-off guide as shown in Fig. 34-4. A stop attachment can also be used. See Fig. 34-3.

11. A wide board can sometimes be put against the cut-off guide by reversing the guide on the table (Fig. 34-5).

Sawing a Miter

1. Set the guide at the angle desired. Most cut-off guides have calibrations (degree markings). Place it in the right or left groove, depending upon which is more convenient.

2. Mark the angle to be cut.

3. Hold the board on the table firmly against the cut-off guide so that the saw cut will be on the waste side.

4. Start the saw, and let it come to full speed.

5. Push the guide and the board forward. The miter can be cut in either the open (Fig. 34-6) or the closed position (Fig. 34-7). The method shown in Fig. 34-7 usually produces a smoother contact area for the joint.

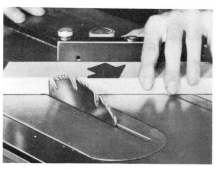

34-7. Making a miter cut in the closed position.

34-3. Crosscutting duplicate short pieces with the use of a stop attachment on the cut-off guide.

34-5. Crosscutting a wide board by reversing the cut-off guide. The guard has been removed to show details.

34-8. Crosscutting a bevel by tilting the saw blade.

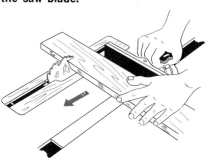

Crosscutting a Bevel

1. Adjust the saw blade with the blade-tilting wheel to the angle of the bevel. Follow steps 1 through 5 given under "Crosscutting."

2. Push the cut-off guide and the board forward (Fig. 34-8), holding the board firmly against the guide and on the table. The pressure of cutting a bevel tends to push the board upward, so it must be held securely against the table top (Fig. 34-9).

3. When a bevel is cut to a compound angle, the crosscut guide and the saw must be set to the desired angles. The saw must be set at the angle of the bevel.

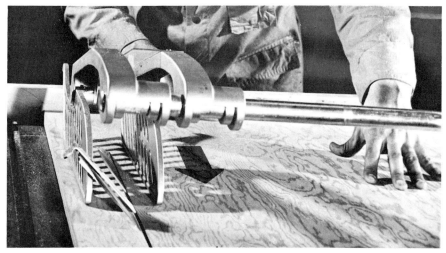

34-9. Sawing a bevel on a sheet of plywood.

Unit 35 Ripping on the Circular Saw

Ripping is the process of sawing a board *lengthwise*. Before attempting to rip a board, make certain that one edge is straight and that one surface is flat and smooth. A board with a crooked or curved edge can cause the saw blade to stick (bind) and kick the piece back toward the operator. It could also buckle (bend or twist) on the saw blade.

35-1. Adjusting the rip fence to the desired width.

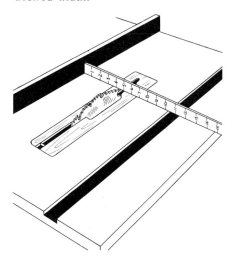

Always follow the safety rules (see Unit 33). These protect you and ensure efficient work habits.

Ripping

1. Adjust the height of the ripsaw or combination blade to approximately ⅛ to ¼ inch above the thickness of the lumber.

2. Arrange and fasten the rip fence at the desired distance from the saw blade (Fig. 35-1). Also test it to make sure it is at right angles to the table top.

3. *Re-measure* the width of the rip cut to see that the rip fence has not slipped.

4. Make a trial cut on a piece of scrap board to check the accuracy. Allow at least ¹⁄₁₆ inch for dressing (planing) with a jointer or a hand plane.

5. Turn on the switch; allow the motor to come to full speed.

6. Place the board firmly on the table top. Press it against the rip fence.

7. Push the board with a steady pressure (Figs. 35-2 and 35-3). Keep

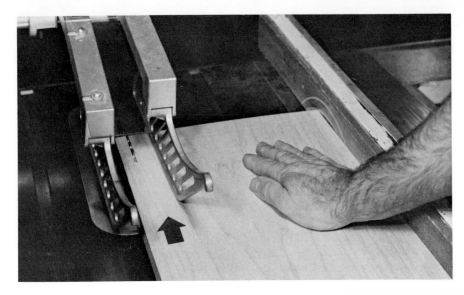

35-2. Ripping a board to width. Note the guard.

35-3. Ripping a large sheet of plywood.

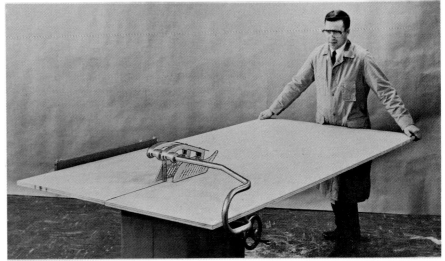

35-4. Using a push stick for safety while ripping narrow pieces.

35-5. Ripping a long board to width. Note the extension on the saw frame to hold long boards.

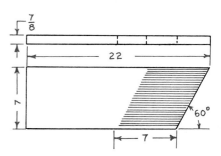

35-7. Details for making a feather board.

35-6. Ripping a board by reversing the board ends.

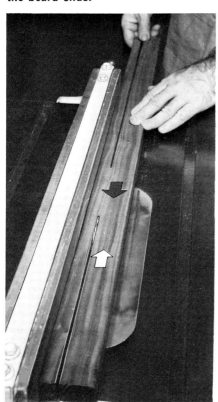

the safety guard in place, and whenever possible, use the antikickback fingers and the splitter attachment. The splitter holds the saw cut open, eliminating binding (sticking).

8. To rip pieces less than 4 inches wide, use a push stick for safety (Fig. 35-4). Sometimes, when a thick board is being ripped, it is wise to set the saw to cut only a part of the thickness the first time. Reset it for a deeper cut; and if necessary, make several cuts to complete the ripping. A splitter cannot be used until the last cut when following this procedure.

9. To rip a long board, provide a means of handling the long stock (Fig. 35-5).

35-8. Resawing a wide board to be completed on the band saw. Use the feather board to hold the stock firmly against the rip fence.

10. Boards can also be ripped by reversing ends (Fig. 35-6).

Resawing

A thick board can be resawed on the circular saw. To do this completely on this machine, the width must be less than twice the capacity of the blade.

1. Follow steps 1 through 6 under "Ripping." Fasten a feather board firmly on the table top to ensure uniform pressure against the board being resawed (Figs. 35-7 and 35-8).

2. If the stock is too wide to be resawed completely on the circular saw, a 1- to 2-inch cut can be made on each edge with the circular saw (Fig. 35-8).

Then complete the resawing on the band saw. See Unit 68, "Straight Sawing and Resawing."

Ripping a Taper

1. Adjust, or make a jig, to shape the desired taper. Study Figs. 35-9 through 35-13.

2. Mark the line of taper on the board so that you can sight your work.

3. Work the board against the jig.

4. Turn on the switch; allow the motor to come to full speed.

5. Push the jig and the board past the saw blade, making the cut to the desired taper, or angle. See Figs. 35-9 through 35-13.

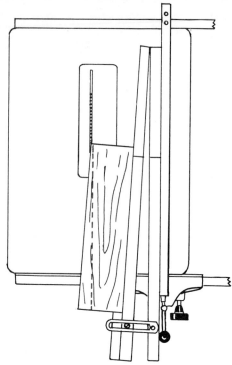

35-10. Setting the rip fence to the combined width of the guide board and the stock to be tapered.

35-11. Ripping the taper with the use of a jig.

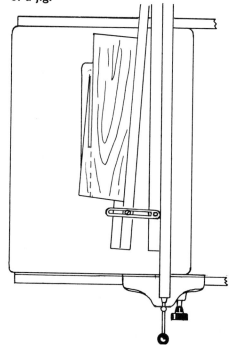

35-9. Details of an adjustable guide to make a taper cut.

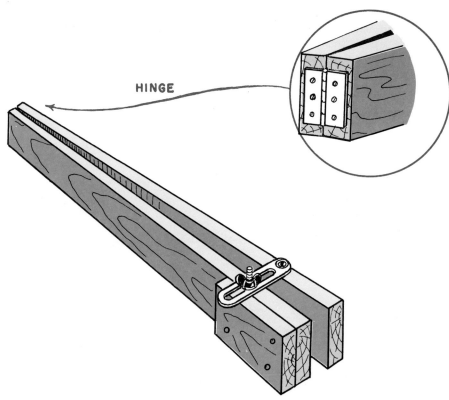

HINGE

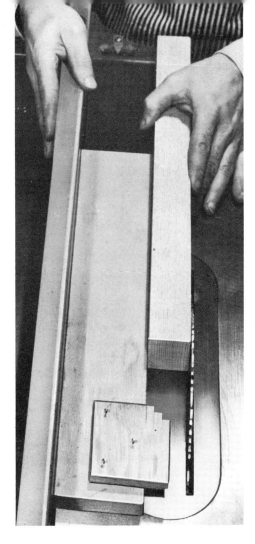

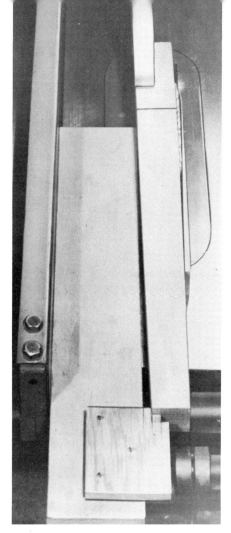

35-12.   Setting the saw for the taper cut, using another type of taper jig.

◀

▶

35-13.   Cutting a taper with the stock placed in the first notch of the jig. Both the jig and the work are pushed into the saw. If the stock is a tapered leg, an adjacent side should be cut in the same manner. Two remaining sides should be cut with the stock, or leg, in the second notch. Do not change the position of the rip fence.

Unit 36 Rabbeting on the Circular Saw

Rabbeting with the saw blade is the process of making two rip cuts of suitable depth, as shown in Fig. 36-1. One way of doing this is on the circular saw.

Procedure

1. Square the stock to the given dimensions. This entails cutting and planing the board or boards to the required thickness, width, and length.

2. Mark the rabbet cut on the end of the piece (Fig. 36-1A).

3. Set the saw to the width of the rabbet. See Fig. 36-2.

4. Adjust the saw blade for depth.

5. Make a trial cut on a scrap.

6. Make the first cut (Figs. 36-2 and 36-1B). Cut the other pieces which have the same rabbet markings.

7. Turn off the saw; readjust it for the final cut. See Fig. 36-1C.

8. Make the final cut on the piece or pieces. See Fig. 36-1C.

A similar procedure can also be used for cutting across the grain.

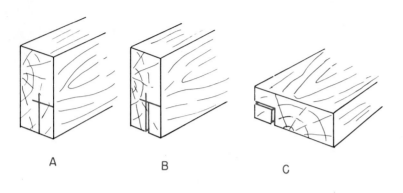

36-1. Details of cutting a rabbet: (A) the marked board, (B) the first cut, and (C) the rabbet cut completed.

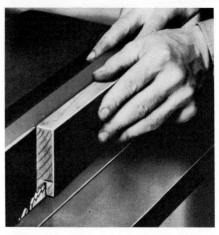

36-2. The first saw cut in making a rabbet.

Unit 37 Making Grooves, Dadoes, Rabbets, and Tenons

The dado head assembly on the circular saw amounts to a thick saw used for making various widths of grooves, dadoes (wide cuts or grooves), rabbets, and tenons. It consists of two outside saws and three or four inside cutters. See Figs. 31-7 and 32-2. The outer blades are usually ⅛ inch thick; therefore, the two used together will cut grooves ¼ inch wide to a specified depth. This is the usual groove for recessing ¼-inch plywood into panels and doors.

Tenons are easily and quickly made with the dado head. The widest combination is often used. It is wide enough to cut the average stub (short) tenon in one pass of the stock. See Fig. 37-6. Tenons can also be made satisfactorily with the crosscut or combination saw blade, as discussed and illustrated later in this unit.

Grooving

1. Assemble a dado, or grooving, head with the blades and cutters as described in Unit 32, "Operating Adjustments."

2. Fasten the dado head on the saw arbor. Refer to Unit 32, "Operating Adjustments." Check to see that the spacer cutters are evenly spaced and that the teeth of the blades and cutters point in the *same direction* as the saw blade just removed.

37-1. Cutting a dado, or groove, across the grain of the wood.

3. Lay out and mark the groove, or dado, on the stock.

4. To crosscut a dado: place the cut-off guide in the table-top groove. To rip a groove with the grain of the wood: adjust the rip fence to the desired distance for making the cut.

5. Adjust for the cutting height of the dado head.

6. Turn on the saw, and allow it to come to full speed.

7. Make a trial cut on a piece of scrap wood.

8. Place the board firmly against the cut-off guide or the rip fence. Make the cut with an even pressure (Fig. 37-1). The groove or dado can be made either with or across the grain.

9. A rabbet can also be cut in one operation by using the dado head (Figs. 37-2 and 37-3). Figure 37-4 shows a dado, or groove, being cut across the grain by using a rip fence.

10. A blind dado can be easily made by using stop blocks clamped to the rip fence (Fig. 37-5).

Making Tenons with a Dado Head

1. Assemble and fasten a wide dado head on the saw arbor. See Unit 32.

2. Clamp a wooden block on the rip fence as shown in Figs. 37-6 and 37-7.

3. Set the rip fence to make the desired tenon length. Measure from the wooden block.

4. Adjust the height of the dado head above the table to cut the shoulder of the tenon.

5. Turn on the saw, and make a trial cut on a piece of scrap wood. Check the cuts for measurement accuracy.

6. Hold the rail, or apron, securely against the cut-off guide; the end is against the wooden block on the rip fence. Push the rail and the cut-off guide slowly over the dado head to make a shoulder cut for the tenon (Fig. 37-7).

7. Turn the rail over; make a corresponding (matching) cut on the other shoulder of the tenon (Fig. 37-8).

37-2. Cutting a rabbet on the dado head.

37-3. Cutting a rabbet on the dado head by using an extra board fastened on the rip fence. This keeps the dado head from cutting into the metal rip fence.

37-4. Cutting a dado, or groove, across the grain of the wood.

37-5. Cutting a blind dado, or groove. Note the stop blocks fastened to the rip fence. The dado head has been reassembled with only the two outer blades to make a ¼-inch groove.

37-6. Making the first cut of a tenon on the dado head.

37-7. Making the second cut of a tenon on the dado head.

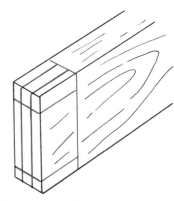

37-8. Layout of a tenon.

8. Make the remaining cuts for the edges of the tenon in a similar manner. This requires resetting the height of the dado head to fit the tenon.

Making Tenons with a Circular Saw Blade

1. Lay out the tenon on the rail, or apron. See Fig. 37-8.

2. Fasten the circular saw blade in place on the arbor. See Unit 32, "Operating Adjustments."

3. Adjust the saw blade to cut the length of the tenon.

4. Adjust the rip fence.

5. Clamp a feather board on the table. The feathered end should press the rail firmly against the rip fence. See Fig. 37-9.

6. Turn on the saw; make a trial cut on a piece of scrap wood. Make any necessary adjustments.

7. Hold the face side of the board firmly against the rip fence. Push it slowly into the saw blade (Fig. 37-9).

8. Repeat this process on other identical tenons to be cut.

9. Stop the machine. Adjust both the rip fence and the feather board to cut the other side of the tenon.

10. Turn on the machine. Make another trial cut on the original piece of

37-9. Making the first cut of a tenon on the circular saw. Note the position of the feather board to ensure a true cut.

37-10. Cutting away the shoulder of a tenon on a circular saw.

scrap wood. Make any necessary adjustments.

11. Again place the tenon piece with the face side against the rip fence. Cut as in step 7.

12. Shut off the power. Always be sure the blades have completely stopped turning before making any adjustments.

13. Reset the rip fence. Make the remaining cuts across the end of the tenon. The feather board is not needed in this process.

14. Place the cut-off guide in the left groove of the table.

15. Adjust the rip fence for cutting away the shoulder. See Fig. 37-10.

16. Set the saw blade at the proper height for cutting away the shoulder. See Fig. 37-10.

17. Turn on the saw. Make a trial cut on the original piece of scrap wood. Make adjustments if needed.

18. Place the rail piece against the cut-off guide. The tenon end should be against the wood block on the rip fence.

19. Hold the stock firmly against the cut-off guide. Turn on the power. Push the stock slowly over the saw blade (Fig. 37-10).

20. Repeat this process to cut away the remaining shoulder pieces from the tenon (Fig. 37-11).

37-11. Cutting off the remainder of the tenon shoulders.

Unit 38 Shaping Straight Edges and Cutting Molding

Shaping straight edges and cutting molding is done quickly and safely with the use of a molding head on the circular saw. The molding head (see Figs. 31-10 and 31-11) has an assortment of molding-head cutters. These fit into molding heads to make almost any pattern on straight shaping or molding. Usually a cut out wood facing is clamped or screwed to a standard rip fence. This allows the cutter-head knives to cut into the wood facing on the fence to make certain patterns (see Fig. 38-1). The circular saw throat plate must be replaced with one that has an opening for shaping.

Procedure

1. Clamp or screw an extra board to the rip fence (Fig. 38-1).

2. Fasten the desired cutter knives in the molding head. Be certain that the knives make up a matched set.

3. Mount and tighten the cutter head on the saw arbor. Place a throat plate with the proper opening in the saw table.

4. Set the rip fence to the width needed for the shaping operation.

5. Start the machine; gradually raise the molding head until it comes to the desired height for making the cut.

6. Make a trial cut on a piece of scrap wood. Adjust the saw or fence setting if necessary.

7. Place the stock to be shaped or molded on the table. Push it slowly and firmly over the molding head (Figs. 38-2 and 38-3). This makes the shaped edge. Shape the end the same way.

38-1. Detail showing an extra wooden facing fastened to the rip fence for shaping and cutting molding.

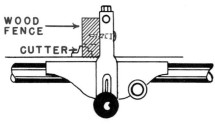

38-2. Shaping the straight edge of a board.

Unit 39 Special Cuts on the Circular Saw

The circular saw can be used to make interesting cuts and shapes. Two of the more unusual ones are the cove cut and saw-cut moldings. The **cove cut** is a concave shape, which might be required in the construction of modern furniture (Fig. 39-1). Sometimes the stock is rectangular in cross section, as shown in Fig. 39-1B; it is then cut in half. Also, the two pieces can be fastened together, turned round (split turned) on the lathe, and then separated for cove cutting.

One attractive saw-cut molding, known as the **zigzag shape**, is shown in Fig. 39-8.

Cove Cutting

1. Determine the width and depth of the cove cut to be made.

2. Make a wood frame, or use a parallel-rule jig, as shown in Fig. 39-2. The inside measurement is set the width of the cut.

3. Set the saw blade at the final height for making the cut (for the intended depth of the cove). This should be half the width of the cove.

4. Place the wood frame, or the parallel-rule jig, over the saw. Turn it until it just touches the front and the rear teeth of the exposed blade (Fig. 39-2). Turn the blade by hand to make certain the teeth barely nick both edges of the frame. This is the proper angle for locating the clamped-on fence (see step 5).

5. Fasten a wooden fence in place on the table top. Use C clamps or hand screws. See Fig. 39-3.

6. Lower the saw blade until it is about ⅛ inch above the table.

7. Turn on the switch; allow the motor to come to full speed.

8. Feed the work against the wooden fence and across the saw blade slowly but firmly (Fig. 39-3).

9. Repeat this operation each time by raising the saw blade about ⅛ inch.

10. Continue making cuts until the depth and the width of the cove have been reached (Fig. 39-4).

11. Dress and sand the cove with a swan-neck shaper blade and coarse sandpaper. Continue sanding with finer grades until it is smooth and the saw marks are removed.

39-1. **Details of rounded corners for the construction of modern furniture.**

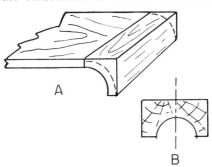

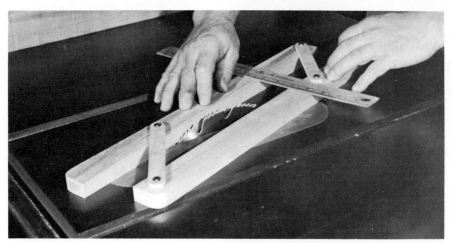

39-2. Placing the parallel-rule jig over the saw to determine the angle for making a cove cut.

The cove can be cut in two and used on the edges of modern furniture, as shown in Fig. 39-1. The outside shaping can be done with a hand plane, scraper blade, and sandpaper, or by split turning, as mentioned in the first paragraph of this unit. The cove-cut piece in Fig. 39-4 was split-turned.

A cove can be sanded rapidly if the abrasive is placed over an object which resembles the contour of the cove.

Saw-cut Molding

1. Square the board to the desired thickness, which will later become the width of the molding strips. The board should be as long as the molding must be to allow for angle waste.

2. Fasten a wood facing to the cut-off guide. See Fig. 39-5.

3. Drive a small nail into the wood facing to act as a guide pin (Fig. 39-5).

The distance from the nail to the blade will determine the spacing of the saw cuts.

4. Set the saw blade to extend above the table the desired height for making the saw kerfs.

5. Place the molding stock against the cut-off guide wood facing. Make the cuts. Repeat cuts are made by alternately turning the work face up and face down, as shown in Fig. 39-6.

6. Place an auxiliary wood table on top of the saw table. Fasten it securely with clamps. See Fig. 39-7. The strips which are ripped will be fragile (delicate), so they will need a solid support.

7. Turn on the switch while the saw blade is below the table top.

8. Gradually turn the hand wheel to raise the saw blade. Allow it to cut up through the auxiliary wood table top until it is high enough to cut through the molding stock.

9. Fasten two clamps as shown in Fig. 39-7. These prevent the molding strips from pushing up and breaking.

10. Plane the edge of the molding strip on a jointer.

11. Feed the molding stock through the saw (Fig. 39-7). Each time a strip

39-3. A wooden fence clamped on the table top for making a cove cut.

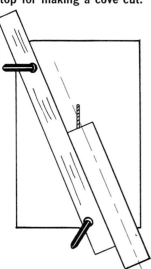

39-4. Cutting a cove by pushing the stock across the saw blade in an angular direction against a wooden fence. This process involves a succession of shallow (⅛-inch) cuts until the depth has been reached.

39-5. A small nail driven into the wood facing of the cut-off guide to serve as a guide pin.

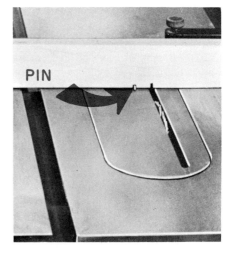

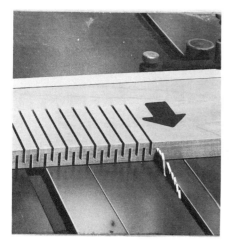

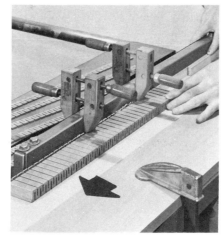

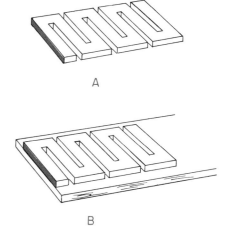

39-6. Saw cuts are made by alternately turning the work face up and then face down. The distance from the nail (guide pin) to the blade in Fig. 39-5 determines the spacing of the saw cuts.

39-7. One piece of molding stock can be sliced and ripped to produce many feet of molding.

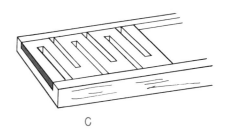

is cut, plane the edge of the stock. It must have a smooth edge to feed against the rip fence.

This molding can be used as an overlay or it can be applied to a heavier backing piece. It can also be inserted in a recess or groove, making an inlay (Fig. 39-8).

39-8. Treatment of saw-cut molding. (A) ripped molding stock; (B) molding fastened onto backing; (C) molding inserted into recess or groove.

DISCUSSION TOPICS

1. How is the size of the circular saw, or table saw, measured? What is the size of the one in your school shop or laboratory? What is the size of the one in your home workshop, if you have one?
2. What are the two general types of circular machines? What makes them different?
3. What is the meaning of the abbreviations **rpm** and **sfm?**
4. What is the range of cutting speeds for the circular saw?
5. Explain the difference between a tilting-arbor and a tilting-table machine.
6. List the name and describe the function of each of the eight essential parts of the circular saw.
7. What are the two general types of circular saw blades? How do they differ?
8. List and describe four types of teeth used on circular saw blades.
9. List and describe two groups of processes which can be performed on the circular saw, aside from single-blade sawing.
10. List 10 important safety rules which should be observed when using the circular saw.
11. What determines the limitation on completing the resawing procedure on the circular saw?
12. How is the feather board used in connection with sawing on the circular saw?
13. How far should a saw blade extend above the work for safe operation of the saw?
14. When is it desirable to use a push stick?
15. Why should a block be fastened on the rip fence when crosscutting several pieces to the same length?
16. What is a dado head?
17. At what angle should the crosscut guide be set for sawing miters to fit a right angle?
18. Visit a sawmill. Report on the types of circular saws in use.

SAWING, DADOING, SHAPING, AND SANDING ON THE RADIAL SAW

Unit 40 General Information About the Radial (Cut-off) Saw

The radial (cut-off) saw is a development of the older swing saw, on which the blade swung back and forth above the work table. The modern radial saw (Fig. 40-1) is a precision machine that is capable of doing an amazing variety of operations. It gets its name because the arm can be rotated 360 degrees right or left. It is a versatile tool for the industrial, school, or home workshop.

This machine, with proper adjustment and the many attachments available, can be used to crosscut, rip, miter, bevel, and compound-bevel. It can rip tapers; plow; cut dadoes, rabbets, grooves, and tongues; and make tenons. It can also be used for molding and router shaping. It also drills, sands, and grinds.

Types

Radial saws are grouped into three major types, depending upon the design and action of the overarm. The **double-arm** design is shown in Fig. 40-1. On this machine the overarm remains in a fixed lateral position; a second, or turret, arm pivots a full 360 degrees. The pivot action of the second arm (the underarm) always moves the saw toward the work.

A second type has a **stationary overarm** that pivots completely around a support column. This type has distinct disadvantages. The arm projects beyond the front of the saw table and interferes with the operator. It also pivots away from the work and off the table, limiting its capabilities.

The third type is the **sliding overarm** design. This machine requires twice the floor space of the other two. It has a sliding arm which rotates completely around the support column.

Regardless of the arm construction of these three types, radial saws have the same basic parts.

Sizes and Speeds

Radial saw sizes are measured by the blade diameter and vary from 8 to 20 inches. The 10- to 14-inch saws are common in home shops and school industrial laboratories. Larger sizes are more suitable for industrial production. The blade is attached by a direct-drive motor arbor to the motor.

Motor speed on most models is between 3,425 and 3,450 revolutions per minute (rpm). The surface speed in surface feet per minute (sfm) varies with the diameter of the blade. This speed can be computed. Multiply the motor rpm by the blade circumference in inches, and divide by 12.

Radial Saw Parts and Uses

■ **Table.** The table is a series of boards held in place with guide fence controls.
■ **Guide fence.** The guide fence provides backing for crosscutting, ripping, and many other operations. This wooden fence guide is removable. It can be positioned between any of the table boards, depending upon the width of the material to be cut.
■ **Base.** The base is usually made of steel. It supports the table and the radial arm.

■ **Yoke.** The yoke holds the electric motor, which hangs from the track arm. The yoke can be moved along the horizontal track arm or held stationary at any point. The blade and other tools are fastened to the motor shaft, or arbor.
■ **Track arm.** The track arm enables the yoke to move back and forth. It is adjustable through 360 degrees right or left.
■ **Overarm.** The overarm is the top horizontal bar which controls the track arm. It is supported by the column at the rear. This arm raises or lowers the cutting blades or tools.

■ **Upright column.** The upright column is the steel cylinder which provides support for the overarm at the rear. It holds the radial arm mechanism above the table and base.
■ **Guards.** The blade guard protects the operator from the blade and cutters. The antikickback attachment has fingers in front of the blade guard that keep a board from kicking back during ripping operations.
■ **Controls and scales.** The several controls are described and illustrated in Unit 42, "Operating Adjustments and Care."

40-1. A 14-inch radial saw.

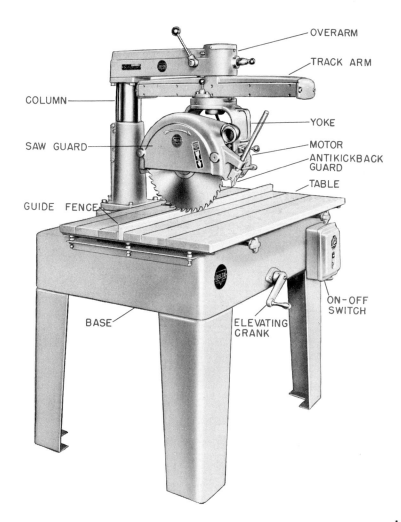

159

Unit 41 Saw Blades, Cutters, and Accessories

Several circular-type saw blades can be used on the radial saw. There are also a number of accessories and attachments, such as dado, molding, and rafter heads; shaper cutters, routers, and bits; sanding disks and drums; and many specialized and customized production blades and cutters.

Types of Saw Blades

The types of saw blades used on the radial saw are the same as those used on the circular saw. These are discussed in detail in Unit 31, "Circular Saw Blades and Accessories." Make sure that the arbor hole in the blade is the correct size to fit the radial saw arbor.

Dado Head

The blades and cutters which make up the dado head are the same as those described in Unit 31, "Circular Saw Blades and Accessories." Make sure that the arbor hole is the correct size to fit the radial saw arbor.

Molding Head

The molding head (Fig. 41-1) is a steel cutter head which holds various shapes of steel knives. The key (wrench) is used to fasten the knives in the grooves. This tool is described in more detail in Unit 31. Other cutter blades are illustrated in Fig. 105-4.

Shaper Cutters

Figure 105-4, Unit 105, "Shaper Cutters, Collars, and Spindles," shows a few of the many three-lip shaper cutters and collars. These offer the possibility of making hundreds of molding shapes on the radial saw. A shaper-cutter adapter (Fig. 41-2) must be used to fit these shaper cutters on the radial saw.

41-2. Shaper-cutter adapter for the radial saw.

41-3. Router bit and adapter.

41-1. A molding cutter head with four sets of knife shapes.

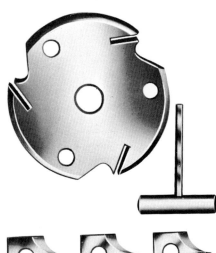

160

Router Bits

Router bits and an adapter (Fig. 41-3) convert the radial saw for router operations.

Rafter-head Cutter

A rafter-head cutter (Fig. 41-4) is used for notching rafters.

Sanding Disks and Drums

Sanding disks and drums (Fig. 41-5) can be used in conjunction with the radial saw. An auxiliary table is needed for disk sanding. See Fig. 46-10.

41-4. A rafter-head cutter.

41-5. Sanding disk and drums.

Unit 42 Operating Adjustments and Care

The versatility, or range of activity, of the radial saw makes it necessary to understand the operation of the various controls and the meanings of the different scales. These scales are shown in Fig. 42-1. Study them in detail before attempting any settings. Those given here for a representative type of radial saw.

Raising or Lowering the Cutting Head

The saw blade and the entire radial assembly above the table can be raised or lowered with the elevating crank handle (Figs. 40-1 and 42-1). On some machines this crank is at the front of the base; on others, it is at the top of the supporting column. One full turn of the crank usually raises or lowers the saw blade or cutting tool ⅛ inch.

Setting for a Bevel Cut

The blade and motor tilt are controlled for bevel cutting with the bevel clamp knob or handle and the bevel latch (Figs. 42-1 and 42-2). Pulling out the bevel clamp releases the lock action of the motor **trunnion** (swivel point). The latch changes the position

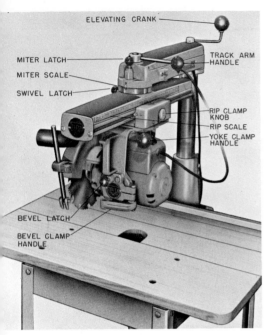

42-1. **Operating controls and scales of the radial saw.**

of the motor. The motor can then be moved by hand to any degree of angle on the bevel scale. Most machines

42-2. **Adjusting for a bevel cut.**

42-3. **Adjusting the radial saw for ripping.**

have stops which locate the vertical and the 45-degree positions.

Adjusting the Radial Saw for Ripping

The radial saw can be set for ripping by the yoke-clamp handle, swivel latch, and rip-clamp handle or knob (Figs. 42-1 and 42-3). The yoke-clamp handle releases the carriage lock action. The swivel latch disengages (releases) the swivel. The rip-clamp handle locks the carriage on the arm in the desired ripping position. This can be set by the rip scale.

Setting Up for Cutting Miters

The track-arm clamp handle and the miter latch are used to set up the radial saw for cutting miters (Figs. 42-1 and 42-4). The clamp handle loosens the lock action of the track arm. The miter latch frees the action of the track arm. This arm should now be swung to the desired miter position on the scale and then tightened with the track-arm clamp handle (Fig. 42-4). On most machines there are stops at zero (0) degrees and at 45 degrees to the right or left.

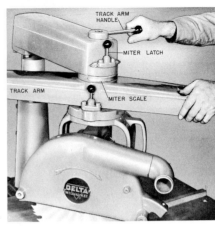

42-4. **Setting up for cutting miters.**

Squaring the Blade to the Table and Fence

The blade (with guard removed) can be squared to the table with a square (Fig. 42-5). Place the square against the blade and on the table. To square the saw blade with the table, pull the clamp handle to release the lock action of the motor, and make the adjustment.

Square the blade with the guide fence by making a trial crosscut in a fairly wide board which has been jointed on one edge. If an adjustment is needed, loosen the track arm (Fig. 42-6) and make the necessary alignment. The two adjustments of aligning the saw blade with the table and the fence are a little more detailed than this. You should read the manufacturer's manual very carefully to learn the technique required.

Mounting Saw Blades and Cutters

Saw blades and most circular cutting tools are mounted directly on the motor arbor of the radial arm saw. First, loosen and take off the guard. To remove a blade or cutting tool, take off the arbor nut (Fig. 42-7). Use one wrench to hold the motor arbor steady;

42-5. Aligning the blade to squareness with the table.

loosen the arbor nut with a second wrench in a clockwise (right) direction. Follow the opposite procedure for mounting and tightening saw blades, cutters, and dado heads. The recessed side of the flanges should be against the blade or cutter. Make sure that the teeth point in the direction of the arrow on the guard. See Fig. 40-1.

42-6. Checking the blade for squareness with the guide fence.

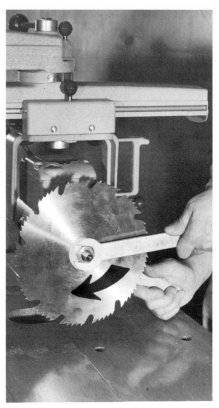

42-7. Mounting a saw blade on the saw arbor.

Unit 43 Safety for the Radial Saw

■ **Permission.** Request permission from the instructor to operate the radial saw.

■ **Clothing and jewelry.** Do not wear loose clothing and hanging neckties. If your sleeves are not rolled up, button them. Tuck in your tie. Remove your ring, if you wear one. It could catch in splinters and injure your hand or simply interfere with your work.

■ **Instruction manual.** Read the instruction manual carefully before you attempt to use the radial saw. Each manufacturer has slightly different instructions on how to make adjustments and perform the various processes on his machine.

■ **Sharp tools.** The teeth of the saw blades and the cutter knives should be kept sharp at all times.

■ **Saw blade and cutters.** Make certain that the teeth of the saw blade or cutters point in the direction of the arrow on the saw guard.

■ **Holding stock.** Always hold the stock firmly against the table-top guide fence.

■ **Protection of hands.** Keep your hands out of the line of the saw blade and cutters. Do not wear rings.

■ **Adjustments.** All operating adjustments should be made and secured (locked) before starting the machine.

■ **Push stick.** Use a push stick when

ripping and cutting grooves and rabbets on narrow stock even though your fingers may fit between the blade and the fence.

■ **Motor speed.** Allow the motor to come to maximum speed before making any cuts.

■ **Saw pull.** Remember that this saw *pulls* itself *into* the work. It is necessary to *push back* on the handle to prevent the saw blade from cutting too fast and choking.

■ **Saw and cutter position.** Always push the cutter head (motor and saw or cutters) back against the post, ready for the next cut. Do not leave it hanging at the end of the arm.

■ **Cutting multiple pieces.** Never put one piece on top of another when cutting two or more pieces at the same time. The top one may kick over the fence. Follow the instructions given in this section on gang, or multiple, cutting.

■ **Antikickback guard.** Make sure that this guard is properly adjusted. When ripping and ploughing, always feed the stock from the opposite end of the anti-kickback guard.

■ **Removing stock.** When sawing and cutting across stock, always return the saw cutter head to its starting position before you remove the stock.

■ **Stopping the machine.** Shut off the power, and do not leave until the saw blade has come to a complete stop.

Unit 44 Crosscutting, Ripping, Mitering, and Beveling

Basic cutting processes on the radial saw are crosscutting, ripping, mitering, and beveling. Compound-angle cutting and taper ripping are also easy to do on this machine. The 360-degree swing of the track arm makes it possible to cut circles and arcs without a jig. Study Unit 42, "Operating Adjustments and Care," before you attempt any of the cuts outlined in this unit.

Crosscutting

1. Set the track arm at zero (0) degrees on the miter scale. Lock the setting securely. See Fig. 40-1.

2. Set the depth of cut by turning the elevator crank. The teeth of the saw blade should barely scratch the top of the table if you wish to cut entirely through the stock.

3. Place the stock (board) on the table top against the guide fence.

4. Turn on the power switch. Make sure the saw blade is *behind* the guide fence.

5. Pull the yoke handle slowly as the saw cuts across the board (Fig. 44-1). Hold the stock firmly against the guide fence. To cut more than one piece to the same length, clamp a stop to the guide fence (Fig. 44-2).

Figure 44-3 shows how to cut several pieces to the same length with one cutting. This is called **multiple,** or **gang,** cutting.

6. Return the saw behind the guide fence before removing the board.

7. Turn off the power switch.

44-1. Crosscutting a board on the radial-arm saw.

44-2. Crosscutting more than one piece to length. Note the stop block clamped to the guide fence.

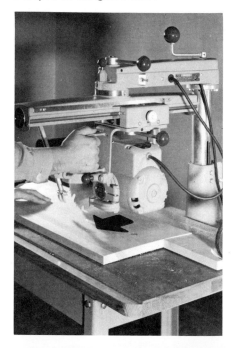

Ripping

1. Set the track arm to the cross-cutting position.

2. Adjust the yoke so that the blade is parallel to the guide fence.

3. Set the depth of cut by turning the elevating crank.

4. Push the carriage along the track arm to the ripping width desired. Lock it in place with the rip-clamp handle.

5. Place the board on the table top against the guide fence.

6. Lower the infeed end of the guard to clear the stock; lock it.

7. Adjust the antikickback guard. Make certain that the points of the fingers are set about 1/8 inch below the surface of the board. See Fig. 44-4.

8. Turn on the power switch.

9. Feed the board into the saw slowly. Make sure that it moves against and along the guide fence (Fig. 44-4). *Do not* feed the stock into the antikickback end of the saw guard.

For **outboard** ripping (Fig. 44-4), the motor is out of the way, and the layout marking is more clearly visible. For **inboard** ripping, the saw head is reversed, and the stock is fed from the opposite direction.

44-4. Outboard ripping.

To rip narrow stock, *always* use a push stick to push away the stock which has been cut.

Plywood can be ripped easily on the radial saw (Fig. 44-5). Likewise, a taper

44-6. Ripping a taper.

can be ripped by using a specially built jig (Figs. 44-6, and 35-9 through 35-13). Figures 35-9 and 35-13 illustrate homemade taper-ripping jigs for use in this process.

44-3. Gang cutting several pieces.

44-5. Ripping plywood.

44-7. Making a miter cut.

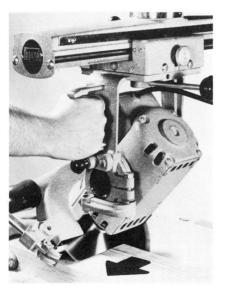

44-8. Crosscutting a bevel.

Cutting a Miter

1. Loosen and swing the track arm to the desired right- or left-hand angle on the miter scale. Lock it securely.

2. Set the depth of the saw cut by adjusting the elevating crank. The cutting edge of the blade should just barely touch the table. This will cut completely through the stock.

3. Place the stock on the table top against the guide fence. See Fig. 44-7.

4. Turn on the power switch.

5. Pull the saw slowly across the board (Fig. 44-7), as in crosscutting. It is always a good idea to check the set-up by cutting a piece of scrap stock first.

6. Return the saw to its position behind the guide fence. Turn off the switch. Always do this before removing the stock.

Crosscutting a Bevel

1. Raise the motor and the cutting head with the elevator crank enough to allow the blade to be tilted.

2. Adjust the track arm and yoke for crosscutting; then tilt the blade to the desired angle on the bevel scale. See Unit 42, "Operating Adjustments and Care."

3. Set the depth of cut by turning the elevating crank.

4. Place the board on the table top against the guide fence. See Fig. 44-8.

5. Turn on the power switch.

6. Pull the saw slowly across the board (Fig. 44-8), as in crosscutting.

Several pieces can be cut to the same length simultaneously, as shown in Fig. 44-9. This is multiple sawing.

Figure 44-10 shows how to saw a compound angle. This is a combination bevel and miter cut that is made in one pass of the saw blade. It requires both a tilt of the blade and a swing of the track arm, either right or left. Study Unit 42, "Operating Adjustments and Care."

Ripping a Bevel

1. Adjust the machine for straight ripping.

44-9. Multiple- or gang-bevel crosscutting.

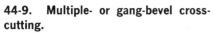

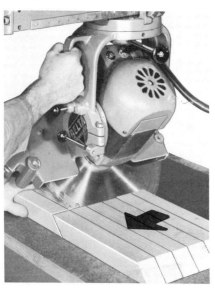

44-10. Sawing a compound angle.

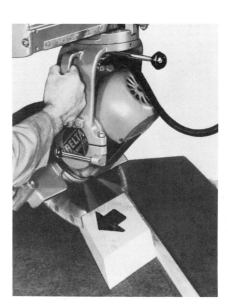

44-11. Making an inboard-bevel rip cut.

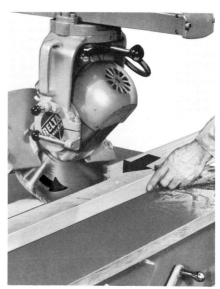

2. Position the carriage on the track arm for proper tilt of the bevel.

3. Rip the angle in the stock (Fig. 44-11) by following steps 5 through 9 under "Ripping."

Making Special Cuts

Stock can be cut horizontally, as shown in Fig. 44-12. Set the track arm and yoke as in crosscutting. The blade is then tilted to the 90-degree setting, parallel to the table top.

Figure 44-13 illustrates how to cut a circular piece of plywood. The stock should be fastened securely to the table top. The 360-degree swing of the track arm makes it possible to cut a circle.

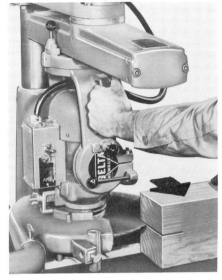

44-12. Making a horizontal end cut.

44-13. Cutting a circle on the radial saw.

Unit 45 Dadoing, Ploughing, and Rabbeting

45-1. Cutting various widths of cross dadoes.

The dado head makes it possible to convert the radial saw to do dadoing (grooving across the grain), ploughing (grooving with the grain), and rabbeting. One can also make tenons. Information about dado heads is given in Unit 31, "Circular Saw Blades and Accessories."

Crossdadoing

Crossdadoing involves the same machine adjustments, setup procedures, and general processes as in crosscutting. Figure 45-1 shows the process of cutting various widths of cross dadoes on the circular saw.

To cut a middle half-lap joint, it is often necessary to make several passes (cuts). See Fig. 45-2. To cut dadoes in several pieces at the same places, use a stop block clamped to the guide fence (Fig. 45-3).

Angle Dadoing

Cutting dadoes, or grooves, at an angle requires adjusting and setting the machine as for cutting miters. Angle dadoes are sometimes also called **gains**. The process of angle dadoing (Fig. 45-4) is the same as for cutting miters except that the dado head does not cut through the board.

Ploughing

Ploughing cuts and shapes a groove lengthwise in a board (Fig. 45-5). The radial saw should be adjusted and set as for ripping. Stock is fed into the dado head the same way as for ripping.

Center grooving (ploughing) can be done successfully by clamping stop blocks to the guide fence (Fig. 45-6). These blocks locate the beginning and end of the cut.

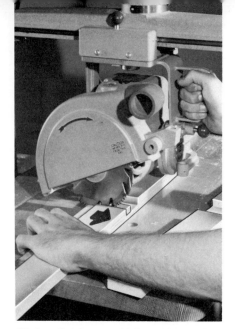

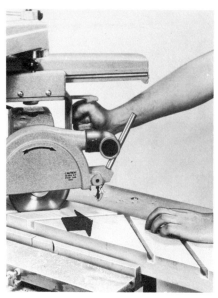

45-2. Cutting a middle half-lap joint.

45-4. Angle dadoing.

45-6. Center grooving with the use of stop blocks.

Rabbeting

Using the dado head, rabbets can be cut in one operation. Set the track arm at zero (0) degrees on the miter scale. Set the yoke to 90 degrees; lo-cate the blade in the inboard position.

Tilt and raise the cutting head to 90 degrees to place the dado head parallel to the table. See Fig. 45-7. Lower the dado head to the desired position, us-ing the elevating crank.

The cutter head remains stationary, and the stock is pushed along the guide fence to cut the rabbet (Fig. 45-7). A bevel rabbet (Fig. 45-8) re-quires a slight tilt of the cutting head to the desired angle.

45-3. Using a stop block for cutting duplicate dadoes.

45-5. Ploughing (grooving) with the grain of the wood.

45-7. Cutting a rabbet.

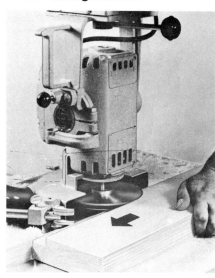

Panel Raising

This process (Fig. 45-9) is used considerably in door and cabinet construction. The dado head is set like the head for bevel rabbeting (Fig. 45-8), but in the *opposite* direction (angle).

Cutting Tenons

The full width of the dado head is used to cut tenons. This reduces the number of passes (cuts) necessary. When a long tenon is cut, a stop block is used, as shown in Fig. 45-10. The *inside cut* is made first.

The spacing-collar method is another way to cut tenons. Figure 45-11 shows the arrangement and assembly of this dado head. The procedure for cutting a tenon by this method is shown in Fig. 45-12. Note that the operator is guiding the stock (rail) with a wider squared board to eliminate kickback.

Cutting a Tongue-and-groove Joint

The dado head and a spacing collar make a good combination for cutting

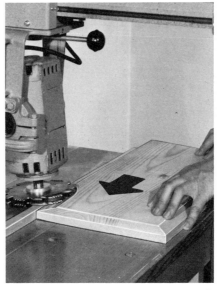

45-9.   Panel raising with a dado head. The guard has been removed.

the tongue of a tongue-and-groove joint (Fig. 45-13). The collar thickness should be the same as the tenon thickness.

A specially prepared auxiliary guide fence should be used, as shown in Fig. 45-13. The opening in the fence per-

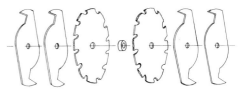

45-11.   An arrangement of a spacer collar with outside dado blades and cutters.

mits the dado head to come through to the desired depth.

A similar setup is used to cut the groove (Fig. 45-14). The width of the groove should be the same as the width of the tongue. This is achieved by combining the outside blades and the center cutters of the dado head.

Cutting a Cove

A cove cut is often required for rounding corners in furniture construction and for making molding. Cove cutting can be done either with the regular saw blade or with a dado head. First, decide the width and depth of the cove. Next, set the radial saw to the desired cove measurements.

45-8.   Cutting a bevel rabbet.

45-10.   Cutting a tenon with the full dado head.

45-12.   Cutting a tenon by the spacer-collar method.

169

45-13. Cutting the tongue for a tongue-and-groove joint, using the spacer-collar method.

45-14. Cutting a groove for a tongue-and-groove joint.

Cut the cove, making *several* passes, each one cutting ⅛ inch deeper. Figure 45-15 is a photograph of a cove being cut with a regular saw blade. The dado head is used to make the cove cut shown in Fig. 45-16.

Rafter Notching

Several rafters can be notched at the same time (Fig. 45-17). Use the rafter-head cutter shown in Fig. 41-4. It fastens on the arbor like a saw blade or a dado head.

45-15. Cutting a cove with a regular saw blade.

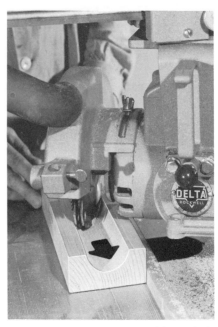

45-16. Cutting a cove with a dado head.

45-17. Notching rafters.

Unit 46 Molding, Shaping, Routing, and Sanding

The scope of radial saw usefulness extends to such woodworking processes as molding, shaping, routing, and sanding. Unit 31, "Circular Saw Blades and Accessories," and Unit 41, "Saw Blades, Cutters, and Accessories," describe molding heads, shaper cutters, router bits, and sanding disks and drums. These accessories perform the several processes mentioned.

Any routing which can be done on a drill press can be done on the radial saw. Refer to Unit 85, "Routing, Inlaying, and Shaping." Generally, however, routing is performed with a machine designed for that purpose, the router. See SECTION 18 "Shaping and Routing with the Portable Electric Router." You should also study SECTION 17, "Shaping on the Wood Shaper."

Occasional sanding jobs can be done on the radial saw, using the drum and the disk sanding accessories. They are fitted directly to the motor arbor or attached by adapters.

Molding

The molding cutter head is fastened on the saw arbor. Position the motor vertically, the cutter head parallel with the saw table. The elevating crank lowers or raises the cutter head to the desired height. Slide the carriage forward or backward on the track arm until the knives in front of the fence give the width of the cut planned.

An effective way to determine the shape of the cut which the cutter head will make is shown in Fig. 46-1. Cutting

46-1. Placing the edge of the stock against the cutter knife to adjust for height and depth of cut.

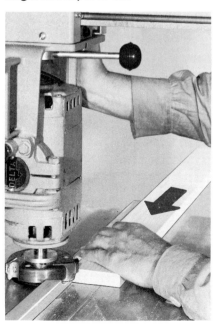

46-2. Cutting a molding on the radial saw.

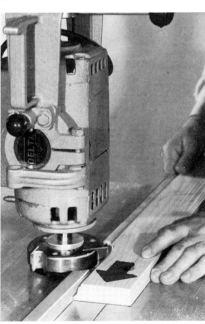

46-3. Molding a circular piece.

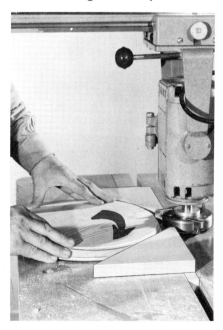

or shaping cuts are made on the side of the stock facing the fence (see Fig. 46-2). Figure 46-3 shows a simple setup for molding circular work. Note that the wooden jig is fastened between the table-top boards in place of the fence guide.

Shaping

Straight and irregular shaping can be performed on the radial saw. The motor should be adjusted vertically. The stock is fed into and against the cutters from right to left. The position of the cutter can be adjusted in the same way as for molding.

Straight shaping is done exactly as that for molding. Note that in Fig. 46-4 an auxiliary board is placed on the table. This raises the shaper cutter, keeping it from cutting into the table.

Irregular (curved) parts can be shaped by using a rub collar (Fig. 46-5). An auxiliary board, fastened to the table top, is required. It should have a hole for the shaper cutter to

work in. Use a guide pin from which to start the cut. **Circular** work can be shaped by using a jig similar to the one shown in Fig. 46-3.

Routing

The routing processes described in this unit are the straight and angular types. **Straight** routing entails moving the piece with the *cutter* remaining stationary (Fig. 46-6). In **angular** routing, the *material* remains stationary, and the cutter moves (Fig. 46-7).

Sanding

Straight-edge sanding (Fig. 46-8) is readily done on the radial saw. The motor should be in a vertical position. Do not hold the edge of the piece being sanded in one position only. If you do, hollow places will be sanded in the edge. Move it continuously. Figure 46-9 shows how to sand freehand curves.

Tilt the motor to the horizontal position for disk sanding. See Fig. 46-10.

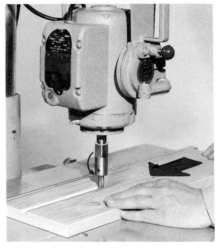

46-6. Straight routing.

A sander table should be built for disk sanding. An easy shop-built table is shown in Fig. 46-10. One side is fastened securely to the table between the boards. This auxiliary table gives a surface on which to work the stock against the sanding disk.

46-4. Shaping straight stock.

46-5. Shaping against a rub collar.

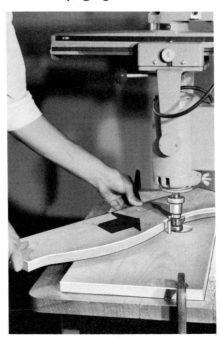

46-7. Angular routing.

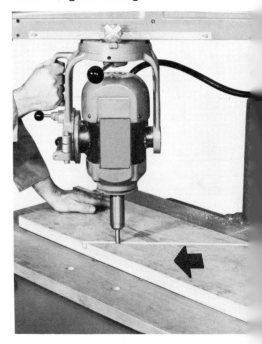

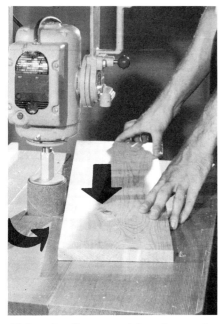

46-8. Sanding a straight edge on the drum sander.

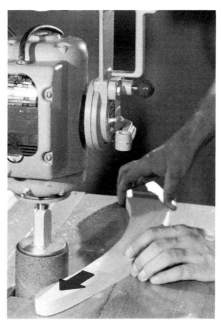

46-9. Sanding curved stock freehand.

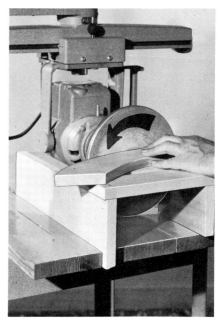

46-10. Disk sanding on the radial saw.

DISCUSSION TOPICS

1. Why is the radial saw so versatile?
2. Explain how the radial-arm saw gets its name.
3. Describe three major types of radial saws. Which type is in your industrial laboratory?
4. What determines the size of this machine?
5. What is the approximate speed of the radial saw motor?
6. What does the abbreviation **sfm** mean?
7. Give the formula for determining the surface speed in feet per minute of the radial saw blade. What is the surface speed of the one in your industrial laboratory?
8. List six radial saw parts. Name their uses.
9. Describe four types of saw blades which can be used on the radial saw.
10. Name six types of cutters and other accessories which can be used on this machine. List a process that each can perform.
11. Explain the functions of four operating adjustments.
12. List six important specifications of the radial saw in your industrial laboratory or home workshop.
13. Name 10 important safety rules which *must* be observed when using the radial saw.
14. Enumerate four different processes which can be performed with the saw blade on the radial saw.
15. Name four processes which can be done with the dado head on the radial saw.
16. Describe the difference between outboard and inboard ripping.
17. Describe the differences between dadoing and ploughing.
18. Illustrate the difference between a miter and a bevel.
19. How far should the saw blade extend into the table top for crosscutting or ripping through stock?
20. What is meant by **gang cutting?**
21. List the sizes of the outside blades and inside cutters of a dado head for cutting a ⅝-inch dado.
22. Visit a large lumberyard, furniture manufacturer, or other wood-products manufacturing plant. Make a report on the radial-arm saw used. List the processes which are done on it. Record the time expended for each operation and determine the number of operations performed daily.

SECTION 6

SAWING WITH THE PORTABLE ELECTRIC HANDSAW

Unit 47 General Information About the Portable Electric Handsaw

The portable electric handsaw (Fig. 47-1) is sometimes called an **electric circular handsaw.** It is used extensively in building construction, and it is especially convenient in that it can be carried to the work. This power tool has been improved with the development of a built-in blade brake. This is a good safety factor and also saves time by stopping the blade quickly so that either adjustments or succeeding cuts can be made. Other safety devices include a kickproof clutch, nondragging telescoping guards, auxiliary front blade guard, and built-in insulated trigger switch. Its balance makes it easy for the operator to use for hours without fatigue.

The cutting action of the blade is up from the underside of the board (Fig. 47-2). It is exactly opposite from the cutting action of the handsaw. Fitted with proper blades or with abrasive disks, this electric tool can be used to cut many materials. It slices ceramics, slate, marble, tile, nonferrous metals, transite, corrugated galvanized sheet, and almost any other kind of building material. It is also useful for cutting grooves, dadoes, and rabbets.

Sizes and Types

The size of the portable electric handsaw is determined by the diameter of the blade it uses. Blades range from $4\frac{1}{4}$ to 12 inches in diameter. The depth of cut varies from slightly over 1 inch to about $4\frac{1}{2}$ inches. An average portable electric handsaw uses a $6\frac{3}{4}$- to $7\frac{1}{4}$-inch-diameter blade. The combination saw blade is most frequently used. It will cut equally well in crosscutting or ripping. See Figs. 31-3 and 31-5.

Electric power handsaws are considered tools rather than machines because they are portable and light in weight. They weigh from 6 to 12 pounds, so they are convenient to carry and to operate. The horsepower rating of the electric motor varies from $\frac{1}{6}$ to $1\frac{1}{2}$.

Parts and Uses

■ **Base plate.** The base plate supports the motor, the handle, the blade, and the entire mechanism of the tool. It is adjustable, controlling the depth and tilt angle of the cut.

■ **Handle.** The handle is contoured (shaped) to give perfect balance in operation. Most handles have a self-contained insulated safety trigger switch.
■ **Motor.** The motor is contained in a body housing which also includes the gear drive that turns the blade. This housing protects the mechanism from dust and handling damage.
■ **Retractable safety guard.** This sprung guard lowers, covering the lower saw teeth when the tool is not in operation. The guard retracts when the tool is in use.
■ **Bevel adjustment.** An index, or bevel scale, is usually found on the front of the tool. It shows when the saw blade is set at any angle from 45 to 90 degrees to the base plate. The adjustment is secured with a tilt lock knob.
■ **Blade.** The combination blade is most frequently used because of the versatility of the portable electric handsaw. This blade is designed for rough and semismooth cutting. A planer blade is used when the cut must be very smooth. For prolonged crosscutting or ripping, a regular crosscutting or ripping blade should be used. See Figs. 31-1 through 31-5. Also see Unit 31, "Circular Saw Blades and Accessories," for detailed information about blades.

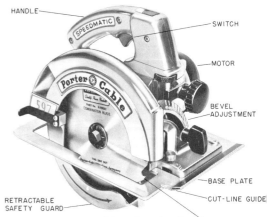

47-1. A portable electric handsaw with a built-in blade brake and other safety features.

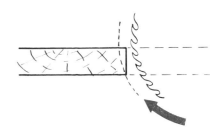

47-2. The cutting action of saw teeth.

Unit 48 Operating Adjustments and Maintenance

The various adjustments on the portable electric handsaw make possible several different positions. It is possible, for example, to change the depth of cut and also to make the different bevel cuts. Figure 48-1 shows a cross section of the various parts and adjustment controls. It is a relatively simple matter to change blades. The motor will give maximum wear if its carbon brushes are inspected often (Fig. 48-3).

Changing a Blade

1. Disconnect the electric cord from the power source.
2. Set the portable electric handsaw on blocks of wood sufficiently high to clear the retractable guard. See Fig. 48-2.
3. Loosen the retaining screw by turning it counterclockwise (to the left). Use the wrench that comes with the

saw. See Fig. 48-2. Hold the blade securely with the front block. This keeps it from turning. Some saws have a built-in blade lock which holds the shaft stationary while the screw is loosened.

4. Push back the retractable guard so that you can lift off the blade and slide it down through the bottom opening.

5. Clean the surfaces of the collars. Make certain that you remember to add a thin film of grease.

6. Place the new or sharpened blade on the arbor. Tighten the retaining screw by turning it clockwise, or to the right (Fig. 48-2). Make it secure with the wrench. The teeth of the blade should point up, toward the front of the saw.

7. Return the retractable blade guard to its proper position.

Adjusting for Depth of Cut

1. Loosen the large, round depth lock knob on the front of the saw by turning it counterclockwise about three-fourths of a turn. See Fig. 48-1. This unlocks the slide.

2. Raise or lower the slide until the blade extends the desired distance below the base plate.

3. Tighten the depth lock knob by turning it clockwise until it is secure. Each manufacturer has specific instructions for making very slight depth adjustments.

Adjusting for Bevel Cuts

1. Loosen slightly the tilt lock knob on the front of the portable electric handsaw. See Fig. 48-1.

2. Swing the body of the saw until the desired angle is obtained.

3. Tighten the tilt lock knob to hold the base in the selected position.

Motor Brush Inspection

1. Remove one brush holder with a screw driver.

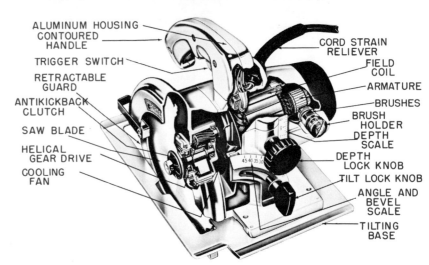

48-1.   A cross section of various parts and adjustment controls of the portable electric handsaw.

2. Withdraw (pull out) the spring and the brush (Fig. 48-3). Note the position of the brush. If the carbon is worn to less than $\frac{1}{4}$ inch in length, it should be replaced.

3. If the old carbon is not worn too much and the spring is not damaged,

broken, or burned, you may reinstall it in its former position. Do not turn it over, however.

4. Be sure to fasten the brush holder securely.

5. Check the opposite brush the same way.

48-2.   Tightening the saw blade.

48-3.   Checking motor brushes for wear.

Unit 49 Safety for the Portable Electric Handsaw

■ **Permission.** Always secure permission to use the portable electric handsaw.

■ **Operator's manual.** Study this manual to learn how to make adjustments and use your particular brand or type of electric handsaw.

■ **Clothing.** Do not wear loose clothing which might get caught in the saw blade. Button or roll up shirt sleeves. Tuck in your tie.

■ **Jewelry.** If you wear a ring, take it off. It might get caught in a splinter and cause injury to your hand.

■ **Grounding.** See that the electrical connection is grounded.

■ **Electric power.** Look to see that the trigger switch is in the off position be-fore connecting the handsaw to the power supply.

■ **Blade.** Make certain that the teeth of the blade are sharp. Study the operator's manual for definite instructions on changing the saw blade.

■ **Cutting depth.** Always check for correct depth adjustment before cutting.

■ **Bevel.** Check for the correct bevel adjustment before making a cut.

■ **Ripping.** When possible, use a guide or a fence for ripping. This is the safest procedure.

■ **Turning off power.** When the cut is completed, always turn off the power switch. Do not take your hands off this tool until the motor and blade have stopped.

Unit 50 Crosscutting and Ripping

The portable electric handsaw is designed to be used with the right hand. The left hand holds the work on sawhorses or on other rigid supports, and the right hand guides the saw across or with the work. Keep in mind that the saw teeth cut *from the bottom* of the board to the top, the reverse of the manual handsaw operation. See Fig. 47-2. Crosscutting and ripping are done very much the same way; however, ripping is a little more difficult, especially when the saw is operated freehand.

Crosscutting

1. Adjust the depth of the cut so that the blade just saws through the board. See Unit 48, "Operating Adjustments and Maintenance."

2. Lay out or mark the board.

3. Plug the cord into an outlet.

4. Put the front of the base plate squarely on the edge of the board. Move the saw forward until the blade just touches the wood at the marked line for the cut. The alignment is made with the cut-line guide, or notch. See Fig. 47-1.

5. Back the saw slightly away from the work. Start the motor with the trigger switch.

6. When the saw has reached full speed, move the blade steadily forward through the board (Fig. 50-1). Do not force the motor. Move the saw only fast enough to keep it cutting.

7. Cut off the power with the trigger switch when the cutting is completed.

8. Stop the blade by pressing down on the blade brake button if the tool is equipped with a brake stop. The brake stops the blade rapidly so that the tool can be laid down or adjustments can be made immediately.

50-1. Crosscutting with the portable electric handsaw.

50-2. The rip guide helps make accurate narrow rip cuts.

Ripping

1. Follow steps 1 through 8 as in crosscutting with this exception: in step 4 the base plate should be put squarely on the end of the board for ripping. It is quite possible to rip freehand while following a straight line, but the use of a guide is recommended for greater accuracy.

2. Attach the rip guide, and set it to the desired width of the cut. This guide is particularly useful in making narrow rip cuts (Fig. 50-2).

3. In order to make wider cuts, use a wooden guide strip. It can be clamped or tacked (nailed) to the board far enough back from the line to serve as a fence to guide the base plate. (Fig. 50-3).

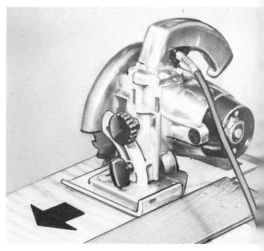

50-3. A straightedge is clamped or nailed to the board to serve as a guide for ripping.

Unit 51 Making Pocket and Bevel Cuts

The portable electric handsaw can be used to cut pockets. It also makes miter, bevel, and compound cuts. The procedure for handling this tool is like that for crosscutting and ripping.

A pocket cut is one which must be made *inside* the area of the material; it does not start from an edge or an end. A bevel cut can be made straight across or at an angle.

51-1. Starting the pocket cut. Note that the retractable guard is pulled back with the left hand.

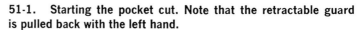

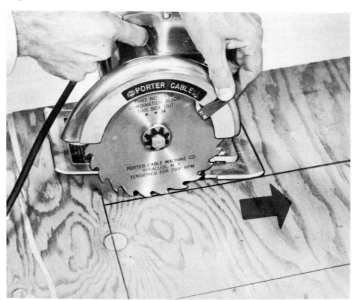

Pocket Cut

1. Mark the area to be cut with clear lines on all sides.

2. Plug the cord into an electric outlet.

3. Start near the corner of one side by placing the front edge of the saw base plate firmly on the work. See Fig. 51-1.

4. Hold the saw up so that the blade clears the material. Be sure you have adjusted the blade for the proper depth of cut.

5. Push the retractable lower guard all the way back so that the blade is exposed (Fig. 51-1).

6. Start the motor, and lower the blade into the board. The front of the tilting base serves as a pivot as the saw blade is lowered.

7. Follow the marked line right up to the corner.

8. Use the procedure described above for sawing the other lines of the pocket cut.

9. Use a compass saw to cut the corners cleanly and accurately.

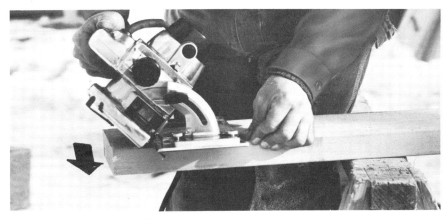

51-2. Making a bevel cut.

Bevel Cut

1. Set the blade at the desired angle to the base. See Unit 48, "Operating Adjustments and Maintenance."

2. Adjust the depth of cut so that the blade just cuts through the piece.

3. Mark the board where it is to be cut.

4. Follow steps 3 through 8 under crosscutting in Unit 50. See Fig. 51-2.

Special Cuts

The portable electric handsaw can also be used for cutting grooves, dadoes, and rabbets. See Unit 31, "Circular Saw Blades and Accessories," which gives information concerning special cutters. The process is generally the same as for crosscutting and ripping except for the use of clamped guides and the depth set of the blade.

DISCUSSION TOPICS

1. Why is the portable electric handsaw so useful?

2. List eight materials this tool can cut when fitted with the proper blades or disks.

3. List six different woodworking processes this handsaw can perform.

4. List and describe the use of at least six parts of the portable electric handsaw.

5. List eight safety rules to follow in using this tool.

6. How does the cutting action of this saw differ from that of the manual handsaw?

7. Explain how you can make a rip guide if the regular one does not extend far enough.

8. Explain two types of adjustments that are readily made on this tool.

9. Describe the procedure for changing a saw blade on the portable electric handsaw.

10. What is the advantage of the blade brake on portable electric handsaws?

11. Explain a pocket cut. Describe the procedure for making a pocket cut.

12. What is the purpose of the retractable guard?

13. How is the size of a portable electric handsaw determined?

14. What is an average size for this tool?

15. What type of saw blade is most commonly used for the portable electric handsaw?

16. Visit a lumberyard, mill and sash company, building contractor, or other wood-products manufacturing plant. Make out a written report on the various types of portable electric handsaws they use. List the different purposes for which they are used.

SECTION 7

PLANING ON THE JOINTER

Unit 52 General Information About the Jointer

The jointer (Fig. 52-1) is an electrically driven power planer. This tool is used mainly to plane the surfaces and edges of boards. It can also be used to plane tapers, chamfers, and bevels; cut rabbets, and make other specialty cuts.

Sizes and Types

The capacity (size) of the jointer is usually determined by the cutting widths of the knives used in the cutter head. These range from 4 inches in even numbers through 16 inches. The jointer front and rear tables are in pro-portionate size to the cutting width of the knives. Most cutter heads have three knives which revolve at a speed between 3,600 and 4,000 rpm.

The table of the jointer consists of two parts: the front, or **infeed,** and the rear, or **outfeed.** Both are usually adjustable for levelness and cutting height. The surface of the rear table must be level (even) with the cutting edges of the knives. If it is higher or lower, the planed edge or surface will not be straight and accurate. The front table is easily adjustable. It can be lowered to provide the depth of cut on the stock.

Jointers used in school laboratories and home workshops are usually of the hand-fed type. Large industrial jointers sometimes have self-feeding mechanisms.

Parts and Uses

The main parts of the jointer are the cutter head, front and rear tables, fence, guard, table adjustments, and base.

■ **Cutter head.** The cutter head (Fig. 52-2) has three and sometimes four fitted knives. Other parts of this portion of the tool are also shown.

■ **Front table.** This is the infeed table, which is easily adjustable for the depth of the cut. It supports the board, which is fed into the knives.

■ **Rear table.** The rear table is also adjustable. For most cuts, it should be even with the cutting edges of the knives. It supports the board after it is planed.

■ **Fence.** The fence is used as a guide. It is usually set at a 90-degree angle to the table to get edges planed at a right angle to the face. It can be set at an angle to produce a chamfer or a bevel.

■ **Guard.** The guard covers the cutting knives. It swings out as the board is planed, thereby protecting the operator. On some jointers there is a back guard which adjusts behind the fence. This is particularly useful when the

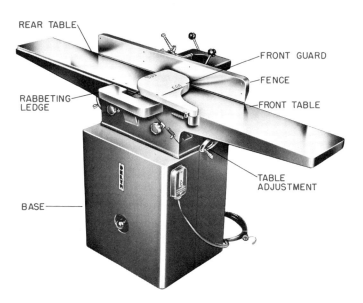

52-1.   An 8-inch jointer.

52-2.   A jointer cutter head.

fence is adjusted to cut rabbets because it covers the cutter head behind the fence.

■ **Table adjustments.** These are conveniently located under or to one side of the front and the rear tables. They raise or lower the tables, according to the type of cut desired.

■ **Base.** The base is the stand, or support, which holds the jointer.

Unit 53   Operating Adjustments

The jointer is a precision machine. In perfect adjustment, it can perform many time-saving planing processes. The preceding unit explained the several parts, including the relationship of the front and rear tables to the cutter head. On some jointers the rear table is fixed (stationary) and cannot be altered. These jointers must have the knives fastened in perfect align-

ment in the cutter head to make the board being planed feed out accurately. On most jointers the rear table raises and lowers with a hand wheel; therefore it must be properly adjusted.

Rear-table Adjustment

To do satisfactory work, the rear table must be even and *exactly level* with the cutting edge of the knives in the cutter head, as shown in Fig. 53-1.

1. Release the hand wheel or handle at the back of the jointer.

2. Raise or lower the rear table until it is even with the knives. Check with a try square (Fig. 53-2).

3. Make a similar check of all knives to see that all project the same distance.

4. If a knife is out of alignment, tap it down lightly, or pry it up. To make this adjustment, slightly loosen the screws which hold the knife in the cutter head so that it can be aligned, as shown in Fig. 53-3. Use a wooden block.

5. When the *rear table* has been adjusted accurately in relation to the knives, tighten the hand or locking wheel. If the rear table is higher than the knives, the jointer will cut a taper on the board, as shown in Fig. 53-4. If the rear table is lower, the knives will make a gouge at the end of the cut, as shown in Fig. 53-5.

Other Adjustments

Make certain that the depth-of-cut indicator or gauge for the front table records accurately the depth of the cut. This indicator (depth scale) can usually be moved slightly to make it accurate.

Check the fence with the table to make sure it is at a right angle (90 degrees). Do this with a try square (Fig. 53-6). There is a tilt scale for checking this accuracy on most jointer fences.

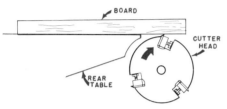

53-1. The correct adjustment of the rear table of the jointer with the cutting edge of the knives.

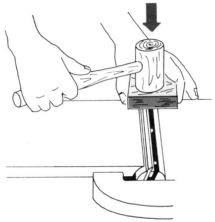

53-3. Adjusting the alignment of the cutter knife with the rear table.

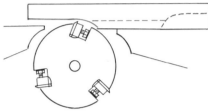

53-5. A gouge cut resulting when the rear table is set too low.

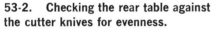

53-2. Checking the rear table against the cutter knives for evenness.

53-6. Checking the fence for squareness with the table.

53-4. A taper cut made with the rear table too high.

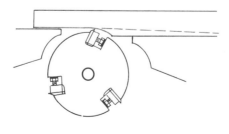

Unit 54 Safety for the Jointer

■ **Permission.** Request permission from the instructor or the person in charge to use the jointer.

■ **Clothing.** Avoid wearing loose clothing. Button or roll up your sleeves. Tuck in your necktie.

■ **Jewelry.** If you wear a ring, take it off. It could catch in splinters and cause injury to your hand.

■ **Sharpness.** Make certain the jointer blades are sharp.

■ **Fence adjustment.** Always check the fence adjustment before planing.

■ **Adjustments.** Make no adjustments of any kind while the jointer is in operation. Check the jointer manual for instructions on adjustments.

■ **Guard.** Keep the safety guard in place and ready to use at all times.

■ **Stance.** Take a firm position at the left of the machine. Never stand at the end of the front table because a board may accidentally kick back. It is a good idea to sweep away shavings and sawdust, especially from a wood floor. This will lessen the possibility of your feet slipping.

■ **Planing.** Plane only boards longer than 12 inches. Shorter boards are un-

safe because your hands might get too close to the cutter knives. Plane these by hand.

■ **Push block.** Use a push block when surfacing (planing) boards on the jointer.

■ **Position of work.** Always hold the board firmly against the fence or on the table of the jointer.

■ **Warpage.** Surface the concave (hollow) side of a warped board first.

■ **Starting.** Always allow the jointer motor to come to full speed before starting to plane.

■ **End grain.** Do not attempt to plane or joint the end grain of boards less than 8 inches wide.

■ **Direction of cut.** Always try to plane in the direction of the grain.

■ **Thickness.** Do not surface a board less than $\frac{1}{2}$ inch thick on the jointer. It might split and shatter.

■ **Depth of cut.** Do not attempt too deep a cut. One-sixteenth inch is a good average cut. The only exception is when cutting a rabbet.

■ **Stopping the machine.** Shut off the power, and do not leave the machine until it has come to a complete stop.

Unit 55 Planing: Surfaces, Edges, Ends

55-1. Steps, or sequence, in squaring a board on the jointer.

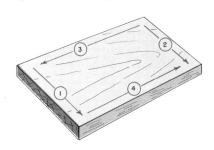

A board can be completely planed on the jointer if the cutter knives can cut the entire width of the board at one time. An 8-inch jointer, for instance, can easily plane the entire width of an 8-inch board because this size of lumber usually measures only $7\frac{5}{8}$ inches in width.

Figure 55-1 shows the steps (sequence) in planing the ends and edges of a board after the faces have been planed. It is considered unsafe to plane the end of a board which is not *at least* 8 inches wide unless you use a guide or jig for safety.

Planing a Surface

1. Adjust the front (infeed) table for a cut of about $\frac{1}{16}$ inch.

2. Check to see that the guard is in place and is working properly.

3. Check the surface of the board for a warp (Fig. 55-2) and/or a wind (slight twist). The concave (hollow) face should be placed down and planed first.

4. Turn on the switch, and allow the machine to come to full speed.

5. Push the stock forward firmly with both hands (Fig. 55-3). When

55-2. A warped board. The cupped face should be planed first.

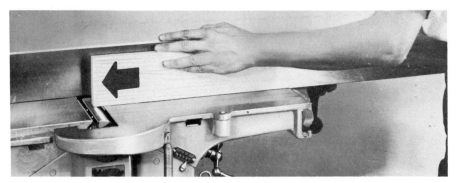

55-5. Start of the cut in edge planing. The guard is removed to show cutting action.

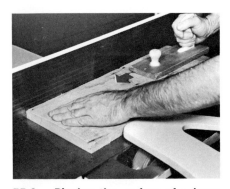

55-3. Planing the surface of a large board on a 12-inch jointer.

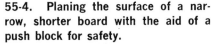

55-4. Planing the surface of a narrow, shorter board with the aid of a push block for safety.

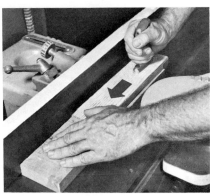

about 12 inches has been planed, move your left hand forward slightly beyond the cutter head. Stand at the left of the front table as you plane. Plane in the direction of the grain. Use a push block for planing surfaces of a narrow, shorter board (Fig. 55-4).

6. Check the planed surface to see that it has been fully planed and is smooth. It may be necessary to make additional cuts to remove the warp, wind, or rough-sawed finish. The final cut should be very shallow.

Jointing an Edge

1. Check the fence with a try square to make certain it is set at a right angle to the table. See Fig. 53-6.

2. Select the best edge of the board to be planed. This should be the one having the fewest irregularities and the one that is the straightest.

3. Adjust the depth of the cut to approximately 1/16 inch. This is done by lowering the front table.

4. Turn on the switch, and allow the motor to come to full speed.

5. Place the board on the front table with the best surface (face side) against the fence. Make certain that you plane *with* the grain.

6. Hold the board against the fence firmly with both hands, and slowly push it over the cutter head (Figs. 55-5, 55-6, and 55-7). Figure 55-8 shows how to plane the edge of a wide board on the jointer.

55-6. Planing an edge. The hand over the rear table presses down so that the planed edge will make contact with the table. The hand over the front table simply pushes the board forward. The guard is removed to show cutting action.

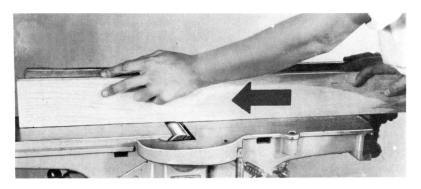

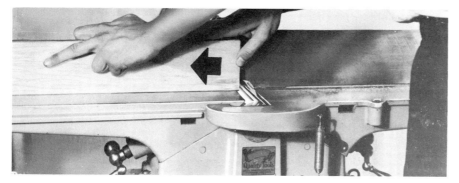

55-7. Completing the edge cut on the jointer. The guard is removed to show cutting detail.

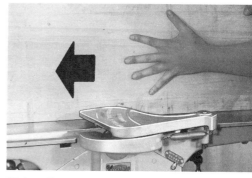

55-8. Edge-planing a wide board.

Jointing an End

1. Check the end of the board with a try square or a framing square.

2. Adjust the depth of the cut by raising or lowering the front table. The depth of the cut should be very shallow: approximately $\frac{1}{32}$ to $\frac{1}{16}$ inch. A deeper setting will tear the grain at the end of the cut.

3. Turn on the switch, and allow the motor to come to full speed.

4. Place the end of the board on the front table with the best face against the fence. Remember: never plane end grain on the jointer if the board is less than 8 inches wide.

5. Hold the board firmly with both hands; slowly push it forward over the cutter head (Fig. 55-9). Jointing completely across the end of a board is satisfactory when squaring up stock, as shown in Fig. 55-1.

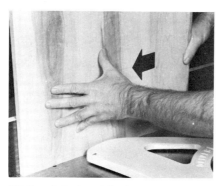

55-9. Jointing (planing) the end of a board.

6. Another method of jointing an end is first to make a short cut of about 1 inch along one end.

7. Reverse the board and joint the end to blend with the cut made in step 6 (Fig. 55-10).

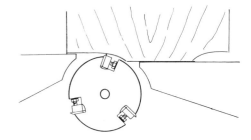

55-10. Another method of jointing an end.

Unit 56 Planing Chamfers, Bevels, Rabbets, Tapers, and Tenons

Although the jointer is primarily used to plane the surfaces and edges of boards, it has other uses. The jointer can be used to make a number of specialty cuts in addition to ordinary planing. This versatile machine can be adapted to plane chamfers, bevels, rabbets, tapers, and tenons.

Planing a Chamfer or a Bevel

1. Set a sliding T bevel to the desired angle for the chamfer or bevel. An angle of 45 degrees is often used for chamfers.

2. Adjust the fence to fit the angle of the sliding T bevel (Fig. 56-1). The

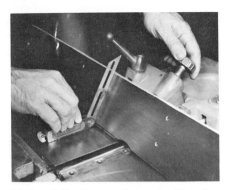

56-1. Adjusting a fence to the desired angle of the chamfer or bevel.

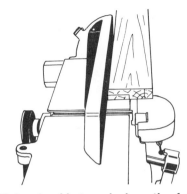

56-4. A rabbet marked on the front edge of a board.

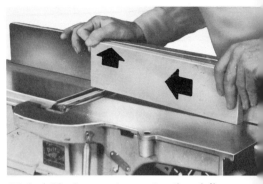

56-6. Planing a taper to the full length of the board. The guard is removed to show cutting detail.

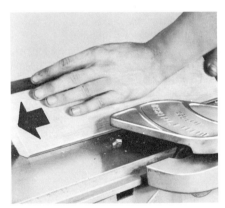

56-2. Planing a chamfer or bevel on the jointer with the fence tilted backward (out).

56-3. Planing a chamfer or bevel on the jointer with the fence tilted forward (in).

fence can be tilted out (backward) or in (forward), as shown in Figs. 56-2 and 56-3.

3. Adjust the depth of the cut by either raising or lowering the front (infeed) table.

4. Turn on the switch, and allow the motor to come to full speed.

5. Make a trial run on a piece of scrap wood; test the angle with the sliding T bevel. Make adjustments if necessary. Hold the stock much as you would in jointing the edge of a board.

6. Plane the chamfer or bevel as shown in Figs. 56-2 and 56-3. Make the number of cuts necessary to shape them. If the chamfer or bevel is to be cut on the ends, as well as the edges, shape the *ends* first, then the edges.

56-5. Planing a rabbet on the jointer.

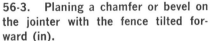

Planing a Rabbet

1. Lay out and mark the exact size of the rabbet on the front edge of the board (Fig. 56-4).

2. Move the fence over to the front edge of the table.

3. Move the guard out of position so that you can see the knives in the cutter head.

4. Turn the cutter head *by hand* until the cutting edge of one of the knives is at the top.

5. Measure in the distance for the width of the rabbet along the top edge of the cutter knife. Move the jointer fence to this point; fasten it to this measurement. Make sure the fence is parallel to the edge of the tables.

56-7. Setting a stop with the table adjusted for tapering a portion of an edge or a leg. The guard is removed.

56-8. Tapering a part of an edge, such as a square leg.

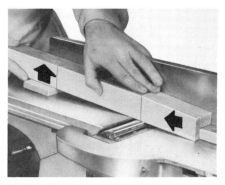

56-9. Cutting a very short taper by pulling the piece toward you.

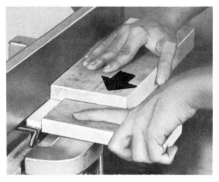

56-10. Shaping a tenon on the jointer.

6. Adjust the depth of cut by lowering the infeed (front) table to the desired depth of the rabbet. If the depth is greater than 3/8 inch, it will be necessary to take more than one cut.

7. Check to see that all adjustments have been secured.

8. Turn on the jointer. Make a trial run for the rabbet cut on scrap.

9. Check the rabbet cut for accuracy. Make adjustments if needed.

10. Plane the rabbet (Fig. 56-5).

Planing a Taper

1. Mark the taper on the stock.

2. Adjust the depth of the cut to the same depth as that of the taper cut. Raise or lower the front table if it is not greater than 1/4 inch. Otherwise more than one cut should be taken.

3. Turn on the motor, and allow it to come to full speed.

4. In tapering the full length of the edge, handle the board in the manner shown in Fig. 56-6. Drop the front edge of the board so that it barely falls on the back table; push it forward to make the taper cut.

5. When tapering only a part of the edge, mark the front line of the taper on the stock (Fig. 56-7).

6. Plane the taper (Fig. 56-8). Use a push block for safety.

7. Very short tapers are most easily cut by *pulling* the work over the cutter head, as shown in Fig. 56-9. The front table should be lowered to the desired depth. The stock is placed on the table so that the start of the taper comes over the knives (Fig. 56-9).

Push the stock down so that the end makes contact with the front table. Slip a block under the free end of the stock to maintain this position, and then pull the piece toward you.

Planing a Tenon

1. Lay out the tenon on the end of the rail or apron. See Fig. 37-8 on page 152.

2. Make the cheek (face, or surface, side) cuts on the circular saw.

3. Move the fence to the front edge of the table. Set it for making the length of the tenon cut. See Fig. 56-10.

4. Adjust the depth for making the cut; raise or lower the front fence.

5. Turn on the motor, and allow it to come to full speed.

6. Place the stock with the tenon end against the fence.

7. Hold the end of the tenon firmly against the fence and on the front table. Move it over the cutter head (Fig. 56-10). To ensure safety as well as a true (accurate) cut, push the piece through with a squared board. See Fig. 56-10.

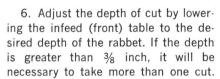

DISCUSSION TOPICS

1. How is the size of a jointer determined? What size or sizes are in your school shop or laboratory?

2. Describe the names and functions of six parts of the jointer.

3. What is the meaning of **rpm?**

4. What are the approximate blade speeds of jointers?

5. Explain what will happen if the rear table is lower than the cutting edge of the knife blades. What will happen if it is higher?

6. List and describe three important jointer adjustments.

7. List 10 important safety rules which should be very carefully ob-

served when using the jointer.

8. What is the shortest length of board which can be planed safely on the jointer?

9. Define **warp** and **wind** in boards.

10. What is the narrowest board which can be safely jointer planed?

11. Which table do you adjust to set the depth of cut?

12. List five unusual types of cuts which can be made on the jointer.

SECTION

8

PLANING WITH A PORTABLE
ELECTRIC POWER PLANE

Unit 57 General Information About the Portable Electric Power Plane

The portable electric power plane (Fig. 57-1) is actually a portable electric jointer. The plane shown in Fig. 57-1 is a heavy-duty, speedy machine that produces a square, smooth surface. The portable electric power plane can be operated much faster than a hand plane, it cuts more accurately, and it is less tiring to use. This plane is being used increasingly as time passes by contractors, carpenters, builders, home renovators, and cabinetmakers. A power block plane, weighing only 3¾ pounds, is shown in Fig. 57-2.

Types, Sizes, and Speeds

Electric plane sizes range from power block planes of 3¾ pounds to heavy-duty planes weighing as much as 16 pounds. Speeds vary from 18,000 to 25,000 rpm.

The cutter used in most machines is a solid body with two spiral cutting edges ground on them. This cutter body can be removed and sharpened with a special tool. These are available from the manufacturer of each machine.

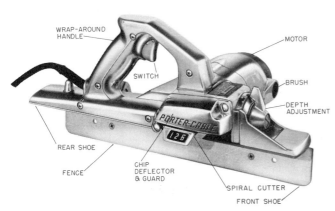

57-1. A portable electric power plane.

57-2. A portable electric power block plane.

The width of the cut in planing varies from $1\frac{13}{16}$ to $2\frac{1}{2}$ inches. The depth of cut on some power planes is from $\frac{1}{64}$ to $\frac{3}{16}$ inch maximum, depending upon the machine.

Parts and Uses

■ **Body.** The body is the housing which encloses the motor and the spiral cutter. It is usually made of lightweight aluminum alloy.

■ **Wrap-around handle.** Handles vary in size and shape, depending on the size and model of the portable electric power plane. It is located for easy handling of this tool, and it also gives the operator control of the trigger switch.

■ **Depth adjustment.** The depth-adjustment lever controls the depth of cut. The markings are calibrated (indexed) to show the exact depth of cut.

■ **Cutter blade.** The cutter blade is a solid piece of specially hardened steel

upon which are ground two spiral edges.

■ **Chip deflector.** This is a part of the body (frame) which throws chips out to the side.

■ **Bevel adjustment.** The bevel adjustment permits setting a plane bed (body) or fence to make outside bevel cuts from zero (0) to 15 degrees and inside ones from zero to 45 degrees. The adjustment is usually made by loosening a lever or wing nuts.

Unit 58 Operating Adjustments

Adjustments differ on the portable electric power plane according to specifications of the manufacturer. Study the operating manual very thoroughly, especially with respect to removal, sharpening, and assembly of the cutter. Other adjustments deal with setting the plane and the depth and bevel of cutting.

Setting the Cutter

1. Set the depth adjustment on the plane to zero (0). Use the adjustment lever located at the front end of the plane. See Figs. 57-1 and 58-2.

2. Turn the plane over (upside down).

3. Place a straightedge (or a try square) across the cutter opening so that it rests on both the front and the rear shoes. See Fig. 58-1.

4. Turn the cutter by hand until it lifts the straightedge (Fig. 58-1).

5. Adjust the lever until the tip of the cutting edge barely touches the straightedge. The cutter is now set at zero. This adjustment must be made every time the cutter has been sharpened and fastened on the plane.

Depth and Bevel Adjustments

1. Advance (turn) the depth adjustment lever at the front end of the plane to obtain the cutter depth desired (Fig.

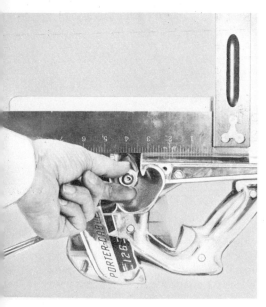

58-1. Setting the portable electric power plane at zero (0) while turning the cutter.

58-2). Most markings are in sixty-fourths of an inch. There are usually two to each number. Placing the lever marking at 1 would make a $\frac{1}{32}$-inch cut. Halfway between 0 and 1 is a marker indicating a $\frac{1}{64}$-inch cut. Setting the lever halfway between 1 and 2 makes a $\frac{3}{64}$-inch cut. See Fig. 58-2. To make a $\frac{1}{16}$-inch cut, set the lever at 2.

2. The bevel adjustment is shown in the lower right in Fig. 58-2. It is made by loosening the two wing nuts on the graduated apron hinges and tilting the apron to the desired angle. Most electric power planes can be quickly set for outside bevel cuts from 0 to 15 degrees and for inside bevel cuts from 0 to 45 degrees. The wing nuts should be tightened securely.

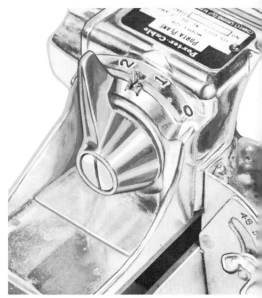

58-2. Depth and bevel adjustments.

Unit 59 Safety for the Portable Electric Power Plane

■ **Permission.** Request permission from the instructor to use the portable electric power plane.

■ **Operator's manual.** Study the operator's manual to learn to make the various adjustments and how to use this power tool properly.

■ **Clothing.** Do not wear loose clothing which might get caught in the plane cutter. Button or roll up your sleeves. Tuck in your tie.

■ **Jewelry.** If you wear a ring, take it off. It could catch in splinters and cause serious injury to your hand.

■ **Grounding.** See that the electrical connection is grounded.

■ **Electric power.** Look to see that the switch is in its Off position before you connect the plane to the power supply.

■ **Cutter replacement.** Do not attempt to replace the cutter or to sharpen it without careful study of the manufacturer's manual.

■ **Power supply.** Always disconnect the plane cord from the power supply before you make any adjustments or replace a cutter.

■ **Cutting depth.** Always check for correct depth adjustment before making a cut.

■ **Bevel.** Check for correct bevel depth adjustment before making a cut.

■ **Turning off the power.** Remember to turn off the switch before taking either hand off the plane after you have made a cut.

Unit 60 Planing with the Portable Electric Power Plane

Planing with the portable electric power plane requires a stance (position of standing) similar to that used with regular hand planing. The difference, however, is that the electric power plane must be properly handled and advanced steadily and evenly along the work. Because the operation of this plane is similar to a jointer, it is rather like operating a small inverted (upside-down) jointer by hand.

Procedure for Planing

1. Adjust the depth for making the cut. See Fig. 58-2.
2. Plug the electric cord into a power outlet. The cord should be grounded for safety.
3. Grasp the plane as shown in Figs. 60-1 and 60-2. The right hand should be on the handle, and the forefinger should be free to control the switch.
4. Place the plane on the board with the cutter slightly back from the edge of the wood. Make certain that the electric cord cannot interfere with the planing process.

5. Turn on the switch. Push the plane to make the cut (Figs. 60-1 and 60-2). Keep more pressure on the front shoe with the left hand than on the rear shoe with the right.
6. Continue planing. Maintain an even pressure with both hands until you have almost completed the cut.
7. To complete the cut, keep a greater pressure on the rear shoe than on the front one.
8. A final cut of 1/32 inch will give a smooth surface which will probably require no sanding.
9. A bevel can be cut by adjusting the fence to the desired angle marking. See Fig. 58-2. The procedure for planing a bevel is the same as for straight planing.

60-1. Planing a door edge with a portable electric power plane.

60-2. Planing the edge of a board.

1. What is the range in weight of portable electric power planes?
2. What is the variation in rpm of the planes mentioned in question 1?
3. Discuss the advantages of the portable electric power plane over conventional hand planes.
4. Describe the cutter used in most of these planes.
5. Describe four essential parts of the portable electric power plane.
6. How much pressure is used at the beginning and at the end of a cut?
7. How is the depth of the cut adjusted?
8. Describe how to set a plane for a 15-degree bevel cut.
9. List six safety rules to observe when using this tool.
10. Visit a building contractor or a wood-products manufacturing plant. Make a careful written report on the various types of portable electric power planes they use. List the purpose for which they are used.

PLANING TO THICKNESS
ON THE SURFACER

Unit 61 General Information About the Thickness Planer

The planer is also called the thickness planer or the **surfacer** (Fig. 61-1). It is a single-purpose woodworking machine used for making a smooth planed surface on a piece of stock. The thickness planer planes, or surfaces, the stock to an even thickness.

Planers are either double or single. The size is determined and listed by the maximum thickness and width of board it can handle. The single surfacer planes one face of a board at a time. It is the most frequently used type in school industrial laboratories.

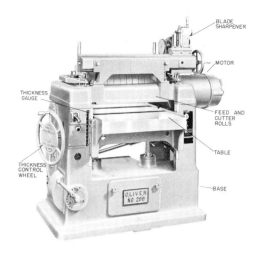

61-1. A 24-inch by 8-inch single planer (surfacer).

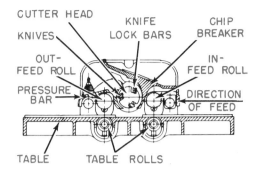

61-2. Detail of the cutter head and rolls on the planer.

The 12-inch surfacer can plane stock up to 4 inches thick and 12 inches wide. Larger single surfacers can plane stock up to 8 inches thick and 42 inches wide.

Double surfacers plane both surfaces of the stock at the same time. The smaller double surfacer handles stock up to 6 inches thick and 30 inches wide. Larger machines can plane stock up to 12 inches thick and 48 inches wide.

Most planer cutter heads have three evenly spaced knives. See Fig. 61-2. Successive cuts are made as the corrugated infeed roll pushes the board through the planer head. The outfeed roll holds the board against the table and the table rolls as it moves forward (Fig. 61-2). The speed of the cutter head varies from 3,600 to 6,000 rpm.

Operating Adjustments

The operating controls of the surfacer are few and simple. An electric switch turns on the power for the machine. A hand wheel raises and lowers the table to adjust for stock thickness. A feed control can be cut on and off to move the board into the cutter head. On some machines this control also regulates the speed from slow to fast. There is a thickness gauge with an indicator (index) which shows the thickness to which the board is being planed.

Other adjustments are considered as maintenance, and these vary according to the sizes and different makes of machines. You should study the manufacturer's manual carefully before making such adjustments.

Parts and Uses

▪ **Feed mechanism.** The head of the planer, contains the feed roll, chip breaker, cutter head, and outfeed roll. These parts are illustrated in Fig. 61-2. A direct-feed motor is usually attached to the planer head.

▪ **Table.** The flat surface on which the lumber rides.

▪ **Base.** The frame which serves as a mounting for the working parts.

▪ **Thickness-control hand wheel.** This adjusts the table, which controls the thickness remaining after the cut.

▪ **Feed control.** This operates the infeed and outfeed rolls which move the stock through the rolls and under the cutter head. On some machines it also determines the speed with which the piece is fed into the planer head.

Unit 62 Safety for the Planer

▪ **Permission.** Request permission from the instructor or the person in charge to use the planer.

▪ **Clothing.** Avoid wearing loose clothing. Button or roll up your sleeves. Tuck in your necktie.

▪ **Jewelry.** If you wear a ring, take it off. It could catch on a splinter and cause serious injury to your hand.

▪ **Inspection.** Inspect the board before planing it. Remove tacks, brads, nails, or anything else which might damage

193

the cutters. The stock should also be free of paint and other finishing materials, which dull cutter blades quickly.

■ **Board sizes.** Do not surface boards less than 14 inches in length and ¼ inch in thickness. The board should be sufficiently long for the outfeed roll to start pulling it before the infeed roll releases it.

■ **Adjustments.** Make all adjustments with the power off.

■ **Stance.** Stand at the side of the board so that you can handle the feed control, thickness hand wheel, and switch. Never bend over to watch the board being planed. Chips may be thrown in your face.

■ **Hands.** Keep your fingers away from the top and bottom sides of the board as it is being fed through the planer.

■ **Planing the first surface.** When possible, do this on a jointer.

■ **Feeding stock.** After the board starts going through the planer, remove your hands and stand aside to avoid possible kickback.

■ **Depth of cut.** Do not attempt to take a deep cut; ⅟₁₆ inch is usually satisfactory.

■ **Planed stock.** When the board comes through the surfacer, be sure to grasp it or see that it feeds onto a table. Do not allow it to fall onto the floor.

■ **Stopping.** Shut off the power, and do not leave until the planer has come to a complete stop.

■ **Shavings.** Be careful to remove shavings only after the power has been turned off.

Unit 63 Planing Stock to Thickness

Very accurate and "true" surfacing of stock on a planer can be done if one side (face) of the board has first been planed on the jointer. This is especially desirable if the board is warped or twisted. A warped board (Fig. 63-1) should have the cupped (warped) face planed first. A board having a wind (Fig. 63-2) should have one face planed flat before it is surfaced.

Boards can be edge-glued together and surfaced to uniform thickness (Fig. 63-3). The width must, of course, be within the capacity of the surfacer.

Lumber that is less than 14 inches in length or ¼ inch thick *should not be planed* in the surfacer. The board should be sufficiently long that the outfeed roll starts pulling it before the infeed roll releases it. Inspect boards to make certain that they are clean and free from tacks, brads, nails, screws, or paint or other finishing materials.

Planing

1. Plane one face of the board on the jointer. This can be done, however, only if you have a jointer which is wide enough. If not, follow the procedure given in the next step.

2. Adjust the table with the hand wheel to the desired thickness. The first cut should be ⅟₁₆ inch *less* than the maximum thickness of the board. Take a shallow cut on hardwoods and

63-1. Plane the cupped face of a warped board first.

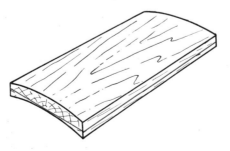

63-2. A board with a wind (twist).

63-3. Boards edge-glued for planing.

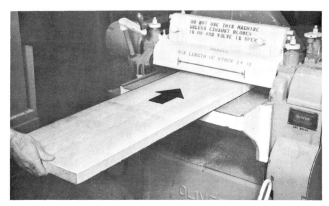

63-4. Feeding a board into the thickness planer.

63-5. Removing a surfaced board from the planer. Note the extension support table.

63-6. Planing a thin board.

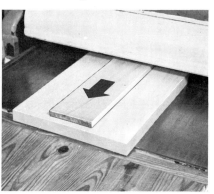

a slightly heavier (deeper) one on softwoods. A good average depth is $\frac{1}{16}$ inch.

If the first face cannot be planed on the jointer, it can be done on the surfacer by placing the cupped face (concave) down. See Fig. 63-1.

3. Check the direction of the wood grain. Try to feed the board so that the cut will be made *with* the grain.

4. Turn on the electric power, and adjust the feed control so that the rollers and the cutter head are turning.

5. Place the board flat on the infeed side of the table. Push it straight forward until the feed rolls pull it (Fig. 63-4).

6. Grasp the surfaced board as it comes off the back table (Fig. 63-5). Do not allow it to fall to the floor.

7. Run the stock through the surfacer as often as necessary. Reduce the board to the planned thickness.

Thin boards can be surfaced by placing them on top of thicker ones (Fig. 63-6).

DISCUSSION TOPICS

1. How is the size of a thickness planer determined? What is the size of the one in your school shop or laboratory?
2. List and describe the names and functions of five essential parts of the planer.
3. What is the speed variation of planer cutters?
4. Name the two types of surfacers.
5. List the three types of operating controls and the purpose of each.
6. Define the words **wind** and **warp.**
7. What are the minimum length and thickness which can be safely handled in a planer? Why are they the minimums?
8. What two other names is the planer known by?
9. What is the purpose of the planer?
10. List six safety rules to observe when using the planer.
11. Why should you stand aside while feeding a board into the planer? To which side of the board should you stand?
12. Visit a large lumberyard, sawmill, mill and sash company, furniture manufacturer, or other wood-products manufacturing plant. Make a report on the surfacers in use.

10

SAWING ON THE BAND SAW

Unit 64 General Information About the Band Saw

The band saw (Fig. 64-1) is a machine which performs many sawing operations. The saw itself is a flexible band of steel with teeth cut on one edge. It can be used for straight sawing as well as for cutting curves.

The band saw used in industry is known as a **band mill.** It has a wide blade and is used to saw logs into planks. Lumberyards and millwork factories use a heavy-duty band saw for resawing thick stock into thinner pieces.

Sizes and Types

The size of the band saw is measured by the diameter of the wheels around which the band runs. For school use, these vary from 14 to 30 inches. Machines with wheels of less than a 14-inch diameter are suitable for home workshops but are not practical for schools or industry. Smaller wheels tend to crystallize the blades in a relatively short time. They break more easily.

196

Cutting speed varies from 3,000 to approximately 6,000 feet per minute (fpm), depending upon the size of the saw.

Some manufacturers make a variable-speed band saw which cuts both metal and wood. This saw is especially popular in the multiple-activity type of laboratory program. The speeds are easily changed. The wood-cutting band saw blade can be replaced with a metal-cutting blade.

Parts and Uses

The essential parts of the band saw are shown in Figs. 64-1, 64-2, and 64-3. There are numerous parts having to do with specific adjustments. These are discussed in Unit 66, "Operating Adjustments." Descriptions of the basic parts follow:

■ **Wheels.** There are two metal wheels whose outer rims are covered with rubber, called **rubber tires.** The band saw blade runs on these rubber tires, which protect the teeth and serve as cushions, preventing the blade from slipping.

■ **Frame.** This is the metal casting which supports the two wheels and all the internal mechanism.

■ **Table.** The table supports the work being cut and serves as the base for the cut-off guide and the rip fence. Most tables are constructed so that they can be tilted 45 degrees to the right and about 10 degrees to the left.

■ **Upper and lower wheel guards.** These guards protect the worker. Some guards are completely removable; others are hinged to permit access to the blade and to the upper and lower wheels.

■ **Blade guides.** There are two blade guides. One is above, the other below, the table (Figs. 64-2 and 64-3). These guide the blade, keeping it from twisting and thus assuring a straight cut. The upper guide is adjustable in height to allow for thickness of cut.

■ **Tension adjustment.** This is generally made on the upper wheel. The pressure on the blade is controlled by operating the hand wheel or a small crank. See Fig. 66-1.

■ **Base.** This is the footing, or metal support, for the machine. On some saws, this is a separate piece; on others, it is part of the frame.

■ **Blade guard.** An angular sheet-metal piece, fastened near the upper blade guide, functions as a blade guard. It protects the worker, covering the blade from the upper guide to the upper wheel guard.

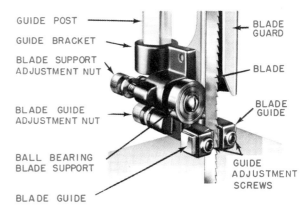

64-2. Upper guide assembly.

64-3. Lower guide and table assembly.

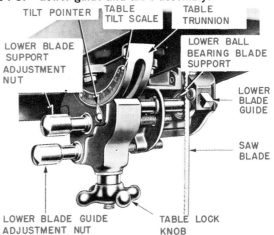

64-1. A 20-inch band saw.

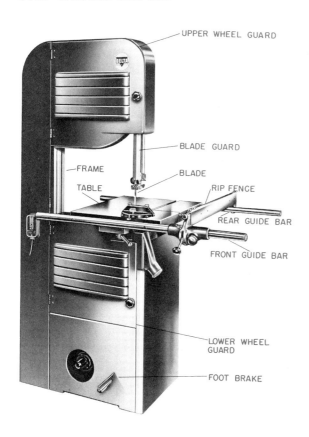

Unit 65 Band Saw Blades

The two most popular tooth styles of band saw blades are (1) the standard, or regular, and (2) the skip-tooth, or buttress. Skip-tooth blades cut faster because the teeth do not clog with sawdust. The teeth of both band saw types are set. Figure 65-1 shows how the teeth are set on a regular band saw blade.

Sizes

The thickness of band saw blades averages .001 inch for each inch of diameter of the wheels on which it will run. A 20-inch band saw would therefore require blades .020 inches thick. This is a general way to arrive at blade thickness; however, both thinner and thicker blades are in use.

Teeth are arranged just like those on the handsaw; there is always one more point than teeth per inch. Five teeth per inch will have six points (Fig. 65-2). Note that band saw teeth have a slight hook, as shown in Fig. 65-3.

Blades vary in width from ⅛ to ¾ inch for home and school use. Width is determined by the diameter of the curve which can be cut on the band saw. Table 65-1 gives data which should be considered before cutting curves. Use a jig saw or drill or bore curves less than ½ inch in diameter.

Folding the Blade

Band saw blades can be easily folded and stored in minimum space by following these instructions: First, release the belt tension and remove the blade from the band saw (Fig. 65-4). Then, follow steps A, B, and C in Fig. 65-5. This series of steps shows how to grasp the blade (with the thumb of the right hand pointed *up* and the thumb of the left hand pointed *down*). If you do not let the blade slip or turn in your hands, it will probably fall into three loops. The right hand should turn away from your body; the left, toward your body, as shown in Fig. 65-5.

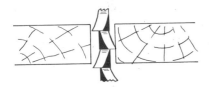

65-1. Teeth are set on band saw blades so that the saw kerf (cut) is wider than the blade. This prevents binding.

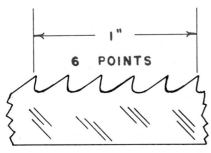

65-2. There is always one more point than teeth per inch on the band saw blade.

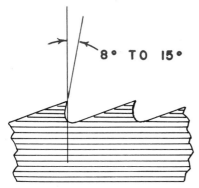

65-3. A slight hook is desirable in band saw teeth.

Table 65-1 BLADE WIDTHS FOR CUTTING CURVES

Width of blade, in.	Minimum diameter of curve, in.
⅛	½
3/16	1
¼	1½
⅜	2
½	2½
¾	3½

65-4. Removing a band saw blade from the band saw. Be sure to release the tension.

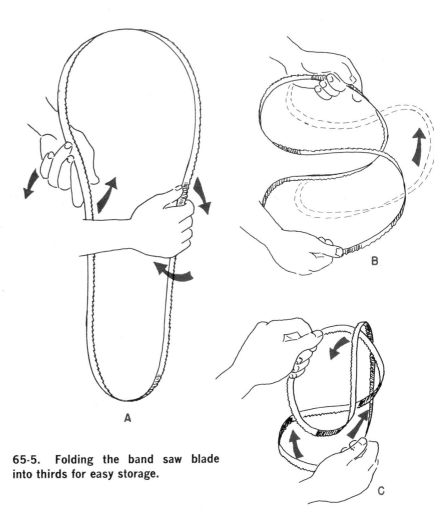

A

B

C

65-5. Folding the band saw blade into thirds for easy storage.

Unit 66 Operating Adjustments

The band saw has several different adjustment devices which must be kept in alignment. Those adjustments described below are typical; they have to be made on most band saws. Before attempting to make adjustments on a particular band saw, be sure to study the manufacturer's data sheet and operating manual. A few of the simpler adjustments are those of the tension on the band saw blade, the blade guides above and below the table, the squareness of the table with the blade, and the cutting action.

Tension Adjustment

The various thicknesses and widths of different band saw blades require different degrees of tension (tightness). The tension adjustment is usually made at the top rear of the saw. A hand wheel or handle (crank) is most often used to make this adjustment. See Fig. 66-1. The handle is turned carefully until the index on the scale matches the width of the band saw blade. After the tension adjustment is made, it should be locked.

66-1. The tension-adjustment handle with a tension scale.

Adjusting Blade Guides

Figure 64-2 shows a detail of the blade guide above the band saw table. Figure 64-3 shows the blade guide underneath. Guide pins on either side of the blade are adjusted to allow a slight clearance for the blade on both sides.

66-2. Proper adjustment of the blade support.

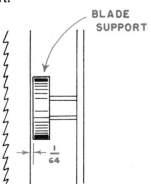

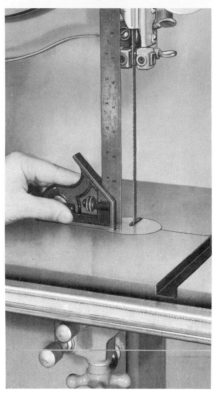

66-3. Checking table squareness with the band saw blade.

The ball-bearing blade support, directly behind the blade, should be adjusted to allow about $\frac{1}{64}$ inch of space (Fig. 66-2). Check to see that the front edges of the guide pins are just behind the saw blade teeth. Similar adjustment should be made almost simultaneously with the blade guide underneath the table.

Table Adjustment

To obtain right-angle sawing, the band saw table must be at a 90-degree angle to the blade. Check this with a try square (Fig. 66-3). The table lock knob underneath the table usually makes this adjustment.

Cutting Action of the Blade

When a piece of wood is pushed squarely into the band saw blade, it should be cut in a straight line. Some-

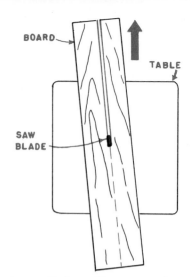

66-4. A blade pulling or cutting to the side, producing a lead.

times, however, the blade **leads** (pulls) to one side or the other (Fig. 66-4). This condition makes it difficult to cut the board satisfactorily. In Fig. 66-4 the blade leads to the right, making it necessary to check the setting of the guides. The blade may have an improper set. If it is the fault of the guides, adjust them slightly tighter. See Fig. 64-2. If it is improperly set saw teeth, lightly hone the side of the blade. Use a fine stone (Fig. 66-5).

66-5. Honing the blade on the lead side.

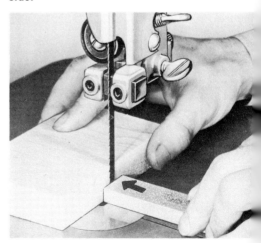

200

Unit 67 Safety for the Band Saw

Permission. Always obtain permission from the person in charge to use the band saw.

Clothing. Avoid wearing loose clothing. Roll up or button your sleeves. Tuck in your tie.

Jewelry. Remove any ring you are wearing. It could catch in splinters and cause serious injury.

Adjustments. Make all adjustments with the power cut off.

Blade tension. Check the tension of the blade, following the manufacturer's specifications.

Safety guards. Keep safety guards fastened firmly.

Blade condition. Examine the blade frequently to make sure it is in good condition. There should be no breaks in it. If there are, this indicates crystallizing (brittleness). A rhythmic click sometimes indicates that the blade is cracked.

Blade lead. Check the blade for lead. The guides may not be correctly set or the blade itself may have an improper set. This can cause it to pull to one side, thereby cutting in that direction (tapering). If this occurs, refer to Unit 66, "Operating Adjustments."

Blade breakage. If the band saw blade should break while the machine is in operation, turn off the power and move away until the machine has stopped.

Sharp blade. It is important that you keep a sharp blade in use on the band saw at all times.

Blade size. Use the correct size of blade for your cutting. A narrow blade is best for cutting sharp curves; a wider one, for larger circles and straight sawing. A $\frac{1}{4}$- or $\frac{3}{8}$-inch blade is a convenient width for most cutting.

Table alignment. Check carefully to see that the saw table is square with the blade.

Upper saw guide. Adjust the upper saw guide to within approximately $\frac{1}{2}$ inch of the stock to be cut. This adjustment should be made before the power is turned on.

Hand protection. Always keep your hand at least 2 inches away from the blade.

Stance. Take a firm, balanced stance (position of standing) slightly to the left of the front of the band saw table. Be sure never to stand at the right side of either the table or the machine. You could be seriously hurt if the blade were to break.

Sawing. Feed the board into the band saw blade firmly, but do not push it too fast. You should usually apply pressure to the work with your right hand, while your left hand guides the stock into the blade.

Freehand sawing. Freehand sawing on the band saw should be attempted only when the work to be sawed is resting flat on the table; this enables you to handle it firmly.

Sawing radius. Make sure the radius of your cut is not too small for the width of the blade.

Relief cuts. Study the layout on the board before cutting. Often you will find that relief cuts must be made before the outline cut is made. Make short cuts first, then longer ones. See Fig. 69-1.

Curves. Cut curves gradually. A short, sudden twist may break the blade.

Completing the cut. Be sure to cut through the waste stock when possible, rather than backing out of your piece with the blade. Backing out of the work could conceivably cause the blade to pull off the wheels.

Removing stock. When it is necessary to back the saw blade out of a long cut, turn off the machine and allow the blade to come to a complete stop. Then remove the board.

Stopping the machine. Shut off the power, and be certain that you do not leave until the machine has come to a complete stop.

Unit 68 Straight Sawing and Resawing

The band saw can be used for straight sawing as well as for cutting curved pieces. Most band saws are fitted with a rip fence and a miter-gauge cutoff (see Fig. 68-8). The widest band saw blade available should be used for both straight sawing and resawing. (Resawing is cutting stock to a narrower thickness.) Resawing is a job that the band saw does better than any other machine.

Straight Freehand Sawing

1. Raise the upper blade guide to clear the lumber being cut. The guide should clear the stock by approximately ½ inch.
2. Mark the board.
3. Turn on the switch. Make certain that you allow the blade to come to full speed.
4. Now feed the lumber slowly through the saw. Guide it gently with one hand; push it with the other (Fig. 68-1). Saw slightly on the waste side of the marked line.

Another method of holding the stock while straight sawing freehand is shown in Fig. 68-2.

Ripping

1. Repeat the first two steps of freehand sawing.
2. Attach the rip fence to the band saw table. Set it to the desired width of the cut to be made (Fig. 68-3).
3. Turn on the switch, and allow the blade to come to full speed.
4. Feed the piece into the saw (Fig. 68-4). Hold it firmly against the fence while pushing it into the saw blade.
5. A square length of wood can be split or ripped in two diagonally. Tilt the table to 45 degrees; push the stock along the rip fence (Fig. 68-5).
6. The band saw is excellent for removing corners of turning squares (Fig. 68-6).
7. Diagonal cuts can be made on the ends of turning squares to mark centers for lathe turning (Fig. 68-7). Make a V-block jig for this purpose. Fasten it to the table, or place it against the rip fence.

Crosscutting

1. Repeat the first two steps of freehand sawing.

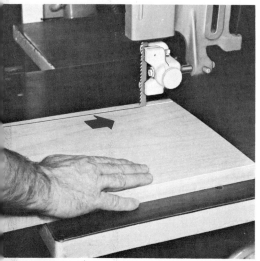

68-1. Making a hand-guided straight cut.

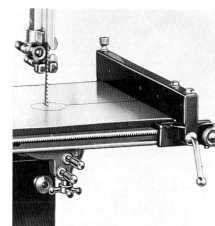

68-2. An alternate method of holding stock while straight sawing freehand.

68-3. The ripping fence adjusted for ripping.

68-4. Ripping stock against a ripping fence.

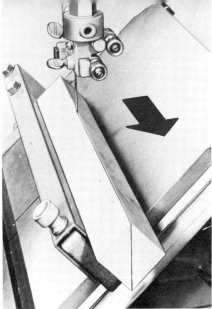

68-5. Ripping stock diagonally.

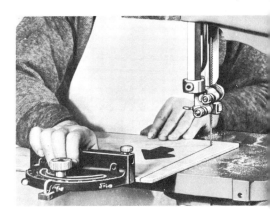

68-7. Marking and cutting two diagonal saw cuts about ⅛ inch deep for lathe turning.

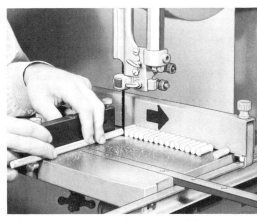

68-9. Crosscutting wide boards by reversing the cut-off guide.

2. Place the cut-off guide on the table in the groove. If the band saw does not have a groove, a wooden extension table can be grooved and fitted to the side, as shown in Fig. 68-8.

3. Turn on the switch, and allow the blade to come to full speed.

4. Hold the stock firmly against the cut-off guide, and feed it slowly into the band saw blade (Fig. 68-8).

5. Crosscut wide boards by reversing the cut-off guide (Fig. 68-9).

6. Make dowel pins uniform using the rip fence as a guide (Fig. 68-10).

Resawing

1. When possible, make preliminary rip saw cuts on the circular saw before resawing on the band saw (Fig. 68-11).

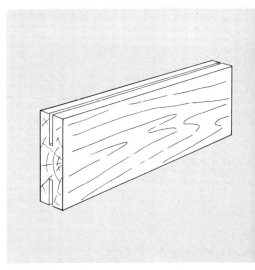

68-10. Cutting dowel pins to uniform length.

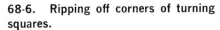

68-6. Ripping off corners of turning squares.

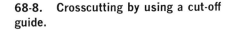

68-8. Crosscutting by using a cut-off guide.

68-11. Ripsaw cuts made on the circular saw make resawing easier.

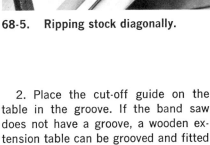

68-12. Resawing along a ripping fence.

68-13. Alternate method of setting up a fence and using a feather board for resawing.

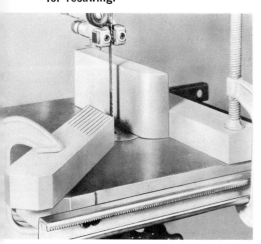

2. Repeat the first two steps of free-hand sawing.

Place the cut-off guide on the table in the groove. If the band saw does not have a groove, a wooden extension table can be grooved and fitted to the side, as shown in Fig. 68-8.

Turn on the switch, and allow the blade to come to full speed.

3. Feed the stock very slowly into the band saw (Fig. 68-12). The edge of the piece being resawed should be planed at right angles to the face. This method of resawing works well if the blade does not tend to lead.

4. Another method of resawing, using a fixed guide, is shown in Fig. 68-13. A shop-built short fence is used. It can be fastened to the regular rip fence or to a longer piece of wood, as shown. This short fence allows for a slight shift in the direction of the feed if the blade does not cut perfectly straight. Note the use of the feather board for holding the stock against the fence.

5. A wooden or metal pivot-block jig fastened onto the saw table is perhaps the simplest guide when resawing stock (Figs. 68-14 and 68-15). The operator can feed the stock in such a way as to offset any lead in the band saw blade. The wooden pivot block or guide can be made easily. The end which serves as the rip guide should be rounded.

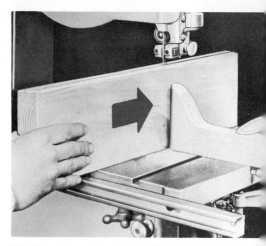

68-14. Resawing stock with a wooden pivot-block jig for a guide.

68-15. Resawing stock with a metal revolving pivot block.

Unit 69 Curved and Irregular Sawing

The band saw is basically designed to cut curves and irregular shapes. Many persons consider this its primary function. Sometimes helpful jigs can be built. Duplicate parts can most easily be made by fastening or nailing several pieces together and then cutting them at one time. It is even desirable to leave the pieces fastened together while dressing down the edges by filing or sanding. This assures that they will be identical.

When cutting circles, be sure that you watch the sawing very carefully. The band saw blade cuts across a grain easily, but it has a tendency to follow the grain when cutting with it. That is, the blade tends to follow the grain when the grain and the blade run in the same direction. Before sawing curves, circles, or irregular parts, study Table 65-1 for the minimum diameters of curves which can be made with different widths of blades.

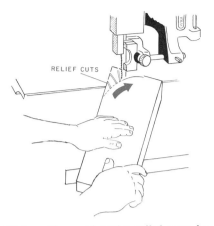

69-1. Plan and make relief cuts before sawing the marked curve.

69-3. Sawing to a curved line.

Freehand Sawing of Curves

1. Raise the upper blade guide to clear the piece being cut.

2. Mark the layout on the board.

3. Turn on the switch, and allow the blade to come to full speed.

4. Study the piece to determine whether relief cuts should be made first (Fig. 69-1). For sharp curves, relief cuts can be made as shown in Fig. 69-2.

5. Feed the piece into the saw blade. Make the cut on the waste side of the marked line (Fig. 69-3).

6. To saw a circle or a disk, follow the procedure shown in Fig. 69-4. Start the cut from the end grain; follow around the marking (Fig. 69-5).

Irregular and Circular Sawing Using Jigs

1. If many identical circular pieces are to be sawed, make a ¾-inch thick plywood jig, as illustrated in Fig. 69-6. Fasten or clamp it to the band saw table. See Fig. 69-7.

2. Select the stock from which the circles are to be made.

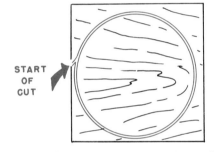

69-4. A suggested procedure for marking and sawing a circle on a piece of wood.

69-2. Relief cuts are desirable when sawing sharp curves.

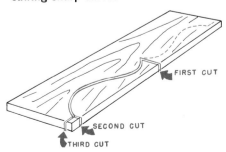

69-5. Sawing a circular piece.

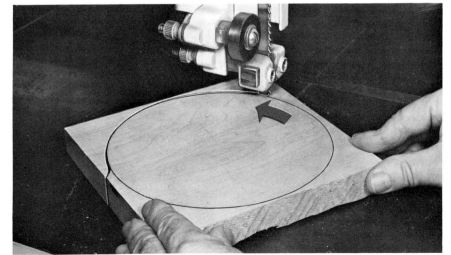

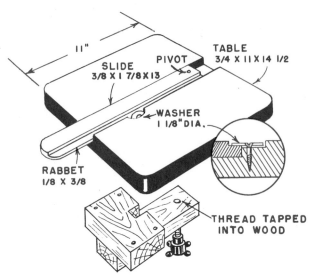

69-6. A plywood jig to be fastened on the band saw table for cutting a circular piece. This one has a sliding pivot bar which can be adjusted to the radius desired.

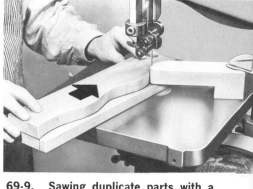

69-9. Sawing duplicate parts with a pattern and a wooden arm jig.

3. Repeat steps 1 and 3 of "Freehand Sawing of Curves."

4. Place the material on the pivot point of the jig; cut out the circular piece (Fig. 69-7). Cut the other pieces the same way.

5. Curved work which is to be ripped to an equal width can be cut on the band saw. Use a pivot guide clamped on the table (Fig. 69-8).

6. A pattern can be used where a number of similar pieces are to be cut.

Figure 69-9 shows a wooden arm jig clamped to the saw table. The end of the arm is cut to a curve, either concave or convex. Center the curve in line with the teeth of the blade. Cut a slight notch at this point for the blade. Fit the pattern with anchor points or brads so that it can be pressed down and held to the piece which is to be cut.

7. Push the pattern and the piece to be cut gently into the band saw blade (see Fig. 69-9).

8. Some work pieces require compound cuts. This means cutting from two or more sides. Figure 69-10 shows how the template, or pattern, was first marked on the wood stock. Figure 69-11 shows this type of freehand sawing.

9. Duplicates can be cut on the band saw. Fasten the several pieces together with brads or nails through the waste portions. Saw the several pieces as one unit (Fig. 69-12).

69-7. Cutting identical circles with the use of a jig.

69-8. Sawing parallel curves with a pivot guide used as a jig.

69-10. Marking compound cuts on wood stock, following a pattern.

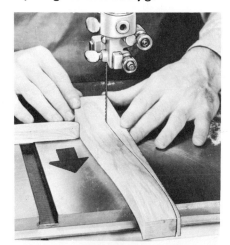

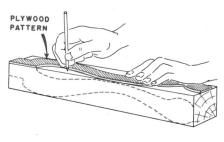

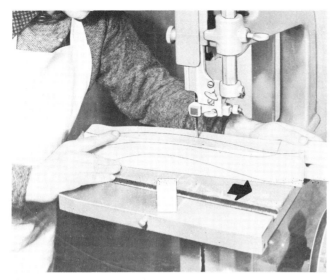

69-11. Sawing compound cuts on the band saw.

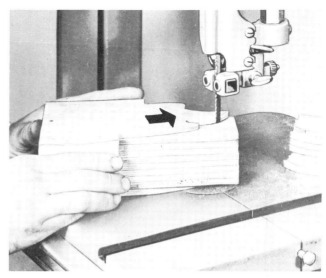

69-12. Sawing duplicate pieces.

DISCUSSION TOPICS

1. How is the size of a band saw measured? What is the size of the one in your school shop or laboratory? What is the size of the one in your home workshop, if you have one?
2. Name the two types of teeth that are widely used on band saw blades. What are the advantages of each?
3. List and describe the name and function of each of the eight essential parts of the band saw.
4. What is the meaning of the abbreviation **fpm?**
5. What is the variation of cutting speed in band saws? What determines the speed?
6. List 12 important safety rules which should be observed when using the band saw.
7. What are the minimum diameters of curves which can be cut with ⅛-, ¼-, ½-, and ¾-inch-wide band saw blades?
8. What is the purpose of relief cuts?
9. Name four types of sawing which can be done on the band saw.
10. When is it necessary to resaw a board?
11. Is it the upper or the lower wheel that is connected to the driving mechanism?
12. What are the gullets of band saw teeth?
13. List and describe three important types of band saw adjustments.
14. What is the purpose of the feather board during resawing?
15. List and explain the function of three types of jigs which can be used in bandsawing.
16. How would you cut several identical pieces?
17. What is meant by the expression **compound cutting?**
18. Visit a large lumberyard, sawmill, mill and sash company, furniture manufacturer, or other wood-products manufacturing plant. Make a report on the types of band saws they use. List the purposes for which they use them.

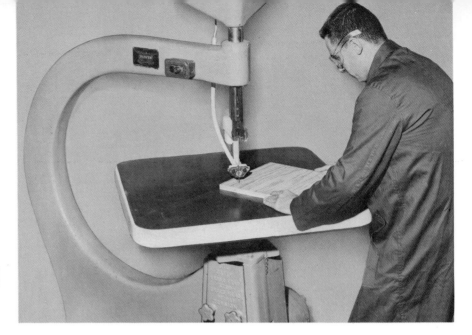

SECTION
11

SAWING ON THE JIG, OR SCROLL, SAW

Unit 70 General Information About the Jig, or Scroll, Saw

The jig (scroll) saw (Fig. 70-1) is used mostly to cut internal (inside) or external (outside) curves in thin wood. The operating principle of this machine is that it changes **rotary motion** (round-and-round) to **reciprocal action** (up-and-down). The reciprocal action operates a moving plunger which has a small, narrow, short saw blade fastened in it.

Sizes and Speeds

The size of the jig saw is measured by the distance from the saw blade to the inside of the curved portion of the overarm. Common sizes are 18 and 24 inches. The latter has the capacity to cut a circle 48 inches in diameter. The usual maximum thickness of stock which a jig saw will cut is 2 inches; however, most are used to cut thin pieces.

A V belt and four-step pulley arrangement makes possible variable speeds from 650 to 1,700 cutting strokes per minute (csm).

Parts and Uses

The main parts of the jig saw are shown in Fig. 70-1. There are also other parts that make specific adjustments. These are discussed in Unit 71, "Jig Saw Blades and Operating Adjustments." Basic parts are listed here.

■ **Base.** The base contains the mechanism which converts rotary motion into reciprocal action. It serves as a mounting for the motor and the table, and it supports the overarm.

■ **Overarm.** Fastened to the base, it holds the upper head, tension sleeve, upper chuck, and other attachments.

■ **Table.** The table is the support for the lumber being cut. It can be tilted 45 degrees to the right or left of horizontal. The table operates on a trunnion, or table tilt (Fig. 70-2). This is part of the table assembly, which also includes the lower plunger mechanism.

■ **Tension sleeve and upper chuck.** The sleeve usually contains a tension spring which pulls the blade up each time after the motor pulls it down. A guide assembly (Fig. 70-3) fastened onto this head has a hold-down guard to keep the stock firmly on the table.

Each manufacturer has instructions for adjusting blade tension.

■ **Belt and pulley guard.** This is a metal protective cover which encloses the V belt and the pulleys of the motor and the jig saw. Most guards can be removed by loosening one hand-operated screw or nut. This is usually necessary when changing the V-belt arrangement to vary the cutting speed of the blade.

70-1. A 24-inch jig saw.

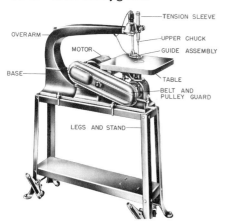

70-2. The jig saw table assembly and lower plunger.

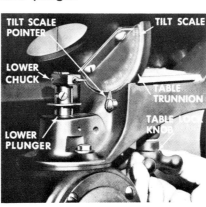

70-3. The guide assembly for the jig saw.

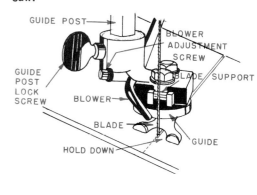

Unit 71 Jig Saw Blades and Operating Adjustments

The jig saw is one of the simplest and safest machines on which to work. Some adjustments must be made and checked each time the machine is used. The few described here are general, so the data sheets and operating manual of the manufacturer should be studied thoroughly. Adjustments require basic knowledge of types of blades and their functions.

Blades

Many different sizes and styles of blades are available for the jig saw. Figure 71-1 pictures seven common sizes. They are classified in two groups: (1) blades which are gripped by both upper and lower chucks, generally known as **jeweler's blades,** and (2) those held in the lower chuck only. These are called **saber blades.**

Jeweler's blades are sometimes called **piercing blades;** they also cut metal. Often the pins are removed from ordinary coping saw blades and the blades used on the jig saw, instead of the jeweler's blades. They are satisfactory and inexpensive.

Fine work, especially on tight curves,

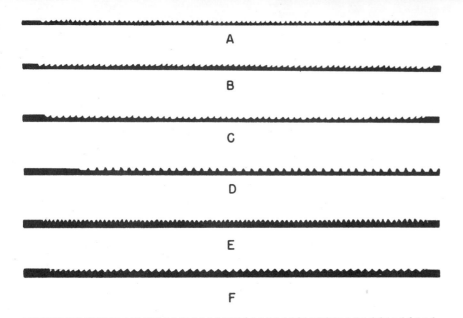

71-1. Seven common sizes of jig saw blades:

A .008 thick, .035 wide, 20 teeth per inch, and 5 inches long
B .010 thick, .048 wide, 18 teeth per inch, and 5 inches long
C .010 thick, .055 wide, 16 teeth per inch, and 5 inches long
D .019 thick, .055 wide, 12 teeth per inch, and 5 inches long
E .020 thick, .070 wide, 32 teeth per inch, and 5 inches long
F .020 thick, .070 wide, 20 teeth per inch, and 5 inches long
G .020 thick, .070 wide, 15 teeth per inch, and 5 inches long

71-2. A homemade blade holder fastened to the overarm.

71-3. The table cut away and the throat plate removed to give an exposed view of a jig saw blade fastened in both chucks.

is most satisfactorily done using jeweler's and coping saw blades. The larger sizes of jeweler's blades are very nearly the same dimensions in gauge and width as the smaller sizes of saber blades. They can cut material up to the full capacity of the saw. Saber blades are heavier and cut faster, so they are used where curves are not too abrupt. A general rule is to use finer teeth for the harder woods and coarser teeth for softer ones. Figure 71-2 shows a homemade jig saw blade holder fastened to the top of the overarm. This makes an assortment of blades available to the operator.

Speed of Cutting

Most jig saws regulate speed with three- or four-step pulleys. This is referred to as a **multispeed drive.** Slow speeds produce a rough cut; higher speeds result in smoother, finer edges. The cutting strokes per minute are regulated by moving the belt from one pair of pulleys to another.

Fastening Blades

Chucks are used to hold blades. There are two chucks for this purpose: one is beneath the table, fastened to the driver plunger; the other, an upper one, is attached to the spring tension sleeve.

Jig saw and jeweler's saw blades are fastened in both chucks (Fig. 71-3). Saber blades are held in the lower chuck only. When using a saber blade, it is desirable that a special guide be added directly under the table, as shown in Fig. 71-4. This extra guide gives more support to the upper guide, since the saber blade is held by only one chuck.

Each jig saw manufacturer provides chucks which adjust a little differently, but the general principle is the same. The blade must be centered in the chuck to make it cut vertically and in straight alignment. Self-centering chucks are available for both the upper and the lower plungers (Fig. 71-5). These are especially efficient where thin, fine-cutting blades are used continuously.

Installing a Regular Jig Saw Blade

1. Remove the throat plate from the table. Refer to Fig. 71-3.

2. Loosen the adjustment on the lower chuck. This will require either a screw driver, an Allen-head wrench, or a special tool which comes with the jig saw.

3. Insert the jig saw blade from the top of the opening on the table. Fasten it securely about ⅜ inch deep in the lower chuck. See Fig. 71-3. The teeth should point *down.*

4. Loosen and push down the plunger and the tension sleeve attached to the overarm so that the upper chuck grasps about ⅜ inch of the blade.

5. Fasten the blade in the upper chuck as you did in the lower one.

6. Pull up the plunger and the tension sleeve until the proper tension is obtained on the blade. Fasten the assembly in the upper arm. Follow the manufacturer's suggestions on the correct amount of blade tension. See Fig. 71-3.

7. Turn the pulley or V belt by hand to make sure that everything is working smoothly.

8. Replace the throat plate.

The procedure of installing a saber blade is similar except that it is fastened in the lower chuck only. Add a special guide, as shown in Fig. 71-4.

71-4. The table cut away and the throat plate removed to give an exposed view of a saber saw blade fastened in the lower chuck, and the addition of a special guide under the table.

Table Adjustments

Most jig saws have a table which can be tilted to permit bevel cutting. It can also be rotated to give clearance space for handling large pieces.

Tilting is easily controlled by the table lock knob under the table (Fig. 70-2). The table can be tilted 45 degrees to the right or left. Figure 70-2 shows in the foreground one of two capscrews on the tilt-scale pointer. It can be loosened to allow the entire table mounting to be swiveled to 90 degrees. Zero on the scale indicates the table is at a right angle to, and perfectly square with, the blade.

Closely allied with adjusting a table is regulating the hold-down attachment (clamp) on the upper guide assembly. This should always be adapted to the top surface of the work being cut. The hold-down clamp can be shifted to fit the piece which is being cut at an angle or a bevel. See Fig. 70-2.

71-5. A self-centering chuck.

Unit 72 Safety for the Jig Saw

■ **Permission.** Request permission to use the jig saw from the instructor or the person in charge.

■ **Clothing.** Avoid wearing loose clothing. Button or roll up your sleeves. Tuck in your necktie.

■ **Jewelry.** If you wear a ring, remove it. It could catch on something.

■ **Hand protection.** Keep your fingers away from the blade.

■ **Adjustments.** Check all adjustments to see that they are correctly set, as directed by the manufacturer's manual. The power should be *off.*

- **Blade size.** Use the proper size of blade for the work that is to be sawed.
- **Blade teeth.** Make certain that the teeth of the jig saw or saber blade are pointing *down*.
- **Blade fastening.** Make sure that the blade is correctly fastened in the chuck or chucks.
- **Tension.** If the upper chuck is fastened to the blade, be certain the tension sleeve has been adjusted properly.

- **Hold-down clamp.** Always regulate the hold-down clamp to exert slight pressure on the top of the piece being cut. Handle the material *firmly* with both hands while sawing.
- **Guide adjustment.** Adjust the upper guide to about ⅛ inch above the material being cut.
- **Plan work.** Lay out and carefully plan your work before sawing.
- **Starting cut.** Keep one hand firmly on the piece being cut as you turn on the power switch.
- **Curve cuts.** When making curve cuts, *do not* push the stock into the blade. *Turn* it on the table until the curve has been cut.
- **Backing out work.** Turn off the switch before backing the blade out.
- **Stopping the machine.** Shut off the power. Do not leave until the machine comes to a complete stop.

Unit 73 External and Internal Sawing on the Jig Saw

The jig saw is ideally suited to making both external and internal cuts. Internal sawing is sometimes called **piercing.** This machine is very simple and safe to operate. A person can stand or sit in front of it and guide his work easily and accurately. A ⅛-inch-wide blade is an average size for doing almost all cutting on the jig saw. It is not limited to cutting wood only; with blades of the correct thickness, it can cut metal, plastics, cardboard, and numerous thicknesses of paper fastened together.

Irregular External Sawing

1. Mark, lay out, or transfer the design to the board or boards. Identical pieces can be cut at the same time by fastening them together with brads or nails in the waste sections.

2. Check to see that the jig saw blade is properly fastened in both chucks. The saber blade is held only by the lower one. Make certain that the teeth *point down*.

3. Place the board or boards on the saw table against the saw blade. Lower and adjust the hold-down clamp so that it barely clears the work. Be sure that the blade is square with (at 90 degrees to) the table.

4. Turn on the power. Gently but firmly move the stock into the saw blade. Start the cut outside the mark or pattern line (Fig. 73-1). This allows

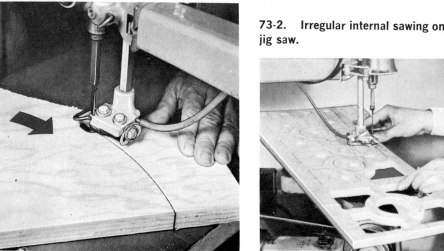

73-1. Irregular external sawing on the jig saw.

73-2. Irregular internal sawing on the jig saw.

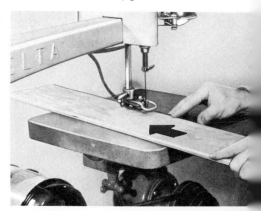

73-3. Straight-sawing a long board from the side of the jig saw.

for edge dressing (smoothing). When sawing sharp turns, apply very little forward pressure and turn the work slowly. It may be necessary to make some relief cuts when sawing an intricate (complicated) design.

5. Continue sawing until all outside cutting is completed.

Irregular Internal Sawing

1. Repeat step 1 of "Irregular External Sawing."

2. Drill or bore a hole in the waste portion of the design.

3. Insert the blade through this hole. Fasten it firmly in the chucks. The saber blade is held only by the lower one.

4. Repeat steps 3, 4, and 5 of "Irregular External Sawing." See Fig. 73-2.

Straight Sawing

Freehand straight sawing can easily ·be done on the jig saw. Figure 73-3 shows straight sawing a board with the chucks and blade turned to the side. This adjustment is necessary when the board is too long to clear the overarm. The chucks of most jig saws can be adjusted to this position.

Straight sawing, with the aid of a rip fence, can be performed as shown in Fig. 73-4. Some band saw rip fences can be adapted to the jig saw for this purpose.

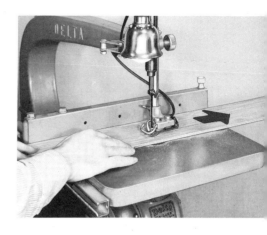

73-4. Ripping a long board on the jig saw table, using a rip fence for a guide.

Unit 74 Making Inlay Designs or Pictures

Making inlay designs or pictures from wood veneers is fascinating. It is not difficult, but it does require accuracy. Inlay pictures or designs make excellent decoration for bookends, trays, coffee and end table tops, and covers of useful small boxes. An inlaid bookend is shown in Fig. 74-1. If a dark and a light piece of veneer are cut on the jig saw at the same time, any piece from one will fit into the corresponding space in the other. That is, the pieces are interchangeable.

Making Inlay Pieces on the Jig Saw

1. Transfer the design or picture, using carbon paper, to a piece of ⅛-inch plywood. Figure 74-1 shows a finished inlay picture on a wooden bookend.

2. Study and plan the most effective color and grain of veneer to use to represent the parts of the picture. Different colors and grains provide the contrast that helps make the design effective.

3. Arrange the pieces of veneer in cross bands between two pieces of plywood, as illustrated in Fig. 74-2. The ⅛-inch plywood with the transferred design marked on it is on the top. A

74-1. An inlaid bookend.

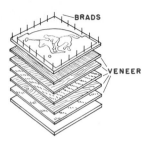

74-2. An exploded view of plywood and veneer pieces to be nailed together for sawing.

74-3. Assembling the inlay pieces on a temporary cardboard mount, using rubber cement.

piece of the same size is on the bottom. Nail this assembly together for sawing. The two pieces of plywood merely serve to hold the decorative veneers together while they are being cut.

4. Using a very thin jeweler's blade, cut out the design or picture on the marked lines.

5. Assemble the pieces face down on a sheet of cardboard, using rubber cement to hold them in place (Fig. 74-3). They are arranged like a jigsaw puzzle.

There will be enough pieces of veneer stock to plan and arrange as many veneered designs as there are sheets of veneer. The contrasts of veneers will be different for each arrangement.

6. Lay out and cut the base to which the inlay assembly is to be permanently glued.

7. Apply glue to the base. Place the inlay assembly on the glued surface (Fig. 74-4). The cardboard should be on top. Clamp the glued assembly (veneer, design, and base) between two pieces of ¾-inch plywood until the glue is dry.

8. Remove the assembly from the clamps. Lift off the cardboard sheet. It will pull off because rubber cement separates easily.

9. Sand the veneered surface until it is smooth.

10. Shape the outside of the piece. Complete the bookend. It should look like Fig. 74-1.

11. Apply a clear finish of shellac, varnish, or lacquer.

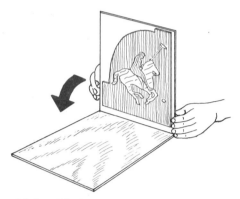

74-4. Placing the cardboard with veneer on the glued permanent base.

DISCUSSION TOPICS

1. How is the size of a jig saw measured? What is the size of the one in your school shop or laboratory? What is the size of the one in your home workshop, if you have one?
2. Name and describe the differences among the three types of blades used on the jig saw.
3. List and describe the names and functions of six essential parts of the jig saw.
4. List eight important safety rules which should be observed when using the jig saw.
5. What is the meaning of the abbreviation **csm?**
6. How many different speeds does your jig saw have, and what are they?
7. What is the procedure for internal sawing?
8. How would you cut several identical pieces?
9. What is a scroll saw?
10. List two types of chucks which can be used on the jig saw.
11. Give the general rule with respect to speed of cutting hardwoods and softwoods on the jig saw.
12. What is the general rule for the types of jig saw blades to use when cutting hardwoods and softwoods?
13. What is the maximum diameter of a circle which can be cut on a 24-inch jig saw?
14. Explain the mechanical principle involved in converting rotary (round-and-round) motion to up-and-down action.
15. What is the process called which involves the fitting together of several types of thin wood, or veneers?
16. Visit a large lumberyard, sawmill, mill and sash company, furniture manufacturer, or other wood-products manufacturing plant. Make a report on the types of jig saws in use. List the purposes for which they are used.

SAWING WITH THE SABER SAW

Unit 75 General Information About the Saber (Bayonet) Saw

The saber saw (Fig. 75-1) is actually a portable electric jig saw, sometimes called a **bayonet** saw. One main feature is that it is portable. It is a very versatile machine tool. It cuts all kinds of wood, plastics, composition board, veneer material, thin metal, cardboard, and even leather. This broad range of work makes it an ideal portable electric saw for use in millwork and cabinet shops, the school industrial laboratory,

and the home workshop. It is a safe tool for everyone to use, and even an inexperienced person can obtain excellent results with only a few minutes of practice.

Sizes, Speed, and Action

The general appearance of the saber saw would seem to indicate that all are the same size. The difference lies in

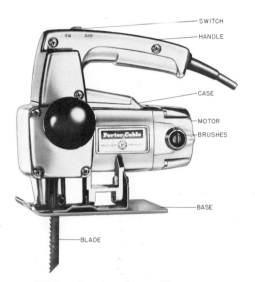

75-1. A saber (bayonet) saw.

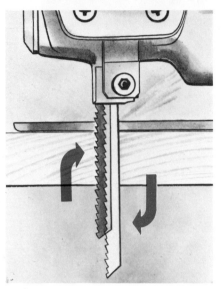

75-2. Orbital (oval) blade motion (action) of a sturdy saber saw.

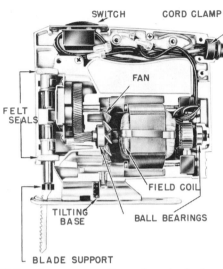

75-3. A cross section of a typical saber saw.

sturdiness of construction, cutting ability, and motor power. The heavy-duty machine readily cuts up to 2-inch-thick stock. Thus, it is particularly useful in building construction.

The portable jig saw (saber saw) weighs between 3½ and 4½ pounds. Most are designed to operate on normal household electric current. The cutting speed is approximately 4,200 strokes per minute (spm).

The action of the better saber saws is an **orbital** (oval) motion, rather than the straight up-and-down motion of the regular jig saw (Fig. 75-2). In this design, the blade cuts only on the up stroke, backing away on the return

stroke. This eliminates return-stroke blade drag. As a result, the teeth stay sharp longer, and the blade does not heat up quickly. It cuts faster, and there is less blade breakage than with the ordinary reciprocating (straight up-and-down) jig saw.

Parts and Uses

The main parts of the saber saw are shown in Figs. 75-1 and 75-3. Figure 75-3 shows a cross section of a typical saw.

■ **Case.** This lightweight-alloy metal housing contains the working mechanism.

■ **Handle.** The handle is the sturdy piece on top which allows the operator to manipulate the saw with ease. It usually includes a fingertip or toggle switch, or other means of turning the power on and off. Some models of saws attach an auxiliary handle on the side. A few of the lighter portable jig saws are built so that the handle is actually a part of the body (case).

■ **Brushes.** These are at the back of the motor housing. They are easily taken out when the cap is removed.

■ **Base.** The base serves as an inverted (upside-down) table. It provides a surface to guide the saw on the work. On most models, it can be tilted.

Unit 76 Saber Saw Blades, Accessories, and Operating Adjustments

It is important that the right blade (Fig. 76-1) be selected for use with the portable jig (saber) saw. The variation in type of blade used depends upon the kind of material to be cut.

Blades

The 10-tooth long blade can be used to cut lumber up to 2 inches thick. The 10-tooth short blade is used to cut small-radius curves and intricate designs. It should be used for material up to only 1 inch thick. Both 10-tooth blades give a reasonably fine-cut (smooth) finish. The 6-tooth long blade is similar to the 10-tooth long blade except that it makes a rougher cut.

This is general information to guide you in selecting blades for working with wood. Table 76-1 gives a partial listing of other types of materials and blade requirements.

Accessories

The bayonet (saber) saw can be used for cutting angles, whether simple or compound. This is done by replacing the regular base with one that adjusts to angles (Fig. 76-2). Straight ripping, crosscutting, and cutting circles require the use of a guide. Some manufacturers make a guide which is used for all three processes.

Adjustments

Aside from motor maintenance, only a few adjustments are needed to make cuts with the saber saw. The installation of the correct type of saw blade for the work to be cut is one. Another adjustment is tilting or replacing the base.

Each manufacturer's product requires a slightly different blade-fastening method. The operator's manual which comes with each saber saw should be studied very thoroughly before an attempt is made to operate the tool. The manual gives specific instructions that are unique to each brand.

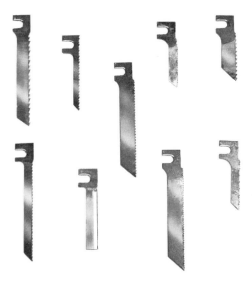

76-1. A typical assortment of blades for a portable jig (saber) saw.

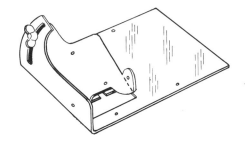

76-2. An angle-adjustment base for a portable jig saw.

Table 76-1 SELECTION OF BLADES FOR CUTTING VARIOUS MATERIALS

Material to be cut	Number of teeth per inch	Type of blade
Aluminum sheet and tubing	14	High-speed steel
Brass sheet and tubing	14	High-speed steel
Copper sheet and tubing	14	High-speed steel
Formica	10	High-carbon steel
Masonite	10	High-carbon steel
Plexiglas and Lucite (acrylics)	10	High-speed steel
Plastics (other types)	14	High-speed steel
Plywood	10	High-carbon steel
Steel sheet and tubing	14 or 24	High-speed steel
Wood (general cutting)	10 or 6	High-carbon steel

Unit 77 Safety with the Saber Saw

■ **Permission.** Always secure permission before using the saber saw.
■ **Clothing.** Avoid wearing loose clothing. Button or roll up your sleeves. Tuck in your necktie.
■ **Jewelry.** If you wear a ring, remove it. It might get caught on something and cause injury to your hand.
■ **Planning.** Lay out and carefully plan your work before sawing.

■ **Blades.** Make sure you have selected the correct type and size of blade for the job to be done.
■ **Adjustments.** All adjustments must be secure before starting this tool.
■ **Electric power.** Disconnect the plug from the electric power outlet before you inspect parts, make adjustments, or fasten the blade.
■ **Electrical grounding.** Check to see

that the electrical connection is grounded.

■ **Holding material.** Hold or clamp the board to be cut so that it cannot vibrate.

■ **Stance.** Maintain a well-balanced position on both feet when operating the saber saw.

■ **Illumination.** Have plenty of shadow-free light on the work.

■ **Stopping.** Once you have turned off the switch, be sure to hold the saber saw with your hands until all the action stops. Then you may safely return the tool to its proper place.

Unit 78 Cutting with a Saber Saw

Some saber saws are equipped with a guide to aid straight ripping or crosscutting. When the guide is turned over and fitted onto a steel guide pin, this saw cuts perfect circles up to the capacity of the guide.

Ripping and Crosscutting with a Guide

1. Fasten the correct blade on the saw. Select it for the material to be cut. See Unit 76.

2. For ripping or crosscutting narrow stock, fasten the guide in place and adjust it to the desired width. See Fig. 78-1. If the piece to be cut off is wider than the guide permits, clamp a wooden fence (guide) on the board. See Fig. 78-2.

3. Hold the board so that the blade can cut through freely.

4. Start the motor. Slowly saw the board. Keep the guide firmly against the edge or the end of the stock, or keep the portable saw against the wooden fence or guide (Figs. 78-1 and 78-2).

Sawing Circles

1. Place the board securely in some position, such as on sawhorses, that allows space underneath for the blade.

2. Lay out the circumference of the circle. Use a compass or dividers.

78-1. Ripping a board with the saber saw and guide.

78-2. Ripping with the saber saw.

3. Drill a 3/16- or 1/4-inch starting hole through the board. This should touch the circle line on the waste side.

4. Fasten the correct blade on the saw for the material to be cut.

5. Drive the circle guide pin into the board at the center of the circle. See Fig. 78-3.

6. Turn the rip guide over, and fasten it in the saw to the radius desired. See Fig. 78-3.

7. Start the motor with the saw in place. Slowly push the saw as it makes the circular cut (Fig. 78-3).

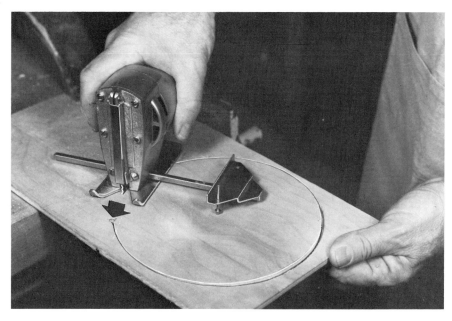

78-3. Cutting a circle with the saber saw, using the rip fence and a circular guide pin.

Unit 79 Freehand Sawing to Marked Lines

The saber saw is a portable electric jig saw used for freehand sawing. Although it is a most versatile tool for cutting many types of materials, it is discussed here because of its usefulness in sawing wood. This unit explains and shows its many uses to the woodworker, cabinetmaker, contractor, electrician, plumber, and hobbyist.

Sawing to Marked Lines

1. Fasten the material to be cut in a bench vise, use clamps to fasten it to a work table, or place it on sawhorses. This is especially important when sawing small pieces. Some cutting will be done directly on floors, walls, and other fixed surfaces.

2. Mark the area to be cut.

3. To start the cut, place the forward edge of the saw base firmly on the edge of the material so that the saw is *tilted* (Figs. 79-1 and 79-2). This is called **plunge cutting.** Do this only when the wood is 1 inch thick or *thinner*.

4. Turn on the motor, and move the saw into the piece of material (Fig. 79-3). Do not force the saw. Let the blade and the saw do the work.

5. Move the machine forward just rapidly enough to keep the blade cutting.

79-1. Starting to saw with a plunge cut.

79-2. Starting to saw in a counter top with a plunge cut.

79-3. Moving the saber saw into the material after the plunge cut.

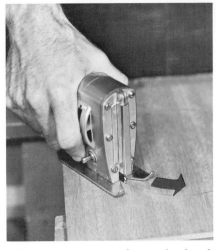

79-5. Making a circular cut freehand.

79-7. A roof rafter notched with a saber saw.

6. The saber saw is ideal for making wall pockets for electric outlets (Fig. 79-4).

7. Figure 79-5 shows the use of a saber saw to make a circular cut freehand.

8. Figures 79-6 and 79-7 illustrate the saber saw being used to cut notches and to fit rafters.

9. Building tradesmen find the saber saw useful for making floor openings for pipe (Fig. 79-8).

10. Letters or numerals are easy to cut out, and they can be fashioned very smoothly by using the plunge cut (Fig. 79-9).

11. Fancy figures can be cut quickly for display purposes (Fig. 79-10).

12. Cutting angles and making compound cuts up to 45 degrees can be done on some saber saws. The regular base must be replaced with an angle-adjusting base (Fig. 76-2). Fig. 79-11 shows this base being fastened.

13. A compound cut can be made accurately with an angle-adjusting base (Fig. 79-12).

79-4. Cutting a wall pocket for an electric outlet with a saber saw.

79-6. Cutting notches and fitting rafters with the saber saw.

79-8. Making a floor opening for pipe, using the saber saw.

79-9. Cutting out letters with the saber saw.

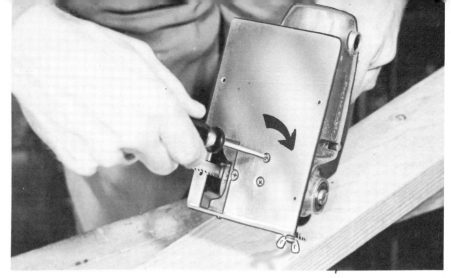

79-11. Fastening the angle-adjustment base.

79-10. Cutting out designs with the saber saw.

79-12. Sawing a compound cut with the aid of an angle-adjustment base.

DISCUSSION TOPICS

1. What other names are sometimes given to the portable jig saw?
2. Name three advantages the portable jig saw has over other means of sawing.
3. Why do the teeth of the portable jig saw point *up?*
4. List six types of materials, and indicate the type of blade and coarseness of teeth for cutting them on the saber saw.
5. What is the maximum thickness which a heavy-duty portable jig saw will cut conveniently?
6. Approximately how many strokes per minute does the average saber saw make?
7. What is the approximate weight of the bayonet saw?
8. What is orbital motion (used by some portable jig saws)?
9. What does the expression **blade drag** mean?
10. List four advantages the orbital-type portable jig saw has over the straight up-and-down (reciprocal) jig saw.
11. List four main parts of the saber saw. Explain the purpose of each.
12. List six safety rules to be observed in using the saber saw.
13. Explain the term **plunge cutting.**
14. Explain the advantage of a base which has angle adjustment.
15. Visit a wood-products manufacturing plant. Make a report on the types of portable jig saws in use. List the purposes for which they are used.

BORING AND DRILLING HOLES, ROUTING, SHAPING, AND SANDING ON THE DRILL PRESS

Unit 80 General Information About the Drill Press

The drill press was originally designed for the metalworking trades, but it has been adapted for woodworking, plastics, and composition materials. It is one of the most versatile and practical power tools. It is most frequently used for drilling and boring holes. The term **boring** usually implies cutting holes in wood, even though twist-drill bits are used. The term **drilling** is usually associated with the process of machining holes in metal. However, the two terms are used interchangeably in modern woodworking practices using the drill press.

Drill presses are made in bench and floor models (Fig. 80-1). The only difference between the models is the length of the upright column.

The many available attachments make it possible to do operations in woodworking other than boring and drilling holes. These are mortising, shaping, routing, and sanding. The process of mortising on the drill press is almost identical with that of mortising on the mortiser. See Unit 94, "Mortising on the Drill Press." Other operations are discussed only briefly in this section because they can be done better or more conveniently on machines designed expressly to do them.

Sizes and Speeds

The more practical sizes of drill presses vary from 12 to 20 inches. The size is determined by the distance from the center of the chuck to the front of the vertical column.

The speed of this machine varies from approximately 300 to 6,000 rpm. On most drill presses, the speed is controlled by shifting the drive belt, or belts, on a set of cone pulleys located in the head. Slow speeds are used for metalworking; faster ones are for woodworking.

The manufacturer's manuals contain charts and tables that show the speeds of numerous belt and pulley combinations. On the drill press shown in Fig. 80-1, only a handle on the head is changed. The speed-guide index indicates the speed.

Parts and Uses

■ **Base.** A heavy cast-iron footing, or support, usually forms the base of the drill press.

■ **Column.** The column is a hollow, rigid tube which fits into the base. It supports the table, motor, and head.

■ **Table.** The flat table holds the work. It is adjustable for angle, and it moves up and down on the column.

■ **Head.** The top assembly is the head. It includes the spindle, pulleys, bearings, and belt. It also supports the motor.

■ **Chuck.** The chuck is usually a geared and keyed device that is fastened to the spindle. It holds the bits. Its capacity ordinarily varies from 0 to ½ inch.

■ **Feed lever or handle.** This part raises or lowers the spindle during drilling operations.

■ **Depth stop.** This consists of double-locking nuts which are used to adjust the depth of the drilled hole.

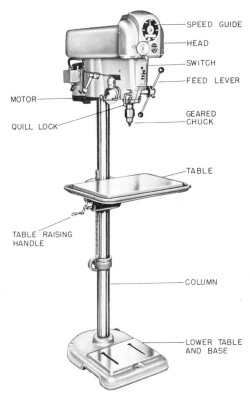

SPEED GUIDE
HEAD
SWITCH
FEED LEVER
GEARED CHUCK
MOTOR
QUILL LOCK
TABLE
TABLE RAISING HANDLE
COLUMN
LOWER TABLE AND BASE

80-1. A 17-inch floor-model drill press.

Unit 81 Bits, Cutters, and Accessories

The numerous jobs the drill press can do depend upon the many types of bits, cutters, and accessories which are available. Several types of bits bore and cut holes in wood. Special-purpose bits and cutters extend the usefulness of the drill press. Mortising bits and chisels, along with the mortising attachment, readily convert the drill press into a mortiser. See SECTION 15, "Mortising on the Mortiser and the Drill Press." Other accessories which fasten on it easily are shaper cutters and small sanding drums.

On some drill presses, the spindle must be changed to attach the accessories. Many are now designed with special arbors which fit into the conventional geared chuck. These are actually spindle extensions which accommodate the numerous drilling and cutting accessories.

The manufacturer's manual gives detailed instructions on the proper spindles to use and how to change them. This is generally easy. The manual should also be studied for correct speeds and how to assemble and fasten the many accessories.

Router bits (Fig. 81-10) come in sizes from 3/16 to 1½ inches in diameter. They are used to rout, or cut, flat-bottom holes.

The **plug cutter** (Fig. 81-10) makes both dowel pins and plugs to cover the heads of recessed screws.

81-1. A straight-shank twist drill bit is available in decimal, number, and letter sizes.

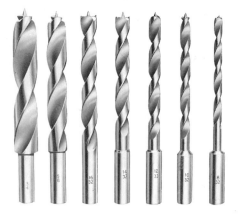

81-2. The double-spur twist bit is the cleanest and fastest cutting wood bit to use on the drill press.

81-3. A wood auger bit may be filed and adapted for the drill press.

81-4. A spade- or power-type wood bit is a speed bit for use on drill presses and electric drills.

81-5. A multispur bit is ideal for cutting holes larger than 1″ in diameter.

81-6. A flat center bit will also cut large holes.

81-7. A quick-cut hole saw may be used to cut holes in wood.

81-8. The counterbore bit comes in numerous sizes. It drills a hole and counterbores a large one at the same time.

81-9. This bit is used to widen the top of a hole to allow for a screwhead.

Accessories and Attachments

Shaper cutters, collars (Fig. 81-11) and a **spindle adapter** convert a drill press into a shaper. A number of satisfactory molding cuts, or edge shapes, can be produced by using solid cutter heads. It is desirable that an auxiliary wood table, with a center hole, be at-

81-10. The drill rack, fastened to a drill press, shows a set of five router bits on the front row. Four plug cutters of different sizes are also shown on the left of the front row and the right of the rear row; a twist drill is at the right on the front row, and a set of double-spur twist bits is in the back row.

81-11. Solid shaper cutters and collars.

tached to the metal table of the drill press for this operation. A fence and hold-down clamps are other accessories used in converting the drill press to a shaper. Figure 85-19 shows a drill press converted for use as a shaper.

Sanding drums of various sizes can be used on a drill press (Fig. 81-12). These are especially useful for sanding curved work. Manufacturers of this equipment also supply sanding sleeves in different grits and sizes to fit the various drums. The drum shanks fit interchangeable spindles or chucks.

81-12. Sanding drums for the drill press.

Unit 82 Operating Adjustments

A few basic adjustments are required before the drill press is used to bore or drill holes. These also apply to other drill press operations when the various attachments are used.

Boring to Depth

Holes are often bored to a specified depth. The best and most accurate method is to use the stop-rod nuts shown in Fig. 82-1. Determine the setting by bringing the drill down alongside the work to a pencil mark showing the desired depth. Adjust and tighten the stop-rod nuts.

Another method is to bring the bit into contact with the wood and then set the depth pointer at a specified mark (Fig. 82-2). The depth of the hole can be figured from this marking as the bit cuts into the wood. Watch the index marking for accurate depth of the hole.

Adjusting the Drill Press Table

Most processes require the drill press table to be set at a right angle (90 degrees) to the bit. Check this with a try square. An adjustment nut underneath the table holds it in position.

Some boring jobs require that the table be set at a tilt. Tilt the table to the desired angle by aligning it to the bit, using a T bevel (Fig. 82-3).

The table is adjusted for height by sliding it up or down and then fastening it to the column. This is usually the first step in obtaining an accurate boring depth.

82-1. Setting stop-rod nuts for depth of hole.

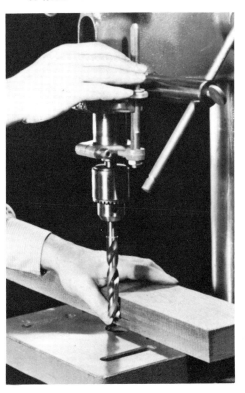

82-2. The pointer used for drilling to depth.

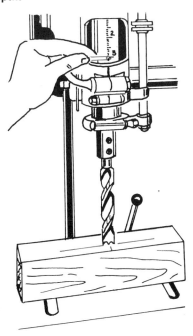

82-3. Checking the tilt of a drill table, using a T bevel.

Unit 83 Safety for the Drill Press

■ **Permission.** Always secure permission to operate the drill press.

■ **Clothing.** Do not wear loose clothing. Tuck in your necktie, and either button or roll up your sleeves. Also, remove your ring if you wear one. This could prevent injury to your hand.

■ **Goggles.** Use goggles or a face shield, especially when operating the drill press at high speed.

■ **Guard.** Keep the guard on the pulleys and the belt to prevent your hair and clothing from getting caught.

■ **Instruction manual.** Follow the instructions of the drill press manual, especially when using the numerous accessories and attachments.

■ **Chuck key.** Always remove the chuck key before starting the drill press.

■ **Adjustments.** Make all adjustments with the power off.

■ **Speed.** Check and adjust the pulley and belt combination to see that the correct speed is set up. Use the recommended speeds for the various processes and material being bored, such as softwoods or hardwoods.

■ **Interchangeable spindles and chuck.** Use the recommended spindle or chuck. Most operations can be done successfully with the 0–½-inch-capacity drill chuck.

■ **Attachments.** When you use routing, shaping, and mortising attachments on the drill press, make certain that they have been properly fastened and adjusted.

■ **Bits and cutters.** Use only the recommended bits and cutters for the job to be done. Never attempt to use an auger bit unless the lead screw has been cut smooth and the square tang cut off. The square tang of a bit cannot be centered in a drill chuck. A lead screw is undesirable when using a drill press because it cuts too fast.

■ **Clamping small pieces.** Clamp small pieces in a drill vise or to the table.

■ **Position of work.** Hold the work firmly so that it will not fly or spin off the table and injure you or someone else. Often it is best to fasten the piece securely with clamps.

■ **Boring and drilling.** Bore and drill holes without using too much pressure. If the wood smokes, release the pressure temporarily and work more slowly.

■ **Stopping.** Shut off the power and clean the table before you leave the machine.

Unit 84 Boring and Cutting Holes

Any of the bits illustrated and described in Unit 81, "Bits, Cutters, and Accessories," can be used to bore and cut holes in wood.

Large-diameter holes are often made with cutting bits and other special tools. The plug cutter, though it cuts holes, is actually used to cut dowels of various diameters, depending on the size of the cutter. These vary from ⅜ to 1 inch.

It is always advisable to put a piece of scrap wood on the table directly under the piece of wood being bored.

Try to keep the hole in the table aligned with the bit so that if the bit goes beyond the scrap wood it will not cut into the metal table top. Fasten the bit securely in the chuck or spindle before boring.

Boring a Hole

1. Lay out and mark the center of the hole. Use an awl.

2. Select the drill or bit of the correct size. Fasten it in the chuck. Make sure it does not wobble.

3. Place the board on the table of the drill press. Put a piece of scrap wood underneath the board.

4. Adjust the table to the correct height and tilt angle. The tilt, of course, depends on the angle at which the hole is to be bored.

5. Adjust for depth of boring. (See Unit 82.) This is especially necessary when the hole is to be bored to a specified depth and is not to go through the board.

6. Turn on the power switch.

7. Hold the board, or stock, securely by hand (or with clamps, if necessary). Apply an even pressure in feeding the bit into the wood slowly (Figs. 84-1, 84-2, and 84-3). If the wood smokes, ease the pressure on the bit until the smoking stops, and then proceed slowly.

8. Figure 84-4 illustrates a unique technique for boring pocket holes (for recessing screws) into the side rail of a table to fasten the top. Note the inset, which shows an end view. Also see Fig. 84-5.

84-1. Boring a hole for screws, using a twist drill.

84-2. Boring a hole with a spur bit.

84-3. Boring a hole with a spade- or power-type type wood bit. Note the ordinary auger bit at the left with a filed lead screw and the tang cut off. This treated wood auger bit may also be used.

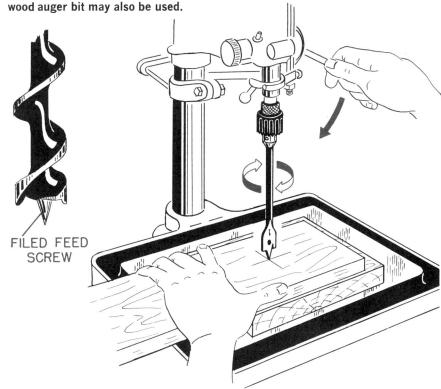

FILED FEED SCREW

84-4. Boring a pocket hole into the side rail of a table with the aid of a wooden jig.

84-5. A pocket hole in a table rail.

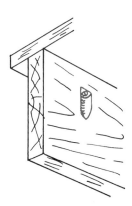

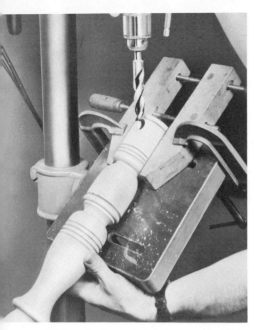

84-6. Boring a hole at an angle. Note the method of clamping stock in position.

9. Figure 84-6 shows a simple method of clamping stock to bore a hole at an angle. Note that the table has been tilted to obtain the desired angle.

10. Figure 84-7 describes how to bore a series of holes freehand for a mortise. This method can be used if a mortising attachment and bits are not available.

11. Figure 84-8 shows one way to hold a long piece of wood for end boring. Note that a depth stop on the bit assures uniform and accurate hole depth. This particular operation is for fitting dowels.

12. Figure 84-9 presents a way to bore a hole that is longer than the length of the drill bit. The simplest method is to work from opposite ends. The table is tilted vertically; the wooden cylinder is aligned and held in place with a V block. The hole is bored first from one end, then from the other. In this way the capacity of a 4-inch twist drill is increased to 8 inches.

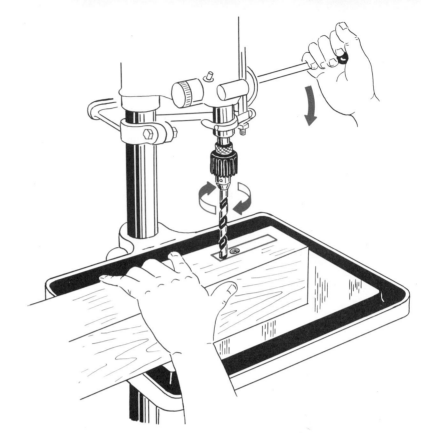

84-7. Boring a series of holes for a mortise.

84-8. Boring dowel holes on the end of a rail. The hand screw is a good device for holding the work on the drill press table.

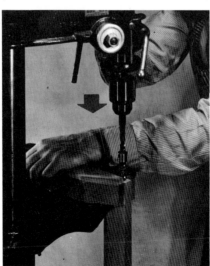

84-9. Boring a hole from both ends with the aid of a V block.

13. In Figure 84-10 a dowel hole is bored at an angle. Make a jig to hold the wood, and clamp it to the table.

Cutting a Hole

1. Figure 84-11 shows a multispur bit cutting a 2-inch hole. The work is clamped to the table because a large bit makes it difficult to hold the work by hand.

2. Figure 84-12 is a photograph of a center bit cutting a large hole. Hold the piece securely with clamps.

3. A large hole can also be cut with a quick-cut hole saw (Fig. 84-13).

Cutting Dowels and Circular Plugs

The plug cutter makes it easy to cut dowel pins. See Fig. 84-14. The full length of the cutter makes dowels up to 2 inches long. In addition, cross-grain plugs can also be made with this cutter. Cross-grain plugs are especially useful for plugging holes in the surfaces or the edges of wood. The design of these plugs makes it possible for the grain of the plug to be lined up in the same direction as the grain of the board. Cross-grain plugs are also used where the heads of screws and bolts are recessed below the surface.

84-10. Boring an angular dowel hole in the end of stock with the aid of a jig.

84-11. Cutting a large hole with a multispur bit.

84-13. Cutting a large hole with a quick-cut hole saw.

84-14. Making dowel pins with a plug cutter.

84-12. Cutting a large hole with a center bit.

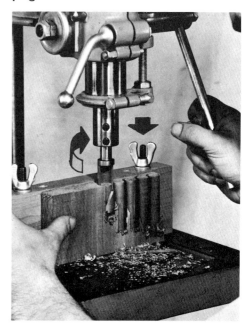

Unit 85 Routing, Inlaying, and Shaping

Routing and shaping can easily be done on the drill press when the proper bits and cutters are used. The speed is increased to approximately 5,000 rpm to get a clean, smooth cut. This speed adjustment is usually made by changing the belt arrangement on the spindle and motor pulleys. Study the manual which comes with the drill press.

Material is always fed from *left to right.* This means that the work must be moved in against the rotation of the cutter. The thrust of the cutter should press the piece against the fence.

The depth of routing should not exceed ⅛ inch per cut, or pass. If a deeper cut is required, repeat the cut with the bit set deeper each time.

Use only small shaper cutters for shaping because most drill press spindles will not withstand a side load, or thrust, as well as a commercial shaper will. The shaping procedure is generally very similar to that recommended in SECTION 17, "Shaping on the Wood Shaper."

Routing

1. Mark and lay out the piece to be routed.

2. Select the correct router or cutter bit. Fasten it in the chuck.

3. Set the depth of the cut by locking the stop nuts on the depth adjustment.

4. Fasten a fence to the table. Adjust it for the location of the cut. See Figs. 85-1 and 85-2.

5. Turn on the power switch.

6. Hold the work firmly against the fence. Feed it slowly into the router bit, from *left to right* (Figs. 85-1 and 85-2).

Figure 85-3 shows how a round rod can be clamped to a straightedge.

7. Crossrouting, such as cutting a dado, requires a specially built feed table which will accommodate a crosscutting guide (Fig. 85-4). This table can be made of plywood and fastened to the drill press table.

The work will have a tendency to creep to the left unless a stop block is used on the crosscut guide. The length of the dado can be controlled with a stop block clamped at the rear.

Routing Ornamental Molding

Figure 85-5 shows a setup, or jig, for cutting ornamental molding. The spacer board is butted against the

85-1.   Direction of feed for routing.

85-2.   Feeding the work along a fence into the router bit. A deep groove, as shown, requires several passes (cuts).

85-3.   Routing a straight cut in a round rod. Note how the rod is clamped.

85-4.   Crossrouting for a dado.

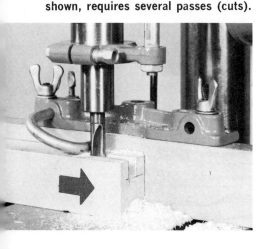

85-5. Routing ornamental molding with the use of a spacer-board jig.

85-6. Another method of routing molding.

85-7. Three molding designs made by routing.

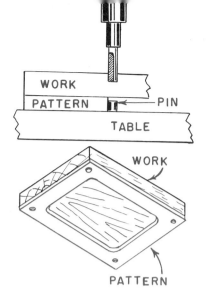

85-9. Detail of the pin-and-pattern method of routing.

85-10. Cutting (routing) a circular recess by the pin-and-pattern method.

fence, and the piece is nailed to this board. The pin in the fence fits into the saw cuts of the spacer board and controls the repeat router bit cuts.

Figure 85-6 illustrates another method, in which the work is simply pivoted on the guide pin.

Figure 85-7 shows three interesting molding designs which can be made with these router cutting methods.

Routing with a Pattern

1. Lay out and cut a full-size template from ¼-inch-thick plywood. See Fig. 85-8.

2. Fasten a suitable router bit into the chuck.

3. Drill a hole and insert a pin (dowel) into an auxiliary wood table. This pin must be the same diameter as that of the router bit, be in line with the bit, and project above the table about ³⁄₁₆ inch (Figs. 85-8 and 85-9).

4. Fasten the plywood pattern to the underneath side of the piece to be routed. See Fig. 85-9. Use short brads.

85-8. The pin-and-pattern method of routing.

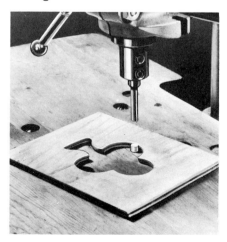

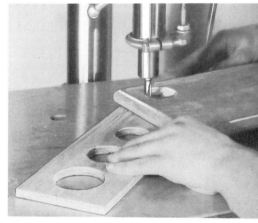

85-11. Routing for an inlay band (strip).

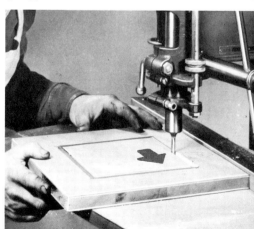

5. Adjust and lock the router bit cutting depth. See Fig. 85-9.

6. Place the work on the table. Turn on the power. Follow the template design to rout the surface piece (Fig. 85-10).

Routing for Inlay

1. Follow steps 1 through 6 above.

2. Figure 85-11 shows the process of routing a groove for simple inlay work. Always guide the work along a fence. The router bit should be the same diameter as the width of the inlay band (strip). The depth of the cut should be slightly *less* than the thickness of the inlay strip.

Figure 85-12 is a photograph of routing a more intricate edge design.

3. Make the routed corners square with a wood chisel (Fig. 85-13). The router bit leaves rounded corners.

4. Cut inlay strips long enough to fit the routed grooves (Fig. 85-14). A mitered guide block helps to get accurate joints.

5. Lay the inlay strip in place (Fig. 85-15). Check to see that all joints fit perfectly. The inlay is now ready to be glued in place permanently.

6. Routing for a circular or curved inlay can be done against a V block clamped to the table.

7. Routing for a freehand design (Fig. 85-16) can be done as shown in

85-12. Making an intricate routing cut for inlay.

85-13. Chiseling a routed corner square for inlay.

85-14. Cutting inlay strips to length, using a wood chisel and a mitered block.

85-15. Laying an inlay strip in place.

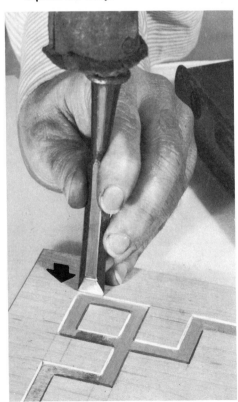

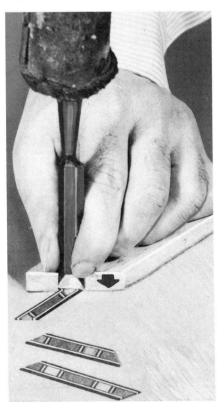

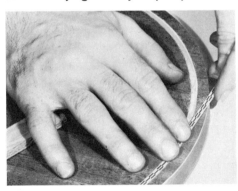

85-16. An inlaid design.

Fig. 85-17. This can also be cut with the pin-and-pattern method. See Figs. 85-8 and 85-9.

Shaping on the Drill Press

An auxiliary plywood shaping table, fence, and hold-down clamps should be fastened to the drill table for shaping a straight edge (Fig. 85-18). Note that the operator is guiding the narrow strip, which is being shaped on the end, with a larger square piece. Figure 85-19 illustrates a method of shaping or smoothing the inside edges of a curved piece. Irregular pieces can be shaped on the drill press by using a rub collar to control the depth of cut.

85-17. Freehand routing for an inlaid design.

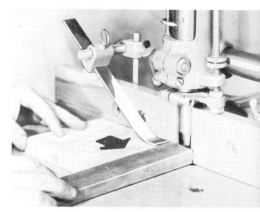

85-18. Straight-edge shaping on the drill press.

85-19. Shaping or smoothing the inside edge of a curved piece.

Unit 86 Sanding on the Drill Press

Drum sander attachments for the drill press are described in Unit 81, "Bits, Cutters, and Accessories." They are shown in Fig. 81-12.

Many sanding operations can be done with this assortment of drums. Figure 86-1 shows a very useful home- or shop-made raised sanding table. It can be attached to an auxiliary wood table or directly to the cast-iron drill press table. This extra sanding table can be cut to any size to give a larger surface. The several different sizes of holes in the top are for the sanding drum to work up and down in.

Sanding

1. Cut wood pieces approximately to outline.

2. Next, dress the sawed edges carefully with a spokeshave, file, or other similar tool. You are now ready to sand them.

3. Fasten a suitable size of sanding drum in the drill press chuck or spindle.

4. Clamp the sanding table to the drill press table. See Fig. 86-1. Locate it so that the sanding drum will go into the correct hole.

5. Place the piece to be sanded on the table. Raise the table so that the drum drops into the hole, or lower and lock the spindle.

6. Turn on the power and sand the edges of the piece, as desired. See Fig. 86-1. The sanding drums can be used to dress inside cuts and holes as well as to smooth outside edges.

Figure 86-2 demonstrates how to sand an edge against a pattern. The edge shown is a ¼-inch plywood ping-pong paddle fastened to a ¾-inch pattern. A plywood disk the exact size of the sanding drum is nailed to the auxiliary wooden table. This must be in line with the sanding drum (Fig. 86-2). The pattern can be moved against the small wooden disk which serves as a rub collar. Do not use the sanding table for this operation.

86-1. Drum-sanding an edge on the drill press.

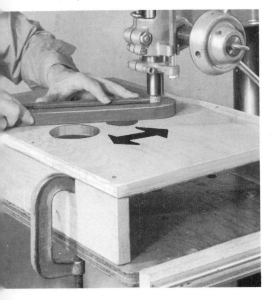

86-2. Pattern sanding on the drill press.

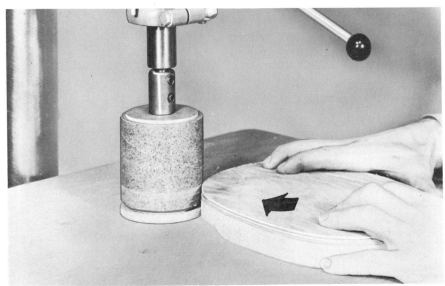

DISCUSSION TOPICS

1. What are the two general types (models) of drill press?
2. List five operations other than drilling for which the drill press can be used.
3. How is the size of a drill press measured?
4. How is the speed of a drill press changed?
5. What variation of speeds can be obtained on most drill presses?
6. How can an auger bit be adapted for use on the drill press?
7. List six important specifications of the drill press in your industrial laboratory or home workshop.
8. List and describe the names and functions of six essential parts of the drill press.
9. Name and give the uses of six types of bits and cutting tools used on the drill press.
10. What is a plug cutter?
11. Describe how you would adjust a drill press to bore to a particular depth and at a particular angle.
12. Name 10 important safety rules which must be observed when using the drill press.
13. Why must a drill press be operated at a slower speed for boring and cutting hardwood than for working with softwood?
14. Name three bits or cutters which are suitable for cutting holes larger than 1 inch in diameter.
15. List and describe four types of bits which can be used for boring holes.
16. Name two methods of boring a hole to a specified depth.
17. What is the difference between routing and shaping?
18. Describe routing with a pattern.
19. Describe how to sand an edge to a pattern by using the drum sander on the drill press.
20. What is the distinction between boring and drilling?
21. Visit a large lumberyard, sawmill, mill and sash company, furniture manufacturer, or other wood-products manufacturing plant in your vicinity. Make a report on the types of drill press in use. List the purposes for which they are used.

SECTION 14

BORING AND DRILLING HOLES WITH THE PORTABLE ELECTRIC HAND DRILL

Unit 87 General Information About the Electric Hand Drill

The portable electric hand drill (Fig. 87-1) is one of the most popular and useful of all portable power tools. It is manufactured in a variety of types, sizes, and capacities. This handy electric tool is used extensively by building contractors and home owners and in school shops and laboratories.

This tool is usually equipped with an electric motor which operates on normal house electrical voltage. It is of the utmost importance, however, that portable tools be used only where they can be grounded. This eliminates the possibility of getting an electric shock as

electricity is conducted from the operator to the ground. Most electrical connections have a third conductor (wire) in the power-supply cord for grounding.

Types and Speeds

There are three basic types of portable electric hand drills: (1) the pistol-grip drill, (2) the D-handle drill, and (3) the spade-handle drill. These types are illustrated in Figs. 87-1, 87-2, and 87-3.

The **pistol-grip drill** (see Fig. 87-1) is perhaps the most common because

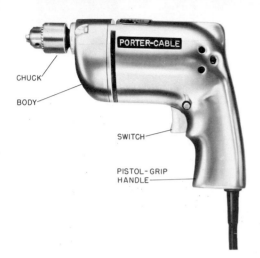

87-1. A pistol-grip portable electric hand drill.

CHUCK

BODY

SWITCH

PISTOL-GRIP HANDLE

87-2. A D-handle portable electric hand drill.

87-3. A spade-handle portable electric hand drill.

it is designed for one-hand operation. It is economical and compact. Various models of this type of drill have different chuck capacities and run at different speeds. Speeds depend upon the type of material being drilled and the kind of drill bit being used. The average drill speed is rated about 2,000 rpm without a load. This lightweight drill has a capacity of up to a 1/4-inch drill bit.

The **D-handle drill** (see Fig. 87-2) also gets its name from the shape of its handle. It is designed for drilling small holes. Its advantage over the pistol-grip drill is its auxiliary handle, which permits more accurate drilling.

The **spade-handle drill** (see Fig. 87-3) also is named because of the shape of its handle. It has the largest chuck capacity, taking up to a 1/2-inch drill bit. It operates at a slower speed than the other two types of drills because it is designed for heavier duty. Its average drill speed is rated at about 600 rpm without a load. Because of its size, both hands are required to use it.

Portable electric drills are designated by the maximum drill diameter that the chuck can accommodate. Sizes vary from 1/4 inch to 1 inch. The drill speed decreases as the size of the drill chuck increases because of the purpose and motor capacity of the drill.

Portable electric hand drills have been developed with self-contained electric power packs for use where electric power sources are not available or convenient.

Drill Parts and Uses

■ **Body or housing.** This part (Fig. 87-4) is usually made of lightweight aluminum alloy. It encloses the power mechanism. It includes the motor and the gears which give the drill the desired speed and power.

■ **Handles.** There are several shapes of handles. All are located to give the operator easy control of the power switch.

■ **Chucks.** Chucks are described and illustrated in Unit 88.

87-4. A cross section of portable electric hand drill parts.

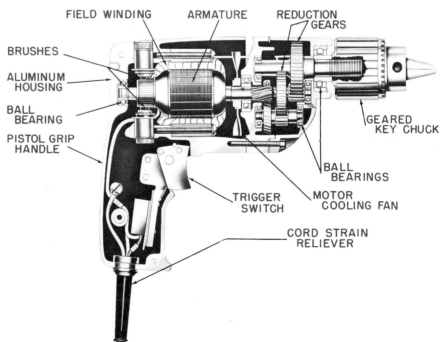

FIELD WINDING   ARMATURE   REDUCTION GEARS

BRUSHES

ALUMINUM HOUSING

BALL BEARING

PISTOL GRIP HANDLE

GEARED KEY CHUCK

BALL BEARINGS

TRIGGER SWITCH

MOTOR COOLING FAN

CORD STRAIN RELIEVER

Unit 88 Chucks and Drill Bits

Chuck sizes are measured by the sizes of the drill bits they can handle. Portable electric hand drills use either key or keyless chucks (see below). Several types of round-shank bits can be used effectively with electric hand drills.

Chucks

The three-jaw key chuck is designed to center the drill bit exactly (Fig. 88-1). The jaws are opened by turning the sleeve counterclockwise (as seen from the bit end). After the bit is inserted in the chuck opening, the sleeve should be turned clockwise until the bit is gripped in the chuck jaws.

The chuck key should be inserted in one of the three holes of the chuck body and turned clockwise until the jaws are tight. It should then be fitted into each of the other two holes until the bit is secure.

A keyless chuck (Fig. 88-2) works in much the same way as the key chuck, but the bit is tightened firmly in the chuck by hand. This chuck is very serviceable, especially when small drill bits are used.

Figure 88-3 shows how the chuck grasps the shank of a dual-purpose unispur auger bit, which is illustrated in Fig. 28-7.

Drill Bits

The types of drill bits which can be used successfully with the portable electric hand drill are (1) straight-shank twist drill bits (Fig. 88-4), which are used in metalworking as well as woodworking; (2) spade-, or power-, type bits, which are used to bore holes in wood; (3) combination wood-drill and countersink bits, which make pilot and shank holes for screws and which countersink for screwheads in one drilling operation; and (4) countersink bits, which set screwheads. These bits are illustrated and discussed in detail in Unit 81.

88-1. A key chuck for the portable electric hand drill.

88-2. Tightening a bit in a keyless chuck.

88-3. A chuck grasping a dual-purpose unispur auger bit.

88-4. A set of drill bits.

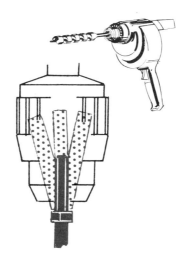

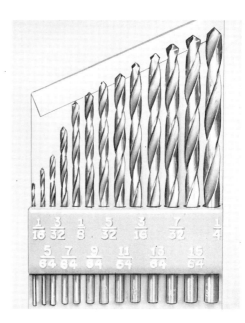

Unit 89 Safety for the Electric Hand Drill

■ **Permission.** Always secure permission from your instructor or the person in charge before using the portable electric hand drill.

■ **Clothing.** Tuck in your necktie so that it cannot get caught in the bit. Either button or roll up your sleeves. Remove your ring, if you wear one.

■ **Planning.** Carefully plan your work and the layout before drilling holes.

■ **Drill bits.** Make sure you have selected the proper size and type of bit for the job. Do not use larger bit sizes than are recommended by the drill press manufacturer.

■ **Chuck.** Fasten the bit securely in the jaws of the chuck before attempting to do any work.

■ **Adjustments.** Disconnect the plug from the electric power outlet before you make adjustments or change bits.

■ **Electrical grounding.** See that the electrical connection is grounded.

■ **Air vents.** Keep the air cooling vents on the drill housing free of dirt and sawdust.

■ **Material.** Hold or clamp the material firmly before drilling holes.

■ **Drilling.** Hold the hand drill with either hand, or with both hands, while drilling. Avoid forcing and breaking the bit.

■ **Stopping drill.** Hold the hand drill until the switch is turned off and the motor has stopped. Then place it on a firm surface, such as a table.

Unit 90 Drilling Holes

90-1. Drilling a hole. A try square helps align the electric hand drill perpendicular to the work.

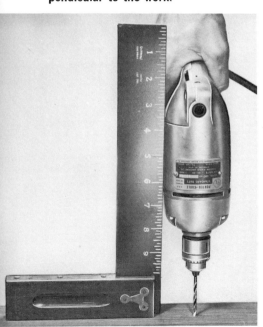

Drilling holes, countersinking, and driving screws are some of the many jobs which can be performed with the portable electric hand drill. With the correct bits, this tool can be used to drill holes in metal, plastics, concrete, and composition materials. Sanding, polishing, grinding, and buffing operations can also be done with this tool and suitable attachments. The main purpose of this unit, however, is to explain how to drill holes and countersink and drive screws.

Procedure

1. Mark the center point of the hole. Use an awl or a nail. This prevents the bit from wandering (slipping) and marring the board.

2. Select the correct size and type of bit. Fasten it in the chuck. Refer to Unit 88, "Chucks and Drill Bits."

3. Connect the electric drill to a properly grounded wall receptacle.

4. Put the point of the bit in the dent made in step 1. Do this before you turn on the motor.

5. Hold the drill perpendicular to the work. Start the motor (Fig. 90-1).

90-2. Drilling a hole, using a block of wood to back (reinforce) the board.

90-3. Drilling a hole with a spade- or power-type bit.

90-4. A portable electric hand drill made into a stationary drill press when attached to a vertical drill stand.

6. Drill the hole. Use just enough pressure to keep the drill cutting into the wood. Let the tool do the work while you use a steady, even pressure.

7. Use a block of wood to back (reinforce) the board, if the hole is to be drilled completely through (Fig. 90-2).

8. Withdraw the bit from the hole with the motor still on; then turn off the switch.

9. Figure 90-3 shows a hole being drilled with a spade-, or power-, type bit.

10. A combination wood drill and countersink bit is an excellent tool for drilling pilot and shank holes for screws and for countersinking in one operation (Fig. 90-5).

11. The portable electric hand drill can be made into a stationary model by fastening it to a vertical drill stand, which is available for most models (Fig. 90-4).

12. Building tradesmen find the self-contained power-pack electric drill extremely convenient and satisfactory for working in places that do not have regular electric power.

13. Screws can be driven with a portable electric hand drill by using a speed-reduction ratchet (Fig. 90-6).

90-5. Drilling a hole with a combination wood drill and countersink bit.

90-6. Driving a screw with a reduction-gear ratchet.

DISCUSSION TOPICS

1. Name the three general types of portable electric hand drills. What is the distinguishing feature of each?
2. Name three advantages of the portable electric hand drill over the drill press.
3. List the two kinds of chucks which can be used with the portable electric drill. What is the most practical use of each?
4. When would you most likely have to use a block of wood to reinforce (back up) the drilling process?
5. List six specification items to consider when purchasing a portable electric hand drill.
6. What are approximate weights of portable electric drills?
7. What is the relationship of cutting speed to the size of the drill bit?
8. What is meant by **grounding?**
9. Discuss three essential parts of the portable electric hand drill.
10. List six safety rules to observe when using this tool.
11. What is the source of power when using the portable drill without a regular electrical system? Where would this tool be most useful?
12. Visit a lumberyard or wood-products manufacturing plant. Make a report on the types of portable electric hand drill in use. List the purposes for which they are used.

MORTISING ON THE MORTISER AND
THE DRILL PRESS

Unit 91 General Information About the Hollow-chisel Mortiser

The hollow-chisel mortiser (Fig. 91-1) is a modern laborsaving machine. It performs two operations at the same time: as the bit bores the hole, the hollow, square chisel which surrounds it trims the wood further, making a square opening. Vertical and horizontal mortisers are used extensively in such industries as sash-and-door plants and furniture factories. Chisel-and-bit combinations make possible efficient production of various sizes of holes.

Types of Mortisers

Many mortisers are equipped with a table which can be adjusted horizon-tally by means of a hand wheel; the stock is moved back and forth by the action of the table. Most mortisers have an automatic mechanism which moves the head assembly (motor, chuck, chisel, and bit) up and down to cut the mortise (square opening) as pressure is applied on the foot pedal. The usual mortiser operating speed is 3,600 rpm.

Figure 91-2 is a cross-section detail showing the hollow-chisel and bit assembly fastened in place on the commercial mortiser. There should always be a $\frac{1}{16}$-inch operating clearance between the bit and the end of the chisel, as shown in Figs. 91-2 and 91-3

Figure 91-4 shows a mortising attachment fastened to a drill press. This converts the drill press into a manually operated mortiser. The stock must be moved back and forth on the table by hand. The cutting of the mortising chisel and bit is controlled by a feed lever. It is very accurate.

Mortising tools for the drill press consist of a hollow chisel with four cutting edges which cut a square hole, a bit without a point which works inside the chisel (Fig. 91-5), and a chisel adaptor, or bushing. Chisel-and-bit sets vary in size from ¼ to ½ inch for mortising on the drill press. Bushings are usually supplied that permit any size of bit to be mounted in the ½-inch hole spindle. Often the bit fits directly into the chuck and does not need a bushing.

Parts and Uses

■ **Motor head.** The motor head consists of a direct-drive motor, chuck, chisel, and bit. This is the mechanism that moves the bit and chisel vertically along the ways (guides).

■ **Table and fence.** This unit moves horizontally; however, on some machines it can be tilted to the right or left 45 degrees so that holes can be cut at an angle. A clamp is provided on the table to hold the stock against the fence.

■ **Column.** The head, table, foot lever, and other parts are rigidly supported by this one-piece casting.

■ **Foot lever.** This controls the action of the motor head.

■ **Chisel and bit.** Chisels, with companion bits, vary in size according to the capacity of the mortiser. For school use, this is usually ¼ to ¾ inch.

■ **Horizontal adjustment.** The hand wheel which is used to control the movement of the table is the horizontal adjustment.

■ **Depth adjustment.** A hand wheel is used to make the depth adjustment; it raises or lowers the table to the correct cutting depth of the chisel.

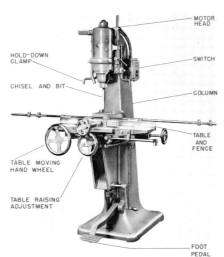

91-1. A hollow-chisel mortiser.

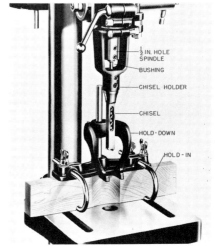

91-4. The drill press converted for mortising.

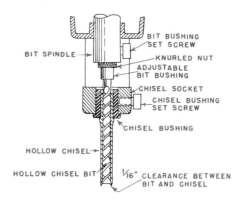

91-2. A cross section of a chisel-and-bit assembly.

91-3. The operating clearance between the end of the chisel and bit should be ¹⁄₁₆ inch.

91-5. A hollow mortising chisel, bit, and bushing to use on a drill press for mortising.

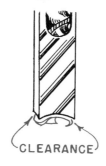

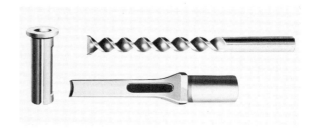

Unit 92 Safety for the Mortiser

- **Permission.** Be sure that you always secure permission before using the mortiser.
- **Instruction manual.** Follow the instructions which are given in the mortising manual or those which are given by the teacher.
- **Clothing.** Do not wear loose clothing. Tuck in your necktie; button or roll up your sleeves. Remove your ring.
- **Hands.** Be careful to keep your hands away from the chisel and bit when you are operating the mortiser.

- **Stance.** Stand firmly in front of the machine with your eyes directed to the mortising cut.
- **Chisels and bits.** Make certain that the chisel and bit are of the same size and that the bit extends beyond the chisel about $1/16$ inch.
- **Position of stock.** Stock must be securely held on the table against the fence. Use either a screw clamp or hold-down clamps.
- **Stopping.** Shut off the power; do not leave until the mortiser has stopped.

Unit 93 Mortising on the Hollow-chisel Mortiser

Mortising is a relatively simple process. The machine must be set with the correct size of chisel and bit, and the table must be adjusted for depth.

Mortising

1. Square the stock to the desired size. Mark the location of the mortise (Fig. 93-1).

2. Install the correct size of chisel and bit into the mortise head. The bit should extend about $1/16$ inch beyond the chisel.

3. Clamp the stock securely in place on the table against the fence.

4. Mark a line on the end of the piece to indicate the depth of the cut. Adjust the vertical height of the chisel to the proper depth (Fig. 93-2).

93-1. Stock squared and marked for a mortise.

93-2. Adjusting the cutting depth of the chisel.

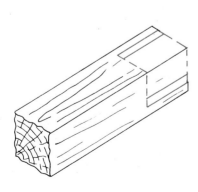

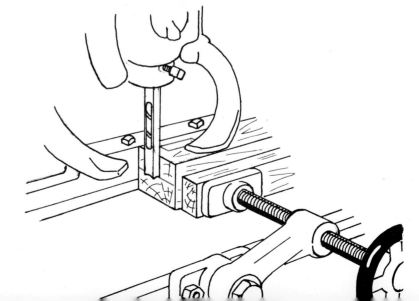

5. Move the table into line with the chisel to make the first cut.

6. Turn on the motor, and make the first cut to only half the final depth. This prevents burning the chisel and bit (Fig. 93-3). The chisel and bit can be made to cut into the wood by the action of the foot lever or the hand control, depending upon the machine.

7. Move the stock over slightly. Make the second cut to the full depth (Fig. 93-4), and then clean out the first cut. Continue making cuts until the mortise has been completed.

Figure 93-5 shows another method of making a series of first passes (cuts). After these have been completed, clean out the remaining portions of the mortise with a final series of passes.

A mortise that is wider than the chisel can be cut as shown in Fig. 93-6.

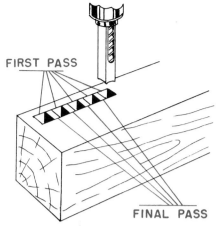
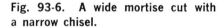

93-5. An alternate method of making mortise cuts.

Fig. 93-6. A wide mortise cut with a narrow chisel.

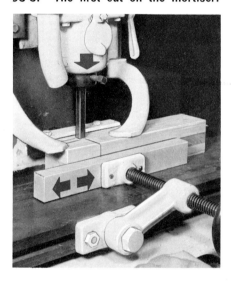

93-3. The first cut on the mortiser.

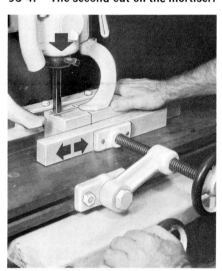

93-4. The second cut on the mortiser.

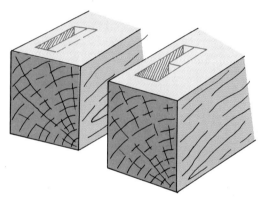

Unit 94 Mortising on the Drill Press

The drill press can be conveniently converted into a mortiser. See Fig. 91-4. Use the chisel and drill bit shown in Fig. 91-5. The instruction sheet or manual which accompanies the drill press and mortising attachments will provide specific instructions for assembling the mortising kit on the drill press. Remember that most mortises are 3/8 inch wide.

The speed of the drill press for mortising should be about 2,250 rpm for softwoods and approximately 1,500 rpm for hardwoods.

Mortising

1. Check the clearance between the chisel and the bit. It should be about 1/16 inch. See Fig. 91-3. There must be some clearance between the bit spurs and the lower end of the chisel; otherwise the bit will heat in operation. On the other hand, if the bit extends below the chisel too far, the chips may be too large to pass through the chisel. The bit should not touch the chisel.

2. Lay out and mark the mortise cut. See Fig. 93-1.

3. Fasten the piece to be mortised on the table against the mortising fence. It should be held down with the hold-down clamp and firmly against the fence with the hold-in clamps. See Fig. 91-4.

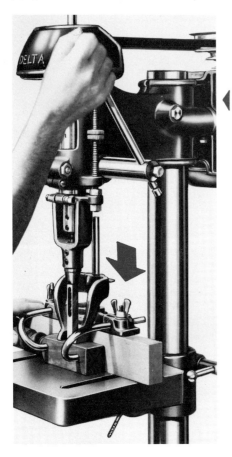

4. Adjust the position of the fence on the drill press table.

5. Adjust the two lock nuts for the depth of the mortise cut. See Unit 82.

6. Turn on the power, and make the first mortise cut. Bring the chisel down to the end of the mortise, and then apply pressure gradually as the drill cuts the wood out and brings it up through the chisel (Fig. 94-1). See the previous unit for the correct procedure.

94-1.   Cutting a mortise on the drill press.

94-2.   Detail of a completed mortise cut.

7. Continue making cuts until the mortise is cleanly cut (Fig. 94-2).

8. Mortises can be cut as shown in Fig. 94-3. Bore a series of holes with the drill bit; clean out the mortise by pushing the piece back and fourth, increasing the depth of the drill bit about $\frac{1}{8}$ inch on each pass. The ends of the mortise can be cut square with a wood chisel, or the tenon can be rounded to fit the mortise.

94-3.   Making a mortise with the drill bit.

DISCUSSION TOPICS

1. What two types of machines can be used for mortising?
2. What is the correct speed for mortising?
3. What is a mortise?
4. Describe the action that takes place when a mortise is cut on a hollow-chisel mortiser.
5. Name six important safety rules which must be observed when using the mortiser.
6. Why should the first mortise cut be made to only about half the depth of the final cut?
7. How much clearance should there be between the end of the bit and the end of the chisel?
8. Visit a mill and sash company or a furniture manufacturer in your community. Make a report on the type of mortiser in use. Describe the exact purpose for which it is used.

WOOD TURNING ON THE LATHE

Unit 95 General Information About the Wood Lathe

The wood lathe is one of the oldest types of power equipment used to fashion wooden objects. Wood turning is an interesting woodworking skill. The lathe, more than any other tool, is in itself a complete unit, capable of producing finished work. Modern lathes (Fig. 95-1) enable craftsmen to produce beautifully formed pieces.

Sizes, Types, and Speeds

Two factors usually determine the size of a wood lathe: (1) the swing of the faceplate, which indicates the maximum diameter of the piece which can be turned (faceplate turning), and (2) the maximum length of a piece which can be turned between centers (spindle

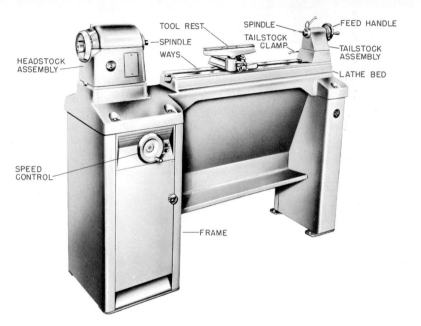

95-1. A 12-inch, variable-speed, wood-turning lathe.

turning). A lathe capable of turning 30-inch-long stock must have a bed long enough to support the tailstock assembly (and on some lathes also the head-stock assembly) in addition to the length needed for holding the wood.

A typical industrial laboratory, school-size lathe is a **12-inch wood lathe with a 4-foot bed.** The next size in common use has an 8-foot bed.

The terms **wood** and **speed** usually apply to the wood-cutting lathes. This avoids confusion with the screw-cutting, metal-turning lathes.

The turning speed is controlled by either (1) a multispeed motor, (2) a variable speed control, (3) spring-loaded pulleys, or (4) three- or four-step pulleys. When step pulleys are used, a V belt must be changed manually for any desired speed. The first three methods of controlling speed usually employ a dial-type speed control. The speed range of the wood lathe is from approximately 350 to 3,600 rpm. The larger the stock to be turned, the slower the speed.

Some wood lathes are equipped with a hand brake which shuts off the current automatically when it is applied. This keeps the work from "coasting" and allows the operator to proceed quickly to his next turning process.

Parts and Uses

■ **Headstock assembly.** This assembly contains the driving mechanism; the spindle for the live, or spur, center; and, on some lathes, the speed control. The headstock of many lathes also includes the motor. If the lathe is belt driven, one of the pulleys is part of this assembly. The other is attached to the motor shaft, usually directly underneath the first one. Figure 95-2 shows a cross section of a typical headstock spindle assembly.

■ **Tailstock assembly.** The tailstock assembly includes the dead center spindle, the dead center, and the hand wheel and locking adjustments.

■ **Lathe bed (ways).** This is the supporting body of the lathe. It holds the head- and tailstock assemblies. It also holds the tool rest (see below) and its support.

■ **Frame or legs.** The upright support on which the lathe stands constitutes the frame. On some lathes, this is a complete base; on others, legs are fastened to the lathe bed.

■ **Tool rest.** This is a horizontal guide. It is held in a tool-rest holder, or support. The turning tool is worked back and forth along the tool rest during the wood-turning operation.

95-2. A typical headstock spindle assembly.

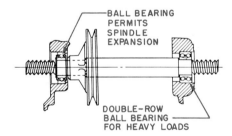

Unit 96 Wood-turning Chisels and Accessories

A standard set of tools (chisels) used in wood turning consists of five basic shapes (Fig. 96-1). There are several sizes for some of these shapes, as described below. These cutting tools are made of a high-grade alloy steel. They

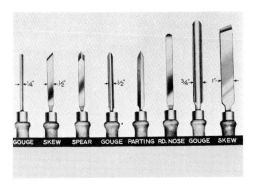

96-1. A set of standard wood-turning chisels.

96-2. A 12-inch tool support.

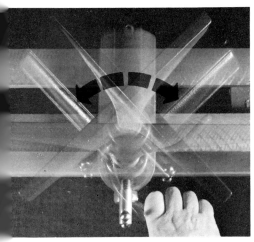

96-3. Phantom view of a tool rest, showing many angle adjustments.

96-4. A right-angle tool rest.

are fitted with long hardwood handles. Several accessories are also available; they are illustrated and discussed.

Turning Chisels

■ **Gouge.** This is the most frequently used lathe tool. It is a roundnose, hollow chisel used for rough cutting and for cutting coves. Gouge tools come in several sizes. See Fig. 96-1.

■ **Skew chisel.** This tool is next in importance. It is a double-ground flat chisel whose end is ground to an angle. It is used to smooth cylinders and to cut beads, V grooves, shoulders, and similar cuts. See Unit 99, "Practice Turning Between Centers." Figure 96-1 shows two sizes.

■ **Diamond-, or spear-point chisel.** The diamond-point (spear-point) chisel is a scraping tool. It is used whenever its shape fits the contour of the piece.

■ **Roundnose chisel.** This is also a scraping tool.

■ **Parting tool.** The parting tool is also a double-ground chisel. It is used to cut off the ends and to make cuts to required diameters.

Accessories

The **12-inch tool support** is the most conventional size of this attachment (Fig. 96-2). It is ideal for general lathework because it can be adjusted to any angle (Fig. 96-3).

The **right-angle tool rest** (Fig. 96-4) is used to turn edges and faces without adjusting the tool rest or support.

The **24-inch tool rest** (Fig. 96-5) is convenient for doing long turnings if you do not wish to move the shorter tool rest. This support requires an extra tool holder or support base.

Figure 96-6 shows 6- and 3-inch-diameter **faceplates**. These permit the turning of different sizes of faceplate pieces.

The **screw-center faceplate** (Fig. 96-7) affords a quick method of mounting (fastening) small faceplate turnings.

96-5. A 24-inch, double-post tool rest.

96-6. Six- and three-inch diameter faceplates.

96-7. A screw-center faceplate.

96-8. A drive, or spur, center.

96-9. A cup, or dead, center.

The **drive** (spur) **center** (Fig. 96-8) and the **cup** (dead) **center** (Fig. 96-9) are used for all spindle turnings.

Horizontal drilling or boring can easily be done on the lathe with the addition of a special **geared chuck.** The geared chuck is inserted either into the headstock of the lathe or the tailstock spindle (Fig. 96-10).

Sanding drums, fitted into the headstock spindle, are excellent for sanding irregular edges (Fig. 96-11).

An **outside spring caliper** (Fig. 96-12) checks the correct diameters of the turning.

The **slip stone** (Fig. 96-13) is an absolute necessity for whetting (sharpening) turning chisels.

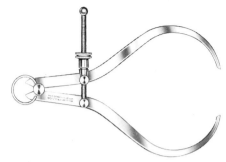

96-12.   An outside spring caliper.

96-10.   A geared chuck.

96-11.   Two sizes of sanding drums.

96-13.   A slip stone.

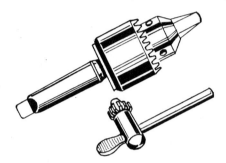

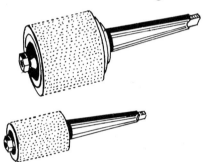

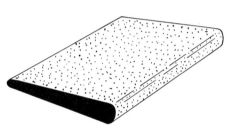

Unit 97 Safety for the Wood Lathe

■ **Permission.** Always obtain permission before using the lathe.

■ **Clothing.** Do not wear loose clothing. Roll or button your sleeves. Tuck in your necktie.

■ **Jewelry.** Remove your ring, if you wear one. It could catch in something.

■ **Instruction manual.** Read and follow the instructions in the lathe manual for maintaining the working parts of this machine.

■ **Adjustments.** Make all adjustments with the power *turned off.*

■ **Lathe tools.** Lathe tools (chisels) must be kept *sharp* at all times.

■ **Tool rest.** The tool rest should be kept as *close as possible* to the stock being turned for better leverage. Do not adjust the rest while the lathe is running.

■ **Speed.** Run the lathe at the correct speed for your work. Lathe jobs should be started at the *slowest* speed, and the stock should be roughed down to form before a faster speed is used.

■ **Wood.** All wood to be used for turning should be examined for knots, checks, cracks, and other defects. The lumber should be clear.

■ **Glued stock.** Glued stock must be *thoroughly dry* before being turned on the lathe.

■ **Rough stock.** Turn rough stock *by hand* after it has been fastened for spindle or faceplate turning. Make certain it will clear the tool rest.

■ **Tailstock.** Adjustments on the tailstock must be secure before you attempt to do spindle turning.

■ **Dead center.** Always add a few drops of oil to the dead center before turning on the lathe.

- **Turning.** Hold turning tools firmly with *both hands* while cutting stock on the lathe.
- **Spindle turning.** Wherever possible, try to cut with the chisels.
- **Measuring with the caliper.** Always *stop* the lathe before you measure with a caliper.
- **Faceplate.** Be sure to use screws only long enough to hold the faceplate to the wood stock (block). When turning this piece, avoid cutting too deeply and striking the screws.
- **Sanding and finishing.** Always remove the tool rest when sanding or applying finish.
- **Stopping.** Shut off the power, and clean the lathe after you use it.

Unit 98 Setting Up to Turn Spindles

Turning done between lathe centers is called **spindle,** or **between-center, turning.** This method is followed to turn any round shape, such as chair and table legs, or other pieces requiring the use of both lathe centers. It is important to know how to center the work and mount it on the lathe.

Centering the Wood Piece

1. Select and cut stock for the spindle turning. It should be approximately square. The ends should also be square with the sides. The thickness should be approximately ¼ inch larger than the diameter of the finished spindle. The length can be the exact length of the desired turning, or it can be ½ inch longer if you wish to cut the ends smooth after the turning is completed.

2. Draw diagonal lines across both ends of the piece (Fig. 98-1). The point of intersection (crossing) is the center. Some woodworkers prefer to do this only on the live-center end and then dent the dead center with an awl.

3. Cut a ⅛-inch saw kerf on the diagonal lines on both ends of the piece (Fig. 98-2).

4. Place the stock on a solid surface or hold it firmly in a bench vise. See Fig. 98-3.

5. Remove the live center from the headstock of the lathe. Use the pin or rod provided for that purpose.

98-1. Drawing diagonal lines to locate the center.

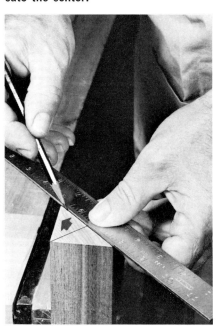

98-2. Sawing on the diagonal lines.

98-3. Driving the live center (spur point) into place.

6. Place the live center (spur point) in the saw grooves. Tap it firmly a couple of times with a mallet to drive it in (Fig. 98-3). This will seat (sink) the prongs (spurs) of the live center in the saw cut.

7. Remove the live center from the wood. Replace it in the headstock of the lathe.

Mounting Stock on the Lathe

1. Place the stock with the grooved end against the live center. Hold it carefully and firmly in position with your left hand.

2. Move the tailstock up to within 1 inch of the end of the wood.

3. Lock the tailstock to the lathe.

4. Turn the hand wheel on the tailstock until the point of the dead center fits either into the hole made with the awl or the center made with the saw cuts. See Fig. 98-4.

5. Tighten the hand wheel on the tailstock until the piece to be turned is fastened securely. Lock the hand wheel, using the adjustment lever. Figure 98-4 shows the piece located between centers.

6. Put two or three drops of lubricating oil on the dead center (Fig. 98-5). Lubricant is not needed if this center is of the ball-bearing type. Oil lessens burning of the wood caused by friction.

98-5. Adding drops of oil to the dead center.

98-4. Spindle stock fastened between centers.

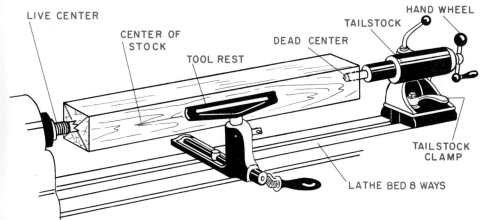

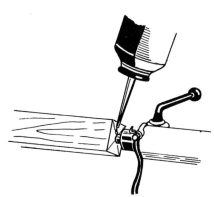

Unit 99 Practice Turning Between Centers

Turning spindles between centers can be done with either a cutting or a scraping action. The chisels that are used for turning are described and illustrated in Unit 96, "Wood-turning Chisels and Accessories." The cutting method is faster and makes a cleaner surface. Much practice is required to learn how to cut; for this reason, many beginners use the scraping method. Most of the processes described and illustrated in this unit use the cutting technique. After you have practiced these cuts, you should be able to make a spindle turning as outlined and illustrated in the next unit.

Roughing the Stock

1. Carefully adjust the position of the tool rest until it is about ⅛ inch away from the piece to be turned and

⅛ inch above the center line (Fig. 99-1). In addition, see Fig. 99-4.

2. Move the spindle stock by hand. Make sure that there is at least a ⅛-inch clearance between all edges of the wood and the tool rest.

3. Turn the speed control to a low speed.

4. Place the ¾-inch gouge on the tool rest. Move it on the tool rest and against the revolving spindle to make the first cut (Fig. 99-2). This cut starts about 2 inches from the tailstock end. Note in Fig. 99-3 that the gouge is rolled over slightly in the same direction as the cut.

5. Make a second cut, starting about 3 inches to the left of the first one. Advance toward the tailstock until you feed into the first cut (Fig. 99-2).

99-1.   The position of the tool rest.

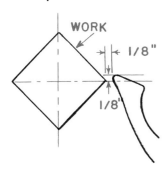

99-2.   The sequence of cuts for rough turning with the gouge.

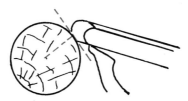

99-3.   The correct way to use a gouge for a shearing cut. Note that the guide hand is held *under* the chisel.

6. Continue to make this series of cuts until you reach a point about 2 inches from the live-center end; then *reverse* direction, and cut off the remainder. After some experience, you should be able to start at one end and make a continuous cut to the other.

7. Continue the rough cutting until the spindle is round and still slightly larger than the maximum diameter of the finished piece (Fig. 99-4). You can move the gouge from left to right or from right to left, whichever is most convenient. The gouge can be held and guided as shown in Fig. 99-2 or Fig. 99-4.

99-4.   Rough-cutting the stock to the approximate diameter.

99-5.   Making a cut with the skew chisel. Note that the guide hand is *under* the chisel.

Smoothing the Wood Spindle with a Skew Chisel

1. Set the caliper to the maximum diameter desired. See Fig. 99-8.

2. Place the large skew chisel on the tool rest; make a fine (accurate) shearing cut as shown in Fig. 99-5 or Fig. 99-6. This cut requires much careful practice. The center of the skew chisel cutting edge should be used for making skew cuts, not the point.

Figure 99-7 shows a common way of scraping with the skew chisel. This method is often used by beginners.

3. Continue making cuts until the spindle is formed to the desired diameter.

99-6.   Making a cut using the skew chisel. Note that the guide hand is *over* the chisel.

99-7.   Smoothing by scraping.

Making a Parting Cut

1. Speed the lathe slightly.
2. Place the parting tool on its edge on the tool rest. See Fig. 99-9.
3. Set the caliper to the desired diameter (Fig. 99-8).
4. Grasp the tool firmly with one hand; push it *directly into* the revolving spindle (Fig. 99-9) to make a scraping groove cut. This is used for cutting to specific depths or squaring ends.
5. Cut until the desired diameter of the spindle has been reached. (Fig. 99-10). Hold the tool in one hand while gauging with the caliper. Figure 99-11 shows how to make a clearance cut when the groove is over 3/8 inch deep. This prevents burning the point of the parting tool.

99-8. Setting a caliper.

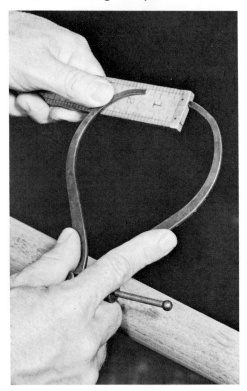

99-9. Making a parting cut.

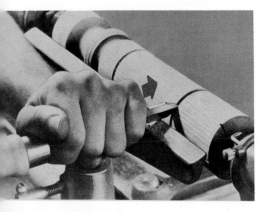

99-10. Cutting and gauging for diameter.

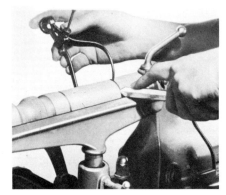

99-11. Making a clearance cut to prevent burning the point of the parting tool.

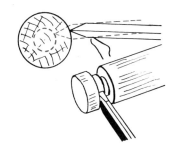

99-12. Removing the surplus wood of a cove with a gouge.

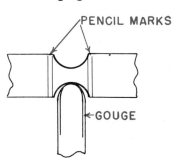

Making a Cove (Concave) Cut

1. Lay out, or mark, the width of the cove with a pencil. See Fig. 99-13.
2. Place a gouge (narrower than the cove) on the tool rest. Push it into the stock to remove the surplus wood (Fig. 99-12). This is a scraping action.
3. Finish cutting the cove with the same gouge (Figs. 99-13 and 99-14).

99-13. Starting a cove cut with the gouge.

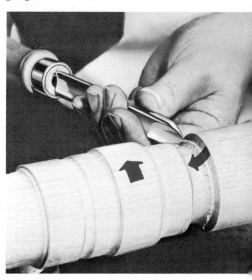

99-14. Finishing the cove cut.

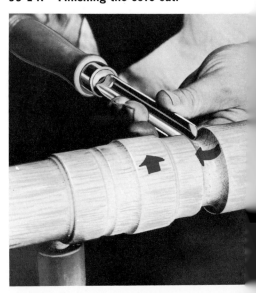

Note the way the chisel (gouge) is *rolled into* the cut.

A beginner may wish to scrape cove cuts, using either the roundnose chisel or the small gouge, until his cutting technique is perfected.

Cutting a Shoulder

1. Cut the wood to within $\frac{1}{16}$ inch of the required shoulder diameter with a parting tool.

2. Smooth the shoulder by using the point of the skew chisel (Fig. 99-15). This makes a clean-cut shoulder face.

V Cuts

1. Mark the cylinder the width of the beads or Vs. See Fig. 99-16.

2. Make the first cut for the beads with the *point* of a skew chisel (Fig. 99-16).

3. Round the beads with the *edge* of the skew chisel (Fig. 99-17).

Figure 99-18 shows V cuts and beads. It also shows how beads and Vs are cut with the skew chisel or are scraped with the spear-point chisel. Scraping is often preferred by beginners.

99-15. Making a side cut with a skew chisel, squaring a shoulder.

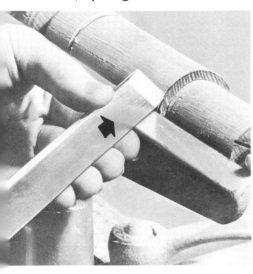

99-17. Rounding beads with a skew.

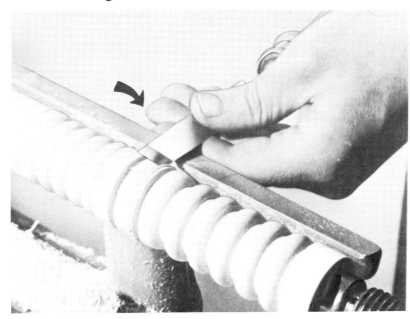

99-16. The first cut in turning beads with a skew.

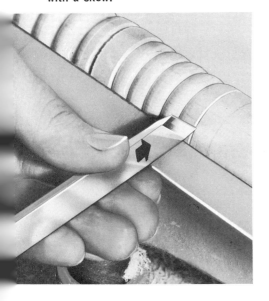

99-18. V cuts and beads.

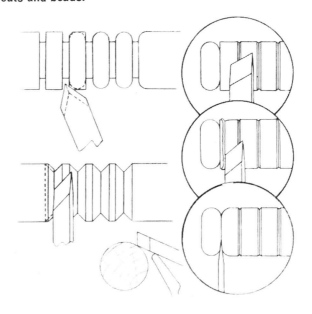

253

Unit 100 Spindle Turning

The previous unit described and illustrated some of the more common shapes which can be cut between centers on the wood lathe. Spindle turnings (between centers) require a general procedure. These steps are presented in this unit. You will find it necessary to refer to the previous unit for details of the various cuts.

Included here is information on **post blocking**. In this process, some extra wood is added to the portions of the spindle where the diameters are greater than the main part of the piece, as is often the case with a lamp column or a table leg. Figure 100-13 shows the effect obtained by use of contrasting woods. The work should be perfectly centered to avoid a lopsided appearance or pattern.

Straight, or Spindle, Turning

1. Turn to the maximum diameter. See "Roughing the Stock" and "Smoothing the Wood Spindle with a Skew Chisel."

2. Mark the required dimension lines along the turning. Use a pencil and a rule (Fig. 100-1). You can also use a full-size template (Fig. 100-2).

3. Cut to the pattern diameters (depths), using the parting tool (cutoff tool) and the gouge (Fig. 100-3). These are the basic cuts that locate the different diameters. They can be gauged with the caliper. You can also make a hardwood diameter gauge. See Fig. 100-3. Figure 100-4 illustrates these cuts on a typical turning design: (A) lines marked on the spindle, (B) first cuts in the spindle, and (C) the completed spindle turning.

100-1. Marking dimension lines with a pencil and a rule.

100-2. Marking dimension lines with a pencil and a full-size template.

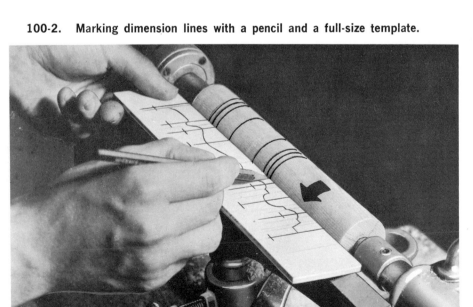

100-3. Cutting and gauging to various diameters (depths).

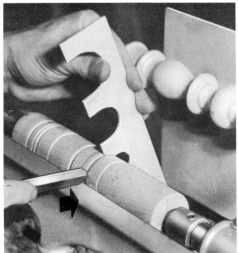

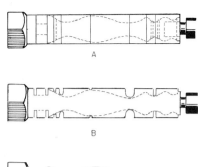

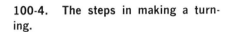

A

B

C

100-4. The steps in making a turning.

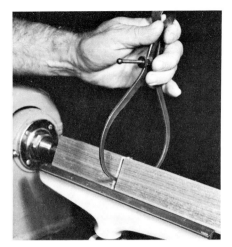

100-6. Gauging the diameter with a caliper.

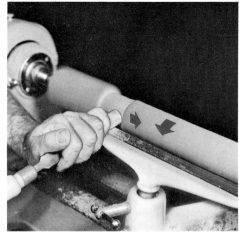

100-7. Rough-cut turning with the gouge. Note that the square portion will not be cut.(Fig. 100-9).

4. Finish the spindle turning by using any of the cuts described and illustrated in the previous unit.

5. Turned legs may have to have a square portion left at the top, particularly if mortise-and-tenon joints are to be used to fasten them to rails. In this case, all turning should begin from the square part, as illustrated in Figs. 100-5, 100-6, and 100-7. The procedure will then be the same as for any straight turning.

Sanding

1. Use a quarter of a sheet of medium-grit sandpaper or emery cloth.

2. Move the tool rest away from the work.

3. Start the lathe at low speed.

4. Sand all shoulders first with the sandpaper or emery cloth folded. Make sure to hold the abrasive paper or cloth so that the shoulders will *not* get rounded (Fig. 100-8).

5. Use extra-fine sandpaper or emery cloth for final sanding.

6. Stop the lathe. Sand the turning *lengthwise* by hand. This removes cross-grain scratches made while the work was revolving.

Post-block Turning

1. Make, locate, and glue extra wood blocks onto the main spindle, as illustrated in Fig. 100-10. These should

100-5. Cutting with the parting tool to separate the square portion from the turned part.

100-8. Sanding a straight turning on the lathe.

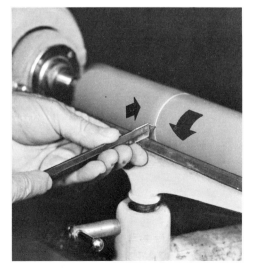

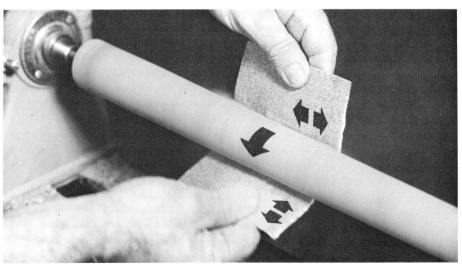

be glued on where extra material is needed. Allow the glue to dry thoroughly before any turning is done.

2. Center and mount the spindle on the lathe. See Fig. 100-11.

3. Shape the spindle (Figs. 100-11, 100-12, and 100-13). The post-block portion should be rough turned before the remainder of the spindle is turned. See Fig. 100-13.

4. Complete all turning on the spindle as explained in the steps in this unit under "Straight, or Spindle, Turning." If necessary, See Unit 99 for a description of the cuts.

100-9. Sanding a turning on the lathe. Note that the abrasive paper or cloth is folded to protect turning details.

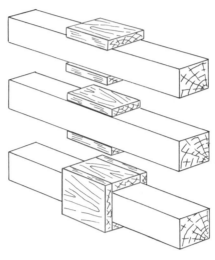

100-10. Steps in gluing on blocks of wood for post blocking.

100-12. Smoothing the post-block turning with a skew chisel.

100-11. Starting the rough cut on a post-blocked spindle.

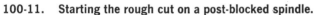

100-13. Post-block rough turned. The remainder of the spindle can now be cut.

256

Unit 101 Setting Up for Faceplate Turning

Faceplate turning is accomplished with the use of either 3- or 6-inch-diameter or screw-center faceplates. These are screwed to the headstock spindle. Wood projects which are most often turned on the faceplate base are bowls, circular trays, and bases for lamps. The several common methods of fastening wood stock to faceplates are described.

Preparing Stock for the Faceplate

1. Select the stock according to the type of wood, thickness, width, and length. Be sure to allow a surplus of approximately ½ inch in both width and length and ⅛ inch in thickness.
2. Rough-cut this piece. See Fig. 101-1.
3. Plane one face smooth.
4. Draw diagonals on the block to locate the center (Fig. 101-1).
5. Lay out a circle to represent the diameter of the bowl or other faceplate turning. Use a compass or dividers. The center is the point where the diagonals described in step 4 cross. See Fig. 101-1.
6. Cut out the turning disk on the jig or band saw. See Fig. 101-4.
7. Select a suitable size of faceplate to fit the wood block.

Fastening Stock or a Turning Disk to the Faceplate

1. Fasten the faceplate with screws to the *smooth face* of the wood block which is to be turned (Figs. 101-2 and 101-3). Figure 101-2 pictures a direct fastening that can be used where the inside of the turning is not to be cut out. Figure 101-3 illustrates the use of a backing block for internal cutting. Be sure the screws *do not go through* the block.
2. Figure 101-4 shows another method of fastening a faceplate to the block of wood. Glue a ¾-inch-thick piece of scrap wood (a backing block) to heavy wrapping paper. The faceplate is screwed to the backing block. Then, glue the paper to the stock to be turned, as shown. When turning is completed, the project can be pried away from the scrap wood easily, since only paper is between the two pieces.
3. Figure 101-5 illustrates how to fasten a screw-center faceplate to a small-diameter (less than 3 inches) turning block.

Mounting Stock

Mount (fasten) the faceplate and the wood-block assembly on the live-center spindle of the lathe head.

101-1. Stock marked for faceplate turning.

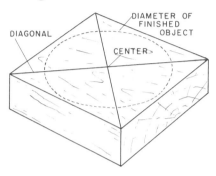

101-2. Direct fastening on a faceplate.

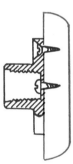

101-3. Using a backing block for fastening stock to a faceplate.

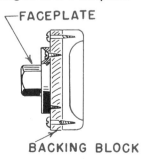

FACEPLATE

BACKING BLOCK

101-4. Turning stock which is glued to a backing block of a faceplate.

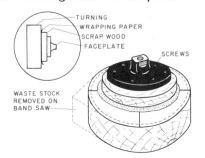

TURNING
WRAPPING PAPER
SCRAP WOOD
FACEPLATE
SCREWS
WASTE STOCK
REMOVED ON
BAND SAW

101-5. Fastening a screw-center faceplate to a small-diameter turning.

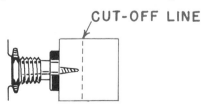

CUT-OFF LINE

Unit 102 Faceplate Turning

Most of the cutting in faceplate work is done with a scraping action. Rough forming (cutting), using a gouge, is similar to that used for spindle cutting. Figure 102-1 shows the correct cutting tools (chisels) to use to make different cuts. Always use the largest faceplate which can be fastened to the block being turned. The processes explained and illustrated in this unit are basic. They can be combined to make intricate faceplate turnings.

Usually, the first cutting shapes the mounted disk (block) of wood to the approximate final diameter. This reduces, and practically eliminates, noticeable vibration.

Turning a Bowl or Tray

1. Fasten the faceplate and the wood-block assembly on the spindle of the lathe head.

2. Adjust the tool rest parallel with the ways of the lathe bed. Set it ¼ inch from the outer edge and down ⅛ inch from the center. See Fig. 102-2.

3. Turn the work *by hand* to see that the wood-block assembly does not hit the tool rest.

4. Turn the speed control to its low speed. Smooth (shape) the edge with either a gouge (Fig. 102-2), a round-nose chisel (Fig. 102-3), a spear-point chisel (Fig. 102-4), or a parting tool (Fig. 102-5). Note that a right-angle tool rest is used in two of the illustrations.

5. Next, turn off the motor. Adjust the tool rest parallel with the piece being worked.

6. Turn on the motor to a faster speed than the speed you used for rough shaping.

7. Smooth the wood face with a gouge (Fig. 102-6), a roundnose turning tool, or a squarenose chisel (Fig. 102-7).

8. Finish the turning (cutting) according to the design or drawing (Figs. 102-8 and 102-9). Use appropriate turning chisels for each type of cut. See Fig. 102-1.

Those turnings which are too large to be cut between the spindle and the lathe bed can be fastened on the *outboard end* of the spindle, as shown in Fig. 102-10. However, in this case a floor stand will be needed to hold the tool rest.

9. Sand the completed faceplate turning. See steps 1 through 6 under "Sanding" in Unit 100, "Spindle Turning."

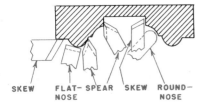

102-1. The use of chisels for faceplate turning.

SKEW FLAT-NOSE SPEAR SKEW ROUND-NOSE

102-2. Shaping the edge with a gouge.

102-3. Shaping the edge with a squarenose chisel.

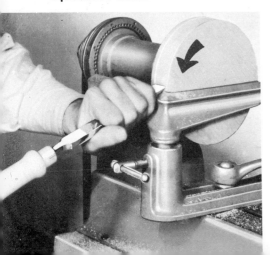

102-4. Shaping the edge with a spear-point chisel.

102-5. Truing the edge with a parting tool.

102-6. Smoothing the face with a gouge.

Cutting a Deep Bowl

Deep bowls and turned jewel boxes (Figs. 102-11 and 102-12) can best be made by using the drill press to bore a hole to the required depth. Turning chisels can then be used off this deep hole to widen the opening. Figures 102-13, 102-14, and 102-15 show the three steps in doing this. Note the position of the tool rest for holding the chisel.

Figure 102-16 shows how to complete cutting the lid of the jewel box.

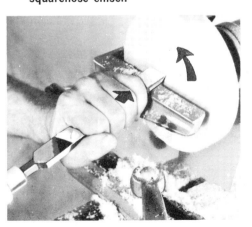

102-7. Smoothing the face with a squarenose chisel.

102-8. Cutting the design into the wood block with the roundnose chisel.

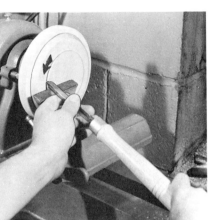

102-9. Shaping the surface design with a parting tool.

102-10. Large faceplate work turned on the outboard end of the spindle.

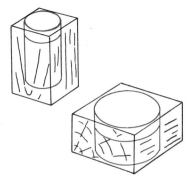

102-11. Novelty turned boxes can be turned with the grain of the block either vertical or horizontal.

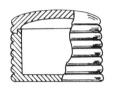

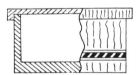

102-12. Design suggestions for turned jewel boxes.

102-13. Cutting the inside for depth, using the skew chisel.

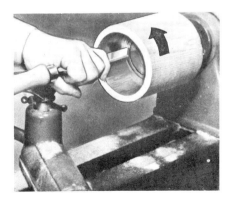

259

102-14.   Smoothing the inside bottom by scraping.

102-15.   Measuring for depth.

102-16.   Final cutting on the lid of a jewel box.

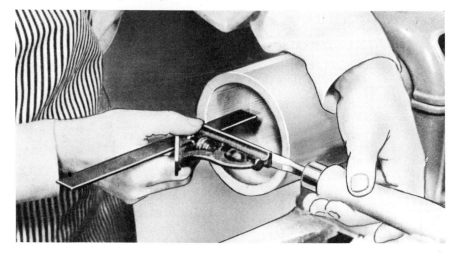

Unit 103   Finishing Lathe Turnings

When the entire project is made on the lathe, it can be finished satisfactorily before it is taken off. One of the best finishes put on in this manner is called **French polish.** The ingredients of French polish are pure white shellac, boiled linseed oil, and denatured alcohol. They are not mixed together; they should be kept in three separate bottles. A soft rag is used to apply the finish.

Applying a French Finish

1. Place the cloth pad over the mouth of the shellac bottle, and tip the bottle until the rag is almost saturated with shellac.

2. Add some denatured alcohol to the pad. Add about half as much alcohol as you did shellac.

3. Then add two or three drops of boiled linseed oil to the pad.

4. Run the lathe at low speed. Hold the pad to the spindle or faceplate turning (Fig. 103-1). Hold it lightly at first, and then increase the pressure until the cloth is almost dry. Move it back and forth along the work while it is turning (revolving).

5. Repeat this process until the surface of the piece is evenly coated.

6. Allow the first coat to dry and harden 24 to 48 hours, and then apply a second one. On successive coats, increase the proportion of shellac, using just sufficient alcohol and oil to prevent rings from forming on the piece. It requires some experience to obtain a smooth, even coating, but the final result will be a smooth, lustrous sheen of pleasing quality.

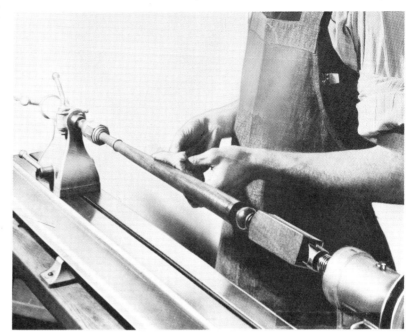

103-1.   Applying a French finish.

DISCUSSION TOPICS

1. What two terms are often applied to the wood-cutting lathe?
2. On what two factors does the size of a wood lathe depend?
3. Name three methods of controlling the speed of a wood lathe.
4. What is the approximate speed range of a wood lathe?
5. List and describe the names and functions of five lathe parts.
6. List at least 10 safety precautions for wood turning.
7. Name and describe five basic turning chisels. Where can each be used to best advantage?
8. Why is oil used on the dead center?
9. What are the two general types of turnings which can be made on the wood lathe?
10. How should a faceplate block be prepared for turning?
11. List three different jobs which can be done on the wood lathe which have not been outlined in this lathe section.
12. What is a general rule regarding speed in wood turning?
13. List four practice spindle cuts, and explain where each might be used.
14. What is meant by **post-block turning?**
15. List two methods of marking dimensions on a spindle turning.
16. What is the name of a finish which can be applied on the turning before it is taken from the lathe? What are the ingredients of this finish?
17. Are cutting or scraping tools preferred on faceplate turning? Why?
18. Why is it advisable to turn the outside or edge first during faceplate turning?
19. Visit a mill and sash company, furniture manufacturer, or other wood-products plant in your area. Report on their lathes. Describe the products which they make on them.

SECTION 17

SHAPING ON THE WOOD SHAPER

Unit 104 General Information About the Shaper

The shaper (Fig. 104-1) is used in woodworking for grooving and shaping on straight or curved edges, for making molding and paneling, and for making almost limitless combinations of decorative cuts. Shaping is done with guides, collars, and patterns, and with the aid of forms, jigs, and fixtures.

Sizes and Types

The size of a shaper is measured by the diameter of the spindle and the size of the table. Most machines used in school industrial laboratories are equipped with $\frac{5}{16}$- to $\frac{3}{4}$-inch spin-

dles. The spindles are usually interchangeable. See Unit 105, "Shaper Cutters, Collars, and Spindles."

The vertical spindle (Fig. 104-2) rotates at a speed of from 7,000 to 10,000 rpm. This makes it important that the shaper be used with every safety precaution observed.

Many shapers have reversible motors to provide rotation in two directions. This permits additional combinations of shapes from the cutters because they must be turned over. The reversing mechanism is usually controlled by a reversing switch.

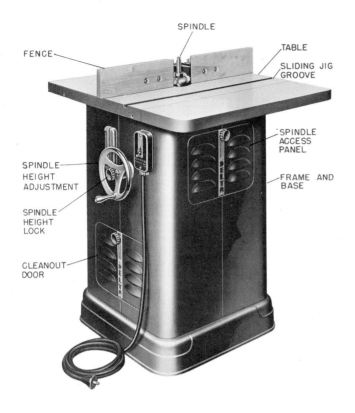

104-1. A heavy-duty woodworking shaper.

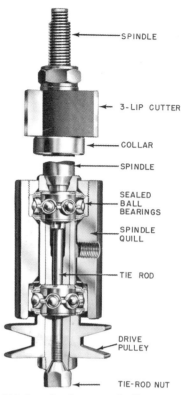

104-2. A shaper spindle assembly.

Parts and Uses

■ **Table.** The shaper table supports the guide or fence and the stock to be shaped.

■ **Frame and base.** These parts enclose the motor and shaping mechanism and hold up the table.

■ **Spindle.** The shaper spindle is the round vertical drive shaft. The cutter head, or cutters, are attached to the spindle.

■ **Spindle height adjustment wheel.** This controls the spindle to which the cutters are fastened.

■ **Fence.** The fence or guide is adjustable. It is located on top of the table; it is used for guiding straight stock.

Unit 105 Shaper Cutters, Collars, and Spindles

There is a wide variety of cutter combinations available. Together, they can do almost any type of shaping. The hollow spindle allows the use of interchangeable spindle heads, which can accommodate many sizes and types of solid-lip cutters, three-knife cutter heads, and open cutter knives in slotted collars. The variety of cutters makes this a versatile machine.

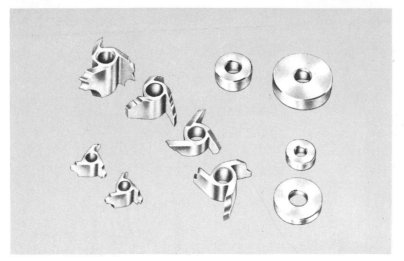

105-1. Solid three-lip cutters, and various sizes of rub collars.

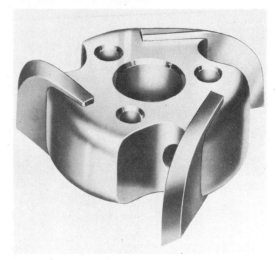

105-3. A three-knife safety cutter head.

Cutters and Collars

Solid three-lip cutters, with ⁵⁄₁₆- or ½-inch holes, are available in a wide selection of shapes. The several types are made from a special alloy steel which has been hardened and tempered in oil. They offer almost unlimited possibilities for making molding designs (Fig. 105-1 and 105-2). These are solid, one-piece cutter knives which can be used singly or together to make intricate molding patterns in one pass through the shaper. Figure 105-2 shows the profiles of many standard solid, three-lip cutters.

Another type of cutter head is the three-knife safety assembly (Fig. 105-3). It is made of alloy steel. It fits a ½- or a ¾-inch spindle. There are interchangeable three-knife sets for use on this head (Fig. 105-4). The knives can be removed and installed with a special wrench.

105-2. Profiles of standard solid three-lip cutters.

105-4. An assortment of three-knife safety cutters.

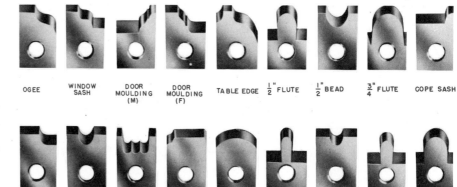

OGEE · WINDOW SASH · DOOR MOULDING (M) · DOOR MOULDING (F) · TABLE EDGE · ½" FLUTE · ½" BEAD · ¾" FLUTE · COPE SASH

BEAD SASH · ⅜" BEAD · BEADED SCREEN · BED MOULD CUTTER · PILASTER FLUTE · ⁵⁄₁₆" FLUTE · ⁵⁄₁₆" BEAD · ⅜" FLUTE · ⅝" FLUTE

⅝" BEAD · ¾" BEAD · ¼" TONGUE · ¼" GROOVE · COVE & BEAD MOULDING · OVAL SASH · OVAL COPE · DOOR LIP

Open knives which fit slotted collars are available for the craftsman who desires to make molding of his own design. The edges of the knives have been ground (beveled) at a 30-degree angle. This has been done so that they will clamp safely between slotted collars (Fig. 105-5). These knives are also available as blanks in matched pairs. The cutting edge of a blank must be ground.

On the right in Fig. 105-1 are various sizes of collars which can be used for spacing or for rub collars when shaping curved pieces. These sometimes vary in thickness and come in an assortment of diameters. Figure 105-6

shows another type of rub collar; this type has different diameters which nest together.

Spindles

Most shapers have several easily interchanged spindles (Fig. 105-7). They permit the use of a rather complete range of cutters. Included, usually, are the $\frac{5}{16}$-inch spindle for small cutters, with $\frac{5}{16}$-inch holes; the $\frac{1}{2}$- and $\frac{3}{4}$-inch spindles for regular cutters, with $\frac{1}{2}$- and $\frac{3}{4}$-inch holes; and the $\frac{1}{2}$-inch stub spindle for cope cutters which fasten on the top of the spindle, as shown in Fig. 105-8.

105-7. Interchangeable spindles.

105-8. A cope cutter.

105-5. Slotted collars and bevel-edge knives.

105-6. A set of nested rub collars.

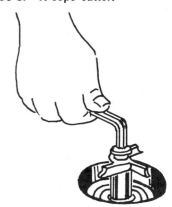

Unit 106 Operating Adjustments

The shaper, like all other machine tools, requires certain adjustments to stay efficient, reliable, versatile, and in alignment. This is a machine on which a number of interesting activities can be performed if certain adjustments are made. The operator should always

be careful to study the manufacturer's data sheet and operating manual before attempting to make any of the various adjustments on the shaper. Although these adjustments are similar on most shapers, the technique for making them will be different.

Interchange of Spindles

Many shapers have hollow vertical shafts which allow interchange of spindles. See Fig. 105-7. The several types of spindles, and their specific purposes, were explained in the previous unit. Interchange permits use of a wider variety of shaper cutters.

Each spindle is fitted with a tie rod (Fig. 106-1) that is threaded at both ends. One end is fitted to the spindle; the opposite end is capped with a tapered nut after it passes through the hollow main spindle. The shank of each spindle is fitted with a keyway which prevents the auxiliary spindle from slipping or turning on the hollow main spindle. When the spindle is in place, it can be fitted with various collars and cutters.

Figure 106-1 shows the mechanism and parts of a heavy-duty shaper. This indicates the location of the spindle assembly. Figure 104-2 shows a detail of the shaper spindle and assembly. On lighter shapers, this assembly is slightly different; however, the same principles of operation apply. Figure 106-2 illustrates a simple method of tapping and loosening the spindle on a light-duty shaper. See also Fig. 105-7. The shaper manual will give detailed instructions on loosening any specific spindle. Figure 106-1 also shows the spindle height-control hand wheel.

Assembling Solid Three-lip and Three-knife Safety Cutters

The several types of cutters and cutter blades discussed in the previous unit require different methods of assembly. Figure 106-3 shows how to mount a solid three-lip cutter. See also Fig. 105-1. The same method is used in mounting the three-knife safety cutter head on the spindle. See Fig. 105-3.

The remainder of the spindle, either above or below the cutter, is filled in with spare collars before the nut is fastened to the top. Collars should be of smaller diameter than the cutting edges of the cutter if a fence is to be used.

106-1.   The mechanism and parts of a heavy-duty shaper.

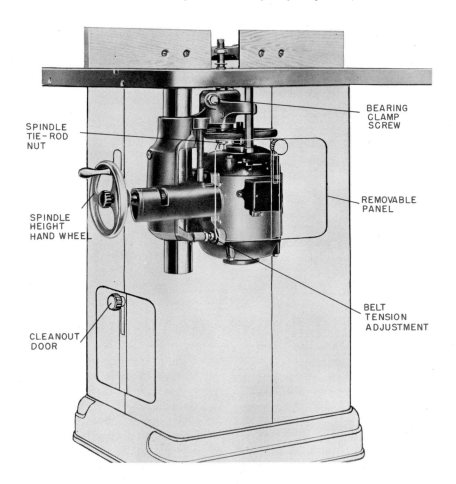

SPINDLE TIE–ROD NUT

SPINDLE HEIGHT HAND WHEEL

CLEANOUT DOOR

BEARING CLAMP SCREW

REMOVABLE PANEL

BELT TENSION ADJUSTMENT

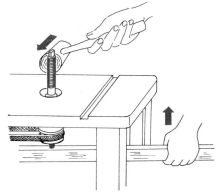

106-2.   Tapping a spindle loose on a typical light-duty shaper.

106-3.   A method of mounting a solid three-lip cutter.

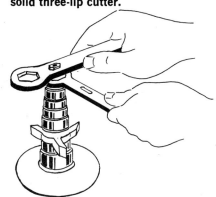

106-4. Knife cutter blades assembled between slotted collar grooves.

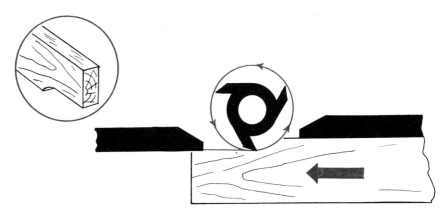

106-7. A top view of the fence-guide adjustment to support an unusual cut.

If you are using one of the collars as a rub collar, place it either directly above or directly below the cutter, depending on where it makes contact with the wood edge to be shaped. There the diameter should be large enough to serve as a fence. This would be used for curved and irregular edges.

106-5. A typical set-up of open-knife cutters fastened between slotted collars.

106-6. A shaper-fence assembly.

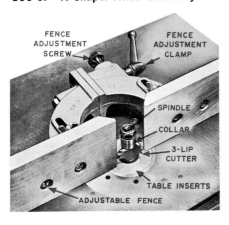

Assembling Open-face Knife Cutters

Open-face knife cutters make possible custom grinding of the cutting edges. Once their edges have been ground and honed, they are fastened between slotted collars. This assembly can be put directly on the shaper with the spindle in place if the spindle can be locked. If not, it is removed and held securely in a vise.

The ground knife cutters should be fastened firmly between the slotted grooves of the collars, as shown in Fig. 106-4. Figure 106-5 gives a typical set-up of open-knife cutters fixed between slotted collars. See also Fig. 105-5.

Fastening the Fence Guide

The fence guide is secured to the table with either stud bolts or a fence-clamp stud (Fig. 106-6). Figure 105-7 shows two fence-clamp studs fastened in place without the fence.

The fence is so constructed that either half can be adjusted. For most work, the halves are in line. The wood faces are usually adjustable, in or out, to accommodate various cutter sizes. The opening should never be any larger than needed to clear the cutter.

Figure 106-7 shows a situation in which the fence guide should not be in line. Here the rear (left half) must be adjusted forward to form a support.

The process shown would involve cutting away the original edge.

Adjusting Safety Clamps

Most shapers are equipped with hold-down devices (spring-type clamps) which provide safety as well as tension against the piece being shaped (Fig. 106-8). Sometimes the work does not permit using either or both. The clamps are regulated with thumbscrews.

When the rub collar serves as a fence guide during the shaping of irregular edges, use a circular fiber ring guard for safety. See Fig. 109-7.

106-8. A spring-type hold-down safety clamp.

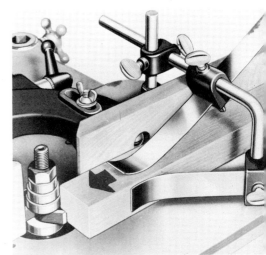

Unit 107 Safety for the Shaper

■ **Permission.** Always secure permission before using the shaper.

■ **Clothing.** Avoid wearing loose clothing. Button or roll up your sleeves. Tuck in your necktie.

■ **Jewelry.** Remove your ring, if you wear one. It could catch on something and cause serious injury to your hand.

■ **Safety goggles.** Always wear safety goggles or a face shield when operating the shaper.

■ **Adjustments.** Make all adjustments with the *power shut off*. Check that all adjustments are tight at all times.

■ **Guards.** Keep the safety guard and hold-down devices in place at all times when it is possible to do so.

■ **Cutters.** Make sure that the cutters are sharp. See that the cutter knives or the cutter are *fastened securely* before you use the shaper.

■ **Cutter knives.** When using separate cutter knives, check to see that both pieces of wood are the same width.

■ **Maintenance tools.** Remove all wrenches and special tools used in setting up the shaper before you turn on the power.

■ **Spindle.** After the cutter head has been securely fastened to the spindle, see that the spindle turns freely *before* turning on the power.

■ **Cutter position.** Arrange the cutter head on the spindle so that the unused portion of the cutters or knives are *below* the table. This is usually possible if the machine is equipped with a reversing switch.

■ **Direction of rotation.** If the shaper has a reversing switch, make certain that the direction of feed will *oppose* the direction of rotation. Always feed *into* the cutting edge.

■ **Stance.** Maintain a well-balanced position on both feet when operating the shaper.

■ **Illumination.** Direct plenty of shadowfree light on the work.

■ **Handling the work.** Hold the board firmly against the fence and the table for straight work. Hold it firmly against the rub collar on the spindle for irregular pieces. Always feed the stock *slowly* into the cutter at an even pressure and speed.

■ **Starting pin.** Make certain that the starting pin is securely in place on the table when shaping against the rub collar.

■ **Starting cut.** When using the rub collar for a guide, start the cut *away* from any corner. This is especially true when shaping around the entire edge of a board.

■ **Moldings.** Plan your work carefully to use the correct sequence (order) of cutter forms to produce the molding pattern desired.

■ **Shaping ends.** Boards *less* than 10 inches wide should not be shaped on the end unless the shaper has a sliding jig to clamp on the board and hold it in place.

■ **Stopping.** Shut off the power. Do not leave the shaper until the motor has come to a *complete* stop.

Unit 108 Shaping Straight Edges

Shaping straight edges will require alignment of the adjustable fence. Using a fence is the fastest, most satisfactory, and perhaps the safest method of shaping. There are only two adjustments: the first aligns the fence (see Figs. 108-1 and 108-2); the second adjusts the height of the cutter (see Figs. 108-3 and 108-4). This type of shaping might cut rabbets and grooves as well as shape edges. The guard and holddown clamps do not appear in many of

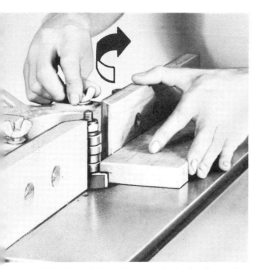

108-1. Adjusting and fastening the fence guide.

the illustrations in this unit so that cutting details can be shown more clearly.

Procedure

1. Select the cutter, cutter head, or knife assembly. Fasten it securely on the spindle. See Unit 106.

2. Sketch the planned cut on the end or the edge of the wood.

3. Adjust the fence guide, and fasten it securely (Fig. 108-1). Make sure the two parts of the fence are in alignment. Check this with a framing square (Fig. 108-2).

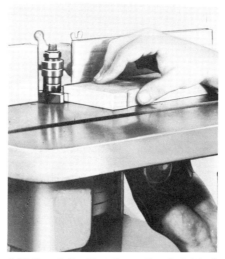

108-3. Adjusting the cutter height of a light-duty shaper.

4. Adjust the cutting height of the spindle for the planned cut (Figs. 108-3 and 108-4).

5. Place hold-down clamps for safety and tension. Adjust these with the work on the table. See Fig. 106-8.

6. Turn on the power. Allow the shaper to come to full speed.

7. Make a trial run on a piece of scrap wood. Hold it firmly in position against the fence. Feed it into the cutter head from *right to left* (Fig. 108-5).

Figure 108-6 shows the top part of the edge being shaped. Occasionally

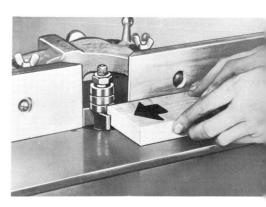

108-5. Starting the shaping cut.

the shaper cuts may be such that the motor should be reversed through the switch, the cutter head inverted (turned upside down), and the piece fed from *left to right*. Figure 108-7 illustrates the difference in making cuts from right to left and left to right. It also shows the direction of the cutter blade.

8. Shape the edge if the trial cut is accurate.

9. When shaping all four straight edges on a board, follow the sequence of cuts shown in Fig. 108-8.

10. Shaping the edge of a wood face is very similar to that of shaping a

108-2. Aligning the two parts of the fence with a framing square.

108-4. Detail of shaping a straight-edge against a fence guide.

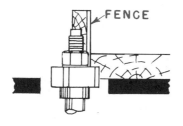

108-6. Shaping the top part of an edge.

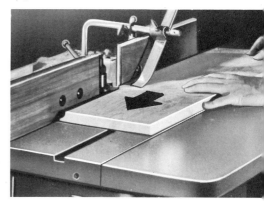

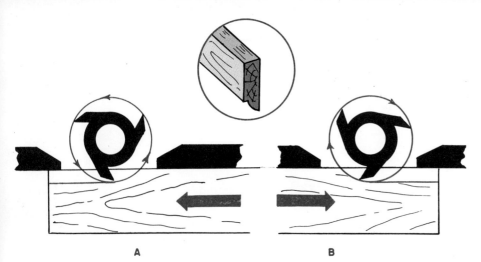

108-10.   Making the first molding cut.

108-7.   Top view showing (A) the work fed conventionally from right to left and (B) the work fed from left to right. The insert shows the shaped edge.

straight edge. Figure 108-9 illustrates the similarity. It is a matter of how the board is placed against the fence and table.

11. Figures 108-10 and 108-11 show how moldings can be cut by planning the sequence from available shaper forms (patterns).

12. Figure 108-12 shows a more complicated molding; this more complicated molding involves several planned passes.

13. Figure 108-13 illustrates how two cutters can be used at the same time in order to make a molding in one pass.

108-11.   Making second molding cut.

108-8.   Steps in shaping all four straight edges of a board.

108-9.   The similarity of face and straight-edge shaping: (A) the face of the board and (B) the edge.

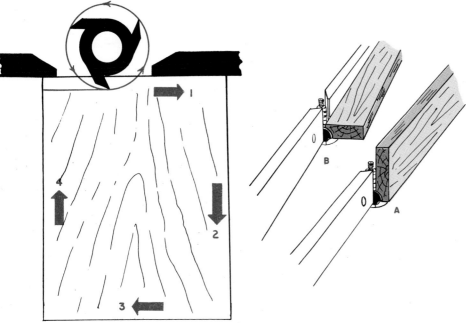

108-12.   The final molding cut.

108-13.   Two cutters used for molding.

Unit 109 Shaping Irregular and Circular Edges

Most irregular shaping requires the use of the rub collar to serve as the guide in place of the straight fence. The rub collar can be used above, below, or between two cutters, as illustrated in Figs. 109-1, 109-2, and 109-3. Work which cannot be shaped against a fence guide is usually shaped against a rub collar. The rim of the collar rides against the piece and limits the depth of the cut. This is one of the most useful techniques in shaping. The only drawback is that the revolving rub collar may score (burn) the wood. To avoid this requires some skill in using the correct amount of pressure in handling an irregular piece.

Circular pieces are shaped much as irregular ones are. However, a wooden jig such as shown in Fig. 109-10 is a very useful guide.

The guard and hold-down clamp do not appear in many illustrations in this unit so that setting and cutting details can be more clearly shown.

Shaping Irregular Edges

1. Select the cutter, or knife blade assembly, and also a rub collar of the correct diameter. Fasten these securely on the spindle. See Unit 106, "Operating Adjustments." In selecting the collar size, remember that the rub collar will serve as a depth gauge for the cut. See Figs. 109-1, 109-2, and 109-3.

2. Sketch the planned cut on the end of the board, if possible.

3. Adjust the cutting height of the spindle so that the shaper cut or cuts will be made where they were planned. Adjust the circular fiber ring guard so that it barely clears the work. See Fig. 109-7. This may not be on all shapers, but it is a good safety precaution.

4. Fasten the starting pin securely in the table. See Fig. 109-4.

5. Turn on the power, and allow the shaper to come to full speed.

6. Make a trial cut on a scrap piece of wood. Place the piece to be shaped firmly in position against the starting pin (Fig. 109-4). Gradually, but firmly, push the wood into the revolving cutter head so that it makes contact with the rub collar (Figs. 109-5, 109-6, and 109-7).

After making full contact with the starting pin and the rub collar, gradually move the board so that you will move away from (not depend upon) the starting pin (Fig. 109-8).

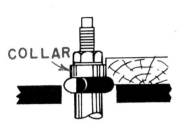

109-1. Detail showing a rub collar above the cutter. This shapes the lower side of the edge.

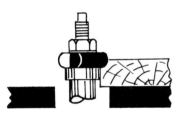

109-2. Detail showing the rub collar below the cutter. This shapes the top side of the edge.

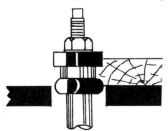

109-3. Detail showing the rub collar between two cutters. This shapes both top and bottom sides with one pass.

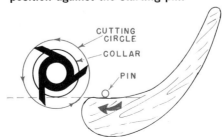

109-4. Detail of an irregular piece in position against the starting pin.

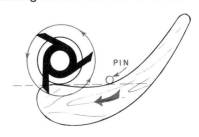

109-5. Detail of an irregular piece making contact with the rub collar.

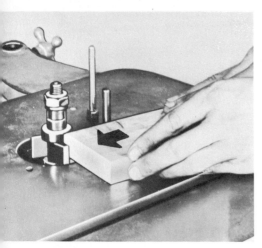

109-6. A board placed against the starting pin and the rub collar. The guard is removed for clarity.

109-7. Shaping an irregular edge. Note the circular fiber ring guard for safety purposes.

7. Shape the entire edge if the trial cut is accurate.

8. When shaping the entire edge of an irregular piece, start the cut as illustrated in Fig. 109-9.

9. Continue to cut carefully and accurately until the desired shaping has been completed.

Shaping Circular Pieces

An excellent guide, which can be used for a wide variety of circle sizes, is shown in Fig. 109-10. It is a flat piece of wood which is as thick as, or thicker than, the piece being shaped. It has a 90-degree V opening cut in the center. The size of the opening should conform, generally, to the size of the circular piece. This guide (wooden jig) can be set for use with pieces of many different diameters. It must, however, provide two contact points for the circular work.

109-8. Detail of a piece being worked (moved) into cutting position and away from the starting pin.

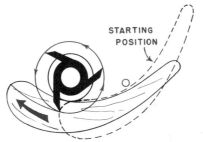

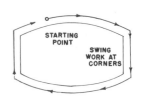

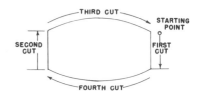

109-9. Detail of continuous shaping around an irregular edge.

109-10. Shaping a circular piece against a shop-made guide.

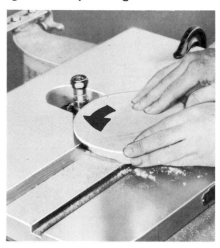

Unit 110 Shaping with an Outline Pattern

Shaping that is guided by an outline pattern (template) is similar to irregular-edge shaping against a rub collar. In this method, however, the *pattern rides against* the collar; the work does not. This eliminates burning, or scoring, of the edges of the piece by friction with the rub collar. The pattern method ensures accuracy for duplicate pieces.

Figure 110-1 shows a detail of shaping when the pattern is fastened to the

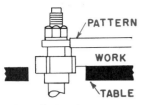

110-1. Detail showing a pattern fastened to the top of the work.

top of the work. Note that the rub collar is fixed on the shaper spindle, and the pattern rubs against it. In Fig. 110-2 the pattern is shown fastened *underneath* the work being shaped, and the rub collar is placed underneath the shaper cutter.

Making the Pattern

The pattern is usually made of ¾- to ⅞-inch thick hardwood. It can be a solid piece, or it can be built up as shown in Fig. 110-6. The pattern form must be the exact outline of the work which is to be shaped or molded. The edges must be dressed smooth and oiled or waxed so that the piece will move smoothly and easily against the rub collar without edge burning.

The pattern is fastened with anchor points to the board to be shaped. The simplest of these is a small brad which

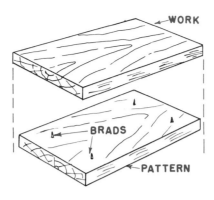

110-3. Relationship of the pattern to the piece being shaped.

will go through the pattern and extend ⅛ to ¼ inch into the bottom side of the piece to be shaped. See Figs. 110-2 and 110-3. The guard and the hold-down clamp do not appear in many illustrations so that setting and cutting details can be shown more clearly.

Shaping with an Outline Pattern

1. Mark, cut, and dress (smooth) the pattern from hardwood. Maple and birch are good woods for this purpose.

2. Drive at least four brads (anchor points) through the bottom side of the

110-4. **Shaping an edge with a pattern (template). Note that only a portion of the edge (thickness) is being cut. The guard is removed to show detail.**

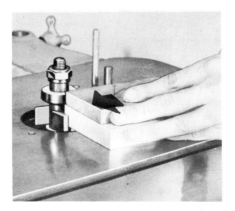

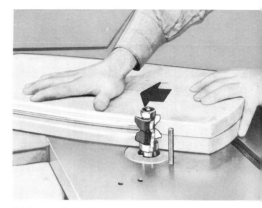

110-5. Shaping an edge with a pattern. Note that the entire thickness of the edge is being cut. The guard is removed to show detail.

pattern. It will probably be necessary to drill holes slightly smaller than the brads through the pattern first. Brads have a tendency to bend in hardwood. They should extend above the pattern about ⅛ to ¼ inch. See Fig. 110-2.

3. Mark, cut, and dress the edges of the board to be shaped. If only a portion of the edge is to be shaped, this piece should be exactly the size of the pattern. See Fig. 110-1.

4. If the entire edge of the board is to be shaped, it should be roughly sawed about 1/16 to ⅛ inch oversize. See Fig. 110-2.

110-6. Shaping an edge of an end table top, following a built-up outline template.

110-2. Detail showing a pattern fastened underneath the work. Note the brad anchor point.

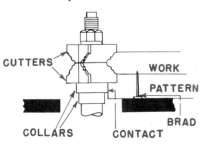

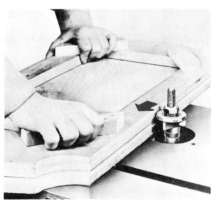

5. Anchor (fasten) the pattern to the board to be shaped. Figure 110-3 shows the relationship of this assembly.

6. Follow steps 1 through 5 in Unit 109, "Shaping Irregular and Circular Edges." Fasten the pattern either below or above the stock, depending upon the type of edge cut planned. See Figs. 110-1 and 110-2.

7. Place the pattern and the piece to be shaped firmly in position against the starting pin. Firmly push the assembly into the revolving cutter head until it makes contact with the rub collar (Fig. 110-4). After making full contact with the starting pin and the rub collar, gradually move the assembly away from the starting pin (Fig. 110-5). Figure 110-6 shows a built-up outline pattern (template) for shaping the edge of an end table top.

8. Continue the cut until the shaping is completed.

Unit 111 Shaping with Jigs and Special Forms

There are some special cuts and grooves which can be successfully made on the shaper. They involve the use of jigs and special types of forms. Some of these can be custom made for the particular job; others are standard accessories which are available from shaper manufacturers. The variety of such cuts and grooves is dependent entirely upon the ingenuity of the operator, the cutters available, and the shape of the specially built forms.

In general, a jig or a form is any device upon which the work is securely fastened by means of clamps, screws, or wedges. Special forms must be built to support irregular pieces, such as legs which require fluting (grooving).

Procedures for making many types of cuts will not be outlined. Each requires an order of procedure developed by the operator for that specific job. A few of the more common cuts, however, are described and illustrated. The guard and the hold-down clamp do not appear in many illustrations in this unit in order to show setting and cutting details.

Shaping with Jigs

Most manufacturers of wood shaper equipment make mechanical clamps available which can be used as jigs. These hold the work while the special cuts are made. Figure 111-1 shows a

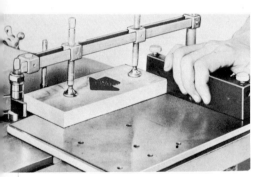

111-1. Shaping with a sliding jig. The front supporting arm is removed to show the cut more clearly.

111-2. Detail of shaping with a sliding jig.

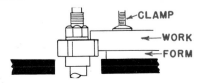

111-3. Holding stock with a jig while cutting a 45-degree end chamfer.

111-4. Cutting a tenon with a sliding tenoning jig.

sliding jig which holds the piece while it is advanced to the cutter head. Figure 111-2 gives the detail drawing to demonstrate this process.

The **sliding jig** is an excellent accessory with which to hold narrow stock while it is being shaped on the end. Figure 111-3 illustrates how to cut a 45-degree chamfer on the end of a square piece.

A **sliding tenoning jig** can be used to good advantage for many shaper operations. Figure 111-4 shows the use of one for cutting the tenon on the end of a formed (bent) laminated leg. This cut is made with one pass by using two cutters on the spindle head. This jig can also be used for holding drawer sides for grooving.

Shaping with Specially Built Forms

Fluting (grooving) a round table leg requires a specially built jig. Figure 111-5 pictures the **fluting jig** (special form) being used to cut flutes in a table leg. Note the stop assembly, which is clamped to the shaper table. This controls the beginning and the end of the cutting operation so that all grooves will be the same length.

The circular piece at the right of the jig is a disk which has equally spaced holes drilled in it. These mark the location for each flute. Figure 111-6 shows a detail of the fluting process.

111-5. A special fluting (grooving) jig for making flutes in a table leg.

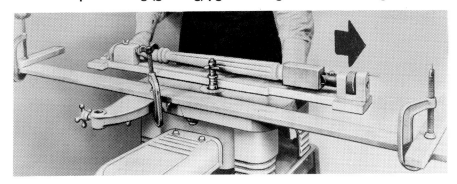

111-6. Detail of the fluting process.

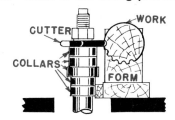

DISCUSSION TOPICS

1. List four methods or types of shaping.
2. How is the size of a shaper determined?
3. What is the approximate speed of a shaper?
4. What is the usual method of reversing the direction of the motor of a shaper?
5. List and describe the names and functions of six essential parts of the shaper.
6. List six important specifications of the shaper in your industrial laboratory or home workshop.
7. Name and describe three types of shaper cutter heads.
8. Describe a jig made for the shaper. How are these jigs used? Describe a tenoning jig.
9. List and describe four essential adjustments which must be made before using a shaper.
10. Name 12 important safety rules to observe when using the shaper.
11. Describe two types of shaping which depend upon the rub collar as a depth guide.
12. What are two advantages in shaping with an outline pattern?
13. What type of wood is most satisfactory for making a shaping pattern? Why?
14. Visit a large lumberyard, sawmill, mill and sash company, furniture manufacturing plant, or other wood-products plant. Make a report on the types of shapers in use. List the purposes for which they are used.

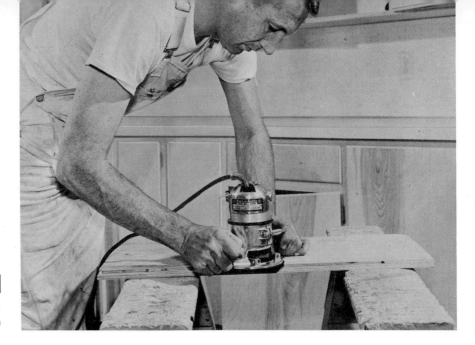

SHAPING AND ROUTING WITH THE PORTABLE ELECTRIC ROUTER

Unit 112 General Information About the Portable Electric Router

The portable electric router (Fig. 112-1) is probably the safest of all portable electric tools. It is a precision-built piece of portable equipment. The electric router cuts to a desired thickness and depth into, and through, wood and many other materials. Accessories make it possible to produce intricate joints, decorative cuts, and inlays. It can also be used to shape edges, cut recesses (gains) for door hinges, and make dovetail joints.

The wide selection of bits and cutters makes the portable electric router an extremely versatile tool. It can be used for freehand cutting by guiding it with the hands alone. It can also be used with various templates.

Sizes and Speeds

The size of the portable electric router is measured by the horsepower (hp) rating of its enclosed motor. This varies from 1/4 to 3 hp. The 3 hp motor is a heavy-duty, industrial type. The speed range is from 16,000 to 27,000 rpm.

Parts and Uses

■ **Motor unit.** The motor is self-contained. Figure 112-2 shows a cutaway view of the many parts, including the motor.

■ **Base.** The base is the platform which rides the surface of the wood and controls the depth of cut.

■ **Hand knobs.** The two knobs or handles are conveniently located for easy grasp and control. Some routers have a handle and a knob, in which case the trigger switch is usually located in the handle. See Fig. 112-2.

■ **Depth adjustment ring.** This is a micrometer depth adjustment control, usually fastened to the base.

112-1. A portable electric router.

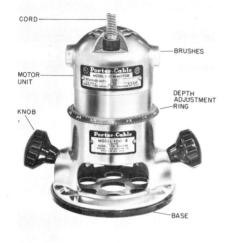

112-2. A cutaway view of a portable electric router.

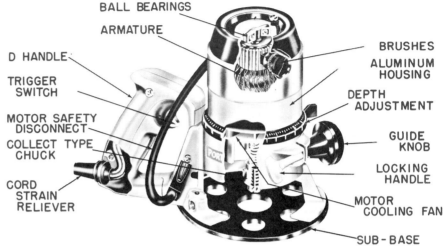

Unit 113 Router Bits and Accessories

There are router bits in sizes and shapes to permit almost any cut desired. Figure 113-1 shows a few of the bit shapes and the cuts they make. The several units in this section discuss and show these and other bits and cutters that are used for specific operations. The numerous accessories make the portable electric router an extremely versatile power tool. They are discussed later in this unit.

Router Bits

Router bits fall into two major classifications: (1) the **one-piece bits,** which

113-1. Some router bits and cuts: (A) rabbet, (B) straight, or groove, (C) cove, (D) ogee, (E) chamfer, and (F) dovetail.

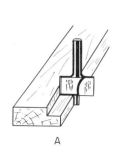
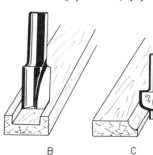
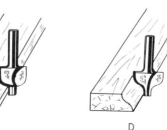

A   B   C   D   E   F

113-2. Router bits with built-in shanks.

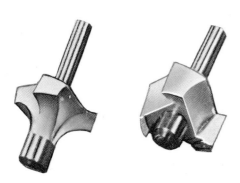

113-3. Screw-type bit with an arbor and a pilot.

113-4. Inserting a bit into the router collet (chuck).

have a shank built into the cutting head (Fig. 113-2) and fit into the collet (chuck) of the router motor; and (2) a **screw-type bit,** with an arbor and a pilot (Fig. 113-3). The pilot screwed into the bottom is used when molding the edge of a board. It controls the horizontal depth of cut by riding along the edge of the piece.

Inserting a Bit into the Router Chuck

1. Select the correct bit for the job. If the bit does not have a shank, add an arbor.

2. Insert the bit (with arbor) all the way into the chuck, and then back it out about $\frac{1}{16}$ inch (Fig. 113-4).

3. Fasten the chuck with the wrenches furnished with the router. Some chucks must be fastened with two wrenches.

4. The depth of cut can be set by measuring with a rule and then adjusting the depth ring (Fig. 113-5).

5. Reverse this procedure when removing the bit or cutter.

Router Accessories

An important router accessory is an **edge,** or **magic guide,** which can be used in cutting an edge, a radius, a groove, or a circle. Figures 116-1 through 116-6 show how it is used.

A highly developed **template** used for making dovetail joints for drawers is shown in Fig. 118-2.

Some router manufacturers make a **shaper stand** that permits the router to be inverted and fastened in the stand, becoming a shaper (Fig. 113-6).

Another important mechanical aid is the **hinge-butt template.** It is used to locate and to serve as a guide in cutting notches (gains) in doors and door frames for butt hinges. See Fig. 119-1.

An electric plane can be made by using the motor unit from some routers with a **plane attachment,** as shown in Fig. 113-7.

113-5. Checking bit depth adjustment.

113-6. Inverted router on a shaper stand, grooving for a drawer bottom.

113-7. A router being converted to make an electric hand plane.

Unit 114 Safety for the Router

■ **Permission.** Always secure permission before using the router.

■ **Jewelry.** Remove your ring if you wear one. It could catch in something and cause injury to your hand.

■ **Eye protection.** Wear goggles or a face shield when using the router.

■ **Hands.** Keep both hands on the handles when you use the portable electric router.

■ **Grounding.** Check to see that the electrical connection is grounded.

■ **Electrical power.** Disconnect the motor unit from the electrical power outlet when you change bits, cutters, or attachments.

■ **Bits and cutters.** Make sure the bits and cutters are sharp. Know the purpose of each one before using it.

■ **Attachments and accessories.** Study the manufacturer's manual for the router. Learn the installation and adjustment procedures before performing any operations requiring their use.

■ **Stance.** Maintain a well-balanced position on both feet when handling the router.

■ **Cutting depth.** Always check for correct depth adjustment before making a cut.

■ **Direction of movement.** Move the router from left to right when you cut straight edges. Move it from right to left when you cut circular or curved edges.

■ **Stopping.** Shut off the power. Do not lay the machine down until the router has come to a complete stop.

Unit 115 Shaping and Routing Edges

One of the most common uses of the router is to cut decorative edges on wood. The wide range of available bits and cutters makes it possible to cut a simple corner round and to make more decorative cove and bead edges. When making cuts on all four edges of a board, make the first cut on the end *across* the grain. If any chipping occurs at the end of a cut, remove it by making the next cut *parallel* to the grain. Tongue-and-groove joints, edge joints, and rabbets can be edge-cut.

Shaping an Edge

1. Decide on the cutter you will use.
2. Fasten the cutter in the chuck, as outlined in the previous unit.
3. Adjust the router for the correct depth of cut. Follow the instructions given in the manufacturer's manual.
4. Make a test cut on a piece of scrap wood.
5. Fasten the board or the project firmly.
6. Place the router base on the board with the cutter or the bit over the edge.
7. Turn on the switch. Push or pull the router against the edge of the board until it hits the bit or the cutter collar.
8. Push or pull the router from left to right (Figs. 115-1 and 115-2).
9. Finish shaping the edge.
10. Turn off the power. Remove the router from the board or project.

Routing an Edge for a Joint

1. Follow steps 1 through 9 above.
2. Figure 115-3 illustrates cutting a rabbet on the edge of a board.

279

115-1. Pushing the router to shape an edge.

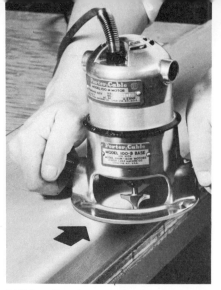

115-2. Routing a **corner-round** with arbor, pilot, and corner-round bit.

115-3. Cutting a rabbet for an edge.

Unit 116 Cutting Grooves and Dadoes with a Guide

The router edge guide is a useful, inexpensive attachment. Modifications of this accessory range from a simple guide to a more elaborate one, called a **magic router guide,** which fits some routers. It is used as an aid in cutting a radius or a circular groove and to cut grooves, veins, and dadoes parallel to edges and ends. Grooves can also be cut in a similar manner for inlaying.

Cutting Grooves, Veins, and Dadoes

1. Decide on the suitable cutter or bit.
2. Fasten the cutter in the chuck.
3. Adjust the router for correct depth of cut.
4. Attach the edge guide; make the necessary adjustments. Study the man-

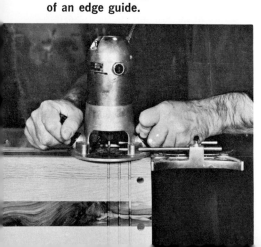

116-1. Cutting grooves with the aid of an edge guide.

116-2. A magic guide in use cutting a groove.

116-3. A router edge guide adapted to cut dadoes.

116-4. A dado joint fitted after having been cut with the router.

116-5. Cutting a curved groove parallel to a curved edge.

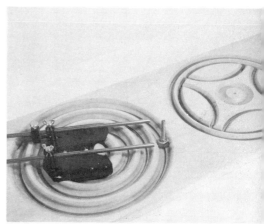

116-6. Circular cuts made with the router and a guide.

ufacturer's manual for specific directions about the router. See Figs. 116-1 and 116-2.

5. Make a trial cut on a piece of scrap wood. Make all of the necessary adjustments.

6. Place the router base on the board. Be very careful; be very sure to see that the cutter or the bit is over the edge.

7. Turn on the switch. Next, begin to move the router slowly and carefully from left to right (Figs. 116-1 and 116-2).

8. Continue making all necessary grooves, veins, and cuts.

9. Turn off the switch. After the router has stopped, you may remove it from the piece of wood.

10. In addition, it is also possible to cut dadoes with the edge guide. However, a slight adaptation is necessary on the guide (See Figs. 116-3 and 116-4).

Cutting Curved and Circular Grooves

1. Follow steps 1 through 9 under "Cutting Grooves, Veins, and Dadoes."

2. Curved cuts can be made parallel to a curved or an irregular edge by using the edge guide (Fig. 116-5).

3. Figure 116-6 shows some circular cuts which were made by using a guide. The router has been removed, leaving only guide and cutter bit.

Unit 117 Freehand Routing

117-1. Freehand-routing a wood carving.

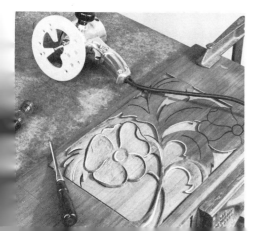

There are a number of routing operations that can be performed by the freehand method. One example is routing (cutting) letters or patterns directly into the surface of a board. Another is cutting out stock from the surface of wood, following a penciled layout.

An example of freehand routing is cutting a groove or dado by simply guiding the router base along a straight piece of wood. On the other hand, one can use a wooden template to cut out the contour of the design and then work the router cutter collar against the template.

Freehand Routing Without a Template

1. Mark or lay out the design to be cut on the surface of the wood.

2. Select a suitable bit.

3. Fasten the bit in the chuck of the router; adjust it for the correct depth.

4. Try out the cut on a piece of scrap wood.

117-2. A freehand-routed name plate.

117-3. Cutting a dado freehand along a straight board, using a template.

117-4. Freehand-routing an irregular pattern, using a wooden template.

5. Turn on the power with the trigger switch. Slowly place the base of the router onto the surface of the wood. Cut out the background as desired (Fig. 117-1).

6. To achieve a carved effect, use chisels and carving tools to shape the parts of the design and to cut accurately and cleanly to the corners.

7. A name plate (Fig. 117-2) can be made in a similar manner.

Freehand Routing with a Template

1. A dado can be routed freehand by guiding the router base along a straight piece of wood which has been clamped on the board (Fig. 117-3).

2. An irregular pattern or design can be cut into a surface with the router by using a precut wooden template as a guide (Fig. 117-4). This could involve cutting a vein (grooved) outline of the design or cutting out (recessing) the entire background to a given depth by using correct bits and cutters.

Unit 118 Making a Dovetail Joint

118-1. Rabbeted (overlapping) dovetail drawer construction.

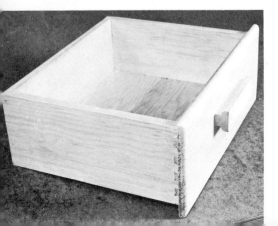

The dovetail joint is one of the most widely used furniture joints. One way to determine quality workmanship in a commercially made piece is to inspect the drawer construction. A dovetail joint (Fig. 118-1) usually indicates well-constructed furniture.

Most router manufacturers make available an inexpensive dovetail template which can be used in conjunction with their tool to make these joints (Fig. 118-2). The one shown will handle stock up to 12 inches wide and from $\frac{5}{16}$ to 1 inch thick. Once set up, this template can be used to cut any number of dovetail joints. A **flush** dovetail joint or a rabbeted (overlapping) one can be made with this template. See

Fig. 118-1. It is always a good idea to practice making a dovetail joint. You may use pieces of scrap wood for this important exercise.

Making a Flush Dovetail Drawer Joint

1. Fasten the broad aluminum base of the template to the workbench or to a piece of plywood. The front overhanging apron of the template base should butt snugly against the front edge of the workbench or a plywood board. Read the instructions which come with the kit on how to assemble the template. Each manufacturer gives slightly different directions.

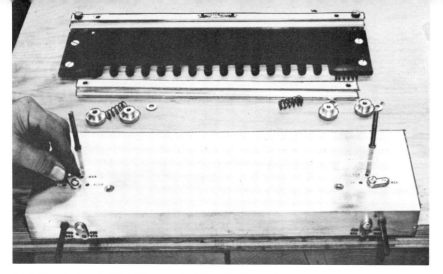

118-2. A dovetail joint template kit, with its parts.

118-3. Clamp front, sides to template.

2. Insert and fasten the proper template guide into the router sub-base.

3. With the motor in the base, fasten the dovetail bit through the template guide and into the router collar. Tighten the collar.

4. Adjust the depth of the bit. The tip should be exactly $1^{9}\!/_{32}$ inch from the bottom of the router base. This depth cuts a ½-inch flush dovetail joint, assuming that the sides of the drawer are ½ inch thick. Different thicknesses require other settings, according to the manufacturer's manual.

5. Fasten the side piece of the drawer vertically against the front apron. The side of the drawer should be temporarily tightened in the template. Butt (press) it firmly against the left stop. About ½ inch of stock should show above the aluminum base.

6. Place the front of the drawer horizontally underneath the plastic "finger" template. Butt it firmly against the left stop and flush against the side of the drawer, which is held by the front clamping bar (Fig. 118-3).

7. Readjust the side of the drawer (the vertical piece). It should now fit snugly against both the left work stop and the plastic template (Fig. 118-4).

8. Plug the cord of the router into the power outlet.

9. As you stand facing the template, place the router firmly on the finger template. The work to be cut is at the left of it. See Fig. 118-5.

10. Turn on the switch. Make the first cut along the entire outside edge of the drawer side, working from *right to left*. Do not rout (cut) into the openings of the finger template (Fig. 118-5). This preliminary cut tends to prevent chipping the edge when the router is moved in and out of the template fingers.

11. Rout between the finger slots. Move the router carefully from *left to right* around the outline of the template (Fig. 118-6). The joint in both the side and the front pieces is now cleanly cut. See Fig. 118-7. It is ready for fitting.

12. Carefully remove the two sections of the drawer, that is, the front and the side sections, from the template. Refer to Fig. 118-7.

13. Fit the front and side drawer pieces together to test snugness (Fig. Fig. 118-8). If the fit is *loose, drop* the router bit approximately ¼₄ inch. On the other hand, if it is *tight, raise* the router bit approximately ¼₄ inch.

14. Reverse the front drawer piece end, and move it to the right-hand side of the template aluminum base. Match the right-side piece of the drawer

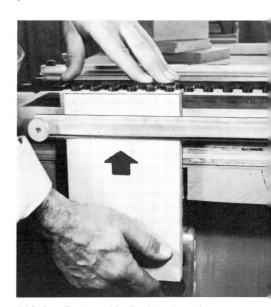

118-4. Fasten side flush to template.

118-5. Cut outside edge from right.

118-6. Cutting between the finger slots from left to right.

118-8. Fitting a dovetail joint for snugness.

against it on the front apron (Fig. 118-9). Proceed to make the dovetail joint for this corner as you did the first one.

15. Make other necessary cuts in the drawer pieces to receive the bottom and the back portions. These will probably be dado cuts.

16. The drawer parts are now ready for assembly.

Making a Dovetail Joint for a Rabbeted Drawer Front

1. A rabbeted, or overlapping, drawer front requires adding ¾ inch to both the length and the width of the drawer front.

2. Cut a ⅜- by ⅜-inch rabbet completely around the inside of the drawer front.

3. Set the stops on the aluminum base and the other parts of the template for making such a joint. Be sure to follow the instructions in the router manual.

4. To cut the overlapping dovetail joint, follow a similar procedure to that for the flush joint. The finished overlapping dovetail joint will look like that in Fig. 118-1.

118-9. The other end of the drawer front and the right drawer side fastened in template, ready for routing.

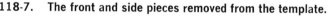

118-7. The front and side pieces removed from the template.

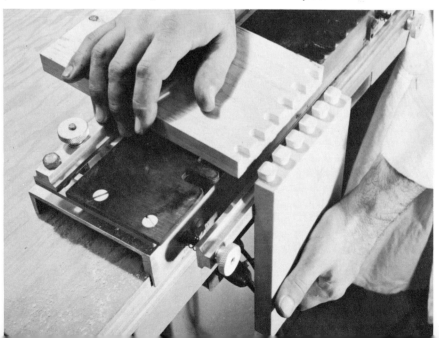

Unit 119 Routing a Hinge Gain with a Template

The hinge-butt template is widely used with a router to cut (rout) hinge gains (recesses) on doors and jambs. The hinge template is like other templates; when properly set, it eliminates guesswork.

Most hinge-butt templates and frame assemblies include three separate hinge-butt sections fastened to a long adjustment rod. This makes it possible to cut out one, two, or three hinge placements alike in several doors or jambs without resetting the template. The illustrations in this unit, however, show the use of only one single hinge-butt template section. The complete template can be adjusted for practically any standard door hinge size, as well as for standard thickness and height.

Routing a Door Edge for Hinges

1. Determine the size of the hinge and the thickness and height of the door. Also find out whether this is to be a right- or a left-hand-opening door.

2. Insert two guide pins in each hinge-butt template section (Fig. 119-1). The pins determine the size of the recess (cut-out area) for the hinge. The holes in the template are marked for size.

3. Select the correct template section for either a right- or a left-hand-opening door.

4. Insert the end-gauge rod through the template clamp of the hinge template. It should touch the guide pin which was inserted in step 2. Tighten it with the wing nut. This automatically provides proper clearance between the top of the door and the jamb.

5. Place this template section on the door edge. Hook the end-gauge plate tightly over the top of the door. Hold the two edge gauges tightly against the door face (Fig. 119-2).

6. Fasten the template to the edge of the door with nails.

7. Locate and fasten the other hinge-butt templates and adjustment rods on the edge of the door in the same way (Fig. 119-3).

119-1. Locating hinge-size guide pins in the template section.

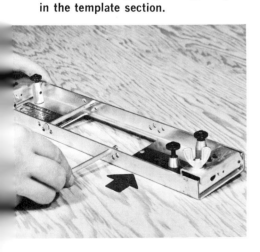

119-2. Locating the top hinge template on the edge of the door.

119-3. Fastening adjustment rod into first template section. Add other section templates and rods as needed.

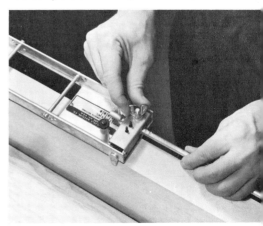

8. Fasten the correct hinge template guide to the base of the router. Install the routing bit in the column. The depth of the bit should be adjusted to cut the thickness of the hinges being used. About ⅛ inch is the thickness of most hinges.

9. Place the router in position on one of the template sections so that the bit is clear of the door (Fig. 119-4). Turn on the motor.

10. Move the router into the door edge, along the right-hand guide pin, about ½ inch. Pull the router back from the door. Take a light cut of about ¼ inch along the edge of the door. Work from right to left until you reach the left-hand guide.

Move the router along the door into the left-hand guide pin until you reach the back of the template. Then move the tool along the back of the template until it rests against the right guide pin. Slide the router over the template to remove all the remaining stock (Fig. 119-5).

11. Repeat this process on the remaining hinge sections.

12. Pull out the nails (Fig. 119-6) which hold the template assembly on the edge of the door. Use a claw hammer. Remove the template assembly.

119-5. A router in position after the hinge butt (gain) has been cut.

119-6. Using a claw hammer to remove the hinge template from the edge of the door.

13. Check the fit of the hinge in the gain (recess) of the door edge (Fig. 119-7). The router bit leaves round corners which fit round-cornered hinges. Square the corners with a chisel if the hinges are square.

Routing a Door Jamb for Hinges

1. Loosen the wing nut that holds the end gauge. Rotate the end gauge until it is parallel with the bottom of the template. Tighten the wing nut.

2. Slide the edge of the template (without the end gauges) over the face of the jamb (frame) until the first or the second row of six jamb-gauge pins is aligned against the edge (Fig. 119-8). The first row is used for 1⅜-inch-thick doors; the second, for 1¾-inch-thick doors.

3. Butt the end gauge against the top of the jamb (Fig. 119-9). Fasten the template with nails. When door stops are already in place, simply fasten the template with the edge against the stop (Fig. 119-10).

4. Rout (cut) the hinge mortises in the jamb as you did when you routed the hinge gains on the door edges.

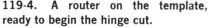

119-4. A router on the template, ready to begin the hinge cut.

119-7. Fitting a round-corner hinge into the butt.

119-8. Jamb-gauge pins locate the template.

119-9. A template nailed to the door jamb.

119-10. A template on the door jamb, butted against a stop.

DISCUSSION TOPICS

1. What makes the router one of the safest portable electric tools?
2. List eight jobs you can do with the router if you have the necessary bits, cutters, and accessories.
3. Name and illustrate six router cuts.
4. Name and describe two types of router bits.
5. What is the purpose of the pilot?
6. Name and describe the uses of the most important templates for cabinetwork and carpentry.
7. What is the horsepower range for routers? What is the horsepower rating of the one in your school industrial laboratory?
8. What is the approximate speed of the router you use?
9. What accessory is necessary to convert the router into a shaper?
10. What are two other names or terms which designate the hinge recess, or cut-out?
11. List and describe the use of attachments and accessories for the router.
12. Visit a mill and sash company, a furniture manufacturer, a building contractor, a cabinet shop, or other wood-products manufacturing plant in your community. Make a report on the types of routers in use and what they are used for.

SECTION
19

HARDWARE AND ASSEMBLY

Unit 120 Fastening with Screws

Wood screws make it easy to assemble and disassemble objects made of wood. They are better than nails as fasteners because they hold better over a longer period of time. To increase their usefulness still more, screws are often used with glue.

Origin of Screws

It is thought that the screw, or spiral, was invented in Greece by Archimedes in approximately 250 B.C. The spiral was used in a pipe to raise water for irrigation. Several hundred years later it was found that screws could be used to exert pressure. They were used in wine and coin presses and eventually in the first printing press, which was made by Johann Gutenberg in 1450. This use of screws led to the development of screw clamps. Wooden screws (pressure clamps) have been used in veneer presses for centuries.

Types

The most common types of screws for woodworking are slotted and have **flat, round,** and **oval heads** (Fig. 120-1C, D, and E). This slotted-type head is very old. A relatively new type is the Phillips, or cross-point, screw (Fig. 120-1A and B). It too has flat, oval, and round heads. The Phillips-head crossed recess provides more screwhead surface against the screwdriver tip than the ordinary screw does.

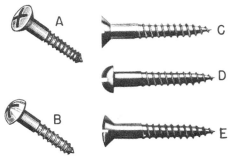

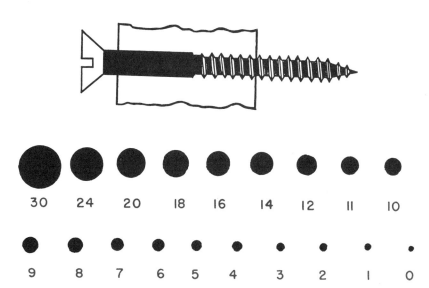

120-1. Types of wood screws: (A) flat Phillips head, (B) round Phillips head, (C) flat slotted head, (D) round slotted head, and (E) oval slotted head.

120-3. Shank (body) sizes of wood screws range from No. 0 to No. 30 ($\frac{1}{16}$ to $\frac{7}{16}$ inch in diameter).

120-2. Boxes of wood screws contain 100 or 144 (one gross) screws.

It holds the tip better and gives more driving surface when the screw is turned into the wood. Special Phillips-head screw drivers or bits are required to drive (turn) these screws. See Fig. 120-9.

Wood screws are made from mild (soft) steel, stainless steel, brass, aluminum, and siliconbronze (an alloy, or mixture, of silicon, copper, tin, and sometimes zinc). Common steel screws rust easily when they are used where humidity (moisture content) is high. To overcome this, screws are made from brass or are steel plated (coated) with a rust-resistant metal such as cadmium (a zinc ore), nickel, or chromium (a metallic chemical element). Brass and rust-resistant plated screws are espe-

cially useful on boats and for ornamentation on projects where the head of the screw is visible.

Screws are usually packaged in boxes containing either 100 or 1 gross (144). The boxes (Fig. 120-2) are labeled to show quantity, length, gauge (diameter of the shank), type of head, material, and the finish when necessary. Flat-head steel screws are often **bright** finished; round-head screws are often **blued.**

There are 20 common lengths of screws (Table 120-1). They range from $\frac{1}{4}$ inch to 6 inches in length. Shank gauges range from number zero (No. 0), which is about $\frac{1}{16}$ inch in diameter, to number 30 (No. 30), about $\frac{7}{16}$ inch in diameter. The relationship of these sizes is shown in Fig. 120-3. The screw

shown is an actual-size No. 16 (about $\frac{1}{4}$-inch shank). The length is usually measured from the point to the bottom of the slot.

Numerous other types of heads and sizes and shapes of screws are available (Fig. 120-4). **Square,** or **hex-head, screws** (Fig. 120-4C and D) are called **lag screws** or **lag bolts;** they are used where greater holding power is needed. A wrench (see Fig. 120-15) is used to drive these into a pilot hole that has been drilled into the wood. A **dowel screw** (Fig. 120-4E) is convenient to use to fasten a small post and shelf (Fig. 120-5).

The **hanger bolt** (Fig. 120-4F) or screw has regular screw spirals on one end and standard bolt threads on the opposite end. It is available in a variety

Table 120-1   LENGTHS MADE IN EACH GAUGE

Length	Gauges	Length	Gauges	Length	Gauges	Length	Gauges	Length	Gauges
$\frac{1}{4}$	0–4	$\frac{3}{4}$	2–16	$1\frac{1}{2}$	3–24	$2\frac{1}{2}$	5–24	4	8–30
$\frac{3}{8}$	0–9	$\frac{7}{8}$	2–16	$1\frac{3}{4}$	5–24	$2\frac{3}{4}$	6–24	$4\frac{1}{2}$	12–30
$\frac{1}{2}$	1–12	1	3–20	2	5–24	3	6–26	5	12–30
$\frac{5}{8}$	1–14	$1\frac{1}{4}$	3–24	$2\frac{1}{4}$	5–24	$3\frac{1}{2}$	8–26	6	12–30

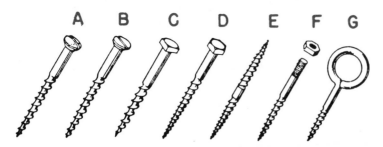

120-4. Special types of screws are used for many purposes in woodworking: (*A*) oval fillister head, (*B*) flat fillister head, (*C*) square head, (*D*) hex head, (*E*) dowel screw, (*F*) hanger bolt, and (*G*) screw eye.

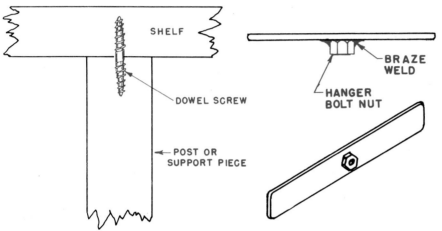

120-5. Posts are sometimes fastened to shelves with dowel screws.

120-7. A specially made tool assists in driving the hanger bolt.

120-6. A table top is easily connected to a post with a hanger bolt.

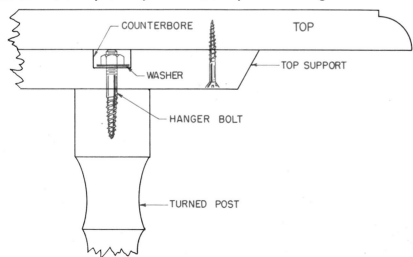

of sizes, and it is especially useful for connecting a complete table top, such as a round, or drum, top, to one or more posts (Fig. 120-6). A special shop-made tool (Fig. 120-7) drives the hanger bolt easily into the wood after a pilot hole of the correct size has been drilled.

Tools

Numerous sizes and types of bits, drills, drilling devices, and other tools are used to drive screws. These hand and power tools include the ordinary screw driver (Fig. 120-8), Phillips-head (cross-point) screw driver (Fig. 120-9), offset screw driver (Fig. 120-10), screw-driver bit (Fig. 120-11), countersink bit (Fig. 120-12), and automatic (ratchet) screw driver (Fig. 120-13). The brace, bits, and drills are discussed in Unit 28.

A combination wood drill and countersink (Fig. 120-14) is a desirable tool. It is available in 24 sizes. The sizes range from ½ inch (No. 5) to 2½ inches (No. 12). It drills the pilot (lead) hole, shank (body) clearance hole, and the countersink enlargement in one drilling operation. It can be held in either a hand or a power tool.

Open-end adjustable wrenches (Fig. 120-15) are available in many sizes. They can be used to turn lag screws or bolts into the work.

Fastening

1. Using an awl, locate and mark the points where screws are to be inserted. Select the type and size of screw. (If the combination drill and countersink is used, steps 2 through 4 can be omitted.)

2. Select the correct size of bit or drill for the pilot hole (Table 120-2).

3. Fasten the drill in the chuck of a hand or power tool. Drill through the first piece of wood and into the second one. This aids in aligning all holes correctly when the screws are no larger than about 10 gauge.

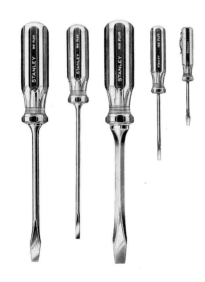

120-9. A short screw driver with crossed point is useful for driving Phillips-head screws in close places.

120-11. A screw-driver shank for a brace.

120-10. An offset screw driver for close places.

120-12. Countersink bits fit many tools: (A) hand and portable electric drills, or drill press; (B) brace.

120-8. Common screw-driver sizes.

Table 120-2 PILOT-HOLE—SHANK-CLEARANCE-HOLE BORING RECOMMENDATIONS

Screw no.	Bit or drill sizes						Auger bit no. (to counterbore for sinking head [by 16ths])
	For shank-clearance holes		For pilot holes				
			Hardwoods		Softwoods		
	Twist bit (nearest size in fractions of an inch)	Drill gauge no. or letter (to be used for maximum holding power)	Twist bit (nearest size in fractions of an inch)	Drill gauge no. (to be used for maximum holding power)	Twist bit (nearest size in fractions of an inch)	Drill gauge no. (to be used for maximum holding power)	
0	$1/16$	52	$1/32$	70	$1/64$	75	
1	$5/64$	47	$1/32$	66	$1/32$	71	
2	$3/32$	42	$3/64$	56	$1/32$	65	3
3	$7/64$	37	$1/16$	54	$3/64$	58	4
4	$7/64$	32	$1/16$	52	$3/64$	55	4
5	$1/8$	30	$5/64$	49	$1/16$	53	4
6	$9/64$	27	$5/64$	47	$1/16$	52	5
7	$5/32$	22	$3/32$	44	$1/16$	51	5
8	$11/64$	18	$3/32$	40	$5/64$	48	6
9	$3/16$	14	$7/64$	37	$5/64$	45	6
10	$3/16$	10	$7/64$	33	$3/32$	43	6
11	$13/64$	4	$1/8$	31	$3/32$	40	7
12	$7/32$	2	$1/8$	30	$7/64$	38	7
14	$1/4$	D	$9/64$	25	$7/64$	32	8
16	$17/64$	I	$5/32$	18	$9/64$	29	9
18	$19/64$	N	$3/16$	13	$9/64$	26	10
20	$21/64$	P	$13/64$	4	$11/64$	19	11
24	$3/8$	V	$7/32$	1	$3/16$	15	12

120-13. An automatic spiral, or ratchet, screw driver.

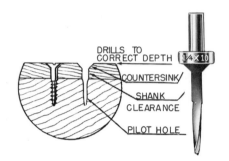

DRILLS TO CORRECT DEPTH

1/4 X 10

COUNTERSINK

SHANK CLEARANCE

PILOT HOLE

120-14. The combination wood drill and countersink is useful for drilling all necessary holes and countersinking in one operation.

120-15. An open-end adjustable wrench is useful for driving lag screws or bolts into the wood.

120-16. The proper size of pilot and shank-clearance holes and countersinking are important to a good fit.

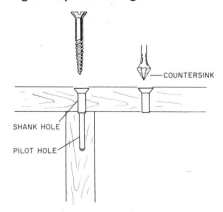

COUNTERSINK

SHANK HOLE

PILOT HOLE

When large shank holes are made with auger bits, it is preferable to perform step 4 *before* performing step 3. The tip of the auger bit then marks the location of the pilot hole in the second piece of wood.

4. Select the correct size of drill or bit for the shank hole (Table 120-2). Place it in the chuck. Remove the top piece of wood, and drill the shank hole through it.

5. Countersink the shank hole (Figs. 120-16, 120-17, and 120-18) if an oval- or flat-head screw is to be used. Counterbore the hole if the screw is to be capped, or plugged with a screw-hole button or plug (Fig. 120-19).

120-17. The countersink bit is easily used in a file handle.

120-18. Countersinking a hole with a brace.

6. Select a screw driver or screw-driver bit to fit the crossed-recess (Phillips-head) or the straight-slot screwhead (Fig. 120-20).

7. Coat the screw lightly with soap, wax, or paraffin to make it turn easily.

8. Hold the screw-driver tip firmly in the slot; drive the screw into place (Fig. 120-21). The brace with the screw-driver bit (Fig. 120-22) and the automatic spiral (ratchet) screw driver (Fig. 120-23) both speed up the job of inserting screws.

Figure 90-6 shows the reduction-gear (reduced-speed) ratchet being used with a portable drill to drive a screw.

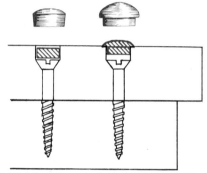

120-19. Counterbored holes are filled with plugs or screw-hole buttons. Note the oval-head plug.

120-20. The screw-driver tip must be held firmly in the straight or crossed slot of the screw.

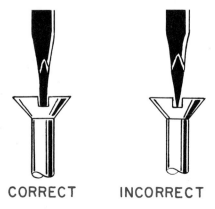

CORRECT   INCORRECT

120-21.   Hold the screw driver firmly.

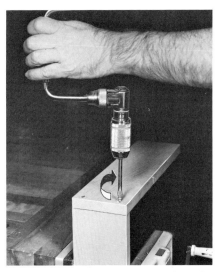

120-22.   Driving a screw with the brace and screw-driver bit. This device speeds up the process considerably.

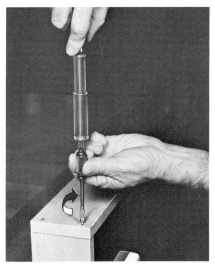

120-23.   Driving a screw with the automatic ratchet, or spiral, screw driver.

Unit 121   Assembly with Nails and Brads

Almost everyone has occasion to drive nails, set nail heads below the surface of the wood, or pull nails. The most widely used sizes, lengths, gauges, diameters, and approximate number per pound of common, casing, box, and finishing nails, and flooring brads are shown in Tables 121-1, 121-2, 121-3, and 121-4. The common size used and the type of head usually determine the use of a nail. Nails are not often used for cabinetwork. They are usually used in rough construction, where they do not detract from good appearance and craftsmanship.

Sizes and Kinds

Nail sizes are indicated by the term **penny,** abbreviated **d,** which designates the weight of 1,000 nails. Sizes range from 2 penny (2d) to 60 penny (60d). For example, one thousand 2 penny (2d) nails weigh 2 pounds.

Common nails (Table 121-1) have relatively thick heads and are larger in diameter than most nails. They are used for all forms of general nailing and especially for construction purposes.

Casing and **box nails** (Table 121-2) generally have the same size designation, but both are smaller in diameter than the common nail. Casing nails have cone-shaped heads. They are used mainly to nail interior trim and painted cabinetwork. Box nails have thin, flat heads that are similar to common nail heads. They are sometimes coated or barbed to increase their holding power. Coated or barbed nails are often used for nailing boxes and light crates.

Finishing nails (Table 121-3) have small heads which are frequently set below the surface. The hole this leaves is then filled with putty, sanding dust and glue, wood plastic, or other suitable filler.

Brads are small finishing nails which vary from ¼ to 1¼ inches in length for smaller sizes. They are useful when small, thin pieces of wood are to be

293

Table 121-1 COMMON WIRE NAILS

Size	Length, in.	Gauge, no.	Dia., in.		Approx. no. per lb.
			Actual	Approx.	
2d	1	15	0.0720	5/64	876
3d	1¼	14	0.0800	5/64	568
4d	1½	12½	0.0985	3/32	316
5d	1¾	12½	0.0985	3/32	271
6d	2	11½	0.1130	7/64	181
7d	2¼	11½	0.1130	7/64	161
8d	2½	10¼	0.1313	1/8	106
9d	2¾	10¼	0.1313	1/8	96
10d	3	9	0.1483	5/32	69
12d	3¼	9	0.1483	5/32	63
16d	3½	8	0.1620	5/32	49
20d	4	6	0.1920	3/16	31
30d	4½	5	0.2070	13/64	24
40d	5	4	0.2253	7/32	18
50d	5½	3	0.2437	¼	14
60d	6	2	0.2625	17/64	11

Table 121-2 CASING NAILS; SMOOTH AND BARBED BOX NAILS

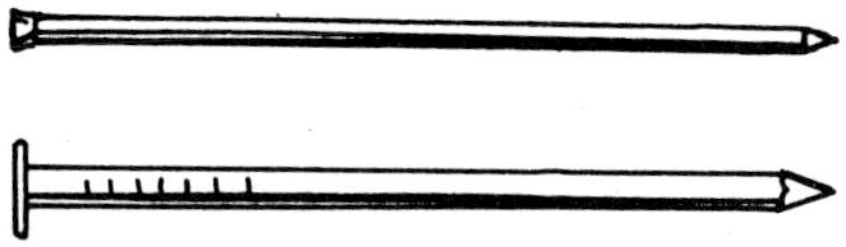

Size	Length, in.	Gauge, no.	Dia., in.		Approx. no. per lb.
			Actual	Approx.	
2d	1	15½	0.0672	1/16	1,010
3d	1¼	14½	0.0760	5/64	635
4d	1½	14	0.0800	5/64	473
5d	1¾	14	0.0800	5/64	406
6d	2	12½	0.0985	3/32	236
7d	2¼	12½	0.0985	3/32	210
8d	2½	11½	0.1130	7/64	145
9d	2¾	11½	0.1130	7/64	132
10d	3	10½	0.1277	1/8	94
12d	3¼	10½	0.1277	1/8	88
16d	3½	10	0.1350	9/64	71
20d	4	9	0.1483	5/32	52
30d	4½	9	0.1483	5/32	46
40d	5	8	0.1620	5/32	35

assembled. Larger forms are called **flooring brads** (Table 121-4); these range in length from 2 to 4 inches. Corresponding sizes are the same as for common nails, but the brad head is similar to the casing head.

Notice in the tables that nails up to 3½ inches in length increase ¼ inch per size. Sizes 20d and above increase by ½ inch for each size.

Tools

The **claw hammer** (Fig. 121-1) is the proper tool for driving a nail. Hammer sizes are measured by the weight of the head. The 12- and 16-ounce sizes are the most popular.

A **nail set** (Fig. 121-2) is used to set (drive in) finishing and casing nails below the surface of the board. They are available in different concave-tip sizes to fit the heads of different sizes of nails.

The **wrecking bar,** sometimes called a **crowbar** (Fig. 121-3), is used to pull very large nails and to help pry large nailed pieces apart.

121-1.   A typical claw hammer with a rubber-covered steel handle.

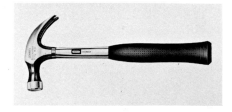

121-2.   A nail set.

Driving Nails

1. Select the correct type and size of nail for the job.

2. Drive the nail with the hammer until it is practically flush (smooth) with the wood (Figs. 121-4 and 121-5). Hold the nail when first starting the driving.

The length of the nail should be about three times the thickness of the first board. If a nail is to be driven through hardwood, drill a very small pilot hole through the first board to prevent splitting.

3. When desired, set the head of the nail about $\frac{1}{16}$ inch below the surface of the wood (Fig. 121-6). Use a nail set. Fill the hole with putty or wood plastic.

Special Nailing Methods

Figure 121-7 shows how to get increased holding power by driving nails at an **angle**.

Driving nails as shown in Fig. 121-8 is **toenailing**.

121-4. A small pilot hole should be drilled before nails are driven into hardwood.

Table 121-3 FINISHING NAILS

Size	Length, in.	Gauge, no.	Dia., in. Actual	Dia., in. Approx.	Approx. no. per lb.
2d	1	16½	0.0582	$\frac{1}{16}$	1,351
3d	1¼	15½	0.0672	$\frac{1}{16}$	807
4d	1½	15	0.0720	$\frac{5}{64}$	584
5d	1¾	15	0.0720	$\frac{5}{64}$	500
6d	2	13	0.0915	$\frac{3}{32}$	309
7d	2¼	13	0.0915	$\frac{3}{32}$	238
8d	2½	12½	0.0985	$\frac{3}{32}$	189
9d	2¾	12½	0.0985	$\frac{3}{32}$	172
10d	3	11½	0.1130	$\frac{7}{64}$	121
12d	3¼	11½	0.1130	$\frac{7}{64}$	113
16d	3½	11	0.1205	$\frac{1}{8}$	90
20d	4	10	0.1350	$\frac{9}{64}$	62

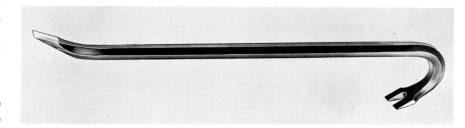

121-3. A wrecking bar is used to pull large nails and pry pieces apart.

Table 121-4 FLOORING BRADS

Size	Length, in.	Gauge, no.	Dia., in. Actual	Dia., in. Approx.	Approx. no. per lb.
6d	2	11	0.1205	$\frac{1}{8}$	157
7d	2¼	11	0.1205	$\frac{1}{8}$	139
8d	2½	10	0.1350	$\frac{9}{64}$	99
9d	2¾	10	0.1350	$\frac{9}{64}$	90
10d	3	9	0.1483	$\frac{5}{32}$	69
12d	3¼	8	0.1620	$\frac{5}{32}$	54
16d	3½	7	0.1770	$\frac{11}{64}$	43
20d	4	6	0.1920	$\frac{3}{16}$	31

121-5. Continue driving a finishing nail until it is almost flush with the wood surface.

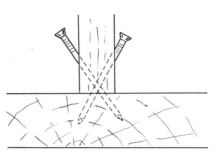

121-8. Nails driven at angles, joining two pieces perpendicularly, is called *toenailing*.

121-10. Attaching a plywood side panel with staples.

121-6. Set a finishing nail below the wood surface with a claw hammer and a nail set.

121-7. Driving nails at an angle helps give more holding power.

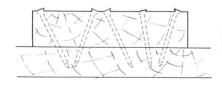

121-9. Nails should be clinched after they are driven through pieces.

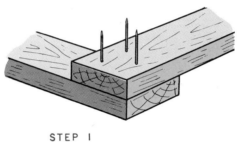

STEP 1

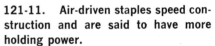

STEP 2

STEP 3

121-11. Air-driven staples speed construction and are said to have more holding power.

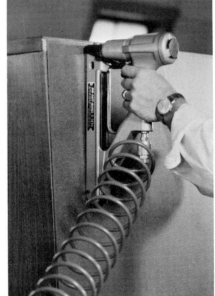

Figure 121-9 describes three steps in **clinching** nails to hold two or more boards securely.

Air-driven staples are also used to attach solid wood braces and panels of plywood (Fig. 121-10) and hardboard (Fig. 121-11).

Pulling Nails

1. Slip the claws of the hammer under the head of the nail. Pull the handle until it is at about a 90-degree angle to the board (Fig. 121-12).

If the nail is too long to pull, slip a block of wood under the head of the hammer to increase leverage (Fig. 121-13).

2. Use a wrecking bar to pry pieces apart or to pull out very large nails. See Fig. 121-3.

121-12.   Drawing or pulling a nail.

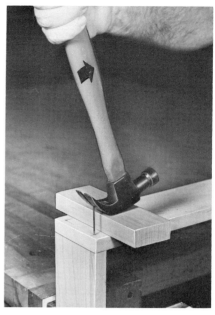

121-13.   Scrap block increases leverage for larger nails, prevents marring.

Unit 122 Gluing and Clamping

Joints which have been well made, coated correctly with a properly prepared glue, and clamped securely are as strong as, or stronger than, the wood itself. Glue is applied to face surfaces of boards which are clamped together for increased thickness (see Fig. 122-5). Board edges are coated with glue and clamped to form wider surfaces (see Fig. 122-11). Decorative paper and plasticlike laminates can be attached to wood and other surfaces with contact cements that do not require clamping. Table 122-1 offers suggestions on the type of cement or glue to use.

Types of Glue

Glues, cements, or adhesives for woodworking can be classified in six categories. Three that are well adapted for use in most woodworking are (1) animal, (2) casein, and (3) synthetic resins. Those that are less frequently used are (4) vegetable (plant starch), (5) fish, and (6) blood albumin. The all-purpose epoxy (plastic) resin and household cements are used for general bonding.

Animal glue is one of the oldest used in woodworking. It is made principally from hides and hooves of cattle. It is available in flake, powder, and liquid forms. Flake and powder forms must be mixed with water and heated before use. Their strength decreases with repeated heatings. The best liquid animal glues are popular because they are strong, ready for immediate use, tough, usually nonstaining, and free flowing. This type of glue is *not* highly water resistant and should not be used on outdoor furniture, boats, or anything else that is exposed to considerable moisture.

297

Table 122-1

Adhesive	Properties	Wood to wood and plywood	Wood veneering	Plastic laminates to wood	Wood boats and marine uses	Wood for outdoor use	Metal to wood	China repair	Patch seal solder	Metal to metal	Paper to cloth	Leather to wood	Rubber to wood or metal	Cloth to cloth or wood	Plywood panels to frame or stud
	X—Best product for this use X—Acceptable for this use														
Titebond	Liquid, ready-to-use aliphatic resin. Tacky, highest strength. Good heat resistance. Durable, tough bond.	X	X	X							X	X		X	
White glue	Liquid ready-to-use polyvinyl acetate resin. Sets fast (20–30 min clamp). Dries clear.	X	X	X							X	X		X	
Liquid hide glue	Liquid, ready-to-use brown animal glue. Reliable. Clamping time 40–50 min.	X	X	X							X	X		X	
Contact cement	Liquid, ready-to-use neoprene based adhesive. No clamping needed. Water resistant.	X	X	X						X		X	X	X	X
Plastic resin	Powdered, urea based. Mixes easily with water. Good water resistance. Requires 6–8 hr clamping.	X	X	X		X									
Waterproof	Two-part resorcinol resin adhesive. Fully waterproof. Requires overnight clamping.	X	X	X	X	X									
Casein	Powdered glue. Mix with water. Water resistant.	X	X	X											
Epoxy cement	Two part: resin and hardener. Bonds almost anything. Requires 8–10 hr setting time.						X	X	X	X					
Household cement	Liquid: clear and fast drying (5–15 min). Vinyl base. Water resistant.							X			X			X	
Liquid solder	Liquid — requires no heat or mixing. Water resistant.								X						

Casein glues are made from casein (powdered milk curd) and certain chemicals. They are made in powder form and are prepared for use by adding water to form a pastelike mixture. Good casein glues are highly water resistant, but they have a tendency to stain woods.

Synthetic resins, which form the basis for a number of plastics, are the most recent development. They are a very popular and durable wood adhesive. The types of resins involved are the **thermoplastic** and **thermosetting.** Thermoplastic resins include the polyvinyls. They are not practical for use in most general woodworking because they often require special handling and equipment. Thermosetting resins are used very successfully for gluing wood. They include the formaldehyde group: urea, phenol, resorcinol, and melamine.

Urea formaldehyde resin is probably the most popular with woodworkers. It is marketed in both powder and liquid forms. The powder type contains wood flour or walnut shell flour as a filler. Urea resin glue possesses high moisture resistance and sets cold. That is, it cures (sets, or hardens) at room temperature.

Phenol formaldehyde resin glue is used in the high-pressure, hot-press method of manufacturing plywood that is intended for use under extreme moisture conditions. Platens (flat plates) used in presses for such operations are heated by electricity, steam, or high-frequency induction. (High-frequency induction is simply electronic waves sent through the platens to create heat.) This resin glue is available in powder and in liquid form.

Resorcinol formaldehyde resin comes in liquid form only. A catalyst (substance to speed the process) must be used to prepare this glue. Resorcinols set at room temperature, but they set more quickly at high temperatures.

Melamine resin glue is the most recent of the synthetic resins. It is available in powder form and is very similar to the phenol type in use, strength, and other characteristics.

Vegetable glue is made in powder form from starches derived from plants. It lacks water resistance, tends to stain, and sets slowly.

Fish glue comes in prepared liquid form, ready to use. It is made from the heads, skin, and bones of fish. It lacks water resistance and is used mostly for small repair jobs that do not require strength.

Blood albumin glue is made from the soluble albumin of beef blood. It is highly resistant to moisture.

Types of Clamps

Clamps are manufactured in numerous shapes for a wide variety of uses. Those most often used in furniture and cabinetmaking are the **cabinet,** or **carriage (C), clamp** (Fig. 122-1); the **bar clamp** (Fig. 122-2); the adjustable, parallel-jaw **hand-screw clamp** (Fig. 122-3); and the **band clamp** (see Figs. 122-18 and 122-19). An adaptation of the bar clamp is called the **multiple-disk clutch clamp** (Fig. 122-4). It can take the place of either the C or the hand-screw clamp.

Gluing and Clamping Precautions

1. Remove dust, oil, wax, or finishes from the surfaces or edges to be glued.

2. Glue and clamp only if the temperature is above 70 degrees Fahrenheit (70°F).

3. Size (pretreat) the end grain of the wood to be glued. Apply a water-

122-1. C clamp.

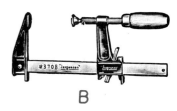

122-3. Parallel-jaw hand-screw clamps

122-4. A special bar clamp called a *multiple-disk clutch clamp.*

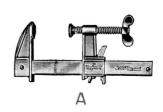

A

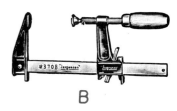

B

122-2. Bar clamp.

thin mixture of glue to the board ends 10 to 15 minutes before spreading on the main film of glue. End grain is absorbent, and the moisture from the main glue layer will soak in if it is applied without preliminary sizing.

4. Put equal pressure on clamps.

5. If possible, use scrap pieces of wood between the metal clamp jaws and the wood being clamped.

6. Apply a thin, even glue coat to surfaces or edges to be clamped.

7. Space the bar clamps 12 to 15 inches apart.

8. Always clean off excess glue before it dries.

Gluing and Clamping for Thickness

1. Mix or prepare the glue according to the manufacturer's directions.

2. Adjust the clamps to fit the job.

3. Make protective blocks for C, hand, and bar clamps.

4. Spread the glue rapidly and evenly on the surfaces of the pieces.

5. Place the glued surfaces together; assemble the hand or C clamps (Figs. 122-5 through 122-8). The correct method of fastening hand clamps is shown in Fig. 122-5. The others show the use of the various clamps for gluing up stock to increase the thickness.

Gluing and Clamping for Width

1. Follow steps 1 through 3 above.

2. Spread glue rapidly and evenly on the edges of the boards.

3. Assemble the boards. The end grain should be arranged as indicated in Fig. 122-9. This reduces the wood's tendency to warp.

4. Fasten the clamps lightly and then tap the boards, as shown in Fig. 122-10. This aligns the boards. Note especially that the clamps are fastened on both sides.

5. Tighten the clamps to uniform pressure (Fig. 122-11). If the boards tend to buckle, keep them aligned as shown in Fig. 122-12. Use multiple-disk clamps, C clamps, or hand clamps.

6. Spot electronic gluing will hold joints sufficiently that clamps can be removed within 30 minutes (Fig. 122-13). In electronic gluing, an electrode (lead) from the machine is placed on each side of the joined pieces. An electric current is applied from the machine which causes a magnetic field and quick heat between electrodes on the joint. As a result, the glue sets (dries) quickly.

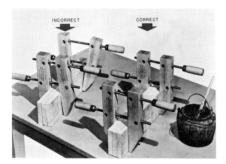

122-5. Hand-screw clamps must be adjusted properly when clamping materials.

122-6. Parallel-jaw clamps can be used on one side to clamp pieces to increase thickness.

122-7. C clamps are very useful.

122-8. Small pieces are easily glued with special clamps.

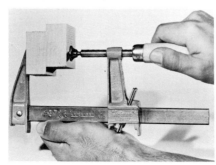

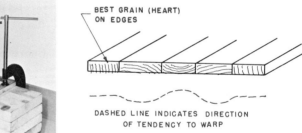

122-9. Alternate the annual rings of wood pieces to help prevent warping.

122-10. Level the boards with a mallet and a scrap block.

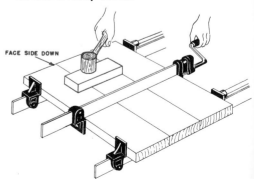

122-11. Bar clamps are placed above and below pieces glued edge to edge to prevent buckling and to increase width.

Special Gluing and Clamping

1. Follow steps 1 through 3 under "Gluing and Clamping for Thickness."

2. Put the parts together and make a trial assembly, using the most suitable clamps for the job.

3. Spread glue rapidly and evenly on all parts to be assembled. Apply glue on dowel pins, splines, and other wooden parts for joints.

4. Assemble all parts and fasten the clamps in place (Figs. 122-14 through 122-16). Figure 122-16 shows the use of a shop-made jig for clamping cabinet

122-15. Long, flat steel bar clamps are used to clamp oversize frames both ways.

122-12. Multiple-disk clutch grips bar automatically at any point. The holding platen helps level boards.

122-14. "I" bar clamps used to clamp a frame.

122-16. Special fixtures help perform clamping operations on large projects.

122-13. An electronic gluing machine spot-heats and speeds up the work.

122-17. Details for a special bar-clamp device.

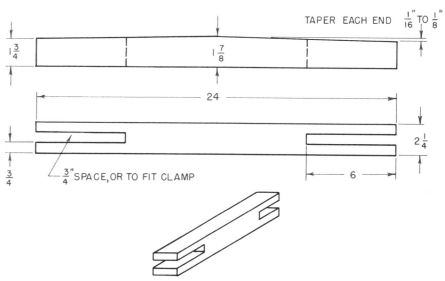

122-18. A canvas band clamp in place on a chair.

122-19. The steel band clamp holds irregular parts together.

parts. Figure 122-17 is a detail drawing for making this special bar-clamp device.

5. Irregularly shaped assemblies can be clamped and held securely with the canvas and steel-band clamps (Figs. 122-18 and 122-19).

6. Miter joints can be held with the miter jig and a hand-screw clamp, as shown in Fig. 122-20.

7. Large surfaces, such as panels and veneers, can be held securely by building a special clamping device (Fig. 122-21). Auxiliary large, flat surfaces, or thick plywood sheets, are used underneath and on top of the stock being glued to exert an even pressure.

122-20. The hand-screw clamp is easily used with the miter jig.

122-21. Special clamping devices are used to glue large surfaces.

Unit 123 Joints and Joint Strengtheners

Joints are used in almost every aspect of woodworking. "Joinery" is another name for cabinetmaking. It is very important to designate the types of joints for use in a project during the stages of planning and making a working drawing. The joints selected for assembly of a project or its parts affect such factors as eventual strength, beauty and construction time. Drawer construction is a good example (Fig. 123-1).

Types of Joints and Uses

The basic types of joints are (1) butt, (2) dado, (3) rabbet, (4) lap, (5) dovetail, (6) mortise and tenon, (7) miter, and (8) tongue and groove (Fig. 123-2).

The dowel and the spline are used to strengthen some of these basic types of joints. Most joints have numerous variations. They are adapted to specific needs within the limitations of the tools available for making them.

Butt joints are used for simple construction. Dowels strengthen this type of joint when it is used instead of the mortise and tenon. However, the doweled butt joint is not as strong as the mortise-and-tenon joint. Butt joints are also doweled to add strength when material is glued edge to edge to form larger solid surfaces (Fig. 123-3).

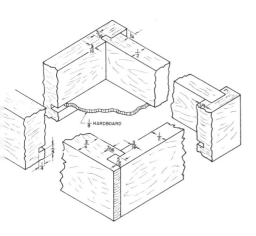

123-1. A typical drawer construction, using several joints.

The **rabbet** (Fig. 123-4A), **dado** (Fig. 123-4B), or combinations of several joints are used when joints stronger than the simple butt are needed.

There are several variations of **lap joints** (Fig. 123-5). The **half-lap joint** is used to connect two pieces end to end in a straight line. **End-, middle-,** and **cross-lap joints** are commonly used when two pieces meet or cross at 90-degree angles. These can replace the butt, doweled butt, or mortise-and-tenon joints when beauty is not necessary.

Dovetail joints (Fig. 123-6) are made on corners where much strength is desired and where pulling strain is involved. Joining sides of drawers to fronts is the most common use of this type in furniture construction. The joint is usually made with a router. See Unit 118, "Making a Dovetail Joint."

Mortise-and-tenon joints (Fig. 123-9) are made where exceptional strength and wearing qualities are needed. They are used especially to join two pieces, such as legs and rails, which come together at right angles (90 degrees).

Miter joints (see Fig. 123-2G) are used on corners of picture frames or when two pieces of trim, molding, or larger surfaces join. The ends of the pieces are cut at a 45-degree angle.

123-3. A doweled-edge joint.

123-2. Eight basic types of joints: (A) butt, (B) dado, (C) rabbet, (D) lap, (E) dovetail, (F) mortise and tenon, (G) miter, and (H) tongue and groove.

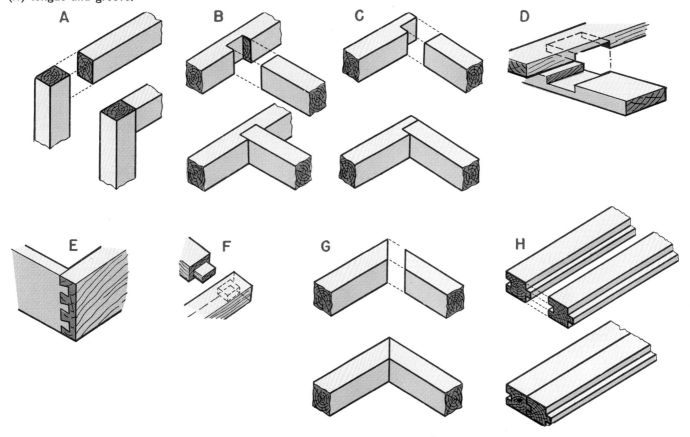

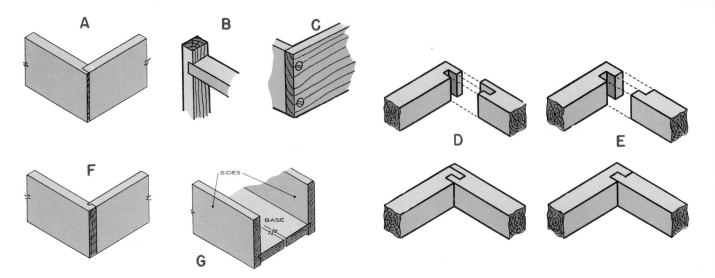

123-4. Combinations of joints are often stronger: (*A*) rabbet, (*B*) dado, (*C*) butt with screws, (*D*) dado, tongue, and rabbet, (*E*) dado and rabbet, (*F*) barefaced tongue and dado, and (*G*) barefaced tongue and groove.

123-5. Lap joints: (*A*) middle lap, (*B*) half lap, (*C*) end lap, (*D*) cross lap, and (*E*) finger lap.

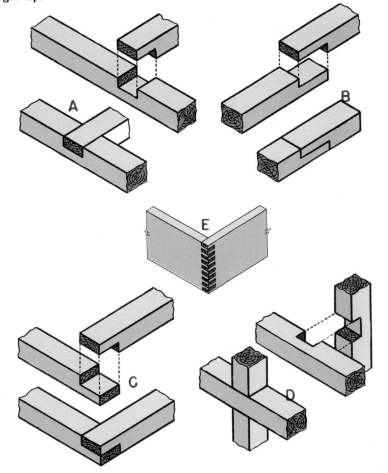

The miter joint is strengthened by using either wood dowels, splines, or special metal clamp nails.

The **tongue-and-groove joint** is often used when the edges of material for table tops and other large surfaces are joined. See Fig. 123-2H. This joint is also found on flooring, center-matched siding, fencing, and some roofing materials. The tongue is frequently used in combination with the dado and the rabbet (Fig. 123-4D,F, and G).

The skills involved in laying out, cutting, and fitting common joints are described in the several sections pertaining to hand tools and machine tools. The basic joint, however, as it is cut and fitted, may need additional strengthening. To provide the extra reinforcement, metal fasteners, wood dowels, splines, and braces are sometimes added.

Metal Strengtheners

Several forms of metal fasteners can be used to strengthen joints. Three of these are the **corrugated fastener** (Fig. 123-7), a special **four-pronged fastener** (Fig. 123-8), and the **clamp nail** (Fig. 123-10B). Metal fasteners detract from

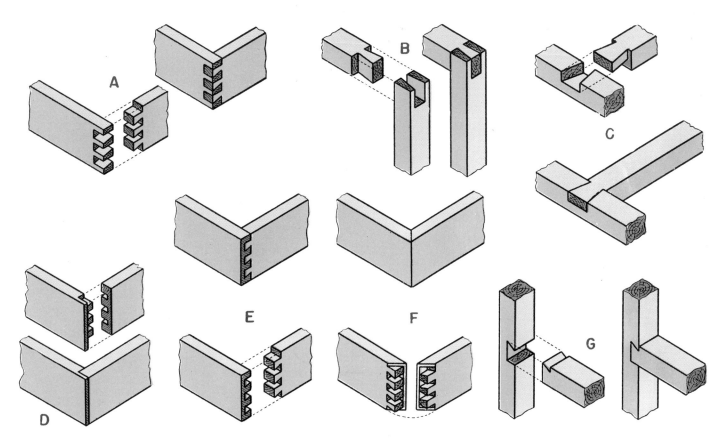

123-6. Types of dovetail joints: (*A*) through multiple dovetail, (*B*) through single dovetail, (*C*) lap dovetail, (*D*) stopped lap dovetail, (*E*) lap, or half-blind, dovetail, (*F*) blind miter, or secret dovetail, and (*G*) dovetail dado.

123-7. Driving corrugated fasteners.   **123-8.** A four-prong metal fastener.

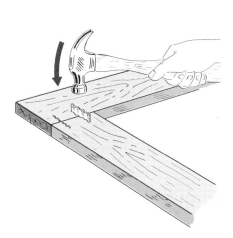

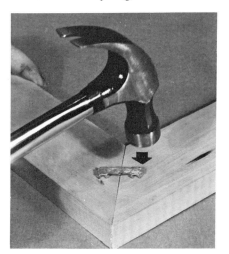

the general beauty of the object, and they do not have the holding power of properly used wood strengtheners. They are sometimes convenient, however.

Dowels as Strengtheners

Wood dowels are frequently used in furniture construction. They strengthen joints when one end of a board is butted to the edge of a second (Fig. 123-10A) and when pieces are glued edge to edge. See Fig. 123-3. Dowels are also used in miter joints.

The best dowel rods are made from birch and maple and come in several lengths and sizes (diameters). The 30-

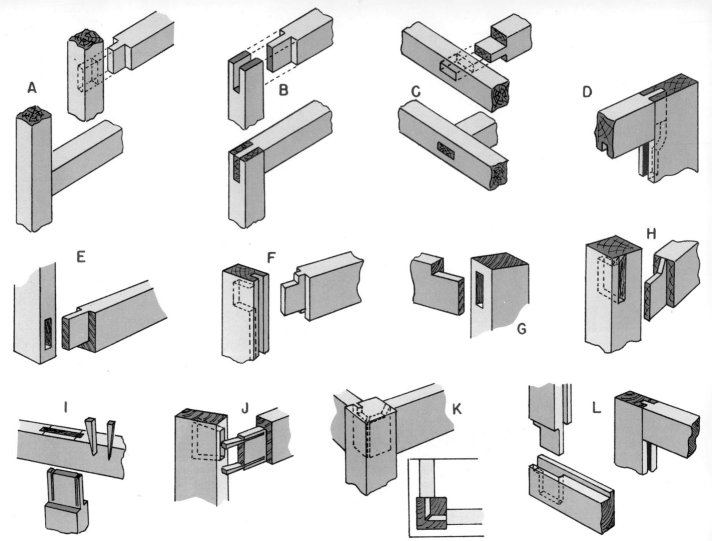

123-9. Common and special mortise-and-tenon joints and their application: (*A*) blind mortise-and-stub tenon, (*B*) through mortise-and-stub tenon, (*C*) open through mortise-and-stub tenon, (*D*) stub tenon in slot (not a true mortise-and-tenon, but easily made for light framing). (*E*) Simple mortise-and-tenon joint used for framing, (*F*) haunched tenon used for grooved framing. The haunch fills the gap made by the full-length groove, (*G*) barefaced tenon has only one shoulder; used when the tenon piece is thinner than the mortised one, (*H*) haunched tenon gives extra strength to the joint without showing a break at the end, (*I*) through wedged tenon; gives added strength where desired, (*J*) blind-wedged tenon; gives added strength where the through-wedged tenon cannot be seen, (*K*) mitered tenon; used to secure maximum length on tenon, (*L*) tenon with long-and-short shoulder used in framework or sash where a rabbet is required.

and 36-inch lengths are common. Many sizes are made, but the usual sizes are ¼, ⅜, ½, ¾, and 1 inch. Special grooved and ungrooved dowel pins (often ⅜ by 1½ inch or 2 inches) can be obtained (Fig. 123-11). The spiral-groove pins hold glue better and strengthen the joint more than smooth pins. When necessary, dowels can be made quickly on a dowel-making machine. If this machine is not available, another method, shown in Fig. 123-12, can be used. Square pieces of wood are driven through a nut having the correct opening for the dowel. The nut is held securely in a vise.

If dowels do not have spiral grooves, they should have a flat place or a

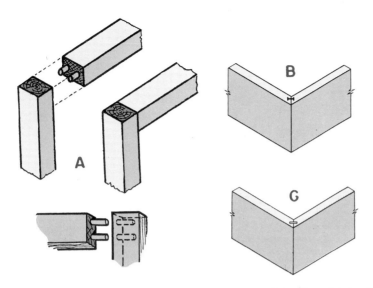

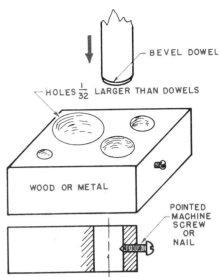

123-10. Joint strengtheners: (A) doweled butt joint, (B) miter joint with a clamp nail, and (C) miter joint with a wood spline.

123-13. Grooving a dowel.

straight groove on one side to allow excess glue to escape from the hole made for the dowel. A groove can be made in almost any length of dowel by driving the dowel through a special jig (Fig. 123-13).

Use of the dowel jig to locate, center, and bore holes on edge joints is discussed in Unit 28, "Boring and Drilling Holes."

Splines as Strengtheners

A **spline** is a thin strip of wood, plywood, or single piece of veneer glued into a special groove (saw kerf) to strengthen joints. A saw cut may run all the way across a joint, or only partially into it (Fig. 123-15). The circular (table) saw can be used (Fig. 123-14) to make matching cuts in two pieces that are to be joined with a spline. The thickness and the width of the cut are determined by the size of the spline and the extra strength needed.

Braces and Strengtheners

Wood braces are frequently used to strengthen joints; they are usually made from scrap pieces of wood. They add additional strength to any type of corner joint, even when mortise-and-tenon joints, dowels, or splines have been used.

Triangular and flat corner braces (Figs. 123-16 and 123-17) add support to the corners of wooden objects. The flat corner brace (Fig. 123-18) strengthens the corner and provides a surface to which leg hardware is attached. Wooden braces are also important in house construction, where they strengthen corners of frames and brace floor joists, rafters, and studs.

123-11. Grooved and ungrooved dowel pins.

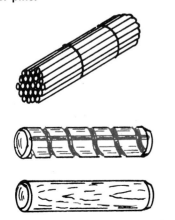

123-12. Making a dowel in a jig.

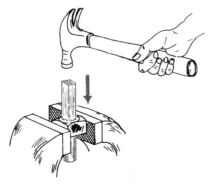

123-14. Cutting kerfs for splines. Note attachment for holding the piece.

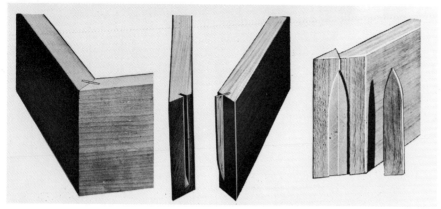

123-15. The saw kerf (cut) for a spline partially cut across a joint.

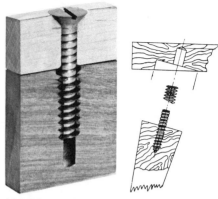

123-19. Self-tapping insert and screw: (1) counterbore base, (2) drill hole partially into base, and (3) install insert for assembly.

Special Connectors and Strengtheners

Knock-down designs and **on-site** assembly of wood products cause special problems of construction and transportation. Special connectors and strengtheners solve some of these.

The **self-tapping insert and screw** (Fig. 123-19) is adaptable for joining legs to bases. The **fishbone connector** offers ease of joint construction. This is shown in Figure 123-20. It is often used with lumber, plywood, and particle board where the capscrew head is visible only from the back.

The **dovetail fastener** (Fig. 123-21) is a wedge-shape metal tenon that is tapped for a bolt. The wood is routed and the bolt connects the pieces.

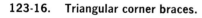

123-17. A flat corner brace.

123-18. Flat corner braces make surfaces on which to attach leg hardware.

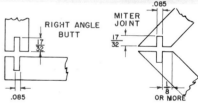

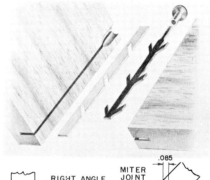

(Heli-Coil Corporation)

123-20. Insert the fishbone connector: (1) saw grooves, (2) cement receiving strips in place, (3) recess for cap screw, and (4) assemble.

123-21. A dovetail fastener permits knock-down construction, flat shipping, and assembly with a screw driver.

(Heli-Coil Corporation)

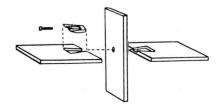

123-16. Triangular corner braces.

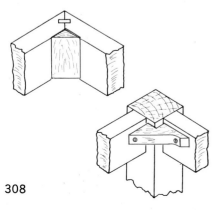

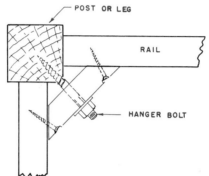

Unit 124 Cabinet Hardware

There is an almost unlimited selection of hardware items for furniture, cabinetwork, and building construction. Typical parts are bolts, screws, hinges, cabinet door catches, locks, metal tips for feet (ferrules), lid supports, drawer pulls and knobs, angle irons, table top fasteners, leg braces, and leg brackets. Larger pieces of very useful hardware are drawer rollers, ball-bearing swivels for lazy susans and chairs, bases to support swivel chairs, and hardware for reclining chairs and platform rockers.

Practically all the hardware is obtainable in many sizes and designs. When hardware is purchased, the necessary screws, pins, and other fastening devices are usually supplied with it.

Furniture and cabinet hardware is used for both decoration and function. It is necessary to be very accurate when locating, drilling, and chiseling the recesses and when making the final attachments (Fig. 124-1). This is usually one of the last operations performed. If hardware is attached before the finish is applied, it is often removed again until all finish work is done. It is then replaced.

Round Tapered Legs

Round tapered legs for tables, chests, and other pieces of furniture can be made or purchased in many materials and sizes. Necessary parts are shown in Fig. 124-2. Combination brackets, as illustrated, allow the leg to be inserted either vertically or at a standard 15-degree angle. Single brackets are also available.

A leg is turned and fitted to the metal cap or ferrule on the tip of the leg. This cap may be plain, or it may have a self-leveling swivel base, or glide.

The top of the leg is prepared for the hanger bolt by drilling a pilot hole. Put soap, wax, or paraffin on the screw threads of the bolt, and use the device shown in Fig. 120-7 to aid in screwing the bolt into the wood easily.

Angle Irons, Plates, Braces, and Fasteners

Flat T and 90-degree flat angle fasteners (Fig. 124-3A and B) are used to strengthen butt joints on the face surface and where edges join at 90 degrees. The bent angle iron is some-

124-1. Fitting doors for hinges before finishing.

124-2. Typical hardware for round, tapered legs.

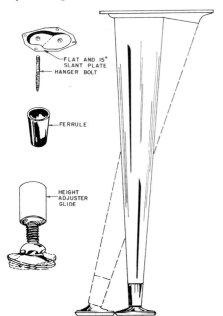

FLAT AND 15°
SLANT PLATE
HANGER BOLT

FERRULE

HEIGHT
ADJUSTER
GLIDE

124-3. Fasteners and braces: (A) T plates, (B) flat corner iron, (C and D) corner braces, and (E) table-top fasteners.

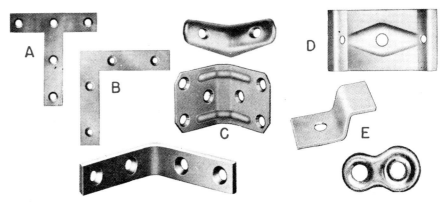

A

B

C

D

E

309

times used to attach table tops. Corner plates and braces (Fig. 124-3C and D) are used for attaching legs to the rails of tables and to strengthen similar corners. Table-top fasteners (Fig. 124-3E) are commonly used to attach a table top to the rails.

Hinges

A few of the many types of common and special hinges in use are shown in Figs. 124-4 and 124-5. A large number of shapes, designs, and finishes are available.

The unswaged-, partial-, or full-swaged **butt hinge** has always been popular and practical. The type of swage (shape) (Fig. 124-4A) determines to a large extent the amount of gain (chiseling out) required. For cutting gains, refer to Unit 119.

124-4. Common hinges: (A) plain strap, (B) T, (C) tight-pin butt, (D) plain-pin butt, (E) loose-joint butt, (F) loose-pin butt, (G) table leaf, (H) round-and-flush, and (I) continuous (piano).

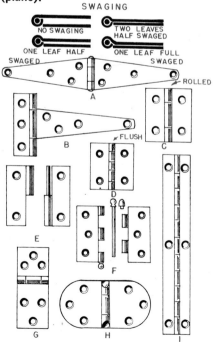

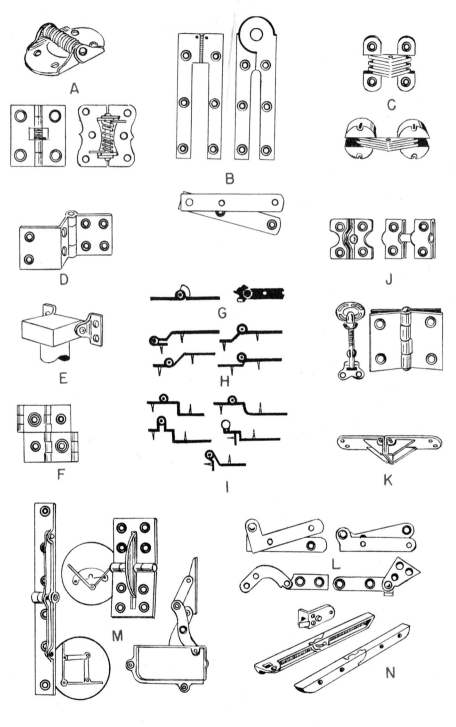

124-5. Special hinges: (A) spring, (B) knife, (C) invisible link, (D) chest, (E) tilt-top table, (F) double action, (G) stop, (H) visible offset, (I) semiconcealed offset, (J) friction, (K) built-in fixture, (L) semiconcealed, (M) combination, and (N) drop-front drawer with catch.

The names of the **half-surface** and **full-surface** (offset) **hinges** (Fig. 124-5H and I) indicate their placement on doors. The hinge is either fully visible on the surface or half hidden behind a door. Surface hinges range from the many-shaped, ornamental types to heavy, rough strap hinges that are found on farm and ranch gates and barn doors.

Invisible hinges are mounted so that they are concealed from view when doors are closed (Fig. 124-6). These are frequently used on quality furniture, such as drop-leaf tables This

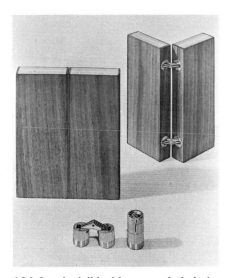

124-6. Invisible hinges and their installation.

124-7. Typical cabinet catches: (A) friction, (B) magnetic, (C) roller, and (D) spring wedged.

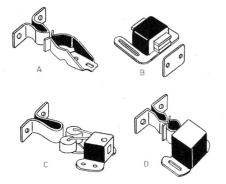

hinge permits perfectly flush mounting so that no hinge parts show. Holes are bored to accommodate the hinge.

Combination hinges (Fig. 124-5M) are often used on desks and chests. They are sold in pairs. This type of hinge operates the lid and has built-in supports to hold the lid open to certain positions.

Cabinet Catches

Four of the many kinds of cabinet catches are shown in Fig. 124-7. These are (1) friction, (2) magnetic, (3) roller, and (4) spring-wedged catches. Probably the easiest to fit and attach is the magnetic catch. It is also noiseless and a very practical way of keeping cabinet doors closed. A spring-wedged catch, offset hinges, and drawer and door pulls are shown in Fig. 124-8.

124-8. A spring-wedged catch, offset hinges, and metal drawer and door pulls, used on many cabinets.

Drawer and Door Pulls

Drawer pulls, door handles, and knobs are made in a great variety of materials, finishes, sizes, and patterns (Fig. 124-9). It is desirable for a person to design and make his own pulls, but he may prefer to purchase commercially made ones. They come complete and ready for mounting and are made of wood, plastic (Fig. 124-10), metal, and composition materials.

Single-post knobs and **pulls** are usually put on small drawers or on doors which open easily. They are installed by marking the location desired and drilling a hole to accommodate the correct

124-9. Antique brass and French gilt (old gold) drawer pulls and knobs.

124-10. Nylon handles, knobs, and hinges are available. They can be dyed to match wood colors with common household dyes.

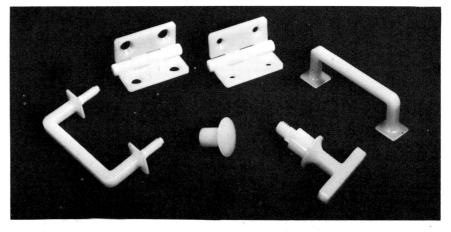

size of screw. Drawer and door pulls with **two posts** and screws require very accurate centering and drilling to make the handle align for a correct fit.

Other Hardware and Accessories

Metal or **nylon glides** (Fig. 124-11) are added to the bottoms of chair and table legs and to other furniture to prevent chipping and wear. **Rollers** mounted in kitchen cabinets and on drawer frames permit easy drawer opening and closing (Fig. 124-12). **Nylon tape** (Fig. 124-13) and **self-adhering plastic glides** are also available for mounting on drawer frames.

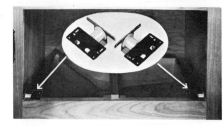

124-12.   Rollers mounted on drawer frames.

124-13.   Nylon tape can be attached to drawer frames for easy drawer glide.

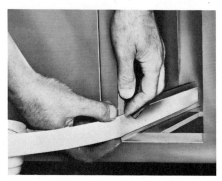

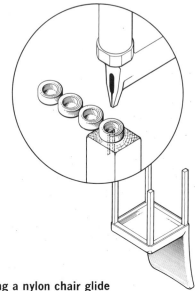

124-11.   Installing a nylon chair glide with a special staple.

DISCUSSION TOPICS

1. Make a sketch to show how the lengths of the different types of screws are measured. Make another one to show how an ordinary screw driver should be shaped for driving slotted screws.
2. What are the advantages of using screws instead of nails?
3. List the information you should have when you buy wood screws.
4. Sketch the heads, list the names, and explain the uses of the common types of nails and brads.
5. What do **6d** and **10-penny** mean?
6. What must you know about nails before ordering (buying) them?
7. What are the five common types of "natural-product" glues?
8. How are the more recently developed synthetic resins classified?
9. Name three kinds of clamps most often used in woodworking. List their specific uses.
10. What is meant by **sizing end grain?** How is it done? Why?
11. Why is it recommended that only pieces that are 4 or 5 inches wide be used in gluing together several boards edge to edge?
12. Sketch one kind of joint in each of the eight categories. Discuss its use in wood construction.
13. List several types of joints used in drawer construction.
14. What are the usual forms of joint strengtheners?
15. From what kinds of wood are the best dowels made?
16. Where are splines used?
17. Explain the purpose of alternating the direction of the annual rings of end-grain pieces being doweled or glued edge to edge.
18. Why are wooden corner braces of value in furniture construction?
19. Name five types of hinges. Where can each be used?
20. Sketch several ways of attaching table tops with metal hardware.
21. What are several types of cabinet catches?
22. List the kinds of hardware used on furniture in your home.

SANDING ON FLOOR-MODEL SANDERS

Unit 125 General Information About Sanding Machines

Power sanders are used extensively. The stationary floor-model sanders which you may have in your shop are (1) the horizontal-belt table sander (Figs. 125-1 and 125-2); (2) the small vertical-belt sander (Figs. 125-3 and 125-4); (3) the disk sander (Fig. 125-5); and (4) the spindle sander (Fig. 125-6).

There are many variations of each of these machines, ranging from the types and kinds illustrated to the fully-automatic ones which require no manual skills, such as the one shown on this page. Sanders are sometimes referred to as **finishing machines.**

Abrasive are in the next unit.

Horizontal-belt Table Sander (Parts and Uses)

A large horizontal-belt sanding machine is shown in Figs. 125-1 and 125-2. It smooths any large surfaces which can be held on a sanding table. The one shown in Fig. 125-1 has a reversing switch which permits the belt to travel in either direction. This machine consists of two major parts: (1) the table, which can easily **be removed** to permit the sanding of large built-up pieces, such as cedar chests, desks, cabinets, and other medium-size furniture; and (2) two pulley columns, or stands. These units can be moved either close together or far apart, depending upon the work to be sanded and the length of the abrasive belt.

■ **Table.** The sander model shown in Fig. 125-1 has a table which can be raised or lowered by turning the hand wheel. On other machines, as in Fig. 125-2, the table is stationary with respect to height, but it slides forward and backward on rollers. The table supports flat surfaces and boards while they are being sanded.

■ **Pulley columns.** Hand wheels on the pulley columns move the pulleys up or down to raise or lower the sanding belt. On some horizontal-belt sanders, the distance between the pulleys is set (fixed), so only one belt length can be used. See Fig. 125-2. This figure shows a common type of horizontal table sander for school use. Both of these sander models are illustrated because they are used in school industrial laboratories.

■ **Idler pulley.** On large sanders, an idler pulley is needed to maintain proper tension on the sanding belt. On smaller machines, however, one of the regular pulleys has a tension adjustment.

■ **Sanding attachment.** This is an optional item. It has an operating lever and a hand pad for pressing the belt down on the surface being smoothed. Usually a sanding (hand) pad is a block of wood with a handle. It is manually pressed against the sanding belt. See Fig. 125-2.

■ **Dust deflector.** The dust deflector is the metal housing that covers one of the pulleys. It sucks the dust away from the work. The deflector is designed to be connected to a dust-collecting system.

■ **Abrasive belt.** The machine shown in Fig. 125-1 accepts a continuous sanding belt 30 feet or longer, in any width not to exceed the width of the pulleys (which are usually 8 inches wide). The abrasive belt speed varies from 900 to 1,800 fpm (feet per minute).

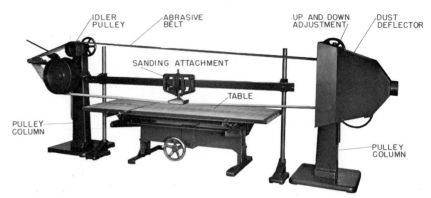

125-1. An industrial-type horizontal belt sander.

Small Vertical and Horizontal Sanders (Parts and Uses)

Figure 125-3 shows a 6-inch vertical-belt sander. A small horizontal sander is illustrated in Fig. 125-4. On some machines, the sanding mechanism can be tilted to a horizontal position. These machines are used to sand flat surfaces. They can be purchased as either vertical or horizontal sanders, or in combination with a disk sander, as shown in Fig. 125-4.

■ **Table.** The table is adjustable to hold the piece being sanded in a vertical position. It also tilts away from or toward the belt to sand bevels.

■ **Fence.** The fence is used only on the horizontal belt sander. It can be tilted to sand a bevel.

■ **Sanding belts.** The sanders shown in Figs. 125-4 and 125-5 use 6- by 48-inch abrasive belts. Other belt sizes vary according to the capacity of the machine. Belt speed is around 3,450 fpm.

125-2. A school-size belt table sander.

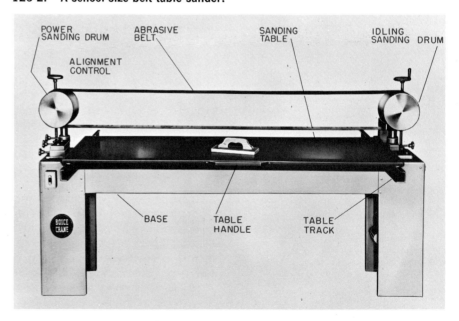

- **Base.** The base is a cast-iron or steel support on which the machine rests.
- **Dust deflector.** This is an attachment on most sanders into which dust from the sanding operation is fed. Often a shop dust-collecting system is connected to the deflector of this machine.

Disk Sander (Parts and Uses)

The disk sander (Fig. 125-5) is used to sand straight and convex (outward curved) edges. The disk diameters range from 8 to 18 inches. Frequently the disk sander is one part of a dual machine, the other part being a small belt sander. See Fig. 125-4.
- **Table.** The table on most sanding machines can be tilted to sand beveled edges.
- **Miter gauge.** A miter gauge makes it possible to hold stock at various angles.
- **Frame.** The disk sander frame is the stand which supports the machine.
- **Motor.** The speed of the motor is usually 1,725 rpm; the disk is directly attached.
- **Abrasive disk.** The abrasive disk is a sheet of abrasive paper on a metal disk. The paper is fastened to the disk with a special abrasive-disk cement, or adhesive.

Spindle Sander (Parts and Uses)

The spindle sander (Fig. 125-6) is sometimes called a **vertical-drum sander.** It smooths (sands) concave (inside curved) edges. Detachable spindles hold drums which vary from ½ by 6 to 6 by 9 inches. On some machines, the table tilts; on others, the spindle tilts.
- **Table.** This is a metal plate on which the piece being sanded rests.
- **Spindle.** The spindle is a rotating shaft which supports the sanding drums. Most spindles are detachable and operate with an oscillating (up-and-down) action. The speed varies from 1,800 to 3,600 rpm.
- **Base.** This is a cast-iron or steel frame which supports the table and the entire working mechanism.
- **Sanding drums.** Steel or rubber sanding drums are used on the spindle sander. The sanding sleeves are fastened to the steel drums with a special adhesive. The sanding sleeves are held tight on rubber drums by means of the air pressure expansion of the rubber.

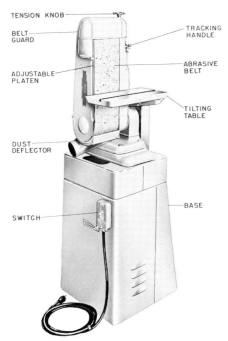

125-3.   A small vertical belt sander.

125-4.   A combination belt and disk sander.

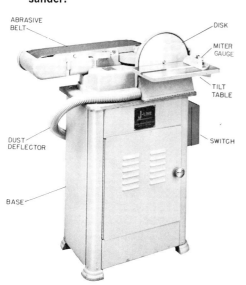

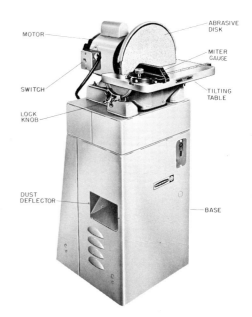

125-5.   A disk sander.

125-6.   A spindle sander.

Unit 126 Abrasives and Adjustments

Adjustments on the several types of stationary (floor-model) sanders vary according to the manufacturer's specifications and the sizes of the machines. The adjustments usually consist of replacing the sanding belts or drums, aligning the idler pulley (the other pulley drives the belt), and regulating the angle of the table or the spindle. The suggestions in this particular unit are general, as they apply to each of the four types of machines discussed in this section.

Abrasives

Abrasive belts and sheet material for use on floor and portable sanders are classified by **grits.** Generally, Nos. 1½ to 2½ are considered suitable for roughing wood stock, 1/0 to ½ for medium-fine finishing (smoothing), and 3/0 to 2/0 for very fine sanding. These numbers refer to the garnet abrasive. Aluminum oxide and silicon carbide equivalents are indicated in Table 126-1.

Large Belt Table Sander

The main adjustments on this machine include *raising and lowering* each of the two pulleys (Fig. 126-1), *tightening* the sanding belt with tension screws, and *aligning* the idler pulley to make the sanding belt track properly. These are all controlled with handles and hand wheels, the placement of which can be seen in Figs. 125-1 and 125-2. *Installing* a new belt requires

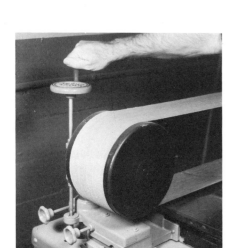

126-1. Adjusting a belt pulley for height above the sanding table.

126-2. Regulating the idler pulley to align the abrasive belt.

126-3. Aligning the table at 90 degrees with the disk.

Table 126-1 ABRASIVE SELECTIONS

Wood	Rough sanding	Medium-fine sanding	Very fine sanding
Hardwoods	Natural 2½–1½ Artificial 36–50	Natural ½–1/0 Artificial 60–100	Natural 2/0–5/0 Artificial 120–180
Softwoods	Natural 1½–1	Natural 1/0	Natural 2/0–5/0

Comparison of *natural* (garnet) grit numbers and *artificial* (aluminum oxide and silicon carbide) sizes of grits:

3 = 24 grit	2/0 = 100 grit
2½ = 30 grit	3/0 = 120 grit
1½ = 40 grit	4/0 = 150 grit
1 = 50 grit	5/0 = 180 grit
½ = 60 grit	6/0 = 220 grit
1/0 = 80 grit	8/0 = 280 grit

removal of the sanding hood (drum guard). Release the tension on the belt, and replace it with a new one of the same length.

Small Vertical and Horizontal Sanders

The angle **tilt** (of the table for the vertical sander and of the fence for the horizontal one) is made with a hand adjustment under the table or at the end of the fence. Both are similar in operation.

Replacement of the sanding belt entails loosening the tension on the idler pulley, removing the outside of the case, and then taking off the worn belt. The new sanding belt should be put over the two pulleys and then the case is placed back on.

The idler pulley should be carefully **regulated** to align the abrasive belt (Fig. 126-2).

Disk Sander

The **tilt** of the disk sander table is adjusted with the handle, which is usually underneath the table. This can be loosened and tightened to adjust the angle. The table is usually set at 90 degrees to the disk (Fig. 126-3).

Installing a new sanding disk requires removal of the worn abrasive paper on the metal disk plate. Sanding disks of the correct diameter are available as replacements.

Usually the worn disk can be peeled off. If it does not loosen, hold the end of a wooden block against the sanding disk while it is revolving. The heat of friction tends to loosen the paper.

If the paper disk has been fastened with wood glue to the metal plate, it will have to be soaked off with water. This requires loosening the metal disk from the motor shaft.

Manufacturers recommend the use of a commercial stick cement which is applied to the revolving plate (Fig. 126-4) to fasten the new paper disk to the metal plate (Fig. 126-5). A band of the stick cement is also rubbed on the outer edge of the paper disk to make it adhere to the metal plate.

Spindle Sander

The angle of **table tilt** is usually the only adjustment that is made on the spindle, or drum, sander. On some machines this is a matter of regulating the table to the desired angle by means of a handle located under it. On others, spindle tilt makes the angle, the spindle being regulated by a hand wheel located under the table. In either case, a calibrated index pointer shows the angle of tilt.

Replacing sanding drums is also an adjustment. On some drums, the abrasive paper or cloth is cemented on; on others, the sleeves are slipped over rubber drums that are held tight by expansion of the rubber under pressure.

126-4. Applying stick cement to the metal plate to fasten the abrasive disk.

126-5. Fastening an abrasive sheet on the disk.

Unit 127 Safety for Floor-model Sanders

■ **Permission.** Always secure permission before using floor-model sanders.
■ **Clothing.** Do not wear loose clothing. Tuck in your necktie. Roll or button your sleeves.
■ **Jewelry.** Remove your ring if you wear one. It could catch on something and cause injury to your hand.

■ **Hands.** Work safely by keeping both hands from getting too near moving abrasive disks, belts, or drums. Your finger tips can be "burned" (abrasion-cut) quickly.

■ **Eye protection.** Wear a face shield or goggles. Sanding dust can be blown into your eyes, harming them.

■ **Adjustments.** Make sure that all adjustments are correctly made and that the parts are locked securely befor you start to sand.

■ **Sanding disk.** Make certain that the abrasive disk is fastened firmly to the metal plate.

■ **Burning the wood or abrasive.** Move the work about to avoid heating and burning a portion of the abrasive disk, belt, or wood.

■ **Belt tension.** Check to be sure that the sanding belt is neither too loose nor too tight.

■ **Abrasive belts and drums.** Make certain that you select the proper grade of grit and the correct size of belt or drum for the sanding desired.

■ **Belt tracking.** Check the installation of an abrasive belt after it has been put on. Make certain it tracks (runs evenly on the pulleys).

■ **Belt direction.** Note the direction in which the belt, disk, or drum turns. This helps you to decide how to hold the piece being sanded or how to hold the pressure of the belt on the project.

■ **Disk direction.** Sand only on the down-stroke half of the disk to control the piece.

■ **Sanding small pieces.** Do not sand small pieces on floor-model sanders unless you have devised a jig to hold them securely.

■ **Push stick.** Use a push stick in sanding small or thin pieces on the small horizontal-belt sander.

■ **Stopping.** Shut off the power, and do not leave until the sander has come to a complete stop.

Unit 128 Sanding on Floor-model Sanders

Sanders smooth wood in preparation for applying finishes. In this process, only a small amount of the material is removed. Where possible, the floor model, or stationary, sander should be connected to an exhaust system to remove sanding dust. It must be remembered that either the piece being sanded or the sanding pad (on large belt sanders) must be continuously moved for even sanding.

Sanding on the Large Belt Table Sander

1. If the machine design permits, adjust the height of the pulleys operating the sanding belt to the desired clearance from the work. On a large machine, the table may even be removed so that a built-up project can be sanded. See Fig. 125-1.

The smaller floor-model horizontal sander permits some vertical adjustment of the pulleys relative to the movable table.

The sanding belt should be about 1 to 2 inches above the piece being sanded.

2. See that the correct abrasive grit is on the sanding belt.

3. Press down on the inside of the moving sanding belt. Use either the hand-stroke belt sander block or the sanding attachment pad (Fig. 128-1). Continue moving the pad and the piece back and forth, and lengthwise, until the surface is smooth and evenly sanded.

Sanding on Small Vertical and Horizontal Sanders

1. Adjust the table (of the vertical sander) or the fence (of the horizontal sander) for the sanding angle desired. This will usually be a 90-degree angle to the sanding belt.

2. Be sure to see that the abrasive belt is of the correct grit. Also check the proper alignment of the belt on the pulleys.

128-1. Sanding an end table top on a large horizontal-belt sander.

128-2. Sanding a smooth surface on a small **horizontal-belt sander.**

128-4. Sanding a bevel on a vertical-belt sander.

128-6. Sanding an end on the disk sander.

3. Move the work on the table slowly into contact with the moving sanding belt. Continue moving the face or the edge much the same way as you did when planing on the jointer (Figs. 128-2, 128-3, and 128-4).

Sanding on the Disk Sander

1. Adjust the table for the sanding angle desired. For most work it should be at a 90-degree angle to the disk.

2. See that the disk abrasive is of the correct grit.

3. Move the piece on the table slowly into contact with the revolving disk. Continue moving it until the edge or end is smooth and even (Figs. 128-5 and 128-6). Feed the work into the disk on the *down side* of the rotation.

Sanding on the Spindle Sander

1. Adjust the table or the spindle for the sanding angle desired.

2. See that the correct grade of grit is on the abrasive drum.

3. Move the piece on the table slowly into contact with the revolving sanding drum. Continue moving the piece until the edge is smooth and even (Fig. 128-7).

See Unit 86 for another method of spindle, or drum, sanding.

4. Figure 128-8 shows a special sanding attachment fastened on a motor for final finishing of turned spindles.

128-7. Sanding an edge on the spindle sander.

128-3. Sanding an edge on a small horizontal-belt sander.

128-5. Sanding a convex (outside) edge on the disk sander.

128-8. Sanding a turned spindle.

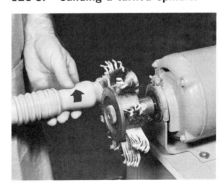

1. Name the four types of floor-model sanders illustrated and described.
2. Name four important parts of each type, and list the uses for each.
3. Why is the belt sanding machine in Fig. 125-1 called a **reversible sanding machine?**
4. What is the purpose of the idler pulley on a belt sander?
5. Which types of floor-model sanders do you have in your industrial laboratory?
6. List 10 safety rules to observe when using floor model sanders.
7. Why is it dangerous to use a disk sander which has a loose sanding disk?
8. Why should you keep the sanding contact with the piece moving continuously?
9. List three general grit classifications for abrasive belts, sheets, and drums.
10. What is meant by **belt tracking?** How is it controlled?
11. What is another name for a spindle sanding machine?
12. Visit a building contractor, mill and sash company, furniture manufacturer, or other wood-products manufacturing plant. Make a report on the types and sizes of floor-model sanders in use. Explain the purposes for which they are used.

Automated assembly-line sanding of plywood panels.

(Timesavers Sanders, Inc.)

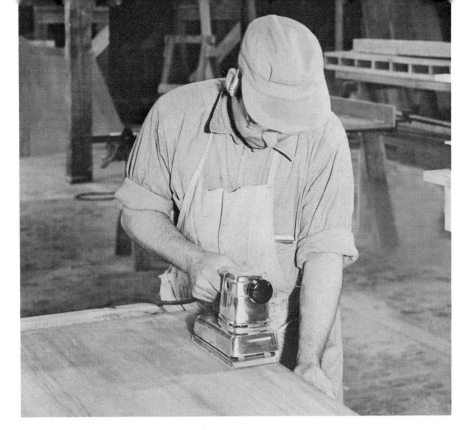

SECTION 21

SANDING WITH PORTABLE BELT AND FINISHING SANDERS

Unit 129 General Information About Portable Electric Sanders

Portable electric sanders are often used to sand wood surfaces smooth. The two described and illustrated in this unit are (1) the belt (Fig. 129-1) and (2) the finishing (Fig. 129-2) sanders. Other types of portable sanders used by building contractors and carpenters are disk and floor models. Each of the two sanders discussed has a specific purpose, and each is somewhat limited with respect to general sanding processes.

Information on the selection of correct abrasives and grits is given in Unit 126, "Abrasives and Adjustments." Each manufacturer has ready-

321

made abrasive sheets which fit his particular brand and model. Replacements can be cut from standard abrasive sheets. Garnet and manufactured abrasives usually make the best coatings for the sheets.

Portable Belt Sander (Parts and Uses)

This lightweight machine is probably the most useful of all the portable sanders. It not only smooths boards but can remove finishing materials (paint, enamel, varnish, or lacquer).

The portable belt sander (see Fig. 129-1) has an abrasive belt which runs continuously over pulleys situated at both ends. The average portable model weighs between 10 and 20 pounds. Its size is usually determined by the size of the belt. Two typical sizes are 3 by 24 inches and 4 by 27 inches.

Lighter portable sanders are available without dust bags. These are often considered home-workshop types. The heavier machine, which is more useful for school and industrial work, is usually equipped with the dust bag.

Figure 129-3 is a cutaway view of a 3 by 24-inch dustless belt sander. The names of its parts are clearly shown on this illustration. They are also seen in Fig. 129-1.

■ **Motor housing.** This housing is usually made of cast aluminum to reduce the weight of the machine. It is the front portion of the frame which houses the motor.

■ **Frame.** The frame is an aluminum casting to which is fastened the motor housing and other parts of the machine.

■ **Traction wheel.** The traction wheel is the rear pulley, which drives the abrasive belt.

■ **Idler wheel.** The idler wheel is the front pulley. It provides tension on the abrasive belt.

■ **Handle.** The handle is usually made of composition or plastic (shockproof) material; it contains the trigger switch. A ball knob or a front handle is also

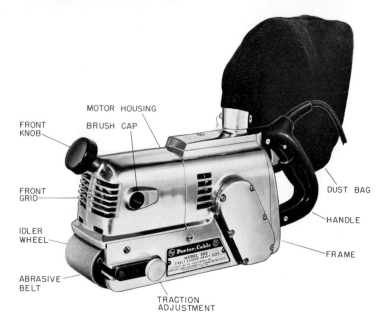

129-1. A portable belt sander.

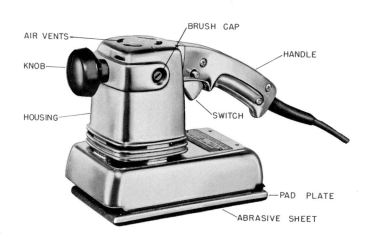

129-2. An orbital finishing sander.

mounted because operation of the sander requires use of both hands.

■ **Dust bag.** This is a removable bag which catches the dust and which can be emptied when full.

■ **Shoe base.** The shoe base is a metal plate over which the back of the abrasive belt moves. It forces the belt to make contact with the wood.

■ **Abrasive belt.** Belts are available in many grits (rough to fine) to fit portable electric belt sanders of different sizes.

Finishing Sander (Parts and Uses)

Finishing sanders are either orbital (circular) or oscillating (back and forth,

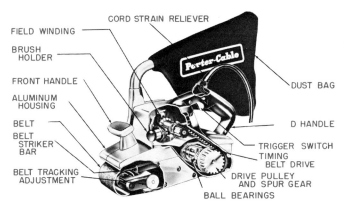

FIELD WINDING
BRUSH HOLDER
FRONT HANDLE
ALUMINUM HOUSING
BELT
BELT STRIKER BAR
BELT TRACKING ADJUSTMENT
CORD STRAIN RELIEVER
Porter-Cable
DUST BAG
D HANDLE
TRIGGER SWITCH
TIMING BELT DRIVE
DRIVE PULLEY AND SPUR GEAR
BALL BEARINGS

129-3. A cutaway view of a dustless belt sander.

BRUSH HOLDER
TRIGGER SWITCH
CONTOURED HANDLE
FRONT HAND KNOB
ALUMINUM HOUSING
CORD STRAIN RELIEVER
PAPER CLAMP
PAPER CLAMP
PAD
BALL BEARINGS

129-4. A cutaway view of a finishing sander.

or vibrating) in motion. Both types look practically alike. Figure 129-2 pictures an orbital sander.

The designation "finishing sander" means that this tool is used for fine sanding. It is sometimes used to obtain a finer surface finish after using the belt sander. The orbital type cuts faster because of the way it moves its abrasive pad.

Finishing sanders vary in size to take one-fourth, one-third, or one-half-sheet sizes of abrasive paper or cloth. Their weights vary from 4 to 10 pounds.

Figure 129-4 is a cutaway view of many parts of the finishing sander. Figure 129-2 also indicates essential parts.

- **Motor housing.** This housing is usually made of cast aluminum to reduce the weight of the machine. It houses the motor and all other parts of the sander.

- **Pad plate.** Abrasive sheets are fastened and locked to the pad plate, which forces them to make contact with the wood.

- **Clamps.** The pad plate has a clamp at each end which holds the abrasive sheet.

- **Handle.** The hand-fitting aluminum handle includes the trigger switch. There is usually a second handle on the front so that this tool can be operated with both hands.

Unit 130 Operating Adjustments

Portable sanders require adjustments when the sanding belt on the belt sander and the abrasive sheet on the finishing sander need replacing. Each adjustment necessitates attention to get maximum wear out of the abrasives. An additional adjustment on the belt sander is a periodic inspection of the carbon brushes. The finishing sander has fewer adjustments.

Adjustments on the Belt Sander

- **Installing an abrasive belt.** Abrasive belts are installed as described below.

1. Lay the sander on its left side. Make sure it is *disconnected* from the power outlet.

2. Release the tension from the idler pulley (wheel). This should be done according to the manufacturer's instructions.

3. Remove the worn-out belt.

4. Slip the new belt over the rear (traction) wheel (Fig. 130-1). The arrow printed on the inside of the belt should point *in the direction* the belt will turn. Be sure to make certain that you have the right belt size and the correct grit.

5. Position the belt so that the outer edge is even with the ends of the wheels.

6. Release the tension so that the idler wheel puts pressure on the sanding belt.

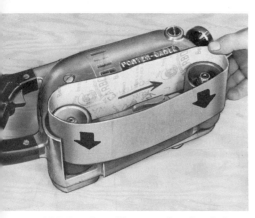

130-1. Installing an abrasive belt on a portable sander.

7. Adjust the belt tracking. Tilt the sander back, start the motor, and turn the belt alignment screw so the outer edge of the belt runs even with the ends of the wheel (Fig. 130-2).

■ **Checking the switch.** Many sanders have a locking trigger in the handle. Learn how to use this before sanding. If the locking button sticks out from the handle, it is off (Fig. 130-3). When it is flush with the side of the handle, it is on. Some machines have a locking button which holds the switch on. You must squeeze the trigger into the handle to release it.

130-2. "Tracking" the sanding belt.

130-3. A locking trigger switch in the handle.

■ **Brush inspection.** The motor brushes should be inspected often for wear. Remove one brush cap; withdraw the spring and brush (carbon). See Fig. 130-4. If the carbon is $\frac{3}{16}$ inch or longer, put it back exactly as it was. If not, put in a new one. Check the brush on the opposite side.

Adjustments on the Finishing Sander

■ **Installing an abrasive sheet.** Abrasive sheets are installed as described in the next column.

130-4. Inspecting a brush (carbon) on a belt sander.

130-5. Stretching an abrasive sheet over the base pad.

1. Release the clamps which hold the worn abrasive sheet. Remove it.

2. Slip one end of the new abrasive sheet around either end of the base pad. See Fig. 130-5. Check to see that you have the proper size and the correct grit.

3. Clamp this end of the sheet in place.

4. Stretch the sheet tightly over the pad (Fig. 130-5).

5. Insert the free end of the abrasive sheet under the clamp at the other end (Fig. 130-6).

6. Fasten the clamp in place.

130-6. Clamping the opposite end of an abrasive sheet to the base pad.

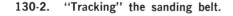

Unit 131 Safety for Portable Electric Sanders

■ **Permission.** Always secure permission before using the portable electric sander.

■ **Clothing.** Do not wear loose clothing. Tuck in your necktie. Roll up or button your sleeves.

■ **Jewelry.** Remove your ring if you wear one.

■ **Eye protection.** Wear a face shield or goggles when using the portable electric belt sander. The motor fan might blow dust from the vents into your eyes.

■ **Hands.** Keep both hands on the handles of the belt sander. This makes it impossible to feel the sanded surface while sanding, thereby endangering your hand.

■ **Electrical grounding.** Check to see that the electrical connection is grounded.

■ **Electric cord.** Arrange the electric cord so that it cannot be caught by the abrasive belt. A good arrangement for safety is to hang the cord over your shoulder. Keep the cord free, and prevent it from being drawn between the abrasive belt and the housing.

■ **Machine protection.** Hold on to the handle of the sander when you plug it into the electrical circuit. This prevents possible damage to the machine. Someone might have turned the switch on without your knowledge. The machine could jerk off the bench.

■ **Belt direction.** When installing an abrasive belt, point the arrow on its back in the direction the belt will turn.

■ **Abrasive belts and sheets.** Make certain that you select the correct size of belt or sheet and the proper grade of grit to do the job.

■ **Changing belts and sheets.** Disconnect the plug from the power outlet when changing abrasive belts or sheets.

■ **Belt tracking.** Check the installation of an abrasive belt after it has been put on. Make certain it tracks properly (is in alignment with the edge).

■ **Starting.** Always lift the sander before starting to sand and also before cutting off the power.

■ **Sander weight.** The weight of either sander is sufficient to do normal sanding. Do not exert more pressure. It might strain the motor too much.

■ **Sander at rest.** Lay the belt sander on its side when you are not using it.

■ **Stopping.** Shut off the power, and do not put down the portable sander until it comes to a complete stop.

Unit 132 Sanding with Portable Sanders

Sanding with portable machines requires carefully planned procedures. Belt and finishing (orbital and oscillating) sanders are easy to operate and control. However, it is important to remember to keep the machines *moving* when they are in use. These sanders have sufficient weight that no additional pressure should be applied. They are guided over the surface of the piece with the hands. *Always lift* the sander from the work before starting and stopping the motor, as shown in Fig. 132-1.

Use a spaced coarse-grain or open-coat abrasive belt or sheet to remove old paint, enamel, varnish, and lacquer from flat surfaces with either type of sander. When working with these ma-

132-1. Lift the sander from the work before starting or stopping the motor.

132-2. Sanding with a portable belt sander.

132-3. Sanding with a finishing sander.

chines to remove finishes, lower them at the far end of the work and pull them back. Raise them, and repeat the cycle in another area.

Portable sanders, with proper abrasive materials, can be used on metals, slate, marble, or plastic materials. The only difference in working on these materials is that there is no grain to consider.

Sanding with a Belt Sander

1. Fasten the board or project firmly.

2. Select an abrasive belt of the proper grit (abrasive coarseness). See Table 126-1. Grit is graded as coarse, medium, and fine. Start with either coarse or medium.

3. Install the belt. Follow steps 1 through 7 in Unit 130.

4. Using both hands, place the sander on the board or project to get the "feel" of it.

5. Lift the sander with both hands, and turn on the trigger switch (Fig. 132-1).

6. Lower the sander to the wood surface. Guide it over the piece with both hands. Work the machine in the direction of the grain (Fig. 132-2).

7. Move the sander forward, backward, and sideways. Do not pause in any one spot while sanding.

8. Turn off the power. Change the abrasive belts. Continue with finer grits until the surface has been smoothed for final finishing.

Sanding with a Finishing Sander

1. Fasten the board or project firmly.

2. Select an abrasive sheet of the correct grit. See Table 126-1. Start with a coarse- or medium-grit sheet.

3. Fasten the abrasive sheet on the base pad. Review the six steps for installing abrasive sheets listed in Unit 130, "Operating Adjustments."

4. Connect the plug to the electrical power outlet.

5. Lift the finishing sander off the board. Start the motor.

6. Set the sander down evenly on the project or piece. Move it back and forth (Fig. 132-3).

7. Guide the sander with the handle. Use both hands until you get the feel of its operation. The weight of the machine itself exerts sufficient pressure for most sanding.

8. Turn off the power. Change abrasive sheets. Continue with finer grits until the surface is smooth.

DISCUSSION TOPICS

1. Which type of finishing sander cuts faster? Why?
2. List 10 sander safety rules.
3. Why is it advisable to lift the belt sander when starting it and when turning it off?
4. Why should you keep a portable sander moving continuously while it is in use?

5. List three general grit classifications for abrasive belts and sheets.
6. Visit a building contractor, mill and sash company, furniture manufacturer, or other wood-products manufacturing plant. Report on the types and sizes of portable electric sanders in use. List the purposes for which they use them.

PREPARATION OF WOOD AND APPLICATION OF FINISHES

Unit 133 Preparing Wood Surfaces and Selecting a Finish

133-1. The furniture manufacturers hand-clean and sand their products before finish is applied.

Wood selected for a project should be chosen for its beauty, strength, and general usefulness. Preparing wood surfaces and selecting the finish the wood will take best are important parts of planning the most efficient procedure. Each craftsman has his personal preferences and methods.

Woods and Finishes

See Unit 3, "Classification and Characteristics of Trees," and Unit 4, "Species of Wood," for detailed descriptions of hard- and softwoods.

The woodworker soon learns that the quality of a finish can be no better than the surface to which it is applied. Stains and natural finishes bring out the beauty of wood grain, but they also magnify defects instead of covering and minimizing them. Minor blemishes, scratches, and planer and jointer marks may appear slight in bare wood, but they are emphasized when the finish is put on.

The design and construction of a project determine whether the entire project can be sanded after assembly or whether parts are more conveniently sanded first.

Sanding Surfaces

Sanding operations are divided into four general categories. The first three are **rough, preparatory,** and **prefinish.** See Unit 29, "Sanding by Hand." Also read SECTION 20, "Sanding on Floor-model Sanders," and SECTION 21, "Sanding with Portable Belt and Finishing Sanders." The fourth category of sanding is **finish.** The final cleaning is done (Fig. 133-1) and the surface is finished "in the white." This expression means that all surfaces are completely sanded and ready for bleaching, staining, filling, or other finishing operations. Proper sanding of the final coat of finish removes dried bubbles, trapped particles, and other blemishes in the finish that might otherwise spoil its beauty.

Finishing Abrasives

Pumice, rottenstone, and tripoli are special powdered abrasives that are derived from natural sources.

Pumice is a powdered volcanic lava that makes a relatively coarse abrasive. It is used for rubbing final finishes to help smooth the surface before using rottenstone or tripoli.

Rottenstone is very fine and much softer than other abrasives. It is made from decomposed limestone shale (fossilized rock); it has a dark grayish color. The name comes from the offensive odor given off when the shale is

133-2.   Blemish-repair materials: (1) lemon oil; (2) French polish; (3) varnish remover; (4) denatured alcohol; (5) touch-up gun; (6) felt; (7) abrasive papers; (8) steel wool; (9) dulling brush; (10) pencil brushes; (11) stick shellac; (12) spirit stain; (13) masking tape; (14) burning-in knife; and (15) alcohol lamp.

broken and ground into powder.

Tripoli is rottenstone that owes its name to Tripoli, Libya, where it is found. It is used with a lubricant, such as lemon oil, for rubbing finishes.

Man-made abrasives for final finishes are **boron carbide** (B_4C), which is next to the diamond in hardness; **silicon carbide** (SiC); and **aluminum oxide** (Al_2O_3). They are the result of heating combinations of chemicals and solids to very high temperatures.

Steel wool is an abrasive of a different type. It is used to remove, clean, or rub and polish finishes. Its grades are No. 3 (coarse), No. 2, No. 1, and Nos. 0 to 4/0 (extra fine). Grades No. 3/0 and No. 4/0 are used to buff and rub down final coats of finish.

Because this material is made of fine steel shavings, there are some disadvantages in using it. For example, the coarser grades can easily cut your hands. The fine grades, on the other hand, permit steel dust particles to fly free in the air, where they can be inhaled. Also, steel wool rusts where there is considerable humidity.

The disadvantages of steel wool have

been overcome by the development of the ultrafine **garnet pad.** It resembles steel wool and is used for the same purposes. The pad is spun until it resembles steel wool. It is soft, resilient, nonrusting, long-lasting, and easy on the hands; it produces a uniformly smooth finish.

Repairing Blemishes before Finishing

Holes from knots and other causes, cracks, scratches, and other imperfections should be repaired either during the initial (first) sanding operation or before the prefinish operation. It is not possible to make the repaired area look exactly like the surrounding grained areas, but the surfaces can be smoothed and the blemishes made less noticeable. Many blemish-repair materials are shown in Fig. 133-2.

■ **Raising the grain.** Serious scratches and deeper impressions can be raised by sponging them with very warm water and then steaming them with a warm iron. An electric iron is useful for this purpose, but do not burn the wood.

133-3. Masking a crack or blemish for repair.

133-4. Heating a spatula or flexible knife and stick shellac to prepare for filling a crack.

133-5. Packing stick shellac into a crack.

■ **Large holes and small, rough knots.** These can be made uniform size by using a wood auger or a Foerstner bit. A plug cutter is used to cut a round plug from a similar piece of wood. Be sure the grain in the plug runs in the same direction as the grain in the area where the plug is inserted.

■ **Screwheads.** It is sometimes necessary to counterbore for screwheads on visible surfaces to make the assembly of parts easier. After sanding the surface, the holes can be plugged with smooth or rounded screw-hole buttons. These fill the holes and at the same time decorate the surface.

■ **Cracks.** Favorite materials to fill cracks and other blemishes are stick shellac and lacquer. These sticks can be purchased in solid white, natural, clear, and more than 70 colors. Stick shellac is heated and worked into the crack or opening with a heated spatula, flat knife, electric soldering iron, or special heating device. The process of repair after finishing is called **burning in.**

These repairs should *not* be done in the finishing room because the materials are flammable.

The device used to burn in should be kept at a constant temperature that is just under the heat that will discolor the stick shellac used. Practice on scrap material to determine the heat needed. It is best to repair the surface *before sanding:*

1. Mask the crack with masking tape (Fig. 133-3).

2. Heat the end of a flexible spatula or knife, and apply the stick shellac (Fig. 133-4).

3. Pack the shellac into the crack until it is full (Fig. 133-5).

4. Remove the tape and cut off the excess shellac (Fig. 133-6).

5. Back up No. 6/0 finish paper with a felt or cloth pad. Dip the paper in alcohol and then in rubbing oil or water. Rub the patch quickly and firmly with five or six strokes (Fig. 133-7).

6. Dull the patch by rubbing lightly with No. 3/0 steel wool.

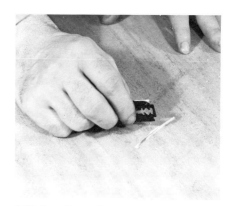

133-6. Removing excess shellac.

133-7. Rubbing the patch or repair mark with rubbing oil, alcohol, and water.

133-8. Spraying on a thin coat of clear lacquer to build up a finish coat over a blemish.

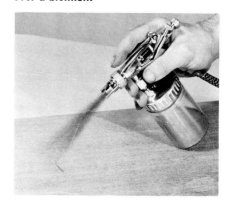

7. If a thin coat results because of rubbing, use spray equipment and spray on a coat of clear lacquer or ether varnish (Fig. 133-8), and rub down the entire surface.

Wood plastic, wood dough, and water putty (a dry powder which is mixed with water) are especially useful for repairing deep blemishes. A prepared surfacing putty can be purchased for use on small imperfections. See Unit 29, "Sanding by Hand," for instructions on the application of wood dough or plastic to fill imperfections.

Although most materials for repairing blemishes shrink very little, many will not allow stains to penetrate. The repaired area never looks exactly like the original wood grain. Plan the work carefully, select good materials, and perform all operations carefully to eliminate errors and blemishes.

Selecting Final Finishes

A final finish can be selected from among oils, waxes, shellacs, lacquers, varnishes, paints, and enamels (Fig. 133-9). Several of these permit different mixtures for special purposes. The choice of a final finish is very important to protect and beautify the wood in the project.

133-9. Lacquer enamels give a bright, clean appearance to older kitchen furnishings.

Brush and spray finishing at room temperature are the methods most often used in the school industrial laboratory and the home workshop. Industries often use hot-spray finishes and infrared drying (Fig. 133-10).

133-10. Hot spray finishes and infrared drying are used by many modern furniture manufacturers.

Unit 134 History of Finishes

Asphalt or bituminous (tarlike natural substance) coatings have been known and used as preservatives for centuries. Skeletons of prehistoric animals were found perfectly preserved in the La Brea asphalt pits near Los Angeles, California, a good example of permanent preservation by moistureproofing. Pitch, asphalt, wax, and paint were used many thousand years ago to protect and preserve surfaces.

History of Varnish

The word "varnish" is derived from the Latin word *vernix*. A translucent fossilized resin which we know as amber was transported from the North Sea to Egypt. It is believed that this substance was named "Berenice" after the Queen of Cyrene, who was married to an Egyptian pharoah. (Cyrene was a Greek city and colony in Cyrenaica, North Africa, about 550 B.C.)

These **fossilized resins** and **copals** (fossilized tree resins) were once favored in the manufacture of varnish. Copals were dug from the earth in the upper African Congo and in India. Chemists have now, however, developed synthetic resins which are more durable than the original fossil gums.

History of Shellac

Natives of India were using shellac to protect surfaces in homes and temples before the time of Julius Caesar

(100–44 B.C.). Europe did not use this substance until just before 1600, although Marco Polo had introduced it several hundred years before.

Once a year tiny insects swarm on the **lac trees** in India. They are carried by wind, birds, and other insects. These small bugs are scientifically called *Tachardia lacca*. They often cluster so thickly that the trees appear reddish in color. By sucking the tree sap into their bodies they literally eat themselves to death.

During this time, the female lays about 1,000 eggs at a time. The sap of the tree is secreted as a gum, which covers both the bugs and the eggs. This liquid hardens and several months later is broken as the eggs hatch and the young move to other trees. The crust is harvested from the tree twigs, put through several purifying processes, and made into a gum which is the basis of commercial shellac.

Shellac is used in drafting inks, lead pencils, electrical wire coating, as a hat stiffener, and as a base coat for other finishes. It is also used to guard against dust, dirt, and wear.

History of Lacquer

Lacquer is a quick-drying product that plays a very important role in wood finishing. It is constantly being changed and improved.

Records show that the Japanese and the Chinese were using lacquer over 2,000 years ago. Plain wooden pieces were often covered with several hundred layers of lacquer until the coating was thick enough to carve. These objects, which are now priceless, often required years of labor to complete. The oriental lacquer needed moisture to cause it to harden properly.

Ancient Chinese lacquer was obtained from the sap of a tree. The tree was tapped, and the sap emerged as a grayish-white liquid that darkened to black when exposed to air. It was eventually pounded, heated, stirred to evap-

orate excess moisture, and then stored in airtight containers.

After World War I, explosives manufacturers had a surplus of gun cotton (nitrocellulose) and butyl alcohol with its esters and other chemicals. From these surplus materials chemists developed a synthetic lacquer which dried very rapidly. This was a valuable characteristic, especially for use in new automobile and furniture finishes. Lacquer also became a valuable finish for shoes and leather products and is often used in hair spray, fingernail polish, and literally thousands of other product finishes.

History of Paint

Paints date back to the cave man. They have been used through the years to decorate surfaces and protect them from the weather. Paint is also used effectively to improve lighting and heating effects for better working conditions. It promotes safety and adds to cleanliness and sanitation.

Water-thinned paints, made from casein and egg white or glue, were used by the Egyptians as early as 3000 to 2000 B.C. Very little progress was made in paint for centuries. In the early colonial days in America, lime and water made a whitewash mixture that was used as paint. In the early part of the twentieth century, animal glue and whiting (chalk from the White Cliffs of Dover, England) were mixed to use as a binder for pigment. This calcimine paint was not highly washable or durable.

Casein paint was developed about the same time as calcimine paint. It was composed of casein, whiting, preservatives, and a hiding pigment (coloring substance). This type of paint was widely used at the Chicago World's Fair.

Vegetable oils made possible the oil-resin and latex-emulsion paints. "Latex" once referred only to a substance extracted from the rubber plant, but it now refers to a variety of synthetic resins.

Oil-base paints are extremely popular. They consist mainly of either white or colored pigments and certain vehicles, or liquids. These paints are used extensively for both exterior and interior work. A good house paint should contain at least 65 percent pigment, the remaining 35 percent or less being composed of the vehicle. Linseed oil is the most important of all drying oils; it is obtained from flax seed. Drying oil is an oily liquid which, applied as a thin film, dries or hardens within 48 hours when exposed to normal weather. This oil should compose 80 to 90 percent of the vehicle, with thinners (turpentine and mixed spirits) and driers making up the remainder. Castor, tung, fish, perilla (Asiatic mints), poppy, hemp seed, and soya are other drying oils which give different characteristics to a particular paint.

Basic carbonate or sulfate of lead (white lead) is widely used as a hiding pigment, and the vegetable, animal, or mineral color pigments are added. Extender pigments do little in covering a surface, but they are necessary to prevent the other pigments from settling into a hard mass.

Some other pigments used are zinc oxide, titanium dioxide, titanium magnesium, titanium barium, and titanium oxide.

Various formulas are derived for different paints. Materials are added to prevent such common paint failures as chalking, checking, cracking and scaling, mildew, blistering, and discoloration.

Paint, a World Development

Materials for paints from the animal, vegetable, and mineral kingdoms have been obtained from every part of the world. Linseed oil from the flax fields, varnish gums from buried prehistoric forests, and tung oil from China and later from the southern United States are some of the ingredients used to manufacture paint.

Manganese, cobalt, lead, zinc, chalk, and iron oxides contribute mineral pigments for paints. Oil and gas fields produce their share of mineral spirits, carbon and lamp blacks, and benzine (naptha).

Beeswax, shellac gum, and some lime from oyster shells are used in paints.

Agricultural implements, mechanical and electrical products, modern buildings, magnificent steel structures, and literally thousands of other products owe their usefulness to paint. Permanence, stability, safety, and beauty are brought about by the uses of paint in the entire scheme of modern science, engineering, and living.

Unit 135 History, Use, and Care of Brushes

Records indicate that the ancient Egyptians were the first to use paint-brushes, which were made from split reeds soaked in water (Fig. 135-1). Greece supplanted Egypt as the center of civilization, and the Greeks utilized the tails and feet of small fur-bearing animals for their brushes. During this time, classic antique art flourished. A decline of civilization during the Dark Ages decreased personal artistry and brought about less use and demand for brushes until the Renaissance.

In the thirteenth century, castle walls were whitened by using a pound of bristles tied to a stick to spread the finish. Brush makers guilds were formed in England and France, and they were given special privileges. Flat brushes did not appear until after 1840. The American brush industry efficiently designed and developed the modern metal-bound paint and varnish brushes during the early part of this century (Fig. 135-2).

Finishing brushes are made in numerous shapes and sizes for specific purposes (Fig. 135-3). Most finishers, however, prefer a chisel-edge brush.

Brush Making

Bristle is the name given to the hair of the wild boar. The unique characteristics of the hair (Fig. 135-4) are not found in the hair of any other animal. The **split end,** or **flag,** and the **taper** from the root to the flag make this hair the most important material used in brush manufacture. The bristle (hair)

is tapered like a flag pole. These qualities of bristle give a brush the ability to hold and carry paint just as a pen carries ink. No natural substitute has been found that is more satisfactory for making brushes than the bristle.

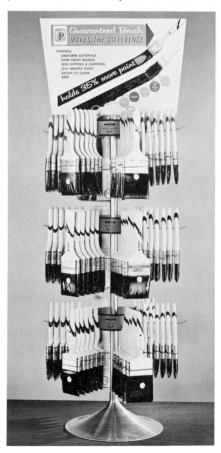

135-2. Common consumer brushes are made in many sizes. Professional painters use more expensive tools.

135-1. Brushes used by ancient Egyptians were made of split reeds soaked in water.

Bristles vary in quality and go through many processes before being formed into the final brush. The hair is collected, cleaned, tied in batches, transported, sorted, mixed (Fig. 135-5), weighed (Fig. 135-6), and combed. Eventually a well-designed brush is assembled by hand (Fig. 135-7) from a mixture of many kinds and lengths of bristle. Some brushes are manufactured by automation (Fig. 135-8).

Coarse brushes (not classified as paintbrushes) are made from many materials other than bristles and soft hair. Some of the materials are horsehair, istle or tampico fibers (cactus family), palmetto and other palms, and rice root. Thousands of different grades of brushes are made from tampico fiber. Rice root is a crinkly root of a large bunch grass that grows in Mexico and Guatamala.

Soft-hair brushes are made mostly from fur-bearing animals of the weasel family. Coarse brushes in this category are made from the hair of the ox and the goat.

The most valuable hair to the brush maker is the red sable, or Siberian mink. Other hairs used are "camel hair" (actually Siberian and Russian squirrel), black sable (civet cat), fitch (tail of the American skunk), American black bear, badger, and genet (dyed hair of the ringtail and other wild cats).

After the bristle and the hair are mixed and worked to shape, size, and specifications, the flag end is "gum set" (set in a gum) temporarily so that it can be more easily handled. Eventually the butt end is dipped in rubber to vulcanize (harden), heated to remove solvents (dissolving liquids), ferruled (banded with metal), drilled, riveted, and attached to the handle, which is usually made of beech or maple wood. The brush is then finished, inspected, and made ready for shipment.

Nylon bristles were developed to replace Chinese boar bristles during

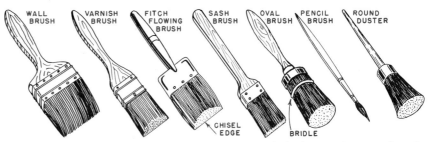

135-3. Many shapes and sizes of brushes are made for amateurs and professional painters and finishers.

135-4. The bristle of the wild boar is the best hair for brush making.

135-6. Stock for a medium-cost brush is weighed and placed in a ferrule, or metal band. A machine performs similar operations to make smaller, low-cost brushes.

135-5. Eight to twelve types of either boar bristle or synthetic filament are required for mixing a good paint brush.

135-7. High-quality paint brushes are assembled by individual workers.

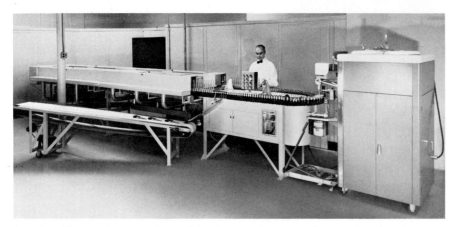

135-8. The equipment pictured is that used to manufacture brushes by automation. Brush parts are loaded on a conveyor, which carries them through the various manufacturing operations to the assembled brush.

World War II. The Chinese bristles had replaced the Russian boar bristles at the time of World War I. The nylon brush is satisfactory in many ways. It lasts much longer than bristle, is uniformly solid, lays a smooth film of paint, and carries paint well. It is resistant to solvents and water, and it can be stored easier without molding. Shellac tends to soften nylon, but the nylon bristles will return to their proper condition if the brush is placed in water after it has been cleaned.

Care and Use of Brushes

Most brushes are discarded because of improper care and use, not because of wear. For longer brush usefulness:

1. Remove loose bristles before using a brush, and dip the brush only part way into the finishing material.

2. Remove excess finish by drawing the flat side of the brush across the lip of the can.

3. Clean brushes immediately after use.

4. Wash completely in the proper solvent. This is usually the thinner for the finishing material used. Wash shellac brushes in alcohol; lacquer brushes in lacquer thinner; varnish, oil-paint, and enamel brushes in turpentine; and water-thinned paintbrushes in water.

5. Squeeze out excess solvent.

6. After the brush is clean, wash it with mild soap or detergent and warm water.

7. Remove excess water, and wrap the brush in clean paper to reshape the bristles as they dry. After drying, wrap the ferrule and bristles in heavy paper and band loosely with a rubber band.

Some painters recommend rubbing a light coat of linseed oil on brushes used in oil-base materials. If the brush is cleaned properly, this is not necessary on nylon bristles. Do not clean nylon-bristle brushes in lacquer thinner or liquids that contain acetone; the nylon would be damaged by the ingredients of these cleaners.

Unit 136 Spray Finishing

The person who supervises and controls spraying operations in industry has a very responsible job. The general beauty and quality of work is largely dependent upon skill of application and knowledge of proper equipment and finishing materials. Spray-gun equipment is used to apply many types of finishes. Stain, tones or shades of color finishes, shellac, and varnish are often sprayed on, as is lacquer. Attention must be given to all this equipment, including the spray gun, containers for finishing materials, hose and connections, air transformers and condensers, and the air-compressor units (Fig. 136-1).

For best results, consult spray equipment manufacturers for answers to particular problems. Only the minimum essentials are discussed here for general spray finishing in small operations.

Safety

Safe practices are absolutely essential in all shops and laboratories, especially in the finishing area. Volatile (vaporizable) finishing materials are very combustible. When improperly used, these materials can cause a fire, or they can explode. The vapors of most solvents should *never* be inhaled for any extended period of time because they can injure the respiratory system.

Follow these safety habits:

1. Place soiled rags and rags saturated with oil, finishes, and solvents in a special closed metal container. Empty the container frequently in some remote area, and see that the rags are burned in a safe place.

136-1. A typical small spray finishing unit.

136-2. Proper respirators give good protection against breathing toxic fumes when spraying finishes over long periods of time.

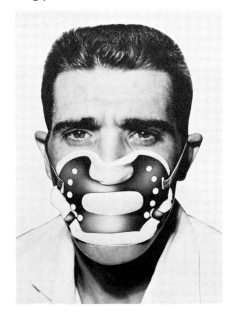

2. Vapor- and arcproof switches, relays, lights, and other electrical devices should be installed in a finish room.

3. Containers of solvents and finishing materials should be securely covered and stored in a fire-resistant or fireproof cabinet. Safety (fireproof) cans should be secured for those liquids which are most highly flammable.

4. Proper fire extinguishers and fire-fighting facilities should be easily accessible. Water, foam, dry chemical, or the soda-acid extinguishers should be available. Consult your local fire marshal to determine which one is best for local use.

Since many finishes and resinous or plastic materials are being used, *do not* use the carbon tetrachloride (CTC) type of extinguisher. When ''carbon tet'' is used on certain plastic fires, a *deadly gas* is produced. *Never* use water on an electrical fire!

5. The finishing area should have proper lighting, ventilation, and exhaust systems.

6. Mechanical, chemical, or combination respirators should be worn for protection against breathing toxic (poisonous) fumes and solid particles (Fig. 136-2).

7. The face, arms, and hands should be covered with a special protective cream or lotion. Hands should be protected by rubber gloves when handling volatile solvents or toxic liquids such as benzol. Cracked skin and infection result when there is too much natural skin oil lost.

8. Clean the floor and walls, and replace or clean the air filters frequently.

9. Label all cans clearly, and store them in an orderly arrangement. Use older materials first, or discard them. Do not use finishes that have been left standing for several years because they often deteriorate (decline in quality).

10. To pour liquids from one small opening in any size of container, turn the can so that the spout or opening is near the top when the can is tilted. Air can enter easily, and the liquid will pour smoothly and freely from the can and will not spatter or gurgle. Wipe all excess liquids off the can or other surfaces.

Spray Guns and Spray Finishing

The **airbrush** (Fig. 136-3) is a small spray gun used extensively in sign painting, finishing, photographs, and artwork. It operates on compressed air and requires exacting artistic technique to obtain satisfactory results.

Electrostatic spraying is used in many industries. This method, which is airless or which uses air broken into smaller particles, is based on the principle of supplying the material to the dispenser by hydraulic pressure (Fig. 136-4). The airless method delivers the finish to the product by centrifugal force. The air-atomized process is based on the law of physics that states that like charges repel and unlike attract. The atomized process can be adapted to nonmetallic products, but it is more successful on metal articles.

The **pressure-feed spray gun** allows air to pass through the gun at all times. This is called a **bleeder gun.** It can be used to spray practically all types of materials from small or large containers. The trigger controls finish flow. This gun is widely used in the automatic-spraying and the air-atomized processes.

136-3. The air brush is used extensively in sign painting.

136-4. Finish is supplied to the airless spray gun by hydraulic pressure and centrifugal force.

136-5. A typical suction-feed spray gun with container.

A **siphon**, or **suction-feed**, **gun** (Fig. 136-5) is probably the most widely used gun in school industrial laboratories, shops, and small operations. This gun is called a **nonbleeder** because the trigger controls both the air and the fluid. It usually has an adjustable external-mix type of nozzle and tip. That is, the air and the finish are mixed just as each comes from the gun. The gun is attached to an air hose, in addition to a quart container that has a special air-vent cap. This vent must be kept open at all times to allow air to come through to create a suction.

The siphon gun operates as a result of the suction created in the cup as air passes through the gun. Only light and thin materials can be sprayed. The principles of feeding and mixing are shown in Fig. 136-6. A variety of sizes of spray heads, nozzles, and fluid needles can be obtained for a general-purpose gun (Fig. 136-7).

Other Spraying Equipment

The **compressor** takes air from the atmosphere, compresses it, and supplies the air pressure needed to operate a spray gun. Compressors may be large or small (Fig. 136-8). They may be portable (Fig. 136-9) or stationary (Fig. 136-10).

Air from the compressor should go into an **air transformer** (Fig. 136-11), where dust, oil, rust, and moisture are removed. These containers and the compressor should be drained of water frequently, and the filters should be cleaned or replaced as necessary.

The transformer is usually equipped with two gauges. One shows compressor-tank pressure. Pressure is greater in the tank than on the spray gun, in order that the spraying pressure may be kept even. The other gauge shows the lesser pressure, the pressure at which the spray gun is successfully and accurately operated for the material which is being sprayed.

A **hose** is connected from the transformer to the gun. The hose material should be of high quality so that it resists swelling or general disintegration that would clog the air passages in the gun. For production work, one hose may be used for air to the gun, another for finish materials (Fig. 136-12). Both hoses contain pressure.

136-6. Principles of feeding and mixing finishes in spraying.

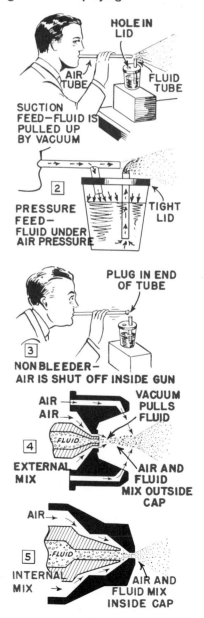

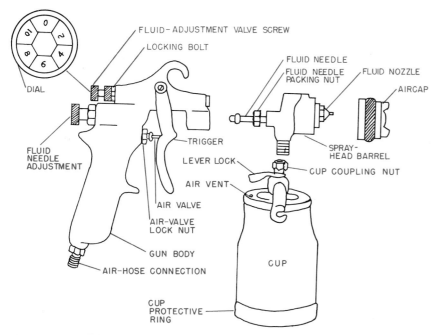

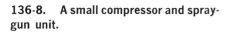

136-7. Parts of the common suction spray gun.

136-8. A small compressor and spray-gun unit.

136-9. A large portable spray finishing unit.

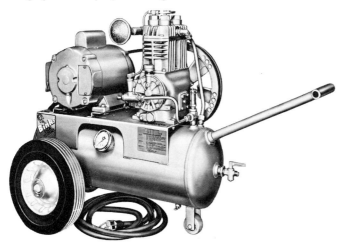

The **suction cup** is attached to a suction-feed gun. Larger containers come in the **gravity** and the **pressure-feed** types; they force finishes to the gun.

Using a Suction-feed Spray Gun

1. Finishing materials and the clean surface should be sprayed at room temperatures of more than 70°F. Finishes work best at a specified consistency, called their **viscosity.** A cupful of properly thinned material should flow from a spray gun in a designated number of seconds for best results, according to the manufacturer's specifications.

2. Strain finishes into the container through cheesecloth or fine window screen if there is any possibility of particles in the liquid. These particles clog a gun. They are often found in cans of finish which have been opened for previous use.

3. Attach the cup to the gun.

NOTE: Spray finishing should be done in a special dust-free area. A spray hood (Fig. 136-13) with exhaust makes an ideal location. Air should enter the area through a filter. It should be cleared properly by exhaust fans designed for that purpose.

136-10. A stationary compressor and tank.

4. Start the compressor, and let the air pressure increase. Open the air line to the regulator. Check the regulator to see that the pressure is somewhat greater than that needed at the gun. There will be an air loss that must be adjusted. The longer the air hose and the smaller the inside diameter, the greater the loss of pressure, regardless of the volume of compressed air generated by the system. The regulator must allow sufficient passage of air.

5. Adjust the regulator on the gun air-hose line for the pressure needed.

Air pressures for spraying are given in Table 136-1.

6. Regulate the fluid-adjustment screw on the rear of the gun. The fluid adjustment screw controls the amount of finishing material which leaves the gun.

136-11. Air transformers have gauges to show pressure and filters to clean the air.

136-12. A hose for air, and one for finish, from a large container are connected to the spray gun in continuous spray finishing operations.

136-13. Hoods help concentrate the spray mist to be exhausted from the spraying area.

Table 136-1

| Size of air hose, inside diameter | Air-pressure drop at spray gun | | | | | |
	5-ft length, lb	10-ft length, lb	15-ft length, lb	20-ft length, lb	25-ft length, lb	50-ft length, lb
¼ in. @						
40 lb pressure	6	8	9½	11	12¾	24
50 lb pressure	7½	10	12	14	16	28
60 lb pressure	9	12½	14½	16¾	19	31
70 lb pressure	10¾	14½	17	19½	22½	34
80 lb pressure	12¼	16½	19½	22½	25½	37
90 lb pressure	14	18¾	22	25¼	29	39½
5⁄16 in. @						
40 lb pressure	2¼	2¾	3¼	3½	4	8½
50 lb pressure	3	3½	4	4½	5	10
60 lb pressure	3¾	4½	5	5½	6	11½
70 lb pressure	4½	5¼	6	6¾	7¼	13
80 lb pressure	5½	6¼	7	8	8¾	14½
90 lb pressure	6½	7½	8½	9½	10½	16

7. Adjust the air cap to the proper externally mixed spray pattern. This could be either a spot or an elongated (elliptical) pattern (Fig. 136-14).

8. Test on scrap paper (Fig. 136-15), and perform steps 5, 6, and 7 until the proper spray is obtained.

9. Hold the spray gun 6 to 8 inches from the surface to be sprayed (Fig. 136-16). Pull the trigger, and make the spray stroke a continuous movement parallel to the surface (Fig. 136-17).

Runs and **sags** result when the gun is held too close, is moved too slowly, or is delivering too much fluid for the operator to control.

When the spray-gun nozzle is held too far from the surface, the material atomizes and too much mist is lost. This results in waste and leaves a cloudy, sandy finish that must be done over.

A deliberate, steady pass which leaves a full, wet coat is desired. Arching and tilting the gun are the two common faults which result in a streaky effect.

10. Corners of projects should be sprayed first (Fig. 136-18). Turn the project so that the gun is always perpendicular to the surface being sprayed (Fig. 136-19). Tilting allows finish to spill from the air vent and eventually will close it. This stopping up prevents operation until the opening is clear.

11. Move the gun to the corner of the project to be sprayed. As it

136-14. Correct and faulty spray patterns.

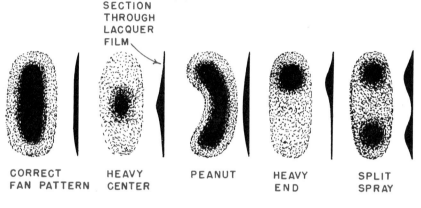

SECTION THROUGH LACQUER FILM

CORRECT FAN PATTERN   HEAVY CENTER   PEANUT   HEAVY END   SPLIT SPRAY

136-17. Keep the spray gun parallel to the surface being sprayed. Swinging the gun in an arc gives uneven coating.

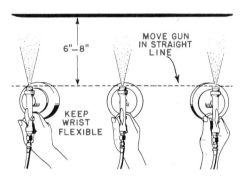

6"–8"   MOVE GUN IN STRAIGHT LINE   KEEP WRIST FLEXIBLE

136-15. Testing a spray pattern before finishing an object.

136-16. Gun must be proper distance from surface for best results.

136-18. Corners of objects should be sprayed first.

136-19. Keep the spray gun perpendicular to the surface being sprayed.

136-20. The gun is held in the same way for spraying round work as in finishing other surfaces.

136-21. Follow the shape of the object when spray finishing.

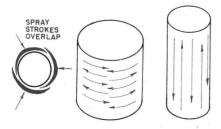

reaches the leading corner or edge, pull the trigger, and release it near the end. Pull it for the next stroke, and release it at the end. This will prevent fatigue and overspraying. Leave flat surfaces to be done last.

12. Use a round spray pattern for table legs and similar round surfaces. When spraying curved surfaces, hold the gun the same way and at the same distance from the work (Fig. 136-20). Follow the curvature of the surface (Fig. 136-21).

13. Study each project or object before spraying it. Decide what procedure will be the simplest, easiest, and require the fewest passes of the gun. Use a round spray pattern on a narrow object or piece; a wide (elliptical) one on larger surfaces.

Cleaning the Spray Gun and Shutting Down Equipment

The spray gun is a precision tool. It should be carefully handled and maintained. The fluid needle packing, the air-valve stem, and the trigger-bearing screw should have a drop of oil on them daily when the gun is in use. Clean the gun as follows:

1. Loosen the air cap slightly, and remove the cup.

2. Pull the gun trigger and release any material in the gun so that it flows back in the cup (Fig. 136-22).

3. Empty the cup, and clean it thoroughly.

4. Put about a cup of the correct thinner into a container. Spray the thinner to clear out the passageways (Fig. 136-23).

5. Remove the cap and tip. Clean them in the proper thinner (Fig. 136-24).

6. Close the air line to the regulators. Bleed off all pressure on the valves and hose. Release the pressure on the regulator screws. These should read zero (0) pressure.

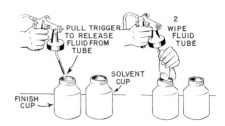

136-22. Simple steps in cleaning a spray gun.

136-23. Spray thinner (cleaner) through the spray-gun passageways to clean out all finish material.

136-24. Clean the cap, tip, and cup in thinner, but do not put the whole gun in the cleaner.

Unit 137 Bleaching, Coloring, Filling, and Sealing Woods

Developments in finishes and finishing have supplied information for complete courses of study and there are a number of books on the many products and procedures. Some of the more popular treatments of wood are presented here.

Bleaching

Dark spots, streaks, and natural wood coloring are removed by bleaching. However, it is sometimes difficult to remove the color without causing injury to the wood fibers. Bleaches are often composed of strong chemicals. They require protection of the skin and utmost safety in use. Bleaching should be done only when necessary to obtain a uniformly light color.

Choose light-colored woods if bleaching is necessary or desired. Darker woods are much more difficult to lighten. Because of their structure and coloring, ash, birch, oak, maple, mahogany, and walnut are easier to bleach than gum, pine, and poplar. Experiment on test strips of the wood (Fig. 137-1).

The use of oxalic acid and sodium hypochlorite as bleaching agents is widely accepted. Borax acts as an alkalizing agent, neutralizing, or counteracting, the acid (Fig. 137-2).

Oxalic acid can be obtained in white crystal form. Approximately 3 ounces dissolved in 1 quart of hot water forms a mild bleaching agent.

The application of the oxalic acid solution is followed by application of **sodium hypochlorite** (ordinary household laundry bleach). It bleaches most woods several shades lighter. After the bleach has been applied and has dried, it should be neutralized: Wash it off with a **borax solution** of about 1 ounce of borax per quart of water. All solutions are made with hot water, but they are cooled before they are put into use.

Commercial two-solution bleaches are usually the most satisfactory. There are several brands on the market, but only two are discussed briefly here. The manufacturer's instructions should be followed exactly.

A common **two-solution bleach** is **oxalic acid** and **sodium bisulfite.** Each is mixed separately in a 5 to 10 percent solution of water. The acid is applied by spray or brush and allowed to dry. The sodium bisulfite is then applied. Mixture of these two chemicals creates the bleach, **sulfur dioxide.**

Potassium permanganate is the second two-solution bleaching process. It is applied in a 2 to 10 percent solution for one or several coats, depending on the effect desired. A brown color appears and is cleared with a 5 to 10 percent solution of sodium bisulfite. To remove the salts of this chemical reaction, the wood is partially neutralized by sponging with clear water.

Most two-solution bleaches are basically alkaline. They have to be **neutralized** with a 5 to 15 percent **acetic acid** (vinegar) solution and then sponged with clear water. If the caustic salts are left on any part of the project, they will injure the finish when it is applied.

Allow at least 48 hours for final drying. The grain of the wood has been raised and must be smoothed. Sand it *lightly* to avoid cutting through the thin layer of bleached wood. Woods can be finished by any of the accepted methods after bleaching, neutralizing, drying, and sanding.

Blonding

Blond finishes are obtained by adding white lacquer to clear lacquer. A

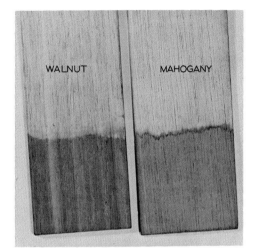

137-1. Experiment on test strips of wood for best bleaching results.

137-2. Common bleaching materials are available at most drug stores.

uniform light coat sprayed on wood as a sealer produces a blond color that does not obscure the wood grain (Fig. 137-3). This technique works very well on light woods, such as maple and birch.

Staining

A stain is used to change the color of a surface, and it often emphasizes the beauty and grain of the wood. It is the first step in the finishing operation after finishing in the white.

Stain is used to match lighter woods with the predominant color and to change the color of the entire object. The lighter sap streaks in woods such as walnut can be stained to match the darker heartwood. Inexpensive woods can be stained to resemble walnut or other more expensive woods. Walnut, cedar, and cherry have suffi-

137-4. Typical furniture finished with colonial maple stain.

137-5. Necessary materials for finishing in colonial maple.

137-3. Blond sealers: Add one part white lacquer to five parts clear.

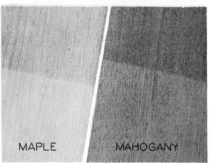

MAPLE   MAHOGANY

cient natural color that they do not require stain.

Some furniture (Fig. 137-4) is stained to give the popular colonial maple color. There is no fixed tone for this maple furniture, however. Necessary materials are shown in Fig. 137-5. The orange-brown antique color is most frequently used. A touch of orange to any medium-brown stain gives the antique maple color.

The object is stained and sealed with a wash coat of orange shellac. A second coat of wiping stain is applied and then wiped, leaving the antique effect. Other finish coats are added to build up the finish.

Many special stains are available in numerous colors. They are divided into four groups: (1) water, (2) oil, (3) spirit, and (4) non-grain-raising (NGR). See Fig. 137-6.

Water stain comes in concentrated powder form. Water-soluble colors (usually aniline dyes) are dissolved in hot water. Use a glass or enamel container to mix this stain. Water stain penetrates deeply, gives greater transparency, has less tendency to fade,

137-6. Powder stains can be purchased which are soluble in water, oil, alcohol, and lacquer thinner.

and does not bleed into coats of finish. It does raise the grain, and it is hard to apply with a brush or by wiping, without streaking.

Spraying is the best method of application. Raising the grain one or more times and sanding or applying a shellac wash coat before application of the stain help eliminate the necessity for resanding.

These powders can be made into non-grain-raising stains. Use less hot water, and then bring the mixture to proper strength by adding alcohol or special solvents. The usual procedure for water staining is shown by steps in Fig. 137-7.

Oil stains are usually classified as **pigmented,** or **wiping** (ground or mixed in oil), and **penetrating** (soluble in benzol, naphtha, or turpentine). They can be purchased either in powder or in ready-mixed forms (Fig. 137-8).

137-7. Steps in the use of water stains.

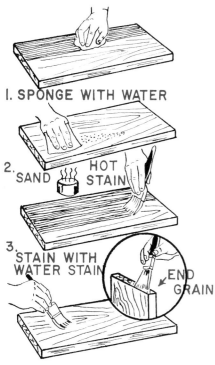

1. SPONGE WITH WATER

2. SAND — HOT STAIN

3. STAIN WITH WATER STAIN — END GRAIN

4. APPLY WASH COAT OF SHELLAC

137-8. A ready-mixed penetrating stain.

Penetrating oil stains are often used to color wood filler. A thin solution of this filler-stain mixture is sometimes rubbed into the wood to stain and fill simultaneously. For the best quality in workmanship, this dual operation is not recommended, especially because oil stain normally penetrates wood less effectively than the many other stains.

Oil stains do not raise wood grain, and they are relatively easy to apply to a uniform color. All excess stain should be removed because it bleeds. Pigmented (wiping) stains are better than the penetrating stains because they fade less.

Apply a coat of boiled linseed oil to all exposed end grain *before* staining. This produces a uniform color when the stain is put on.

Spirit stains are mostly aniline dyes that are soluble in alcohol. They are difficult to apply evenly, they fade quickly in sunlight, they bleed, and they cut through most finishes. Because they penetrate easily, they are popular for use in refinishing old furniture.

Staining for Refinishing

1. Remove the old finish with a prepared remover and steel wool (Fig. 137-9). A wood file, emery cloth, and steel wool are used to remove finish and clean in close places (Fig. 137-10).

2. Sand all areas with wet-dry sandpaper.

3. Mix a penetrating stain. Test for the desired color on scrap wood (Fig. 137-11) or on the bottom of the project (Fig. 137-12).

4. Apply the stain with a brush to all parts of the object.

5. Remove all excess stain before it dries (Fig. 137-13).

137-9. Removing an old finish.

137-10. Several items are necessary to remove old finish or to smooth irregular surfaces.

137-11. Mixing and testing stains on scrap wood.

Shading and Highlighting

Shading is done by spraying or wiping shading materials on the finished work and wiping it off to give a highlighted or aged (antique) appearance. Wiping or shading stains, tinting colors, and shading lacquers are common materials (Fig. 137-14). Dye is often added to clear lacquer or varnish for use over sealer coats to give a uniform transparent color. Spray shading is used to give a uniform overall tone to make different species of woods look the same (Fig. 137-15).

When pigment instead of dye is added to varnish or lacquer, the finish becomes opaque. Opaque enamels cover the grain, giving a painted effect.

Bone white is a typical **shaded finish** (Fig. 137-16). When the white color is dry, spray on a coat of wiping stain (Fig. 137-17). Wipe off before the stain reaches the tacky (sticky) stage. This leaves **highlights** (Fig. 137-18). Highlighting is also done by sanding spots with steel wool or abrasive paper, blending wiping stain with a brush, or detail shading with a special spray gun (Fig. 137-19).

137-12. Matching stain to unexposed surfaces of the project to be stained.

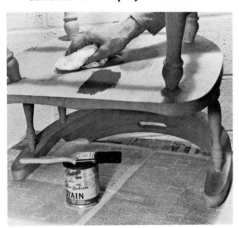

137-13. Remove excess stain before it dries.

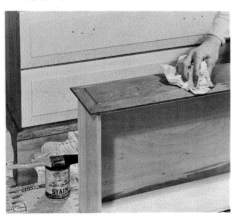

137-14. Common shading materials.

137-15. Spray shading to produce a uniform color.

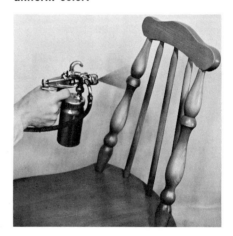

137-16. Spraying on a bone-white shaded finish.

137-17. Spraying a wiping stain to highlight a bone-white finish.

137-18. Wiping off excess stain and leaving a highlight effect.

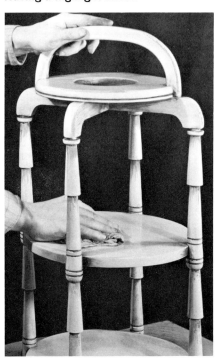

Filling

Most of the materials used to fill and seal wood pores are shown in Fig. 137-20. Only two or three, however, are used in one finishing operation.

After thorough sanding, and also after staining when desired, the most important operation in obtaining an excellent built-up finish on open-grain woods is the application of a good filler. Filler is *not* a coat of finish; it is a material that fills the pores of the wood.

Wood filler is a product made from **silex,** a ground quartz (flint) silica mixed with a drier, a solvent (thinner), and a vehicle. Silex and boiled linseed oil were the main ingredients of the older fillers. Small amounts of japan drier and turpentine were added, and wood flour replaced silex, making a different kind of filler.

Two types of filler for wood pores are paste and liquid. **Paste filler** dries

137-19. Other highlighting materials.

slowly because of the linseed oil it contains. It can be thinned as desired with this oil and turpentine, but it requires from 12 to 48 hours drying time, depending on the oil content, before a sealer should be applied. The oil has a tendency to expand and provides a good lubricant in filler application, and it helps enrich the natural color of the wood.

A shellac sealer coat is the best kind to use over this type of oil-paste filler because lacquer-type sealers tend to check and have an "orange-peel" texture if the filler is not perfectly dry.

137-20. Common filling and sealing materials.

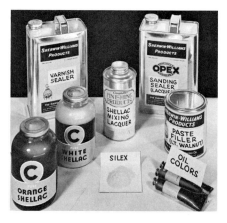

137-21. White and tinted filler produce accents to oak and ash grain fiber patterns.

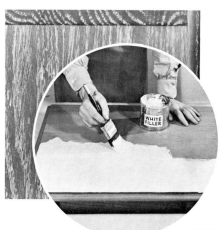

345

137-22. **Brush on filler with the wood grain.**

137-23. **Rub, or "pad in," filler across the grain.**

137-24. **Remove all surplus filler.**

Some craftsmen prefer to apply a **wash coat** of shellac (1 part shellac to 6 or 7 parts alcohol) *before* filling wood that has exceptionally large pores, such as mahogany and ash.

Newer paste fillers are very fast drying because of their synthetic resin-base vehicles. A good general-purpose thinner for most of these fillers is **varnishmakers and painters naptha** (VM&P naptha). A minimum drying time of 2 hours is suggested, depending on the driers and reducers (thinners) used to thin the paste or liquid.

Liquid filler is usually made from cheap varnish and a small amount of silex. It is often used on inexpensive work in medium close-grain woods. A thin paste filler is more satisfactory for all work, however.

The following procedure is useful in properly filling the pores for natural colors or toned effects:

1. Apply a wash coat of shellac over stain, or natural-colored woods with large pores (ash, oak, mahogany), before filling.

2. Thin the filler to a workable consistency. Color or tint it as necessary. For example, a white-tinted filler accents the beautiful grains of oak and ash (Fig. 137-21).

3. Apply filler *with* the grain to 1 or 2 square feet, or to one piece, of a project at a time (Fig. 137-22). Use a cloth or a brush.

4. Let the filler dry until it has a dull appearance. *Do not* allow the filler to dry on top of wood surfaces. It will harden and often require scraping and sanding to remove.

5. Rub the filler *across* the grain, using burlap, coarse rags, or the palm of your hand (Fig. 137-23). Apply ample pressure to push the filler to the bottom of the pore holes. Filler that catches only in the top portion of the pores may drop or wash out when dry, especially during brush finishing. Air that is trapped in pores that are not completely filled may break through the finish, causing bubbles and blisters in the surface finish coats.

6. Rub flat surfaces *across the grain* with clean burlap or excelsior (wood wool). This both removes most of the surplus filler and works it more deeply into the pores (Fig. 137-24).

7. Remove surplus filler from all corners, using a cloth, a stick, or a putty knife (Fig. 137-25).

8. Use cheesecloth or any other soft fabric to wipe *with the grain* to remove streaks and *all* remaining filler on the surface (Fig. 137-26).

9. Allow the filler in the pores to dry thoroughly before completing the remaining finishing operations.

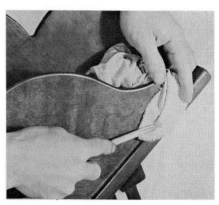

137-25. **A piece of wood (picking stick) wrapped in a soft cloth will help remove surplus filler from corners.**

137-26. **Use a soft cloth, and rub with the wood grain to remove all streaks and remaining filler from surface.**

Sealing

Close-grain woods do not require fillers. They do, however, need a sealer coat on which to build finish. Open-grain woods require a sealer after filler has been rubbed in.

One or more sealing coats are used. They prevent bleeding of the stains or fillers and seal (close) pores and fibers, making a good base for subsequent finish coats. As the first coat of the finish, sealers prevent moisture absorption as well as absorption of other finish coats.

Lacquer sealers and **shellac** are common sealing materials. Both can be brushed or sprayed. Shellac is available in cuts (mixtures) ranging from 2 to 12 pounds. A common grade is termed **four pound cut.** This means that 4 pounds of lac resin are dissolved in 1 gallon of alcohol. One part of four pound cut shellac to three parts alcohol or a mixture of half alcohol and half shellac (two pound cut) can be easily brushed or sprayed.

Because oil-base materials tend to bleed, a **shellac-type sealer** should be used over all oil-base stains and fillers. This sealer coat should dry at least 2 hours. Varnish sealers should dry overnight before they are sanded.

Unit 138 Applying Oil and Wax Finishes

Wax that is used as a finish or to polish and protect other finishes must be renewed periodically to keep a shining surface. It cannot withstand water or excessive heat.

Carnauba (Brazilian) wax is the most important natural polishing agent. It is obtained from a species of palm tree growing in Brazil. It is the hardest of the natural waxes, melting at 185° F. Carnauba wax is usually mixed with other waxes, such as beeswax (a fairly hard wax produced by honey bees), ceresine (a hard hydrocarbon wax), or paraffin (a soft wax obtained from petroleum), to make it softer and easier to use.

Turpentine is the most common solvent or thinner for waxes.

Raw **linseed oil** is extracted from crushed flax seed. It often takes raw linseed oil a week to dry, but it leaves a tough film on wood. Linseed oil for furniture finishing is kettle-boiled to emulsify (mix smoothly) the film-forming particles. This oil dries in 12 to 24 hours.

Oil or oil-and-wax finishes are used to obtain a beautiful surface on walnut, cedar, and dark-red cherry woods. This attractive finish does not necessarily depend on the amount of oil used; rather it depends on repeated rubbings between coats. This finish is popular on dark-colored antique furniture. It does not offer the protection of other finishes, however, and many days are required to secure a beautiful sheen (gloss). Stains bleed through, so they are not recommended under an oil finish.

Oil Finish

1. Dust the wood surfaces and other parts thoroughly.

2. *Very carefully* heat a mixture of one or two parts boiled linseed oil and one part turpentine. Heat in a double boiler, because both are highly flammable.

3. Apply the heated mixture with a soft cloth tied to a dowel or some other piece of wood. Use only enough oil to soak readily into the wood. Wipe off the surplus.

4. Allow the oil coat to dry about 15 minutes.

5. Rub briskly with a lint-free, rough-textured cloth until the surface shines brightly.

6. Be sure to let the surfaces dry two or more days before repeating steps 3 and 4.

7. Between 5 and 10 applications may be needed before a beautiful sheen glows on the surface. Brisk rubbing and thorough drying of each coat are essential to obtain the proper oil finish.

Oil and Beeswax Finish

1. Cut about 1 ounce of beeswax into fine shavings. Put them into ½ pint of turpentine. Let the mixture stand overnight.

2. Heat the mixture. Observe the safety precaution given in step 2 under "Oil Finish."

3. When the mixture is warm, stir in about ½ pint of boiled linseed oil. *Heat over hot water* until all the wax is dissolved.

4. Carefully apply a thin coat of the hot beeswax-turpentine mixture to the wood. Use a brush or a soft cloth to apply the mixture. Rub the surface hard with a soft cloth.

5. Let the wood dry 12 hours or more.

6. Reheat the solution. Repeat step 4 several times. The wax and oil tend to fill the pores on open-grain woods. Hard rubbing of each coat and the careful removal of excess wax is the secret of producing a beautiful satin finish.

Unit 139 Applying a Shellac Finish

Shellac is particularly valuable as a sealer over oil and bleeding stains, oil-base fillers, and resinous knots. These bleeding knots are found frequently in pines and other conifers.

Lac resins are dissolved in special formulas of denatured alcohol to form shellac in its natural orange color. White shellac is made by bleaching the resins. The cloudy appearance is caused by the natural wax in the shellac. When this wax is taken out, a transparent, or clear, shellac results, which is called **French varnish.** Shellac is actually a **spirit varnish.**

Shellac Finish

1. Dust all surfaces. Be sure that the stain or filler is thoroughly dry.

2. Pour some shellac into a container. Mix with an even amount of alcohol to make a thin mixture.

3. Remove drawers and other removable parts of the piece. All removable parts of the work are to be finished separately.

4. Brush (Fig. 139-1) or spray on the first coat of shellac. Begin at the top; work toward the bottom of vertical surfaces. Leave the top horizontal surface to the last. Apply the mixture from one side of a piece to the other. Shellac dries rapidly. Apply the coat evenly and quickly, with as little overlapping as possible.

5. Allow the coat to dry from 2 to 6 hours.

6. When it is dry, rub this coat of finish smooth with No. 2/0 or No. 3/0 steel wool. Rub *with* the grain if possible. Smooth each coat. Do not rub through the shellac on edges and corners.

7. Succeeding coats should dry longer. Dilute the shellac from the container by adding one-fourth alcohol. Very soft woods and those with large pores may require three to six coats to obtain a satisfactory built-up shellac finish.

8. The final coat should dry 8 to 10 hours. Sand it smooth with No. 6/0 wet-dry paper and rubbing oil. *Do not use water* as a rubbing lubricant because it will turn the shellac white. The final coat may also be rubbed lightly with steel wool.

Apply a coat of good paste wax. Allow the wax to dull, and then rub it briskly to a luster. Use a soft cotton cloth.

139-1. Applying shellac with a brush.

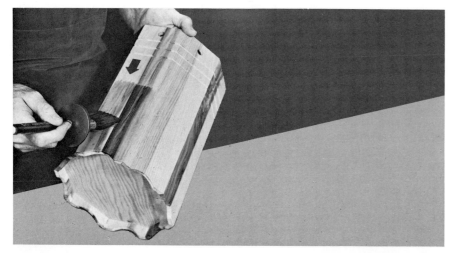

Unit 140　Applying a Varnish Finish

Varnish has the excellent qualities of transparent depth, durability, and hardness. It dries slowly and requires a dust-free area both when it is being applied and while it is drying.

Materials in Varnish

Materials in varnish include resins or gums, oils, turpentine (for thinning), and drying agents.

Resins or **gums** are the solid portion of varnish, giving the film hardness and luster. They vary in hardness and are blended for each particular kind of varnish. Originally, all good varnishes used imported fossilized gums. Recent developments have produced varnishes based on synthetic (man-made) resins that dry more quickly.

Oils serve as vehicles in varnish. Oil from tung nuts of the Chinawood tree and linseed oil act as binders for the resins, giving the varnish film elasticity (stretch). Larger amounts of oil make the film tougher, more durable, and more water resistant.

Turpentine is the solvent used for thinning varnish (Fig. 140-1) so that it can be sprayed with light equipment or brushed. It dries by evaporation.

Drying agents are made from oils and from salts of various metals. They

140-1. Turpentine is the correct thinner for varnish.

140-2. Several kinds of varnish.

speed up the drying process of the vehicle or of the oils. Japan drier, for example, is a compound of lead or manganese salts.

Types of Varnish

Varnish formulas are available in three general classifications, according to oil content: long-oil, medium-oil, and short-oil varnishes. There is no all-purpose varnish, but several kinds take care of most requirements (Fig. 140-2). This finish is called **oleoresinous** because it is essentially a mixture of oils and resins.

Long-oil varnishes include spar varnish. As much as 100 pounds of oil can be mixed with an equal amount of resins. This varnish is recommended for exterior surfaces that are exposed to water and weather. Spar varnish is slightly darker, it is slow drying, and it gives a moderate gloss. It requires 12 to 24 hours to dry.

Medium-oil varnishes are floor-type finishes. They contain up to 40 pounds of oils per 100 pounds of resin. They are harder and dry faster than the spar type. Normal drying time is 12 hours.

Short-oil varnishes include rubbing, pale rubbing, and polishing varnishes. They contain up to 10 or 12 pounds of oils per 100 pounds of resin. Polishing varnish contains hard resins, takes a high polish, and rubs and sands clean without gumming. Drying time is 24 to 48 hours.

Special varnishes are made in several types for specific uses. **Table-top** varnish is very hard; it is heat- and waterproof. The drying time is about 18 hours. Bar-top varnish, often referred to as **bakelite** varnish, is similar to table-top varnish, but it is usually synthetic, drying hard in about 4 hours. Mild acids, water, and alcohol do not affect it. Flat varnish is for interior use, drying to a dull finish in about 12 hours. **Dammar** varnish is a colorless spirit varnish, used in photography. It is quick drying (2 hours), but it is softer and less durable than the others. **Mastic** varnish is made from aromatic resins of a small Mediterranean evergreen tree. It is similar to dammar varnish in use and characteristics.

Shellac is the most important and best known of the three spirit varnishes. The others: dammar and mastic.

Tack Cloths in Varnish Finishing

Cleanliness in finishing is an absolute necessity to obtain quality results. A **tack cloth** helps clean the project or piece. This is a chemically treated piece of cheesecloth prepared for this specific use. It picks up particles of steel wool, dirt, lint, and sanding dust that an ordinary dry cloth does not.

If a commercially treated tack cloth is not available, make one from a lint-free soft cotton cloth. Soak the piece in warm water, wring it out lightly, and sprinkle it with turpentine. Pour about 2 teaspoons of varnish on it; fold, twist, and wring the cloth nearly dry. To keep tack cloths in good condition, sprinkle them lightly with water and turpentine; store them in an airtight jar or container.

Varnishing

1. Remove the drawers and other separate parts to finish separately (Fig. 140-3). Dust all parts carefully with a soft brush (Fig. 140-4), particularly the corners. Carry the project to a very clean finishing room.

2. **Tacking** is the final dusting operation. Use a tack cloth (Fig. 140-5) to pick up all remaining dirt and dust.

3. Varnish can be thinned and sprayed. It is somewhat difficult to spray varnish so that it does not run or ripple. Heating it in a double boiler before spraying will lessen this possibility (Figs. 140-6 and 140-7). The flow is increased, and the mixture sets more quickly. However, sometimes this does not allow sufficient time for proper tipping (see step 8).

140-4. Clean out corners carefully with a soft brush before varnishing.

140-6. One method of safely heating varnish.

140-3. Drawers should be removed before finishing a chest.

140-5. Tack cloths clean the project of all dust and other particles.

140-7. Extreme care should be used when varnish is heated.

Varnish can be applied over shellac or lacquer, but *do not* apply lacquer over varnish. The ingredients in the two finishes do not mix, and the finish will raise and peel.

4. If you brush on varnish, *do not* use it directly from the can (Fig. 140-8). Use an aluminum saucepan about 4 inches across and 2 inches deep to hold the varnish. Add a wire to the pan on which to stroke the brush to remove excess varnish (Fig. 140-9). Cut the handle of this pan, and fold it over to form a loop (Fig. 140-10).

5. Pour a small amount of varnish into the pan. Do not shake the can or stir the contents. Bubbles are formed which will be carried by the brush onto the surfaces being varnished. A brush should be dipped into the varnish only a little over one-third the length of the bristles (Fig. 140-11).

6. The first step in brushing technique is **lining in,** or **cutting in** (Fig. 140-12). Start at the corners of the piece and brush toward the center. Varnish flows best in the temperature range of 70 to 90°F.

7. The second step is to apply a full coat by **cross brushing.** Begin at either

140-8. Varnish should not be used directly from the can.

140-10. Form the handle on the pan so that it is easy to hold.

140-12. Line-in, or border, the areas with varnish.

140-9. A wire through the pan makes an excellent strike-off bar to remove excess varnish from the brush.

140-11. Dip the brush into the varnish about one-third the length of the bristles.

140-13. Cross-brush with a full coat of varnish.

side, and brush toward the middle (Fig. 140-13). Brush from the second side, and lift the brush as soon as the strokes overlap. Cross brushing is usually omitted on top surfaces because the varnish flows together smoothly.

8. The third step is **tipping**. Wipe the brush on the wire, and then use only the tip to finish lightly with the grain (Fig. 140-14).

Use a smaller brush to finish edges. This prevents the bristles from spreading over onto the top surface. Turned

140-14. Tipping is smoothing the varnish with the bristle tips.

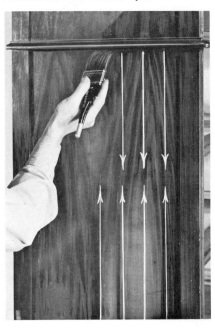

parts are brushed around and around to eliminate sagging, especially on sharp parts.

9. As the work progresses, pick out any dust particles which show up on surfaces. Do this with either a sliver of wood or a ball of burnt varnish on the end of a stick (Fig. 140-15). Do not wait until the varnish becomes tacky (sticky). Most bubbles will disappear as the varnish sets (drys).

Pour all unused varnish into another container to store. Never pour unused portions back into the original can because it may have accumulated dust and other particles.

10. Allow each varnish coat to dry completely before the next one is applied. In damp weather, more than 2 days may be needed for drying. The

140-15. Remove all dust and particles from the surfaces before the varnish dries.

usual time is around 36 to 48 hours, but some varnishes dry hard in 4 to 6 hours. When the varnish coat resists the impression of the thumbnail, it is ready to rub or for another coat (Fig. 140-16).

Each coat of varnish should be sanded lightly with very fine wet-dry finishing paper. A milky appearance will remain after rubbing until the next coat is put on. If surfaces have been properly sanded, filled as needed, and sealed carefully, two coats of varnish should give a good surface. Better-quality work will need three or four coats.

11. When the final coat has dried hard, complete the finishing according to the procedure in Unit 144, "Rubbing and Polishing Finishes."

140-16. Test the varnish coat with the thumbnail for dryness before applying another one.

Unit 141 Applying a Lacquer Finish

Most lacquer is synthetic, being made by treating nitrocellulose (cotton and certain wood fibers) with nitric and sulfuric acid. A clear, water-white lacquer is produced when the materials are blended with suitable solvents. Mixtures of various quantities of cer-

tain chemicals, gums, and resins make possible synthetic lacquers with any characteristic desired.

Lacquers are relatively low in cost and are durable, transparent, and hard. They can be made acid resistant and waterproof. A lacquer coat dries dust-free in a matter of a few minutes and dries hard in 30 minutes to 2 hours.

At least 250 synthetic resins have been developed. Finishes in this classification represent a wide variety of products. Some materials for lacquer finishing are displayed in Fig. 141-1.

Lacquers

A few of the many lacquers are (1) gloss, (2) semigloss, (3) flat, (4) water white, (5) rubbing and polishing bar top, (6) bronzing, (7) shading, and (8) novelty.

Thinners for one brand or type of lacquer may not work with another. Consult the person selling thinner or the manufacturer to get the correct ones.

Basic lacquer finishing differs very little from the varnish schedule. The wood is stained, if desired, and filled as needed; then lacquer is used instead of varnish. The proper lacquers can be secured for brushing or spraying and for application to either wood or metal, with successful results. It is usually sprayed. See Unit 136, "Spray Finishing."

141-1. Common materials for lacquer finishing.

Spraying Tips

1. Thin lacquer only when the directions on the can call for it.
2. Make a test spray pattern, and adjust the spray gun properly. A heavy, wet center surrounded by globs means orange peel, poor atomizing, and breaking up of lacquer. Correct this by thinning the lacquer, increasing the air pressure, and possibly by cutting the fluid feed.

Peanut-shaped or heavy-end patterns mean a dirty gun. Clean the air cap, or remove the obstruction from the fluid needle tip.

The split spray is caused by too much air pressure. See Fig. 136-14.

Lacquer Finishing

The lacquer finish should be preceded by the basic procedures of sanding, staining, and filling. This depends on the type of wood and the kind of finish desired.

1. Apply a coat of sanding sealer, or use thinned shellac as a sealer. See Unit 137, "Bleaching, Coloring, Filling, and Sealing Woods," and Unit 139, "Applying a Shellac Finish."
2. Sand with No. 5/0 dry garnet paper when the sealer has dried.
3. Spray on two to four coats of lacquer. Allow 1½ to 2 hours for each coat to dry. Sand lightly between coats with No. 5/0 dry garnet paper. See Unit 136, "Spray Finishing," for details.
4. Let the final coat dry at least 24 hours before rubbing and polishing.

Unit 142 Applying Paints, Enamels, and Decorative Finishes

Paints and enamels are used on less expensive woods. They cover, protect, and beautify woods when natural, clear finishes are not desirable or appropriate. Paint is used on both exterior and interior surfaces. Enamel usually produces a harder, smoother finish. Linseed oil and other ingredients are used as vehicles for paint. Varnish or lacquer and synthetics colored with pigments are the bases for enamel.

Painting and Enameling

1. Clean all surfaces thoroughly. Sand if necessary.
2. Read and follow the manufacturer's directions on the can for mixing, thinning, and applying. Numerous color mixtures can be blended at local supply sources (Fig. 142-1). A primer coat may be needed to seal wood pores before other coats are applied.

3. Shake the can vigorously to mix all ingredients thoroughly. If the paint is not completely mixed, pour some of the top solution into another container.

4. Stir the base mixture in the can until it is smooth. Gradually blend in the top solution. A drill press with a stirring device in the chuck is useful in mixing paint (Fig. 142-2).

5. Select a good brush of suitable size. Dip about one-third of the bristle length into the finish. Strike (press) off excess paint.

6. Apply the paint or enamel with long, smooth strokes. Start at the top and work down on vertical surfaces (Fig. 142-3). Paint the inside areas first, and then exterior sides, front, and top (Fig. 142-4).

Start painting across the grain. Finish brushing with the grain. Do not allow the material to run, but keep sufficient paint on the brush to cover smoothly and evenly.

7. Allow the coat to dry according to the directions. Sand lightly between coats, but do not sand the final coat. Use No. 2/0 garnet or flint paper if more than one coat is applied.

Decorative Finishes

Flock is the name of pulverized wool, silk, cotton, rayon, or nylon used to decorate surfaces. Various colored powders and other materials can also be used. Short fibers are used most, but fibers are available in lengths from $\frac{1}{64}$ to $\frac{1}{2}$ inch.

Brush or spray varnish or enamel on the surface to be flocked (Fig. 142-5). Apply the flock to the tacky (sticky) surface by blowing through a special container (Fig. 142-6) or sifting (Fig. 142-7).

Stencils are often made and painted, stippled, or flocked to add decoration (Figs. 142-8 and 142-9).

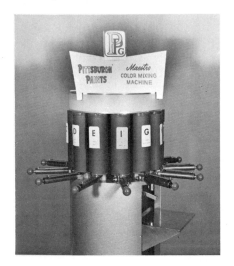

142-1.   A typical color mixing and blending machine.

142-2.   A stirring device in the chuck of a drill press makes mixing paint easier.

142-3.   Begin at the top and paint down on vertical surfaces.

142-4.   Paint the top last, and keep sufficient paint in the brush to prevent "dragging."

142-5.   Spraying on varnish or enamel in preparation for flocking.

142-6.   Blowing on flock.

Textured walls are adaptable to many styles of attractive decorative effects. Oil- or water-base paint is brushed on a wall. This heavy-body (thick) paint should be $\frac{1}{16}$ to $\frac{1}{8}$ inch thick. A wood float is applied to the surface and pulled straight back to give a pleasing texture (Fig. 142-10).

Troweling this surface flattens the points to produce a milder effect (Fig. 142-11). Two-tone effects are obtained by going over this same surface with a contrasting color applied with a rubber roller (Fig. 142-12).

Spattering is a technique that uses a special spray-gun nozzle or brush.

Load the brush with paint, and strike it sharply against your hand or a stick (Fig. 142-13). Several different spatters of blending colors, applied in successive coats, are attractive on some surfaces.

A spatter variation is obtained by brushing a regular pattern lightly with a brush after the paint has set slightly. Figure 142-14 shows a two-tone spatter being spread.

142-7. Sifting flock on a surface.

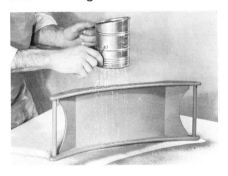

142-8. Spraying paint through a stencil to decorate a wall.

142-10. A float produces a textured finish.
142-11. A trowel smooths a textured finish to produce another effect.
142-12. A roller can be used to apply a two-tone color to textured walls.

142-13. A brush spattering technique.

142-14. Smoothing a spattered two-tone finish.

142-9. Interesting designs can be painted on furniture by using stencils.

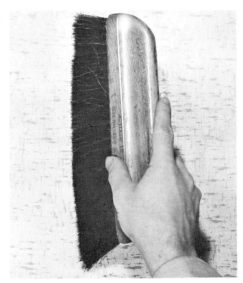

Unit 143 Applying a Penetrating Finish

Penetrating finishes are made thin so that they can be absorbed into the pores of the wood. A wear-resistant, natural appearance is the feature of this type of finish. Several coats build up a satisfactory surface. It is an easy finish to apply because it can be brushed, sprayed, or wiped on.

Wiping on a Penetrating Finish

1. Prepare the wood as in other finishing operations.
2. Pour a small amount of the finish into an open container.
3. Apply generously with a cloth. Wipe off excess liquid with a dry cloth after the penetrating finish has set 10 or 15 minutes.
4. Allow the first coat to dry overnight; then rub it carefully with fine steel wool.
5. Open-grain wood may be filled before a second coat of finish is put on, if desired. Two to four coats make a durable surface. Rub each coat with steel wool; allow 2 to 4 hours between coats, under normal conditions. Finishes dry more slowly in cool, damp air than they do in warm, dry air.
6. Smooth the last coat with steel wool.
7. Apply a coat of furniture wax. Polish.

Unit 144 Rubbing and Polishing Finishes

The use of sandpaper, steel wool, pumice, and other abrasives is often termed **rubbing.** Smoothing the finish between undercoats makes a uniform surface to which the final coat adheres evenly. Rubbing the final coat eliminates imperfections, dust specks, and ripples. A perfectly smooth, glasslike surface is obtained.

Study Tables 144-1 and 144-2 to learn rubbing schedules and rubbing and polishing materials.

Rubbing and Polishing

1. Rub the first coat with *dry* abrasive. If water were used, it probably would get under this first thin surface. Use No. 4/0 or No. 5/0 **garnet paper.** Tear a standard sheet into eight pieces. Rub these small pieces together to dull the grit (Fig. 144-2).
2. Rub the second and succeeding coats, up to the final one, with No. 5/0 or No. 6/0 garnet paper (Fig. 144-3). **Steel wool** (No. 2/0) is excellent for rubbing shellac (Fig. 144-4).

Wet-dry silicon carbide paper and a lubricant are used on lacquer and varnish finishes. *Oil* should *always* be used to lubricate shellac, *never water.*

Water is the easiest lubricant to use for finishes (except shellac). Back the paper with a felt or cork pad (Fig. 144-5). This helps to obtain a smooth, level surface. Rub with the grain as much as possible.

3. Clean the rubbed surface with a damp chamois or a soft cloth. Rub spots that need additional smoothing.
4. Grades No. 2F to 4F **pumice** are used for the first rubbing of the **final coat of varnish.** Use a small sifter-top can (such as a salt shaker) to sprinkle generous amounts of pumice powder on the surface. Wet it and make a paste mixture. Keep it wet to prevent balls of fresh abrasive from forming and scratching the surface that has been rubbed. Rub with the grain.
5. Lacquer is harder to cut than varnish, and the final coat can be

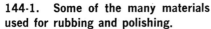

144-1. Some of the many materials used for rubbing and polishing.

Table 144-1 RUBBING SCHEDULES*

Varnish	flat	First coat, 5/0 garnet finishing paper, dry. Second coat, No. 1/2 or 1 pumice and water. Third coat, No. FF pumice with water or oil.
	satin	Same as above, but third (last) coat No. FF pumice with water, followed by rottenstone and oil or No. 4F pumice and oil.
	polished	Sand filler with No. 3/0 dry garnet. First varnish coat, No. 5/0 dry garnet. Second coat, No. 6/0 waterproof paper with water. Third coat, same. Final coat rubbed as follows: 1. FF pumice and water 2. Rottenstone and water 3. Clean with benzine; let dry 24 hr 4. Rub with polishing oil 5. Spirit-off with denatured alcohol
Shellac	flat satin polished	Same as above but No. 00 steel wool for all undercoats and oil rub for finish.
Lacquer	satin	Scuff all undercoats with 5/0 paper. Sand final coat with 8/0 waterproof paper with naphtha.
	polished	Follow above with lacquer rubbing compound. Remove compound haze, and polish with lacquer polish.

*SOURCE: Delta Power Tool Division, Rockwell Manufacturing Company.

Table 144-2 RUBBING AND POLISHING MATERIALS*

Rubbing felt	One piece of soft pressed felt, ½ by 3 by 5 in. for general rubbing. Several smaller pieces.
Abrasive papers	Grits 4/0 and finer, waterproof garnet (for varnish), or waterproof silicon carbide (lacquer or varnish).
Pumice	No. 1 for coarse rubbing; Nos. FF and FFF for fine rubbing.
Rottenstone	For fine rubbing.
Rubbing oil	Lubricant for rubbing. Purchased ready mixed. Paraffine oil, crude petroleum, or light motor oil thinned with benzine can be used.
Naphtha	Also sold as benzine. Used for cleaning up rubbing slush.
Polishing oil	For obtaining high polish after rubbing. Purchased ready mixed. Typical formula is half olive oil (sweet oil) and half denatured alcohol. Standard furniture polishes can be used.
Lacquer rubbing compound	For rubbing lacquer. In paste form, ready mixed.
Lacquer polish	For cleaning up compound haze. A large number of ready mixed products are available.
Alcohol	Used to spirit-off polishing oil. Should be denatured (grain) alcohol of average paint-store grade.

*SOURCE: Delta Power Tool Division, Rockwell Manufacturing Company.

sanded with No. 6/0 to No. 8/0 **waterproof paper** backed with heavy felt lubricated generously with water. Naphtha can also be used as the lubricant on lacquer for a beautiful satin finish.

6. Wipe a clean place occasionally with the side of your hand to inspect the rubbed surface. After all the areas are rubbed, clean with water and a soft cloth or chamois.

Remove the slush from all corners and recesses by using a cloth or a sliver of wood.

7. Repeat the rubbing operation, this time using rottenstone with oil for the lubricant. Rottenstone polishes but does not cut.

Rub the mixture with your fingers, the heel of your hand, a sponge, or a soft cloth. After the final rubbing, clean with water and, finally, with a soft cloth dampened with benzine (naphtha).

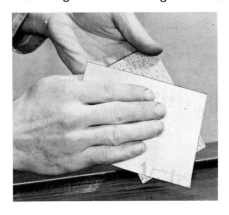

144-2. Finishing abrasive papers are rubbed together to dull the grit.

144-3. Sand between coats with No. 5/0 or 6/0 garnet paper.

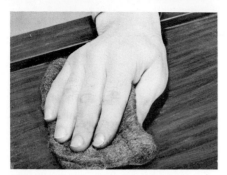

144-4. Steel wool is an excellent rubbing material for shellac finishes.

8. Apply one or more coats of a high-grade furniture wax. Let the surface become dull (about 10 minutes). Rub to a high sheen with a soft cloth. Apply wax only to a small area at a time. Let the polished wax dry several hours. Repeat the operation with one or more coats.

144-5. Back rubbing and polishing materials with a felt pad.

DISCUSSION TOPICS

1. Name five porous or semiporous hardwoods and five nonporous softwoods; discuss the proper finishes for each.
2. Besides the wood selected for a project, what factors should influence the selection of a finish?
3. What products are used in repairing blemishes?
4. What are some commercial finishing methods that are not practiced in small operations?
5. Compare steel wool and the garnet pad in relation to use, materials, and advantages.
6. Discuss the derivation of the word **varnish.** What is the main ingredient used in its manufacture?
7. Explain how shellac is produced.
8. What are the basic ingredients of lacquer?
9. Explain the development and differences of water-, casein-, and oil-base paints.
10. When is shellac used specifically as a sealer?

11. What modern product has been developed to replace bristles?
12. Describe precautions which will give longer wear to brushes.
13. Explain the different types of spray guns and spray-finish methods.
14. Be able to explain thoroughly the procedure for using the suction-feed spray gun.
15. What are the important steps in cleaning the spray gun? In shutting down the other equipment?
16. Why is it necessary to bleach some woods?
17. Discuss the advantages and disadvantages of the various types of stains.
18. What are the kinds of wood filler? What are their main ingredients?
19. What is the purpose of wood filler?
20. What makes the bristles of the wild boar especially useful as material for the best brushes?
21. Name the common types of sealing materials.
22. Explain what is meant by **four pound cut shellac.**
23. What is the most important natural wax?
24. Name three other sources of wax.
25. What is the most common solvent, or thinner, for wax?
26. What woods are successfully finished with oil? Oil and wax?

27. Why is rubbing oil used instead of water to smooth shellac finish?
28. What special characteristics does varnish have in relation to other finishes?
29. Explain the difference and uses of long-, medium-, and short-oil varnishes.
30. Why is it not advisable to apply lacquer over new varnish?
31. What are the three steps in brushing technique for varnishing?
32. How is synthetic lacquer made? What raw materials are used?
33. Why is lacquer not recommended as a finish over varnish?
34. What are the special uses of paint and enamel?
35. How are different design effects produced on textured walls?
36. Discuss the advantages and disadvantages of a penetrating finish as related to varnish and lacquer.
37. Explain the purpose of sanding between applications of finish coats.
38. Why is water not used as a lubricant when sanding or working a shellac finish?
39. Why is the first coat dry rubbed?
40. Discuss the proper procedure and purpose of using pumice, rottenstone, and wax on the final coat of finish.

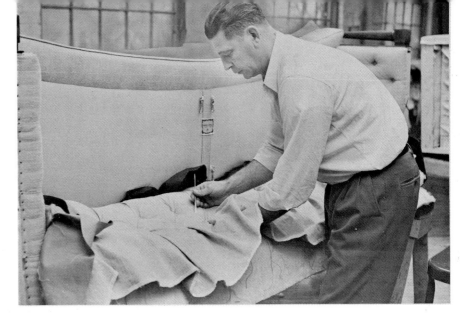

UPHOLSTERING

Unit 145 Forms of Upholstery

Upholstery is usually classified into three categories: (1) **padded** (or slip), (2) **spring,** and (3) **overstuffed** forms of seats and backs. Each of the basic types is designed for specific purposes. When frequent change of outer fabric is necessary, the simple padded method of upholstering is usually preferred.

Padded Seat and Back

There are two types of padded slip seats: the solid base (Fig. 145-1) and the webbed-frame base (Fig. 145-2). Comfort in a padded slip seat depends on the kind and amount of padding or stuffing used. The procedure of upholstering is basically the same. The frame-type padded seat may also be used on a simple ottoman, as shown in Unit 148, "Upholstering the Padded Seat."

Spring Base and Back

The spring base or back may be made of coil springs tied together or the no-sag zigzag type of wire spring (Fig. 145-3). If properly installed, spring seats make a comfortable, soft base and back on furniture.

Coil springs can be attached to solid bases, sewn or clipped to webbing, or mounted on special steel bars. They are tied together with special spring coils, wire clips, or tying twine. This method of mounting coil springs is sometimes called **tied,** or **tight-spring construction.**

145-1. An electric stapler speeds upholstery work on padded solid bases.

Overstuffed Construction

Overstuffed construction of seats and backs on chairs and divans (Fig. 145-4) is the softest and most comfortable of the three upholstered forms. Special springs are often used under cushions in both the seat and the back. These are filled with cotton, foam rubber, plastic foam sheets, or spring units wrapped in cotton. Overstuffed construction is ideal for living-room suites, lounging chairs, and divans.

Before attempting to upholster, study the following information on basic tools, equipment, materials, supplies, and techniques.

145-2. Webbed-frame bases are used on better dining room chairs.

145-3. No-sag spring wire can be used in seats and backs.

145-4. Overstuffed furniture construction is the softest of the three forms of upholstery.

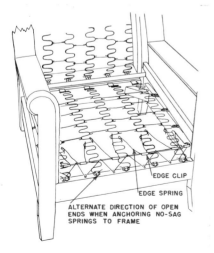

EDGE CLIP
EDGE SPRING
ALTERNATE DIRECTION OF OPEN ENDS WHEN ANCHORING NO-SAG SPRINGS TO FRAME

Unit 146 Upholstering Tools and Equipment

A complete set of tools makes upholstery processes easier and faster. However, all the tools and equipment discussed are not absolutely necessary for most basic jobs.

Essential Tools

Basic tools needed for the various forms of upholstery are the upholsterer's tack hammer, a webbing stretcher, a regulator, and upholsterer's shears (scissors). See Fig. 146-1. Additional tools which are very helpful are the steel-webbing stretcher (Fig. 146-2), tack lifter (Fig. 146-3), ripping chisel (Fig. 146-4), needles and skewers (Fig. 146-5), and cushion irons (Fig. 146-6). Most of these tools can be made in the school industrial laboratory or shop.

The **upholsterer's tack hammer** (Fig. 146-1A) is one of the most important tools. The special shape of the head makes it easy to use in many close places. The double-face type, with one magnetic face, is recommended.

The **webbing stretcher** (Fig. 146-1B) can be purchased or made. This tool, or the **webbing pliers** (Fig. 146-1C) is used to stretch jute webbing on open frames. A **steel-webbing stretcher** (see Fig. 146-2) is useful for stretching steel webbing.

A **regulator** (Fig. 146-1D) is similar to a very large needle. It is used to smooth out irregularities in loose padding or stuffing after it has been covered with burlap.

Upholstery shears (Fig. 146-1E) are heavy-duty scissors, serviceable enough to cut coarse fabrics, tying twine, and burlap.

The **tack lifter,** or **tack claw** (Fig. 146-3), has a V notch on the bevel end. This notch makes it easy to get under tacks which have not been driven completely into the frame.

A **ripping chisel** (Fig. 146-4) is similar to the tack lifter, but it has a solid, single-bevel end. It helps to remove tacks which have been driven completely into the wood.

Needles of assorted shapes and sizes (Fig. 146-5) are very useful. The curved needle (Fig. 146-5A) ranges in size from $1\frac{1}{2}$ to several inches in circumference. The 2- and 3-inch sizes are adequate for sewing corners and for most other purposes.

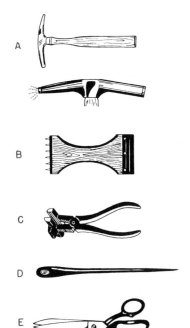

146-1. Basic upholstery tools: (A) upholsterer's tack hammer, (B) webbing stretcher, (C) webbing pliers, (D) regulator, and (E) trimmer or upholsterer's shears (scissors).

146-2. A steel-webbing stretcher.

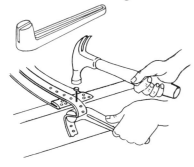

146-3. A tack claw (lifter).

146-4. A ripping chisel helps remove tacks which have been driven completely into the wood.

146-5. Assorted needles and skewers are useful to sew and pin different types of upholstery work.

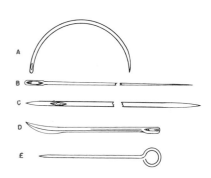

The straight needle (Fig. 146-5B) is available in numerous sizes with single or double points. An 8-inch double-point needle (Fig. 146-5C) is useful for sewing back and forth through stuffing or other materials without turning it. The bent packing needle (Fig. 146-5D) sews heavier packing materials.

Skewers (Fig. 146-5E) are pins that come in lengths of 2½ to 4 inches. Each has a loop for a head. Skewers pin the final fabric cover in place for tacking and sewing.

Cushion irons, or hand irons (Fig. 146-6), serve in place of a cushion-filling machine. They can be made or purchased. A unit of cushion springs is wrapped in cotton or other filler; it is placed inside the folded iron and compressed. The cushion box (upholstered cover) is fitted around the outside of the irons. The unit of springs with filler is then pushed into the cover.

Miscellaneous Tools

The Klinch-It tool (Fig. 146-7), hammer tacker (Fig. 146-8), spring-driven or compressed-air driven staplers, and hog-ring and spring-clip pliers (Fig. 146-9) are special tools. They are used in industry (Figs. 146-9 through 146-12).

Equipment

A special **work table** is useful and convenient to lay out, cut, and handle fabrics up to 54 inches wide. It should have a top approximately 5 by 8 feet, and it should be 30 to 34 inches high. Space underneath the top makes a good material storage area.

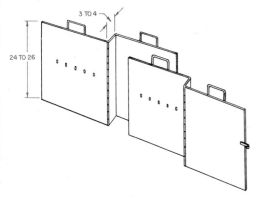

146-6.   Cushion irons help compress padding in cushions so that the covers can easily be put on.

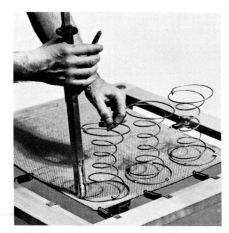

146-7.   Coil springs are easily attached to webbing with a Klinch-It tool.

146-8.   A hammer tacker.

146-9.   Hog-ring and spring-clip pliers.

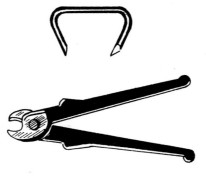

146-10.   The staple hammer helps speed production.

146-11.   The spring-driven stapler can be used to attach wood strips, as well as upholstery material.

146-12.   Air-driven staples and brads are used to attach corner blocks and trim on this furniture frame.

A heavy-duty **sewing machine** and a **cushion-filling machine** (Fig. 146-13) make work easier and faster.

Padded **trestles,** or **horses** (Fig. 146-14), are convenient to set the work on.

146-13. A cushion-filling machine.

146-14. A padded upholstery trestle, or "horse," prevents exposed wood from being scratched.

Unit 147 Upholstery Materials and Supplies

An immense variety of materials and supplies used for upholstery are available. The finished products vary according to personal needs, ingenuity, and desires.

Tacks

There are three common kinds of tacks: (1) upholstery, (2) webbing, and (3) gimp. Their sizes and lengths are given in Table 147-1.

The **upholstery tack** (Fig. 147-1) has a flat head and a smooth, tapered shank. It is used for tacking most fabrics and for anchoring tying twine. Sizes range from 1 ounce, which is about $\frac{5}{32}$ inch long, to 24 ounce, which is $1\frac{1}{8}$ inches long. The 4-, 6-, 8-, and 12-ounce sizes are commonly used.

Webbing tacks have barbed shanks which give more holding power to tack webbing. The 12- and 14-ounce sizes are commonly used. The larger (14-ounce) size is about $\frac{3}{4}$ inch long.

Gimp tacks have small, round heads. They range in size from 2 ounces (about $\frac{5}{16}$ inch long) to 8 ounces (about $\frac{5}{8}$ inch long). The 3-, 4-, and 6-ounce sizes are commonly used. They tack decorative gimp (Fig. 147-2).

Decorative nails (Fig. 147-3) are tacks used where the heads will show.

Compressed-air driven **staples** are used by many manufacturers instead of upholstery tacks.

Webbing

Three basic types of webbing are (1) jute, (2) steel, and (3) decorative.

Jute webbing is the most frequently used, is exceptionally strong, and stretches very little. It is available in rolls that range from 3 to 4 inches wide; the $3\frac{1}{2}$-inch width is the most common. The webbing is interwoven into cross bands as a base support for stuffing on open frames and cushions. Loose coil springs can also be attached to webbing.

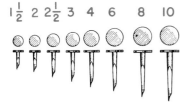

147-1. Common upholstery tacks have tapered shanks and very sharp points.

147-2. This is one of many designs of decorative gimp used over seams and edges of upholstery material.

Table 147-1
SIZES AND LENGTHS OF TACKS

No.	Length	No.	Length
1	$\frac{3}{16}$	10	$\frac{5}{8}$
$1\frac{1}{2}$	$\frac{7}{32}$	12	$\frac{11}{16}$
2	$\frac{1}{4}$	14	$\frac{3}{4}$
$2\frac{1}{2}$	$\frac{5}{16}$	16	$\frac{13}{16}$
3	$\frac{3}{8}$	18	$\frac{7}{8}$
4	$\frac{7}{16}$	20	$\frac{15}{16}$
6	$\frac{1}{2}$	22	1
8	$\frac{9}{16}$	24	$1\frac{1}{8}$

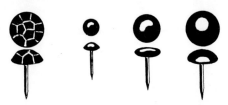

147-3. Decorative nails are often called tacks. They are used to tack on outer materials where the heads are visible.

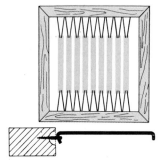

147-4. The first of four methods of arranging and fastening rubber webbing.

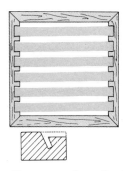

147-5. The second method of arranging and fastening rubber webbing.

147-6. The third method of arranging and fastening rubber webbing.

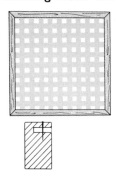

Steel webbing is about ¾ inch to 1 inch wide. It is used to support jute webbing. It can also be used in combination with small springs to form a semisolid base support.

Decorative webbing is usually made from plastic or rubber. The plastic type is made in many patterns and colors. It is used on lawn furniture, folding chairs, and other pieces where the webbing serves as the complete seat or back. Rubber webbing often serves as a base for cushions; it is most often seen on Swedish and Danish Modern furniture.

Four representative patterns for arranging and attaching rubber webbing are shown in Figs. 147-4 through 147-7.

Springs

Upholstery springs are manufactured in single coils, zigzag rolls, bars, and in special groups called **marshall units; base,** or **deck, units;** and **back units** (Fig. 147-8). Single coils are purchased by weight; zigzag rolls, by the foot; and bars, by the number of springs per bar.

Springs are classified according to their shape, their firmness, and the way the tips of their coils arc handled. They are selected for their intended use, the load they are to carry, and the depth of the frame in which they will be placed.

147-7. The fourth method of arranging and fastening rubber webbing.

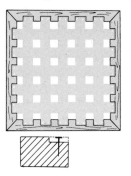

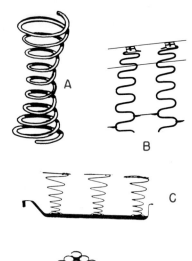

147-8. Types of upholstery springs: (A) single coil, (B) zigzag, or no-sag, (C) bar, and (D) marshall unit.

Coil springs come in three types: (1) seat, (2) back, and (3) cushion. Single-coil **seat springs** (Fig. 147-9A) are loose and smooth at both ends. They are made soft, medium, and hard as to their firmness. They range from about 4 to 14 inches in height, and are

147-9. Coil springs: (A) loose seat, (B) back, and (C) marshall unit.

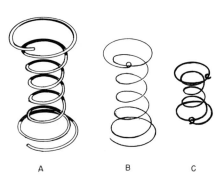

147-10. The foam slab resembles a loaf of bread in continuous production.

147-11. A worker is topping a foam bun to provide a block, slab, or sheet of almost any dimension.

(Nopco Chemical Company)

147-12. Different shapes of foam padding: (*A*) slab, (*B*) crowned, (*C*) cored, (*D*) full molded, and (*E*) reversible "T."

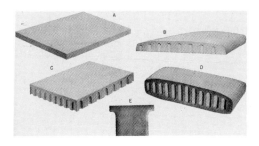

usually made of 9-gauge (larger) to 11-gauge (smaller) wire. If the center of the spring coil is smaller than the outside, the spring is harder; if it is larger, the spring is softer. An example of a medium-hard spring is shown in Fig. 147-9A).

Back and **cushion springs** (Figs. 147-9*B* and 147-9*C*) in many types of special units are made of small wire (12 to 15 gauge). They are tied together by wire or helicals (small springs) to form units for seat decks and backs. Their height ranges from 4 to 8 inches. Cushion springs for marshall units (Fig. 147-8*D*) are sewn into individual pockets of muslin.

The **bar-spring unit** (Fig. 147-8*C*) is convenient because no other spring support is necessary. The seat or back spring units are ready to tie; they are already spaced and attached to steel wire or bars. These units are easily mounted on a frame with nails, webbing tacks, or screws.

Twine

The best **spring-tying twine** is made from hemp. It has a wax finish. It is commonly purchased in 1- or 5-pound balls. The best twine should be used because it is under great strain. When the springs are correctly tied, the twine lasts indefinitely.

147-13. Rubberized curled hair.

Sewing or **stitching twine** and **thread** are made from nylon or flax, and they may have a wax finish. They are exceptionally strong and are used to sew springs to webbing and to stitch padding materials in place to prevent movement. Another use is to sew edge rolls to spring wire edges. Thread is used to sew the final fabric.

Padding

Padding material is referred to as **stuffing.** It should be clean and strong. Padding makes the seat, back, and arms of furniture soft and attractive.

Foam rubber and **plastic foam sheets** are preformed materials. The foam is manufactured in a continuous slab (Fig. 147-10). It can be molded, split, and cut (Fig. 147-11) to provide shapes and sizes of almost any dimension (Fig. 147-12).

Hair is one of the oldest and best stuffing materials. It comes from hogs, cattle, and horses. Hog hair, alone, is least desirable, so it is mixed with other types. Rubberized curled hair is made in many thicknesses, widths, and lengths of prepared flat strips and rolls (Fig. 147-13).

Moss is a vegetable material obtained from trees in the South. A fine, wirelike hair is obtained after it is heat-treated. It is sold by the pound.

147-14. Cotton batts for padding are formed in many shapes and sizes.

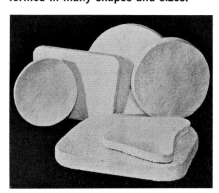

Cotton felt, or **batting,** is prepared in sheets or layers about 1 inch thick and 27 inches wide. It weighs about 1 pound per yard. Batts are made soft, medium, and firm, and they are obtainable in various shapes (Fig. 147-14). Cotton is often used as the only padding for solid-base seats. It should be pulled apart because a hard edge results from cutting.

Stuffing materials other than those listed above are **tow** (from flax stalks), **sisal** (from flax leaves), **palm fibers, coco fibers, excelsior, kapok, down** (soft feathers), and **cotton substitutes** (made from wood).

Other Upholstery Materials

Edge rolls can be purchased by the foot. They require only sewing or tacking into place. Rolls are made by using various fillers inside a burlap covering. Round rolls are used around edges of arms and other places where a soft edge is required. Spring-tied edge rolls are shaped like teardrops. They are easily made. This type of roll is sewn to the burlap which covers the edge wire around the foundation or the deck springs.

Burlap covers the springs after they are tied. It is made from jute yarn. The 8- to 10-ounce weight is very satisfactory; the 40-inch width is useful. Stuffing is placed over a burlap base. It is then covered with muslin or burlap if loose material or rubberized hair is used.

Muslin comes bleached and unbleached. It is from 35 to 54 inches wide. It covers cotton and other stuffing material before the outer fabric is put on. For this reason, it is sometimes referred to as a "temporary covering."

Welt cord can be bought in many sizes. It is made from strong twisted paper or twisted yarn. It is sewn into the final fabric to form a bead around seats, cushions, or other trim areas.

A **tacking strip** is made of stiff cardboard. It is $3/8$ to $1/2$ inch wide. These strips are used in blind tacking of straight welt seams and where the final cover must be blind tacked. In blind tacking, the tack is driven into place so that the material can cover the head of the tack.

Cambric is a starched or stiff glazed cotton fabric. It is usually tacked underneath seats to close the bottom. It prevents stuffing particles from eventually falling to the floor when they work loose.

The **final covering** of upholstered furniture is chosen from an almost unlimited number of materials, designs, and colors. Friezes, tapestries, and velours are easily worked. Leather is a beautiful but expensive covering; however, durable leather substitutes and numerous forms of plastics have been successfully developed.

Some synthetic products, without cloth backing, are more difficult to work than the fabrics. Plastic or vinyl materials are sometimes bonded to specially woven fabric backings. These are strong, serviceable, and soft, and they stretch and form readily. The interesting design shown in Fig. 147-15 shows the versatility of fabric-backed vinyl covering materials. Figure 147-16 shows the suggested amount of final covering to buy for some shapes of furniture.

147-15. A metallic-finish "scimitar" design on this vinyl material appears to be a fabric.

147-16. Suggested amounts of upholstery material for different sizes and shapes of furniture.

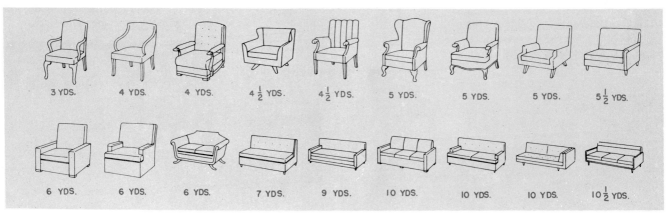

3 YDS. 4 YDS. 4 YDS. $4\frac{1}{2}$ YDS. $4\frac{1}{2}$ YDS. 5 YDS. 5 YDS. 5 YDS. $5\frac{1}{2}$ YDS.

6 YDS. 6 YDS. 6 YDS. 7 YDS. 9 YDS. 10 YDS. 10 YDS. 10 YDS. $10\frac{1}{2}$ YDS.

Unit 148 Upholstering the Padded Seat

Simple padded construction is often used, especially on the seats and backs of kitchen and dining chairs. The upholstering is done on a solid base or an open frame (slip-seat construction). This type of upholstery permits frequent, easy changes of the outer fabric. An ottoman may also use the open frame with slip-seat webbing and padding, as shown in this unit.

Upholstering an Open Frame

1. Construct or obtain an open frame for a seat. If the frame is made to fit a particular opening, allow ⅛ inch of space on each side for the thickness of the upholstery materials. If it is to be a chair slip seat, make it from ¾-inch stock. The dowel butt joint is a good choice for corner construction. (NOTE: Follow only steps 8 through 15 when a solid base is used.)

An open frame can be built as shown in Fig. 148-1. This frame can be adapted for either a webbed, padded seat or for coil or no-sag springs.

2. Round all corners slightly to help prevent wear on the upholstery material.

3. Determine how many strips of webbing are needed. Space them from ½ to 2 inches apart. The space between the frame edge and the first webbing strip should be approximately the same as the space between the strips.

Do not cut the webbing into strips until after each is fastened. Tack one end of the 3½-inch jute webbing roll to one side of the frame (Fig. 148-2). Use No. 12 webbing or upholstery tacks. Space three tacks evenly. Allow about ¾ to 1 inch excess length of webbing for folding back over these tacks. Anchor this fold with two more tacks (Fig. 148-3).

4. Stretch the webbing tight, using the webbing stretcher. Tack it to the opposite side of the frame with three tacks (Fig. 148-4).

5. Release the webbing stretcher. Cut the webbing about ¾ to 1 inch beyond the three tacks. Fold it back over them. Secure the end with two more tacks, as in step 3.

6. Continue fastening other strips of webbing in a basket-weave pattern until the frame is covered (Fig. 148-5).

7. Cover the webbed frame with one thickness of closely woven burlap (Fig. 148-6). Tack snugly in place with No. 6 or No. 8 upholstery tacks. Space them about 1½ inches apart. Some seats need an edge roll around the edges.

8. Cut a section of 1-inch foam rubber, plastic foam sheet, or rubberized hair to fit the seat (Fig. 148-7). If loose stuffing is used, tear it apart and

148-1. Open frames can also be adapted for use with most kinds of springs.

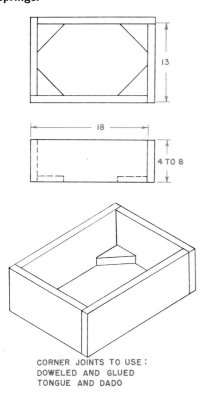

CORNER JOINTS TO USE:
DOWELED AND GLUED
TONGUE AND DADO

148-2. Tack an end of the webbing roll to the frame.

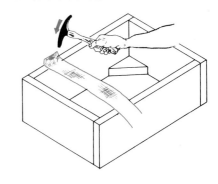

148-3. Anchor the fold with two additional tacks.

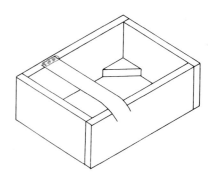

cover the seat evenly to a depth of about 2 inches. Be sure that all foreign particles are removed.

9. Cover the rubberized hair (or other stuffing) with burlap. Drive the tacks in only about halfway so that they can be easily removed if necessary. Moss or other loose padding is adjusted to a smooth layer with a stuffing regulator.

10. Cut the surplus burlap from the corners to eliminate a bulge under the final cover.

11. Tighten the burlap. Drive in the tacks.

12. Cover the burlap with a layer of cotton felt or batting. Some craftsmen prefer to use only the rubber or plastic foam sheet. This eliminates use of the cotton and rubberized hair.

13. Cover the cotton with a piece of muslin. Tack it to the frame.

14. Cut the final upholstery, and place it over the muslin. Pull it smooth and snug, and tack it underneath the frame.

15. Tack the cambric to the under part of the frame. Attach the legs.

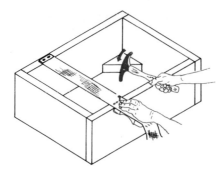

148-4. Stretch the webbing and tack it to the opposite side of the frame.

148-5. Cover the frame with strips of webbing in a basket-weave pattern.

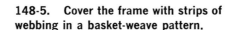

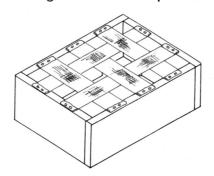

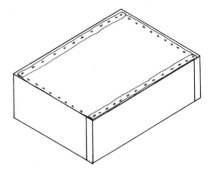

148-6. Cover the webbing with burlap.

148-7. Rubberized hair or foam sheets make smooth layers of padding.

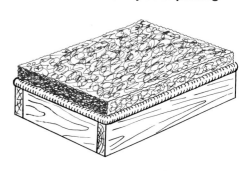

Unit 149 Spring Upholstering

No-sag springs are widely used in upholstering. The 9-ounce weight (size) is used for seats and the 11-ounce for backs. This form of upholstery is relatively simple, fast, and preferred by many craftsmen.

No-sag Spring Construction

1. Make or obtain a wood frame for a chair (Fig. 149-1) or an ottoman.

2. Tack clips on opposite sides of the frame so that the lines of no-sag spring stock will be about 4 inches on center. Use barbed webbing tacks for better holding power. On chairs, place the springs from back to front or from top to bottom.

Handle the spring wire carefully. It is steel and will therefore be difficult to handle. It will be necessary to get someone to assist you.

3. Place one end of the spring stock into a metal clip. Roll out the length to the opposite side. The spring contour should rise above the frame from 1 to 2 inches, depending on the softness of the seat desired.

4. Cut the stock to the required length. Make a notch with a file, a hacksaw, or a bolt cutter. The no-sag stock is made of spring steel and will break easily where it is notched. *Hold the ends in a vise,* or with other tools, to prevent the resulting sharp ends from springing loose.

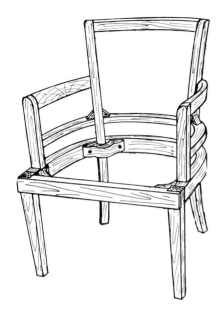

149-1. Some chairs are adaptable for upholstering with pad, no-sag spring, or coil-spring construction.

149-2. No-sag springs hold in the clips easier when the ends are slightly bent.

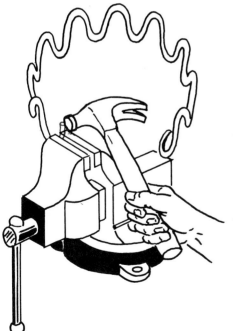

5. Check the first piece of spring for proper length. Cut all the others.

6. Grind the ends of the pieces smooth. Place the tip ends of the spring pieces in a machinist's vise. Bend them slightly (Fig. 149-2) to hold better in the metal clips or the hinge links (Fig. 149-3).

7. Place the no-sag springs in the clips. Anchor the clips permanently with webbing tacks (Fig. 149-4).

8. Tie the rows of no-sag springs with connecting wire springs. Clothes-hanger wire is very good for tying the middle rows together. Special helicals (small springs) can be used for all, or part of, the tying on the sides. See Fig. 149-4. Regular upholstery spring-tying

twine can also be used for tying the rows crosswise.

9. Cover the no-sag springs with a layer of burlap (Fig. 149-5).

10. Tack and sew an edge roll around the frame edges to build up the seat and to protect the final covering from wear. This roll can be purchased or built up (Fig. 149-6).

11. Continue building the edge roll until the desired height is obtained (Fig. 149-7).

12. Add layers of filler padding (foam rubber, plastic sheeting, or rubberized hair). Cover the entire seat with burlap (Fig. 149-8). Chalk lines show where to sew through the top layer of burlap down to the spring-

149-3. Some of the special hardware used with no-sag springs.

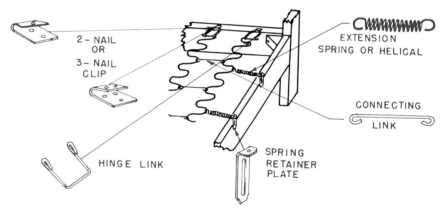

149-4. Clips should be anchored well to the frame. Note how the wires and springs hold the no-sag rows.

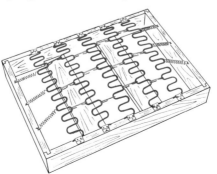

149-5. Springs covered with burlap.

covering burlap to make filler compact.

13. Add a layer of cotton or foam padding. Cover it with muslin (Fig. 149-9). Tack it underneath firmly.

14. Complete the seat by covering with upholstery material (Fig. 149-10). The corners of the final covering fabric should be shaped as illustrated in Fig. 149-11. A bead, or welt cord, sewn in the fabric gives the final covering a finished appearance. The entire silhouette can be changed by using less depth in the frame and padding and a different style of legs (Fig. 149-12).

Tight-coil Spring Construction

Coil springs can be mounted with clips to webbing, on wood slats (Fig. 149-13), or on metal bars. Decide how high the seat is to be built and how soft it is to be. Test several sizes of

149-6. A padded roll placed around the edges builds up the seat and reduces wear of the final covering.

149-9. Add a layer of cotton or foam padding and cover with muslin.

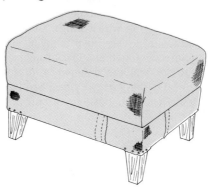

149-12. Different frames, legs, and height change the appearance of similar upholstered pieces.

149-7. The additional edge roll adds height and comfort.

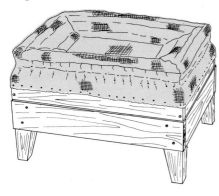

149-10. Many types of upholstery material are available as a final cover.

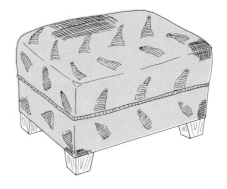

149-13. Easy attachment of coil springs.

149-8. Add filler padding and cover the whole seat with burlap.

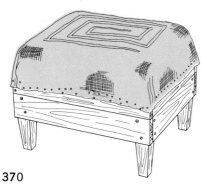

149-11. One method of shaping corners.

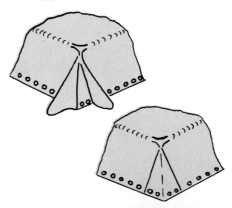

149-14. Coil springs properly tied.

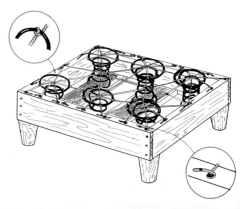

springs. Determine the size and number needed for the frame. Openings between springs should be no greater than the size of a spring coil. This open area will be crossed by wires or hand ties to prevent the padding from sagging.

1. Make a suitable furniture frame to be upholstered with coil-spring construction. See Fig. 149-13.

2. Select the springs. Mount them in the frame. Check the rows for alignment and spacing. Loose springs are attached to a wood base with staples. Burlap is placed underneath the spring to act as a silencer. Springs are attached to a webbed base with sewing twine or wire clips.

3. Drive a No. 8 or a No. 10 upholstery tack about halfway into the frame edges in line with the center of each row of springs.

4. Cut several pieces of tying twine to the correct length. This is about 2½ times the length or width of the frame.

5. Wrap one end of the twine around a tack. Drive it in securely. Leave about 1 inch of surplus twine. Anchor it with a second tack (Fig. 149-14, *right detail*).

6. Hold the first spring in the position for the height of seat desired. Pull the tying twine over the spring edge nearest the tack. Tie the twine to the spring with the spring-tying knot (Fig. 149-14, *left detail*).

149-15. The bar spring, or drop-in, unit is easy to attach to the frame with screws.

DROP-IN SPRING UNIT

7. Tie to the opposite side of the spring. Proceed across the row of springs with the same pattern of tying. Fasten the twine to the opposite frame edge with the same knot.

8. Continue tying rows of springs crosswise (two-way tie) and diagonally (four-way tie) as shown in Fig. 149-14. A smooth contour will result.

9. Cover the springs with a layer of closely woven burlap. Fold the edges. Tack it to the frame.

10. Follow steps 8 through 15, Unit 148, "Upholstering the Padded Seat."

Wire-edge Coil-spring Construction

1. Make a frame for the kind of springs and mounting desired. The procedure explained is for bar-spring (drop-in) units, but it is virtually the same as other operations after the springs are mounted.

2. Mount bar-spring, or drop-in, units to the frame with screws (Fig. 149-15).

3. Bend a piece of spring-steel edge wire to the shape of the wood frame. It should fit the outer edges of the springs when they are standing straight.

4. Tie the edge wire to the outer edges of the coil springs. Follow the procedure shown in Fig. 149-16.

5. Drive a No. 8 or a No. 10 upholstery tack about halfway into the frame edge, aligned with the center of each outer spring. Loop one end of the spring-tying twine around the tack. Drive it in to hold the twine securely.

6. Start another tack into the frame near the first one. Wrap the loose end of the twine around it. Drive the tack into place (Fig. 149-17).

7. Tie the surplus end of the twine to the wire edge to obtain the proper height for the springs. The rows are then ready to be tied together. Lengths of the twine should be about 2½ times the length or width of the frame.

8. Repeat step 7, working around the frame. The wire edge should be level all around.

149-16. Procedure for tying edge wire to coil springs.

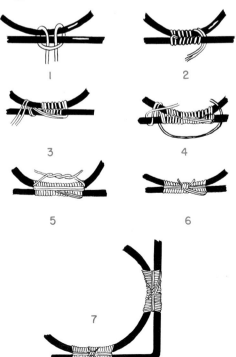

1

2

3

4

5

6

7

9. Tie the springs with the long end of the tying twine, as shown in Fig. 149-17. Continue tying the coils with the spring-tying twine crosswise and diagonally until a smooth, flat seat is obtained.

10. Cover the springs with a layer of closely woven burlap. Tack it to the frame (Fig. 149-18).

11. Sew a hard teardrop edge roll to the burlap around the edge of the wire frame (Fig. 149-19).

12. Pad the seat with rubberized hair and cotton or foam padding. Cover it with muslin.

13. Complete the upholstered seat by covering it with the final upholstery material.

149-17. Attaching tying twine to the frame.

149-18. Cover springs with burlap.

149-19. Sew a hard tear-drop edge roll over the edge wire to prevent wear and add comfort.

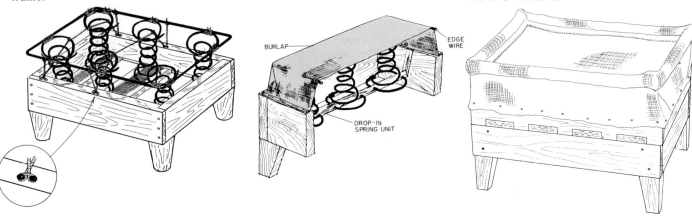

Unit 150 Upholstering Overstuffed Furniture

Many types of springs are used in overstuffed furniture construction. Seats and backs are built up in many ways. Coil springs can be mounted on steel webbing and tied (Fig. 150-1) to form a base. The seat and back can be made with sets of springs as a complete unit (Fig. 150-2) or as separate units with loose cushions.

Cushions are upholstered as separate units for either seats or backs. Marshall-unit springs, or formed-foam units, are also used to form cushions.

Much modern overstuffed furniture has been developed for functional, multipurpose use. Typical examples are (1) the sofa-sleeper unit (Fig. 150-3), (2) the reclining chair (Fig. 150-4), and (3) the two-seat settee (Fig. 150-5). Mechanical hardware action speedily converts the settee into a guest bed (Fig. 150-6), a chaise lounge, or any of a number of other positions.

150-1. Coil springs mounted on steel webbing.

150-2. Some chairs do not use loose cushions.

(The Seng Company)

150-3.   Metal frames fold out to support a mattress.

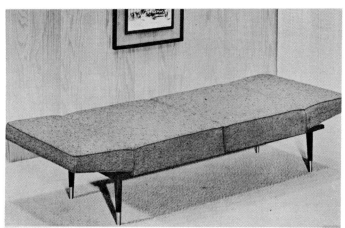

(The Seng Company)

150-4.   Special hardware converts a chair into a recliner.

150-5.   A multipurpose settee.

(The Seng Company)

150-6.   Settee converts to a guest bed.

(The Seng Company)

Constructing Overstuffed Furniture

Many of the operations mentioned in this procedure are the same as in pad and simple spring construction. Additional operations are explained for one type of overstuffed furniture. Refer to special books on upholstery for additional information and operations. Cutaway and cross-section views of overstuffed furniture are shown in Figs. 150-7 and 150-8.

1. Make (or obtain) a strong chair frame. The chair should have two arms (Fig. 150-9) or no arms (Fig. 150-10). Or you may use two chairs together. Each of these chairs has one arm. They form sectional furniture. (Fig. 150-11).

2. Attach and fasten coil springs in the seat and no-sag springs in the back (Fig. 150-12).

3. Add the wire edge to the seat springs. Tie the coil and no-sag springs (Fig. 150-13) as explained in Unit 149.

4. Cover the springs on the seat and back with plain burlap or burlap with interwoven wire See Fig. 150-14.

5. Interweave and attach webbing to the inside of the chair arm.

6. Sew an edge roll to the open sides of the seat. Tack a smaller roll to the frame around the back and over the chair arm (Fig. 150-14).

7. Place a layer of rubberized hair or other padding on the arm. Cover it with burlap (Fig. 150-15). Repeat this padding on the seat and back. More

than one layer of padding is necessary when cushions are not used.

8. Add one layer of cotton or foam on the arm and one or more on the seat and back. Cover each part separately with muslin (Fig. 150-16).

9. Cover the cushion units, and upholster all parts (Fig. 150-17). The order of upholstering is (1) seat, (2) front of back, (3) inside of arm, (4) outside of arm, (5) back, and (6) cam-

bric underneath. Welt cords are sewn into the outer fabric to add a decorative, beadlike appearance.

10. Cover the fronts of the arms with panels. To make panels, saw $\frac{1}{4}$-inch plywood to the shape desired. Cover it with a thin layer of cotton; then cover this with upholstery material.

11. Nail the panel in place with small finishing nails or wire brads. Use

a center punch to set the nails beneath the fabric so that they are out of sight.

12. Cover the outer side of the arm and back with the same upholstery material. Use tacking strips. Use gimp tacks or decorative nails, or sew with a blind stitch to overlap material to attach this material smoothly to the frame (Fig. 150-18).

13. Tack cambric to the frame underneath the seat.

150-7. Cutaway section of an upholstered chair with the cushion removed.

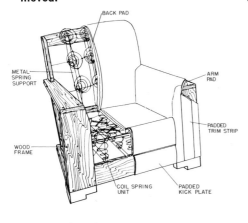

150-9. Chair arms and legs which are to be seen on finished upholstered furniture are built into the final frame.

150-11. One arm is built on opposite sides of sectional units.

150-8. Cross section of an upholstered chair, showing the deck, back, and loose cushion.

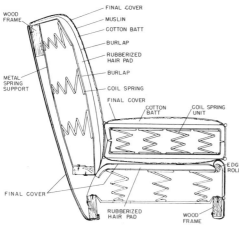

150-10. Arms are left off some chairs and center portions of sectional furniture.

150-12. Coil and no-sag springs can be mixed on different upholstered parts.

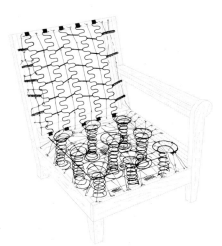

150-13. Loose coil springs in a chair seat need an edge wire and proper tying to hold the seat in place.

150-14. An edge roll gives protection from wear.

150-15. A chair arm also needs padding.

150-16. Cotton or foam padding is covered with muslin.

150-17. Cushions can be loose or covered and attached as a one-piece unit.

150-18. Furniture has a finished appearance when the back is covered with the same material.

DISCUSSION TOPICS

1. What are the advantages of each type of upholstery classification?
2. Describe the assorted sizes and shapes of needles.
3. Where are skewers used?
4. List some special tools which would be convenient to use in upholstering furniture.
5. Give the names and purposes for some special machines and equipment used in upholstering.
6. Name and explain the differences between, and the uses of, the kinds of upholstery tacks.
7. What are the three kinds of webbing?
8. In what shapes or quantities can upholstery springs be purchased?
9. Name five stuffing or padding materials.
10. What type of joint is recommended for slip-seat frames?
11. Why is a basket-weave pattern used when webbing is attached to a frame?
12. Name the tools used in no-sag spring construction.
13. Why is no-sag spring wire dangerous?
14. What are the minimum and maximum heights this spring wire should rise above the frame?
15. What is an edge roll for?
16. What tools and materials are used in coil-seat construction which are not needed for a padded seat?
17. What advantage does the four-way tie have over the two-way tie?

THE BUILDING CONSTRUCTION INDUSTRY

Unit 151 Common Building and Carpentry Terms

The terminology selected for this unit includes words and terms that are frequently used in carpentry and building construction. The nomenclature is divided into groups according to the major components (parts) of a building. Examples of many terms are seen in the various drawings and photographs.

General Building Terms

■ **Batter boards.** These are boards nailed to posts at the corners of the proposed building. Strings stretched between them indicate the outline of foundation walls.

■ **Brace.** A brace is any piece of wood fastened to two or more pieces. The brace usually forms a triangle with the other pieces to give greater strength.

■ **Building code.** This is composed of the legal requirements designed to protect the general welfare, health, and safety of those in and around buildings.

■ **Scaffold.** A scaffold is a temporary platform built to assist workmen in reaching high places.

■ **Sheathing.** Sheathing is narrow boards spaced on rafters to which shingles are attached. It is also boards, plywood, or other wallboards placed solidly over studding or rafters.

- **Sheathing paper.** This is a paperlike material placed over subfloors, on walls, or on roof sheathing to help prevent air passage.
- **Toenailing.** Nailing at an angle through one surface into another is termed **toenailing**. It is usually done when one piece is perpendicular to another.
- **Trim.** Trim is exterior or interior finish materials, such as moldings placed around windows, doors, floors, and ceilings.
- **Vestibule.** This is usually an enclosed entrance to a house or building.

Foundation Terms

- **Footing.** Footing is the lower portion of a foundation wall or pier. It is usually made wider than the wall to distribute the load.
- **Foundation.** The foundation is a footing, wall, or piers which support the remainder of the building.
- **Ledger strip.** The ledger strip is the piece nailed to girders or beams. The ends of the floor joists rest on it.
- **Sill.** The sill is usually a horizontal member which rests on the foundation. It supports the uprights of the frame. It may also form the lower part of an opening, as a window sill does.

Flooring Terms

- **Bridging.** Bridging pieces, equal to the width of the joists, are fitted between floor joists. Crossed pieces, placed in pairs between joists from the top of one to the bottom of an adjacent joist, brace and distribute loads.
- **Joists.** These are 2- by 6-inch (or heavier) parallel beams on 16- or 24-inch centers. They support floor and ceiling loads and are themselves supported by bearing walls, girders, or larger beams.
- **Subfloor.** A subfloor is straight-edge or matched lumber placed diagonally across joists over which the finish floor is laid. It may also be made of plywood or some other sheet-wood product.

Wall Terms

- **Bay window.** Any window space projecting outward from the regular wall, in various shapes, is called by this name.
- **Baseboard.** A board placed around the bottom of a wall to finish and decorate between the wall and the floor is a baseboard.
- **Base shoe.** The base shoe is a molding or carpet strip placed next to the floor against the baseboard.
- **Jamb.** This is a frame that surrounds and contacts the window or sash. It is supported by framing.
- **Girder.** This term is often used interchangeably with **beam** to mean a large structural member which supports a heavy load in walls, a roof, or floor.
- **Header.** A header is often called a **lintel**. It is a horizontal beam placed perpendicularly between joists over window and door openings or in framing for a chimney or stairway opening.
- **Partition.** A partition is any wall-dividing unit within a building. If it supports a load, it is a **bearing partition;** if it is **nonbearing,** it supports only its own weight.
- **Siding.** Siding can be beveled or lap, strong drop siding (tongue-and-groove joints), or shiplap (rabbeted or lap joints) for use as exterior wall covering.
- **Sole plate.** This is usually a 2-by 4-inch wood piece laid flat, on which wall and partition studs rest.
- **Stud (also studding).** Studding pieces are the vertical members of walls and partitions, usually placed on 16- or 24-inch centers.
- **Wallboard.** This is plywood, wood pulp, and other material made into large, rigid sheets. It is fastened to internal and external walls, partitions, roofs, and the framing of a building.

Roofing Terms

- **Beam.** A beam is sometimes called a **girder.** It is a structural member which supports a load in the roof, walls, or floor.
- **Gable.** This is an inverted V formed between the slopes of two roof sections.
- **Pitch.** Pitch is the ratio of the total rise of the building to the total width. In addition, pitch is the number of inches of vertical rise to each foot of horizontal run.
- **Rafters.** Rafters are the framing pieces on which other roofing is placed. **Common** rafters are those which run square from the top of the wall plate to the peak (ridge) of the gable. **Cripple** rafters are pieces cut to fit between valley and hip rafters. **Hip** rafters extend from corners, or the outside angle of the wall plates, to the apex of the roof. **Jack** rafters are those which run square from the wall plate, or ridge board, and intersect hip or valley rafters, respectively. **Valley** rafters extend from the inside angle of wall plates to the ridge center line of the building.
- **Rise.** This is the height of a roof measured vertically from a point on the outside face of the top wall plate to the ridge of the roof.
- **Roof.** The roof covers the top of a structure.
- **Run.** A run is half a span (see **span,** below). It is the horizonal distance from the face of one wall to the ridge of a roof.
- **Shingles.** Shingles are wood pieces, and various other materials, cut and packaged in standard thicknesses, widths, and lengths.
- **Span.** A span is the horizontal distance between any structural supports, such as outside walls, columns, beams, girders, piers, or trusses.
- **Square.** This is a unit of measure of 100 square feet of roofing and sidewall materials. These roofing and sidewall materials are often packaged and sold by the square.
- **Truss.** A truss is a structural frame of rafters and other parts, usually in triangular form. Trusses are laminated or curved units which are used to support roofs or other heavy loads over long spans.

Unit 152 Construction Lumber

About three-fourths of the lumber produced for interior and exterior construction of homes and buildings comes from the many softwoods. Some of these are cedar, cypress, fir, hemlock, larch, pine, redwood, and spruce. Softwood lumber is classified by **manufacture, use, size,** and **grade.**

152-1. Suggested uses of lumber for standard construction.

(Douglas Fir Plywood Association)

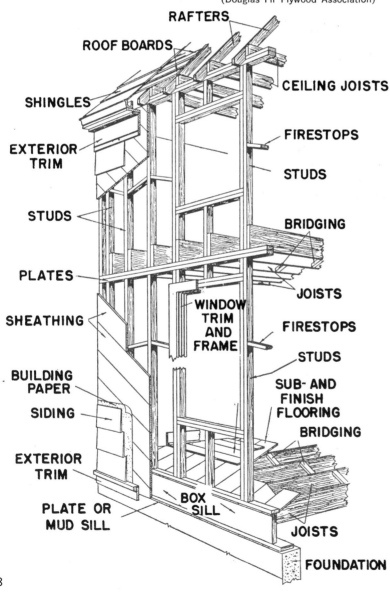

RAFTERS
ROOF BOARDS
CEILING JOISTS
SHINGLES
FIRESTOPS
EXTERIOR TRIM
STUDS
STUDS
BRIDGING
PLATES
JOISTS
WINDOW TRIM AND FRAME
SHEATHING
FIRESTOPS
STUDS
BUILDING PAPER
SUB- AND FINISH FLOORING
SIDING
BRIDGING
EXTERIOR TRIM
PLATE OR MUD SILL
BOX SILL
JOISTS
FOUNDATION

Manufacture Classifications

Rough lumber has not been dressed (planed). It has been sawed, edged, and trimmed, and it usually shows saw marks on all its longitudinal surfaces.

Surfaced, or **dressed, lumber** has been surfaced or planed to a uniform size on one or two sides (S1S or S2S), one or two edges (S1E or S2E), or a combination of sides and edges (S1S1E, S1S2E, S2S1E, or S4S).

Worked lumber has been dressed and worked for a particular purpose in a matching machine, molder, or other special equipment. Examples of worked lumber are rabbeted edges for shiplap, tongue-and-groove matching, and molding.

Use Classifications

Yard lumber in all sizes and patterns is intended for general-purpose building.

Factory and **shop lumber** is worked into doors, windows, and similar millwork.

Structural lumber is used where stress and heavy loads are supported.

Size Classifications

Boards are called **strips** if they are less than 6 inches wide. This grouping includes pieces less than 2 inches thick and 1 or more inches wide. Examples are fencing, sheathing, subflooring, and roofing.

Dimension stock is from 2 inches up to, but not including, 5 inches thick and 2 or more inches wide. Included in the group are joists, studs, and rafters.

Timbers are pieces with a minimum dimension of 5 inches. They include beams, posts, and sills.

Lumber dimensions are smaller than the common sizes by which they are known because of seasoning and surfacing. Minimum thicknesses and widths for actual sizes are specified for each type of softwood lumber in the American Lumber Standards. For example, a standard dressed 2- by 4-inch piece actually measures only $1\frac{5}{8}$ by $3\frac{5}{8}$ inches. However, the standard size is used in all lumber sales and bookkeeping. Such a piece is referred to as a **two-by-four**.

Grade Classifications

The exact grading rules for all species of lumber, both softwoods and hardwoods, are established by agencies maintained by the lumber industry. These grading rules cover the appearance and the performance of individual species of wood. The agencies maintained by industry also supervise grading and inspection.

Select grades are intended for finish purposes. A and B grades are usually combined and sold as **B and Better.** C and D grades are more economical, and they serve many purposes just as well as the higher grades.

Common grades are utilized where knots and other surface characteristics are decorative. These are intended for general construction purposes.

Dimension grades of softwood are classified according to the natural characteristics which affect their stiffness, strength, and other load-bearing qualities. The appearance of joists, studs, and heavy construction parts is usually of secondary importance.

Structural lumber is 2 or more inches in thickness and width. A separate grading system, based on strength characteristics, is used.

General suggestions in the choice of lumber for standard building construction are indicated in Fig. 152-1.

Unit 153 Planning and Constructing the Foundation of a House

Three main essentials are needed to build a satisfactory house: (1) correct planning, (2) proper materials, and (3) sound construction. These principles apply to a house of any design, size, or cost. Some of the acceptable building practices and established methods of construction are explained. Construction details vary in different localities, but the fundamental principles apply anywhere.

Location and Excavation of the Site

Compare the size of the building plot to the size of the house desired. Check local building codes for minimum setback from streets, side clearance, and back (or alley) requirements. Building permits are usually necessary.

Determine subsoil and drainage conditions and depth of water-table

153-1. Batter boards are used at the corners of a plot to stake and lay out a house.

(USDA booklet 73, *Wood-frame House Construction*)

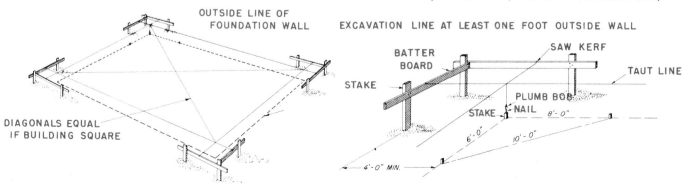

level before beginning any construction. The depth of a basement and the location of sewer pipes may depend on the natural ground water line, or water table.

Small stakes are located at each corner of the proposed house. Batter boards (Fig. 153-1) are placed at the corners outside the planned foundation lines. A common excavation plan is shown in Fig. 153-2.

Footings and Foundations

The footings and foundation walls are usually made of poured concrete or some other masonry product. The thickness and type of construction are controlled by local building codes, and the thickness varies from 6 to 12 inches. When basements are planned, 6 to 10 feet should be the minimum

height from the basement floor to the bottom of the floor joists.

Tight forms must be made, braced, and tied. The concrete is poured into these forms for the footings and foundation walls. The forms hold the fluid concrete in place until it hardens. A typical method of handling forms is shown in Fig. 153-3.

Frames and Forms

Frames for basement windows or doors are set in place when the concrete forms are built. Nails are placed in the top of the form to show the level to which the concrete should be poured. Pouring should be a continuous operation.

Forms are removed after the concrete has set (hardened) sufficiently to support loads. A week of drying is pre-

ferred. Hot tar and similar materials are used to waterproof the outside walls from above the surface grade line to the footing.

The joists and other floor structures are anchored to the concrete walls (Fig. 153-4). Bolts should be placed in the concrete before it hardens.

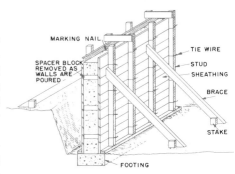

(USDA booklet 73, *Wood-frame House Construction*)

153-3. Typical formwork for pouring concrete walls.

153-2. A common excavation plan, showing the use of batter boards and chalk lines for layout.

(USDA booklet 73, *Wood-frame House Construction*)

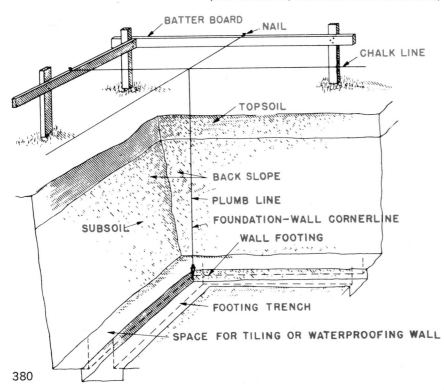

153-4. Anchoring joists and floor structure to the foundation.

(USDA booklet 73, *Wood-frame House Construction*)

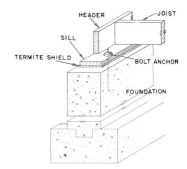

Unit 154 Floor Framing

Floor framing uses posts, beams or girders (Fig. 154-1), sills, joists, bridging, and subfloors. Chemically treated lumber should be used for all floor framing in areas where termites are a problem. Untreated materials can be partially protected by metal termite shields.

Posts and Beams

Steel or **wooden posts** are used to support beams or girders (Fig. 154-2). The beams support the inner ends of the first-floor joists, and they often rest on either masonry pieces or wooden posts (Fig. 154-3).

Beams can be either solid or box (Fig. 154-4) and can be built up (Fig. 154-5) with two or more pieces of 2-inch-thick dimension lumber. The end joints are staggered, but they usually join over a post.

Short beams can be butt-joined by using special metal connectors (Fig. 154-6). At least 4 inches of the beam end should rest (bear) on masonry walls. The top of the beam should be flush (level) with the sill plate unless notched joists are set on ledger strips (Fig. 154-7). Girders are specially spaced to allow for utility lines between them.

Sill and Floor Joists

The two common types of construction used over the foundation wall are platform and balloon. **Platform** construction (Fig. 154-8) uses a single sill anchored to the foundation. In **balloon** construction the joists and studs both rest directly on the double sill or the sill plate (Fig. 154-9).

Studs are nailed to both the joists and the sill. A nailing strip or fire stop must be placed between the studs when diagonal subflooring is used in balloon construction. Balloon framing is preferred when the outer construction is to be stone or a brick veneer because there is less potential shrinkage of exterior walls.

The selection of joists depends on the strength and stiffness required to eliminate annoying vibration. Joists

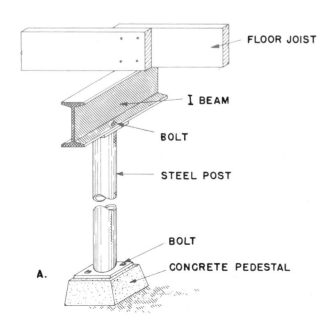

(National Lumber Manufacturers' Association)

154-1. Floor joists, beams, and two types of bridging are shown in this house framing.

154-2. Posts and beams: (A) steel post and I beam, and (B) wood post and built-up wood beam.

(USDA booklet 73, *Wood-frame House Construction*)

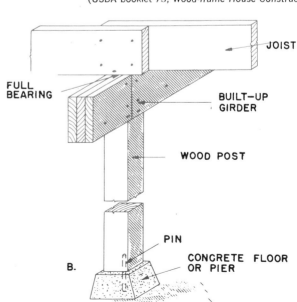

154-3. Joists rest on beams and wood posts to raise this coast resort home above ground level.

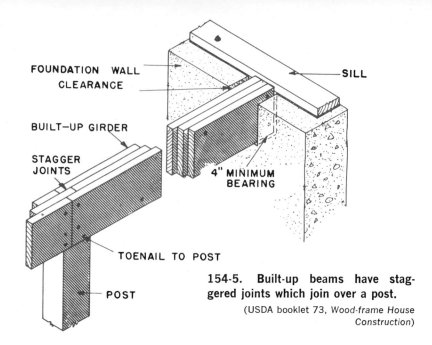

FOUNDATION WALL CLEARANCE

SILL

BUILT-UP GIRDER

STAGGER JOINTS

4" MINIMUM BEARING

TOENAIL TO POST

POST

154-5. Built-up beams have staggered joints which join over a post.

are usually 2 inches thick and 6, 8, 10, or 12 inches wide. The choice depends on the load to be carried, the length of the span, the spacing between joists (16 or 24 inches on center), and the species or grade of lumber used. Joists used under load-bearing partitions and as framing around fireplace openings, stairwells, and other openings should be doubled.

Bridging and Subfloors

Bridging is used between joists to stiffen the joists and to help distribute loads. Bridged pieces are used at mid-span, but not over 8 feet apart. Long spans will certainly require several lines of bridging (Fig. 154-10). These bridged pieces are themselves the same width as the joists.

Smaller pieces can be cut at an angle to fit diagonally between joists. They are nailed to the top and bottom of the joists. The bottom is frequently not fastened until the house framing is complete. Bridging and other floor framing for platform construction are shown in Fig. 154-10.

Subflooring is made of ¾-inch construction plywood or square-edge or

154-4. Plywood box beams, solid beams, posts, and other footing are often mixed in one construction job.

154-6. Metal connectors can be used to connect building parts. Uses are shown in Fig. 154-4.

154-7. Ledger strips are nailed to beams or girders to support joists.

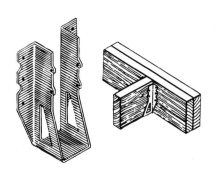

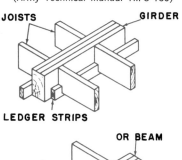

JOISTS

GIRDER

LEDGER STRIPS

OR BEAM

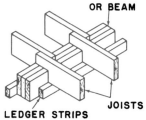

LEDGER STRIPS

JOISTS

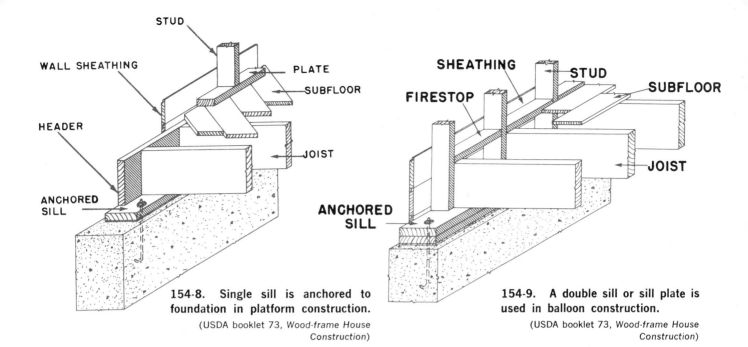

154-8. Single sill is anchored to foundation in platform construction.

(USDA booklet 73, *Wood-frame House Construction*)

154-9. A double sill or sill plate is used in balloon construction.

(USDA booklet 73, *Wood-frame House Construction*)

tongue-and-groove boards. Boards should be no wider than 8 inches in standard 1-inch surfaced lumber. They should rest on at least two joists and be laid diagonally. The usual angle is 45 degrees. The end joints of adjacent lines of boards should not be together on the same joists.

The finished floor can properly be laid parallel or perpendicular to the joists when subfloor boards are laid diagonally in relation to the joists. If subfloors are laid at right angles (in a perpendicular position) to the joists, the finished floor itself should be laid at right angles to the subfloor. Figure 154-11 illustrates the use of plywood and boards for subfloors.

154-10. Typical platform floor framing.

(USDA booklet 73, *Wood-frame House Construction*)

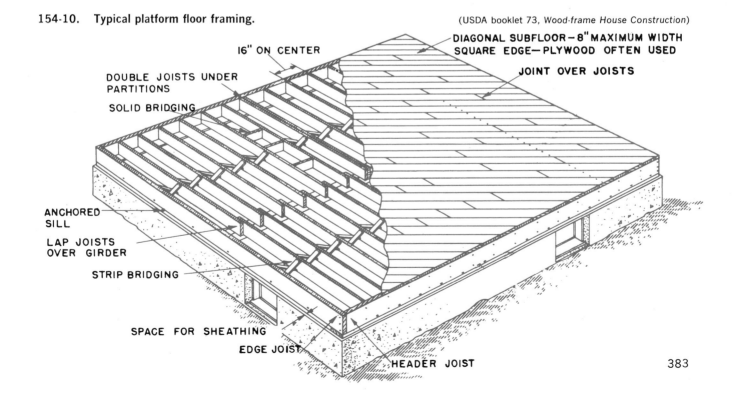

383

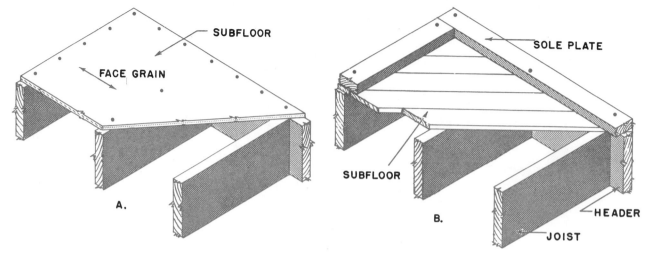

(Housing & Home Finance Agency booklet, *Technique of House Nailing*)

154-11. Subfloor material is called underlayment: **(A)** plywood, **(B)** boards.

Unit 155 Wall Framing

"Wall framing" refers to the use of vertical and horizontal two-by-fours for exterior and interior walls. These serve as a base for nailing on wall-covering materials and support the upper floors, ceilings, and roof. Where large plumbing pipes are placed in a wall, it is recommended that two-by-sixes be used for studs for either the entire wall or a portion of it. Wall-framing lumber should be good grade, seasoned, stiff, free of warp, and easily worked, and it should possess nail-holding power.

Ceiling heights are preferably 8 feet. Studs are generally placed on 16-inch centers, but they are placed on 24-inch centers in some one-story buildings. Different wall framing is used on one- and two-story platform construction (Figs. 155-1 and 155-2).

Framing Corners

Posts made of multiple studs should be used at exterior corners and at intersections of walls. These posts provide a nailing base, especially for interior wallboard.

Figure 155-3 shows a common arrangement of studs on an exterior

155-1. Single-story platform wall framing.

(USDA booklet 73, *Wood-frame House Construction*)

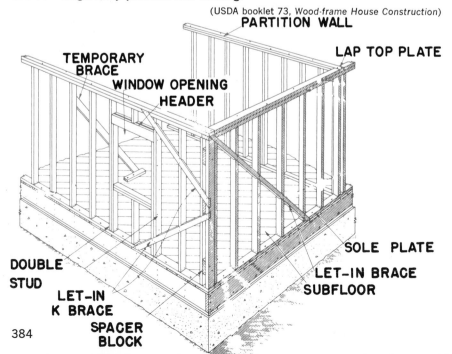

384

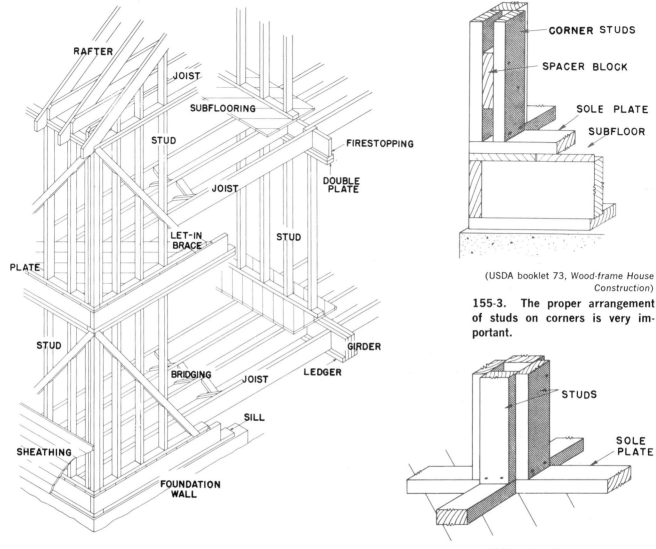

RAFTER
JOIST
SUBFLOORING
STUD
FIRESTOPPING
JOIST
DOUBLE PLATE
LET-IN BRACE
STUD
PLATE
STUD
GIRDER
BRIDGING
JOIST
LEDGER
SILL
SHEATHING
FOUNDATION WALL

(National Lumber Manufacturers' Association.)

155-2. Two-story platform wall framing.

CORNER STUDS
SPACER BLOCK
SOLE PLATE
SUBFLOOR

(USDA booklet 73, *Wood-frame House Construction*)

155-3. The proper arrangement of studs on corners is very important.

STUDS
SOLE PLATE

(USDA booklet 73, *Wood-frame House Construction*)

155-4. Studs must give proper nailing surfaces where interior walls cross.

corner. They are arranged to give good nailing surfaces where interior walls cross (Fig. 155-4) and where a partition meets another wall or partition (Fig. 155-6).

Braces on walls and corners are usually made of one-by-fours (1 x 4) set into the studs or two-by-fours (2 x 4) cut and placed at an angle between the studs. See Figs. 155-1 and 155-2. If sheathing is placed at an angle on exterior walls, the braces can be eliminated.

Framing Doors and Windows

Extra strength is needed to carry vertical loads over window and door openings. Double lintels, or headers (usually 2 x 6), should span the open-ing at the top. These headers rest on studs at each end.

Metal framing anchors are some-times used without the double stud when an opening is less than 3 feet wide. Triple studs are recommended when the opening exceeds 6 feet, with the ends of the lintel resting on two studs. Typical door and window fram-ing is shown in Figs. 155-5 and 155-7.

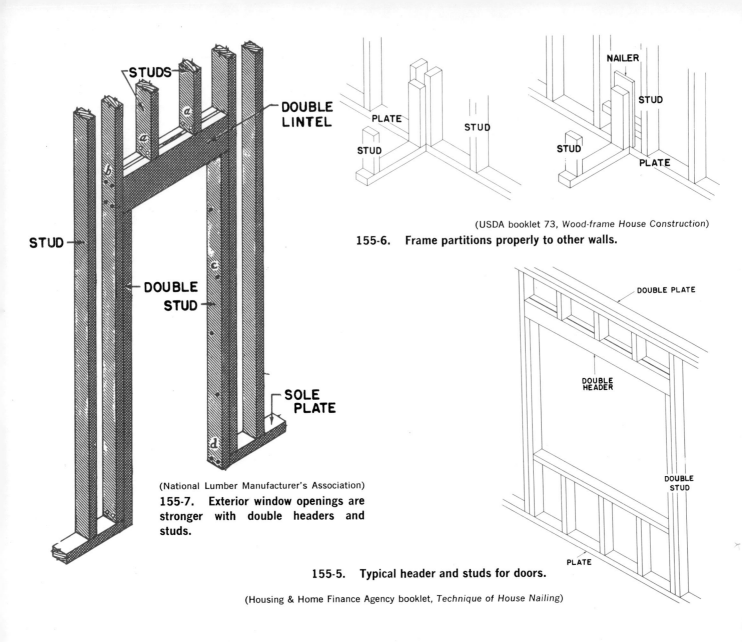

(National Lumber Manufacturer's Association)

155-7. Exterior window openings are stronger with double headers and studs.

(USDA booklet 73, *Wood-frame House Construction*)

155-6. Frame partitions properly to other walls.

155-5. Typical header and studs for doors.

(Housing & Home Finance Agency booklet, *Technique of House Nailing*)

Unit 156 Ceiling and Roof Framing

Ceiling joists are nailed to each rafter to act as ties between exterior walls and interior partitions. Joists and rafters are often put together as roof trusses. In two-story structures, joists support the ceilings on the first floor and help to support the second floor. All parts of the roof should be securely tied together to the exterior and in- terior walls. Roof construction should be exceptionally strong to withstand all types of unfavorable weather conditions.

Types of Roofs

There are two general types of roofs: **flat** and **pitched.** Both have vari-

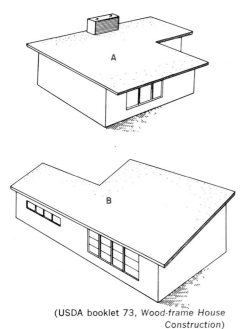

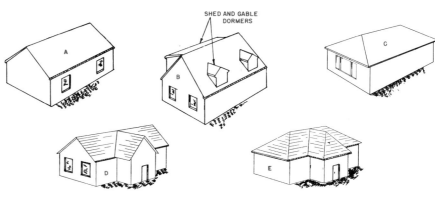

156-2. Simple and combined pitched roofs: (A) gable, (B) gable with shed and gable dormers, (C) hip, (D) gable and valley, and (E) hip and valley.

(USDA booklet 73, *Wood-frame House Construction*)

156-1. Flat roofs: (A) rafters and ceiling joists are same pieces, (B) rafters and ceiling joists are separate.

156-3. Special construction is needed on a flat roof when the combination rafter and ceiling joist is used.

(National Lumber Manufacturers' Association)

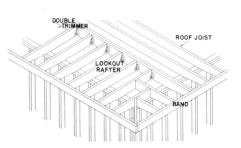

ations. Joists of flat roofs serve both as rafters and as ceiling supports. The joists are laid level, or they are laid with a very slight slope to provide better drainage.

The flat roof and the variable flat shed roof are illustrated in Fig. 156-1A and B. A flat roof with overhang requires special construction and arrangement of the combination rafter and ceiling joists (Fig. 156-3).

The simplest pitched roof is the **gable** (Fig. 156-2A). Others are the gable with **shed** or **gable dormers** (Fig. 156-2B), **hip** (Fig. 156-2C), **gable and valley** (Fig. 156-2D), and **hip and valley** (Fig. 156-2E).

Valleys in a Roof

A **valley** in roof construction is formed when the slopes of two sides of a roof join. The roof part connecting these slopes is the valley rafter. If the two slopes are equal in size, this rafter is doubled to carry the roof load. It is

156-4. Gable roof framing.

(Stanley Tools)

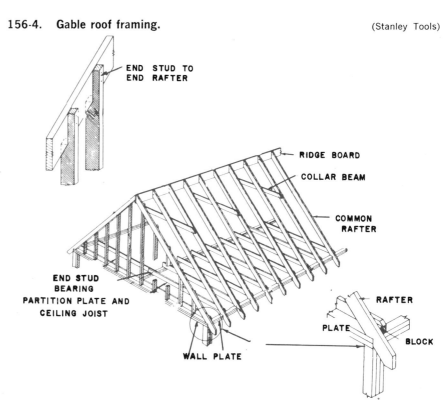

387

2 inches wider than the common rafter to permit the full end of the jack rafter to come in contact with it. Framing for the various pitched-roof types, including the valley, is pictured in Figs. 156-4 through 156-7.

Types of Rafters

There are three major types of rafters which extend from the wall plate to the ridge board: (1) **common**,

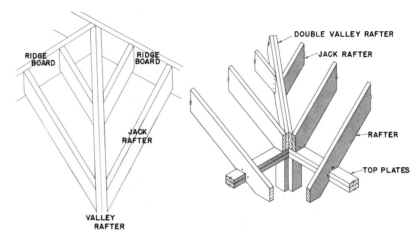

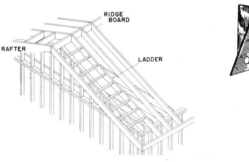

(USDA booklet 73, *Wood-frame House Construction*, and National Lumber Manufacturers' Association)

156-6.   Framing a valley.

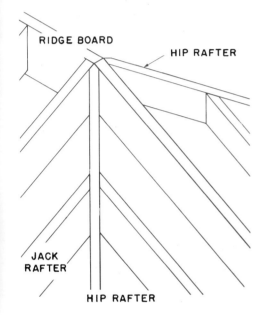

(National Lumber Manufacturers' Association)

156-7.   Framing a gable and over-hang.

(Timber Engineering Company)

156-8.   Special fasteners are some-times used to join rafters to wall plates.

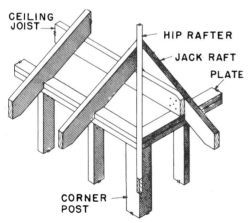

(USDA booklet 73, *Wood-frame House Construction*)

156-5.   Hip roof framing.

156-9.   Use of different rafters in hip-and-valley roof framing.   (Stanley Tools)

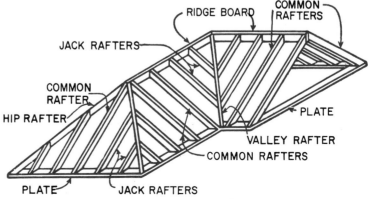

(2) **hip,** and (3) **valley.** They are nailed to the wall plate or attached with special fasteners (Fig. 156-8).

The **jack rafter** (a variation) is shorter than the common rafter, and it does not extend from the ridge board to the plate. See Fig. 156-9. There are three kinds of jack rafters. The **hip jack** extends from the ridge board to a hip rafter. The **cripple jack** extends from a hip to a valley rafter, but it does not touch the plate or ridge. The **valley jack** is sometimes called a **cripple rafter.** See Fig. 156-9 for all except the cripple jack.

Unit 157 The Framing Square

The framing square is an indispensable tool of the builder and the carpenter. It is made in the form of a right angle. The principles of roof framing are based on the geometric principles of the right triangle.

The Framing Square

The steel framing square is used to lay out lengths and cuts on various rafters used in framing the roof. Its main parts are the **blade** (body) and the **tongue** (Fig. 157-1). Study the scales, divisions, and tables given on the face and back of this square.

Figure 157-2 shows how the roof-framing terms relate to gable roof members and the framing square. Study the definitions of these terms in Unit 151.

Brace Length

The length of a brace is quickly measured on the steel framing square by consulting the **brace measure table.** It is measured along the center on the back of the tongue (Fig. 157-3).

For example, find the length of a brace when the run on the post (or stud) and beam (or plate) is 48 inches. To solve, find $\frac{48}{48}$ 67 ^{88} on the table. The length of the brace, then, is 67.88 inches, or 67⅞ inches for practical uses.

Board Measure

Board-foot (bd ft) measure for most sizes of construction lumber is on the **board measure table** on the back of the steel square body.

Inch graduations along the outer

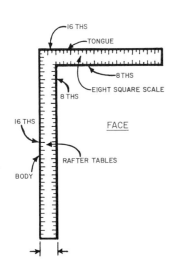

157-1. **Parts of the steel framing square.**

(Stanley Tools)

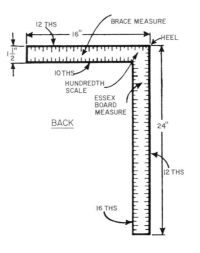

157-2. **Span, run, rise, and pitch of a gable roof.**

(Stanley Tools)

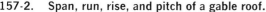
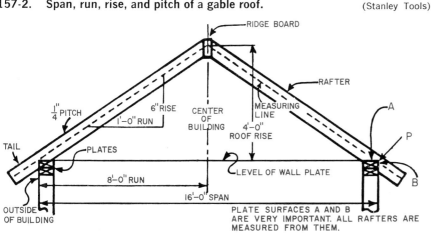

edge of the square are used in combination with numbers along the seven parallel lines beneath these graduations. *The 12-inch mark is the starting point for all calculations* (Fig. 157-4).

The number 12 represents a board 1 inch thick, 12 inches wide, and 12 feet long, or 12 board feet. The inch graduation on *each* side of the 12 represents the *width* of the boards. The numbers *beneath* the 12 indicate the *length* of the boards.

The board measure tables are given for boards 1 inch thick. For other thicknesses, multiply the figure given in the table by the thickness of the lumber.

Follow this procedure:

1. Find the *length* of the piece under the number 12.

2. Locate the standard *width* of the piece along the inch graduations.

3. Follow the line on which the length is stamped until it intersects the line of figures under the given width. The figure stamped at this point is the board measure in the piece.

For example: What is the board measure in a piece of lumber 10 feet long and 11 inches wide?

To solve, find the number 10, representing the length, in the vertical column under the 12-inch mark. See Fig. 157-4. Follow the horizontal line to the left until it intersects the column of figures under the 11-inch mark, representing the width. The number at this point is 92 (9-2) or $9\frac{2}{12}$. The number of board feet in the piece is $9\frac{1}{6}$.

Using the framing square, find the answer to the following problem: How many board feet are in 3 pieces of standard lumber 2 inches thick, 4 inches wide, and 14 feet long?

To solve, find the 14 (length) under the 12-inch mark on the square. Following to the left under the 4 (width), find the number 48 (4-8). This number represents $4\frac{8}{12}$, or $4\frac{2}{3}$ board feet for 1-inch lumber. Multiply by the 2 (thickness), then by the 3 (pieces).

$$\frac{\cancel{3}\,\text{Pcs} \times 2 \times \cancel{4} \times 14'}{\cancel{12}} = 28 \text{ bd ft}$$

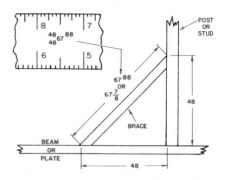

(Stanley Tools)

157-3.   Use of the brace measure on the square saves time in calculating the length of a brace needed.

157-4.   The board measure table on the square is easy to use.

(Stanley Tools)

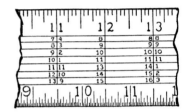

Unit 158 Roof Pitch and Rafter Layout

Roofs of the same width can have different pitches, depending upon the height of the roof. The principal pitches (Fig. 158-1) show the amount of rise in inches per foot of run, or the ratio of rise to span.

Special acknowledgment is due the Stanley Tool Company for the contents of this unit.

Determining Pitch, Rise, and Run

Pitch, rise, and **run** can be determined from a basic formula when two of the quantities are known. For example: If a building is 24 feet wide and the rise is 8 feet, the pitch is one-third ($\frac{1}{3}$).

$$P \text{ (pitch)} = \frac{R \text{ (rise)}}{S \text{ (span)}}$$

$$P = \frac{8}{24} \text{ or } \frac{1}{3}$$

$$R \text{ (rise)} = P \text{ (pitch)} \times S \text{ (span)}$$

$$R = \frac{1}{3} \times 24 \text{ or 8 ft}$$

Using the same 24-foot span, the rise in inches for each foot of run can be determined: the rise is 8 feet, or 96 inches (8′ × 12″). The run is one-half ($\frac{1}{2}$) the span, or 12 feet ($\frac{1}{2}$ × 24). Therefore:

$$\text{Rise per ft of run} = \frac{96''}{12} = 8 \text{ in.}$$

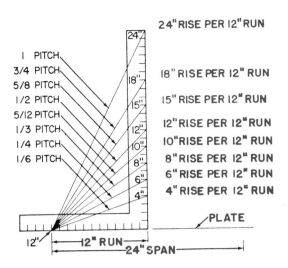

24" RISE PER 12" RUN

1 PITCH
3/4 PITCH
5/8 PITCH
1/2 PITCH
5/12 PITCH
1/3 PITCH
1/4 PITCH
1/6 PITCH

18" RISE PER 12" RUN

15" RISE PER 12" RUN

12" RISE PER 12" RUN

10" RISE PER 12" RUN

8" RISE PER 12" RUN

6" RISE PER 12" RUN

4" RISE PER 12" RUN

PLATE

12"   12" RUN   24" SPAN

rafter into three parts. The length of a rafter per foot of run will be different for each pitch. Therefore, the rise per foot of run must be known before rafter length can be established.

Rafter lengths can be obtained by three methods other than tables on the square. They are (1) mathematical calculation, (2) measuring across the square, and (3) stepping off with the square. However, by using tables on the framing square, time for calculation and the chance for error are lessened.

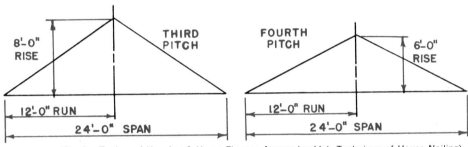

8'-0" RISE

THIRD PITCH

12'-0" RUN

24'-0" SPAN

FOURTH PITCH

6'-0" RISE

12'-0" RUN

24'-0" SPAN

(Stanley Tools and Housing & Home Finance Agency booklet, *Technique of House Nailing*)

158-1.   Pitches of a roof.

Determining Common Rafter Length

The length of the common rafter is the shortest distance between the center-line point of the ridge to the outer edge of the plate. This length is taken along the measuring line (Fig. 158-3).

Inches and sixteenths of an inch ($\frac{1}{16}$) are found on the outside face of the square on both the body and the tongue. The first line on the body gives the length of common, or main, rafters per foot of run (Fig. 158-4).

The rise in inches per foot of run is always the same for ordinary pitches:

Pitch			
½	⅓	¼	⅙
Rise per foot of run			
12″	8″	6″	4″

158-2.   The relationship of rafter length to foot of run.

(Stanley Tools)

Rafter Length Tables

The rafter tables on the steel framing square are based on the rise per foot of run (length). Numbers in the table show length of common rafters for any rise, as indicated in Fig. 158-2.

The roof illustrated has a span of 6 feet. The run (divided into three equal parts of one foot), the rise, and the total rafter length represent a right triangle *ABC*. Vertical lines through each part of the run also divide the

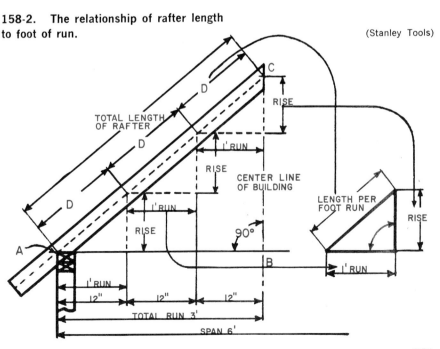

TOTAL LENGTH OF RAFTER

CENTER LINE OF BUILDING

LENGTH PER FOOT RUN

90°

1' RUN   12"   12"   12"

TOTAL RUN 3'

SPAN 6'

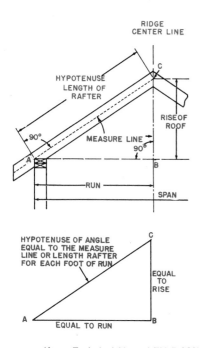

(Army Technical Manual TM 5-460)

158-3. Figuring the true length of a common rafter.

The 17 main rafter tables begin under the 2-inch mark and continue through 18 inches.

To find the length of a common rafter, multiply the number of feet of

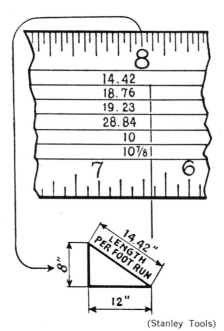

(Stanley Tools)

158-5. Using the rafter table to determine the length of a common rafter per foot of run.

run times the length given in the table. As an example: If rise equals 8 inches per foot of run (⅓ pitch) for a building 20 feet wide (span), the run is 10 feet.

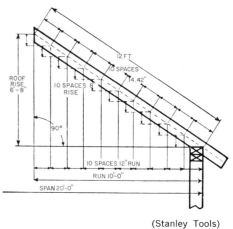

(Stanley Tools)

158-6. Determining the length for a common rafter.

Solution:

1. Find the 8-inch (8″) mark on the body of the square.

2. On the first line under the 8 will be found the number 14.42 (Fig. 158-5). This is the length of the common rafter in inches per foot of run.

3. Multiply 14.42 × 10 feet of run to secure 144.2 inches of rafter.

4. Divide 144.2 inches by 12 inches per foot; the common rafter length will be 12:01, or 12 feet for practical use (Fig. 158-6).

158-4. Rafter tables on the face of the framing square. (Stanley Tools)

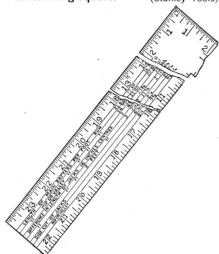

158-7. A large imaginary square shows how the heel and plumb cuts are made on a common rafter. (Stanley Tools)

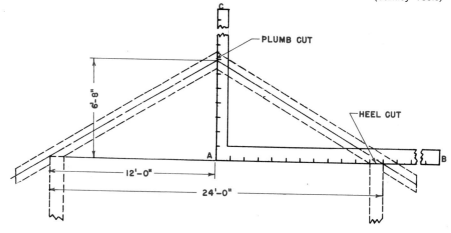

Top and Bottom Cuts on Common Rafters

The top cut on the rafter is the place where the upper end rests against another rafter or the ridge board. This cut is parallel to the center line of the roof. The bottom, or **heel**, cut is at the lower end of the rafter, horizontal with the plates. This makes the top and bottom cuts at right angles to each other.

The manner in which the cut is made is illustrated in Fig. 158-7 with a large imaginary square placed on the rafter. The tongue coincides with the top, plumb, or ridge cut; the blade coincides with the bottom, heel, or plate cut.

To obtain the layout of the heel and the plumb cuts, use the 12-inch mark on the body and the rise per foot of run on the tongue (Fig. 158-8). The horizontal cut is marked along the body of the framing square, and the vertical cut is marked along the tongue.

The lengths of rafters obtained from the tables are actual length from the center line of the ridge to the outside edge of the plate, when there is no overhang. When a ridge board is used, deduct half the thickness of this board from the total length of the rafter before the top cut is made (Fig. 158-9). The correct and incorrect methods of measuring rafter length are shown in Fig. 158-10.

After the total length of the rafter has been established, both ends should be marked. Add length for the overhang. Subtract half the thickness of the ridge board if this board is used. For example, if a rafter is 16 feet 6 inches long and the rise is 9 inches per foot of run, how are the top and the bottom cuts obtained?

Procedure for layout of cuts:

1. Study Fig. 158-11. Points A and B are the rafter ends.

2. For the bottom, or seat, cut, lay the square on the rafter so that the 12-inch mark on the body coincides with point A and the 9-inch mark on the tongue coincides with the rafter edge.

3. Mark along the body to obtain the line for the seat cut.

4. Move the square to the top end of the rafter. Place it in the same position coinciding with point B.

5. Mark along the tongue to obtain the line for the top cut.

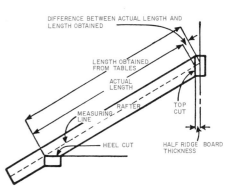

(Stanley Tools)

158-9. Allowance in length of the rafter must be made when the ridge board is used in construction.

6. Deduct half the thickness of the ridge board at the top end. This deduction, at C, should be at right angles to the plumb cut.

7. Add tail overhang length to the bottom end.

8. Cut two rafters. Place them on the building to check their accuracy. Correctly cut rafters can be used to lay out all the others.

If a common rafter must be cut for a roof that has an odd number of inches in the span, such as 24 feet 10

158-8. Laying out the heel and plumb cuts. (Stanley Tools)

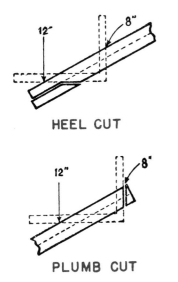

HEEL CUT

PLUMB CUT

158-10. The length of a rafter must be measured accurately. (Stanley Tools)

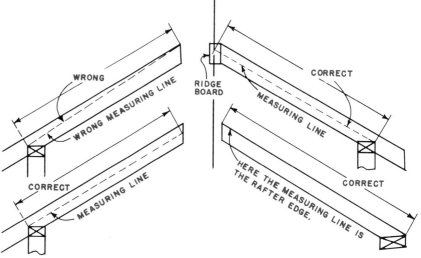

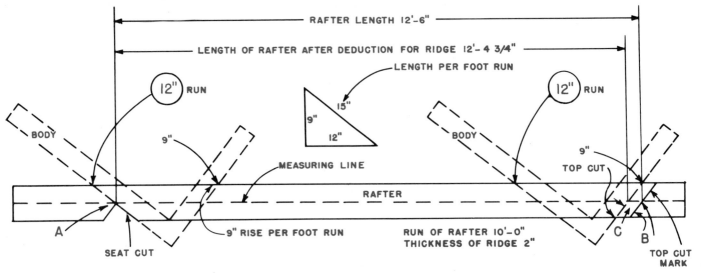

158-11. Correct layout is necessary for top and bottom cuts on a rafter.

(Stanley Tools)

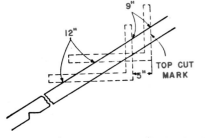

(Stanley Tools)

158-12. Add odd inches to the lengths of common rafters.

158-13. "The square of the hypotenuse is equal to the sum of the squares of the other two sides" is a principle of the triangle often used in mathematics, and it also applies to rafter layout.

(Stanley Tools)

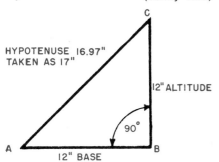

inches, this is done by following the example in Fig. 158-12. The run of such a building would be 12 feet 5 inches. The additional inches can be added as illustrated. They are added at right angles to the last plumb line after the numbers obtained from the square for each foot of run are measured.

Determining Hip and/or Valley Rafter Length

The relation of hip and/or valley rafters to common ones is the same as that of the sides of a right triangle. If the sides forming a right triangle are 12 inches each, the hypotenuse, or side opposite the right angle, is equal to 16.97 inches, usually considered to be 17 inches (Fig. 158-13).

The position of the hip rafter, as related to the common rafter, is illustrated in Figs. 158-14 and 158-15. The prism has a base 5 feet square and a height of 3 feet 4 inches. *D* is the corner of the building; *BC* is the total rise of the roof; *AB* is the run of the common rafter; *AC* is the common rafter; *DB* is the run of the hip rafter; and *DC* is the hip rafter.

Figure *DAB* is a right triangle whose sides are the portion of the plate *DA*, the run of common rafter *AB*, and the run of the hip rafter *DB*. The run of the hip rafter opposite the right angle *A* is the hypotenuse, or the longest side of the right triangle.

Assume a 1-foot run of common rafter and a 1-foot plate length, and the right triangle *H* is formed. See Fig. 158-15. The sides are each 12 inches long, and the hypotenuse is 17 inches. The hypotenuse of this small triangle *H* is a portion of the run of the hip rafter *DB*, which corresponds to a 1-foot run of common rafter.

Remember the rule that the run of the hip rafter is always 16.97 inches for every 12 inches of run of the common rafter. The total run of the hip rafter therefore, will be 16.97 inches multiplied by the run, in feet, of common rafter.

The lengths of hip and/or valley rafters are found on the *second* line of the rafter table, "Length of hip and valley rafters per foot run." Numbers in this table indicate the length of hip and valley rafters per foot of run of common rafters.

394

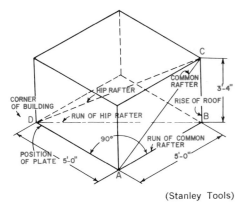

158-14. Position of the hip rafter in relation to the common one.

(Stanley Tools)

To find the length of a hip or valley rafter, multiply the length given in the table by the number of feet of run of the common rafter. For example, find the length of a hip rafter where the rise of roof is 8 inches per foot of run. This indicates a one-third (⅓) pitch when the building is 10 feet wide. See Fig. 158-15.

Proceed in the same way as for common rafters. Find the number along the edge of the square corresponding to the rise of roof, which is 8. On the second line under this figure is 18.76. This is the length of the hip rafter in inches for each foot of run of common rafter for a one-third pitch.

The common rafter has a 5-foot run. Therefore, there are five equal lengths for the hip rafter, as seen in Fig. 158-15.

The length of the hip rafter is 18.76 inches per 1-foot run. Its total length will be 18.76 × 5 = 93.80 inches. This is 7.81 feet, or, for practical purposes, 7 feet 9⅝ inches.

Top and Bottom Cuts on Hip and Valley Rafters

To obtain the top and bottom cuts of hip or valley rafters, use 17 inches on the body and the "rise per foot run" on the tongue. The numeral 17 on the framing square body will give the seat cut, and the figure on the framing square tongue will give the vertical, or top, cut (Fig. 158-16).

158-15. The length of the hip rafter is related to its position.

(Stanley Tools)

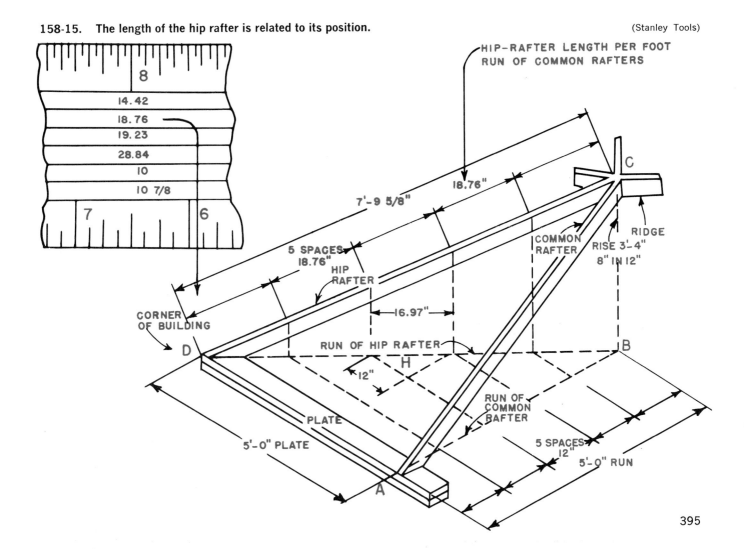

395

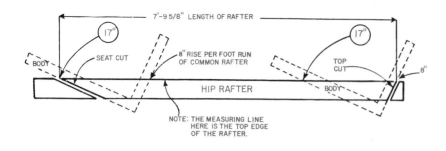

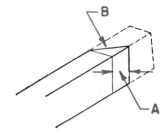

(Stanley Tools)

158-16.   Laying out top and bottom cuts on hip and/or valley rafter.

(Stanley Tools)

158-17.   Laying out the side, or cheek, cut on a hip rafter.

Measuring Hip and Valley Rafters

The length of all hip and/or valley rafters is always measured along the center of the top edge or back. Rafters with overhang are treated like common ones except that the measuring line is the center of the top edge.

Deduction from Hip or Valley Rafter for Ridge

The deduction for the ridge is measured like that for the common rafter except that half the diagonal (45 degrees) thickness of the ridge must be used.

Side Cuts

Hip and valley rafters must also have **side,** or **cheek,** cuts at the point where they meet the ridge. These side cuts are found on the *sixth* (bottom) line of the rafter tables, which is marked "Side cut hip or valley—use." The numbers given in this line refer to the graduation marks on the "outside edge of the body."

The numbers on the framing square have been derived by determining the number to be used with 12 on the tongue for the side cuts of the various pitches. From a plumb line, the thickness of the rafter is measured and marked at right angles (Fig. 158-17A).

Square a line across the top of the rafter; the diagonal points connect (Fig. 158-17B). Line *B* (side cut) *is* obtained by marking along the tongue of the square.

To obtain the **side cut** for hip or valley rafters, use the number given in the table on the body of the square and 12 inches on the tongue. Mark the side cut along the tongue where it coincides with the point on the measuring line.

As an example, find the side cut for a hip rafter when the roof has 8 inches rise per foot of run (one-third pitch). Figure 158-18 represents the position of the hip rafter on the roof. With the rise of roof 8 inches per foot of run, locate number 8 on the outside edge of the body. Under this number in the bottom line is $10\frac{7}{8}$. This number is used on the body and 12 inches on the tongue. The square is applied to the edge of the back of the hip rafter. The side cut *CD* is along the tongue.

Deduct for half the thickness of the ridge in the same way as for the common rafter except that half the diagonal (45 degrees) thickness of the ridge must be used.

In making the **seat cut** for the hip rafter, an allowance must be made for the top edges of the rafter. These edges would project above the line of the common and jack rafters if the corners of the hip rafter were not removed, or backed. The hip rafter must

be slightly lowered by cutting parallel to the seat cut. This amount varies with the thickness and pitch of the roof.

The 12-inch mark on the square tongue is used in all angle cuts at the top, bottom, and side. The number taken from the fifth or sixth line in the table is the only other one to remember when laying out side or angle cuts. The side cuts are always on the right hand, or tongue side, of rafters.

Odd Inches of Hip and Valley Rafters

Additional inches in the run of hip or valley rafters are added in a way similar to that explained for common ones (Fig. 158-12). The diagonal (45 degrees) is used. Approximately $7\frac{1}{16}$ inches for 5 inches of run is added.

Determining Jack Rafter Length

Jack rafters are common rafters which have been "cut off" by the intersection of a hip or valley before reaching the full length from plate to ridge. They lie in the same plane as common rafters and are usually spaced the same and have the same pitch. They also have the same length per foot of run as the common rafters.

Jack rafters rest against the hip or valley rafter. When equally spaced, the second jack must be twice as long as

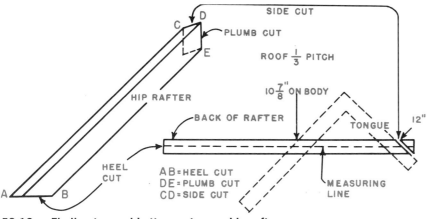

158-18. Finding top and bottom cuts on a hip rafter.

(Stanley Tools)

Labels in figure: SIDE CUT; C; D; PLUMB CUT; ROOF ⅓ PITCH; E; HIP RAFTER; 10 7/8" ON BODY; BACK OF RAFTER; TONGUE; 12"; HEEL CUT; AB=HEEL CUT; DE=PLUMB CUT; CD=SIDE CUT; MEASURING LINE; A; B

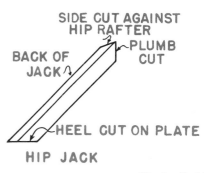

158-19. Side cut for hip jack rafter.

(Stanley Tools)

Labels in figure: SIDE CUT AGAINST HIP RAFTER; PLUMB CUT; BACK OF JACK; HEEL CUT ON PLATE; HIP JACK

the first one; the third is three times as long as the first. This length multiple continues for each additional jack rafter.

Lengths of jack rafters are given in the third and fourth lines of the rafter tables on the framing square, as follows:

Third line: "Difference in length of Jacks—16-inch centers."

Fourth line: "Difference in length of Jacks—24-inch centers."

Numbers in the table indicate the length of the first, or shortest, jack, which is also the difference in length between the first and second, and between the second and third jack, and so on for each rafter.

To find the length of a jack rafter, multiply the value given in the tables by the number indicating the position of the jack. From the obtained length, subtract half the diagonal (45 degrees) thickness of the hip or valley rafter.

For example, find the length of the second jack rafter when the roof has a rise of 8 inches to 1 foot of run of the common rafter spaced 16 inches apart. Solution: On the outer edge of the body, locate number 8, which corresponds to the rise of the roof. On the third line under this number, locate 19.23. This indicates that the first jack rafter will be 19.23 times (×) 2, or

38.46 inches. For practical use, the length is 3 feet 2½ inches. From this length, deduct half the diagonal thickness of the hip or valley rafter, as on the hip rafter for the ridge. The same procedure is used when jack rafters are spaced on 24-inch centers.

Top and Bottom Cuts on Jack Rafters

Jack rafters have the same rise per foot of run as common rafters. The method of obtaining the top and bottom cuts is the same. Use 12 inches on the body and the rise per foot of run on the tongue. The 12 inches will locate the line for the seat cut; the figure on the tongue will locate the plumb cut.

Side Cut on Jack Rafters

A side cut is required on a jack rafter where the end meets the hip or valley rafter. Side cuts for jacks are found on the fifth line of the rafter tables. It is marked "Side cut of jacks —use."

To obtain the side cut, use the number shown in the table on the body of the framing square and the number 12 on the tongue. Mark along the tongue for the side cut.

As an example, find the side cut on jack rafters for a roof having an 8-inch rise per foot of run (one-third pitch).

See Figs. 158-19 and 158-20. Under 8 on the edge of the square, locate 10 in the fifth line of the table. Use this 10 on the outside edge of the body and 12 inches on the tongue. The two will give the line for the required side cut.

Trusses for Pitched Roofs

The lightweight roof trusses (Fig. 158-21) are installed as complete units (Fig. 158-22). They save material and time. Trusses are designed according to accepted engineering practices. They are joined with glue, nails, staple nails (Fig. 158-23), bolts, and special connectors (Fig. 158-24).

Trusses eliminate the need for interior load-bearing partitions. In this type of construction, gable ends are usually framed in the conventional

158-20. Layout of a side cut for a valley jack rafter. (Stanley Tools)

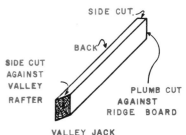

Labels in figure: SIDE CUT; BACK; SIDE CUT AGAINST VALLEY RAFTER; PLUMB CUT AGAINST RIDGE BOARD; VALLEY JACK

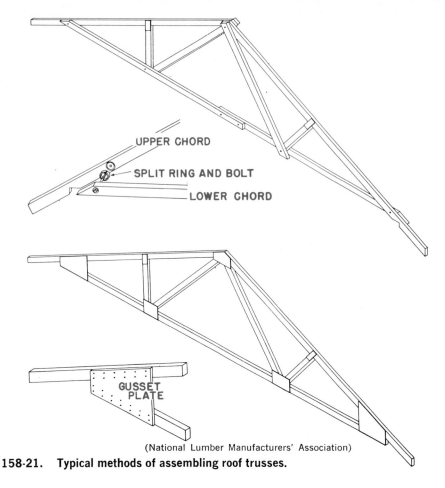

UPPER CHORD

SPLIT RING AND BOLT

LOWER CHORD

GUSSET PLATE

(National Lumber Manufacturers' Association)

158-21.   Typical methods of assembling roof trusses.

(Spotnails, Inc.)

158-23.   A gusset plate is attached to parts of a truss with staple nails.

158-22.   Roof trusses are assembled on the ground or at the factory. They are easily installed as complete units.   (Southern Pine Association)

manner, using a common rafter to which the gable and the studs are nailed. Overhangs at eaves are provided by extending the upper chords of the trusses beyond the wall (Fig. 158-26) or by nailing the overhang framing to the upper chords.

Where hip and valley construction is necessary, modified trussed rafters or conventional framing is used. Trusses are spaced 16 to 24 inches apart. This depends on the type of truss and roof sheathing and the ceiling covering used.

Ventilation of Attic Space

Moisture condensation in cold weather, and heat in hot weather, are eliminated or reduced by ventilating the attic space. For gable roofs, screened louvers can be used. The net area of the louver opening should be about $\frac{1}{300}$ of the area of the ceiling below. A sheet-metal ventilator

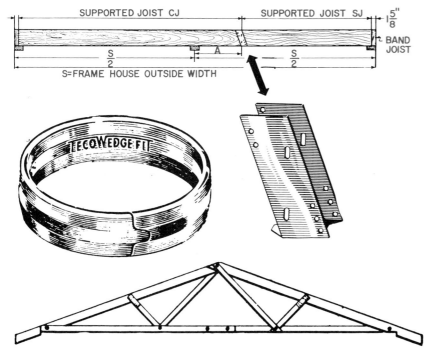

158-24.   Special connectors can be used to join parts of a truss.

(Timber Engineering Company)

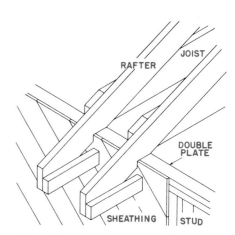

(National Lumber Manufacturers' Association)

158-26.   Rafter extensions or upper truss chords form the roof overhang.

near the peak of the roof and a $\frac{3}{4}$-inch slot beneath the eaves are used on hip roofs. The net area of the inlet should be $\frac{1}{900}$ of the ceiling area below; that of the outlet, $\frac{1}{1600}$ of the area.

For flat roofs, blocking and bridging should be arranged to allow free movement of air. Such roofs can be ventilated along the overhanging eaves. The net opening area should be $\frac{1}{250}$ of the area of the ceiling (Figs. 158-25 and 158-27).

158-25.   Roofs must have openings for proper ventilation.

(National Lumber Manufacturers' Association)

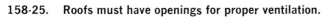

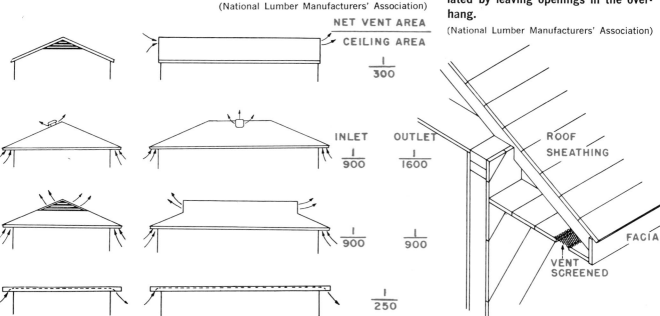

158-27.   Roofs are frequently ventilated by leaving openings in the overhang.

(National Lumber Manufacturers' Association)

Unit 159   Bay Windows, Dormers, and Stairs

Bay windows and dormers are functional. They provide additional space, lighting, beauty, and ventilation (Fig. 159-1). Stairs serve as passages to different levels of a building. They should be designed to afford safe, comfortable passage to the occupants, and sufficient space in which to move furniture should be allowed.

Bay Windows and Dormers

Bay window projections are arranged so that floor joists extend beyond the foundation wall (Fig. 159-2). The extension should usually not exceed 2 feet. Additional support of the roof over this window opening is necessary.

Dormers should be framed when a house is first constructed. Extra framing must be added (Figs. 159-3 and 159-4). This framing is similar to that already explained, but it should be planned in advance of construction. Dormers provide lighting and ventilation and make possible future expansion or additional attic rooms. It is also possible to obtain additional light by using skylights (Figs. 159-5 and 159-6).

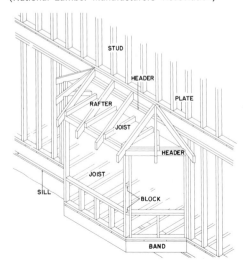

(Fred Reuton, Inc.)

159-1. Dormers add beauty, lighting, and ventilation.

159-2. A properly framed bay window.

(National Lumber Manufacturers' Association)

159-3. Framing a shed dormer.

(National Lumber Manufacturers' Association)

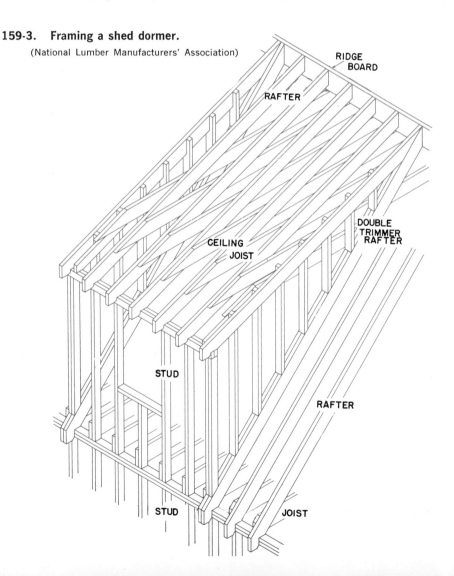

Laying Out Steps and Stairs

Principal stairs should provide comfort and convenience. Service stairs to attics and basements are usually steeper and often are constructed of less expensive material.

Stairs can either be built in place or as separate units and then set in place. They can be built in a winding pattern; in a straight, continuous run (Fig. 159-7); or with an intermediate platform (Fig. 159-8). The latter two forms are considered safer and are most often used in homes. Safe stair designs and terms used are shown in Fig. 159-9.

The fundamental layout for straight stairs is shown in Fig. 159-10. Dimensions for the riser and the tread (a **tread** and a **riser** make a "step") are selected to make stairs easy and comfortable to ascend or descend. Follow these pointers in stairway layout:

1. Determine the height, or rise, from the first-floor level to the next.

2. Figure the run, or distance, measuring horizontally.

3. Lay out the risers and treads on a stair horse, or stringer, for a preliminary plan. Fractions of an inch often result. See Fig. 159-10.

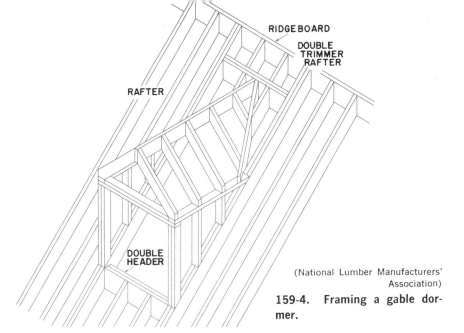

(National Lumber Manufacturers' Association)

159-4. Framing a gable dormer.

Example:

total rise 8 feet 3¾ inches, or 99¾" divided (÷) by 14 = 7.125 inches, or 7⅛ inches for each riser

4. Lay out, or space off, the number of treads wanted in the horizontal distance, or run. There is always one less tread than there are risers. If there are 14 risers, there are only 13 treads.

For example, if the tread is 10 inches wide and the riser is 7 inches, the stair stringer (stair horse) would be laid out (stepped off) with the framing square, ready for cutting (Fig. 159-10).

The thickness of the tread should be deducted from the first riser. This is done so that the first step will be made the same height as all the others.

159-5. Skylights add natural light.
(American Cyanamid Company)

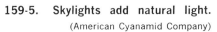

159-6. Skylight adds beauty to roof and natural light to interior areas.
(American Cyanamid Company)

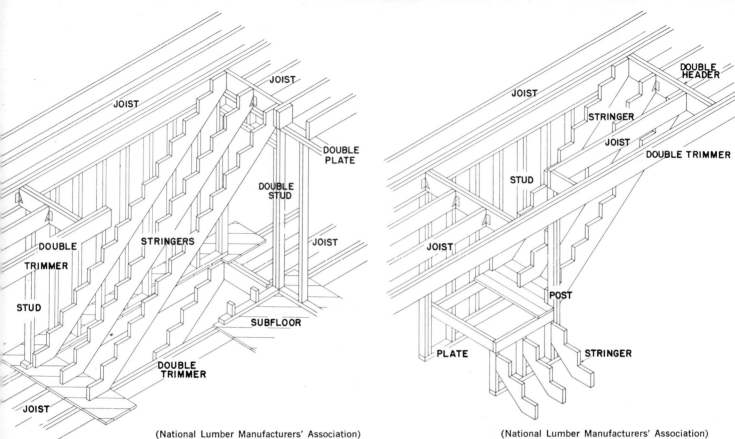

(National Lumber Manufacturers' Association)

159-7. A typical layout and framing for a straight-run stairway.

(National Lumber Manufacturers' Association)

159-8. Intermediate-platform stairway framing.

159-9. Some of the terms used in stair design.

(USDA booklet 73, *Wood-frame House Construction*)

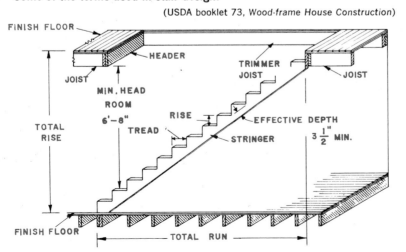

159-10. A fundamental layout for straight stairs.

(Army Technical Manual TM 5-460.)

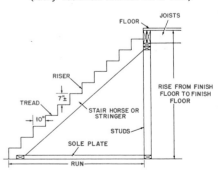

Unit 160 Wall, Roof, and Floor Coverings

Coverings for exterior (Fig. 160-1) and interior walls, ceilings, roofs, and floors add beauty, strength, and insulation to various parts of a building. Sheathing serves as the underlayment, or base, for nailing on roofing, siding, and interior coverings. Experiments show that wood-frame construction and insulation reduces heating or cooling losses.

Sheathing Roofs and Walls

Four types of roof and wall sheathing are commonly used in modern construction. These are (1) **lumber** (Fig. 160-2), (2) **plywood** (Fig. 160-3), (3) various **fiberboards** (Fig. 160-6), and (4) **gypsum board.** Lumber is put on walls and roofs either horizontally or diagonally (Fig. 160-4). Plywood, fiberboard, or gypsum board can be at-

160-3. Plywood panels weighing as much as 1,300 pounds were used as sheathing on this modern church.

(Douglas Fir Plywood Association)

(Koppers Company, Inc.)

160-1. Treated lumber was used to cover the exterior walls of the United Nations General Assembly Building.

160-4. Sheathing lumber is attached horizontally or diagonally.

(USDA booklet 73, *Wood-frame House Construction*)

160-2. Lumber is used as a sheathing material on this building.

(Southern Pine Association)

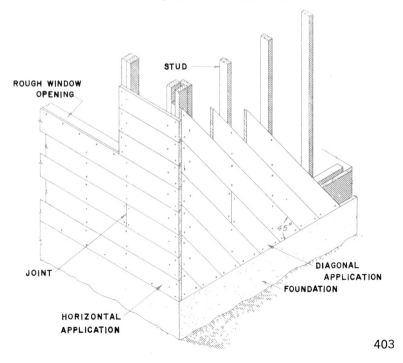

ROUGH WINDOW OPENING

STUD

JOINT

45°

DIAGONAL APPLICATION

FOUNDATION

HORIZONTAL APPLICATION

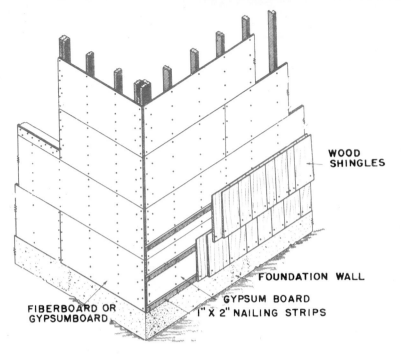

WOOD SHINGLES

FOUNDATION WALL

GYPSUM BOARD

1" X 2" NAILING STRIPS

FIBERBOARD OR GYPSUMBOARD

(USDA booklet 73, *Wood-frame House Construction*)

160-5. Walls can be sheathed horizontally with two- or four-foot by eight-foot sheets of plywood, fiberboard, or gypsum board.

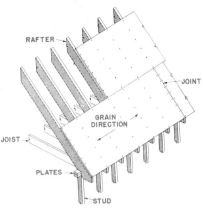

RAFTER

JOINT

GRAIN DIRECTION

JOIST

PLATES

STUD

(USDA booklet 73, *Wood-frame House Construction*)

160-8. Roofs can be sheathed with plywood.

160-7. Sheets are also used to sheath walls vertically.

(Housing & Home Finance Agency booklet, *Technique of House Nailing*)

160-6. Fiberboards for wall sheathing are strong and help insulate and eliminate noise.

(The Sheet Metal Worker)

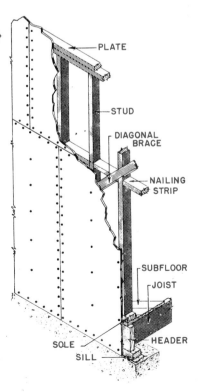

PLATE

STUD

DIAGONAL BRACE

NAILING STRIP

SUBFLOOR

JOIST

SOLE

SILL

HEADER

tached to walls horizontally or vertically (Figs. 160-5 and 160-7) and to roofs as shown in Fig. 160-8.

Sheathing materials are made in numerous thicknesses and widths. Common sheet rock is usually manufactured in 2- and 4-foot widths and in lengths of 4, 8, and 12 feet (Fig. 160-9). These sizes can easily be fitted and nailed to framework placed on centers of 16 and 24 inches.

160-9. Sheathing materials may be as long as 12 feet.

(Insulation Board Institute)

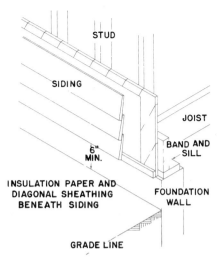

(National Lumber Manufacturers' Association)
160-10. Clearance should be made between the siding and ground level.

160-11. Typical kinds of siding and methods of nailing.

(National Lumber Manufacturers' Association)

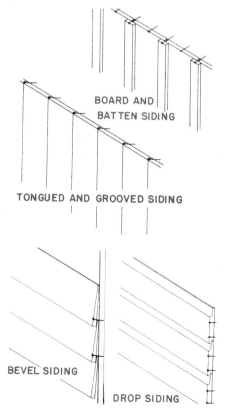

BOARD AND BATTEN SIDING

TONGUED AND GROOVED SIDING

BEVEL SIDING

DROP SIDING

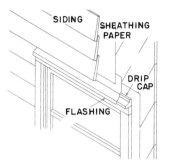

(National Lumber Manufacturers' Association)
160-12. Bevel siding above a window over diagonal lumber sheathing.

Siding for Walls

Numerous types of exterior siding are available. Several kinds of wood siding, methods of nailing, and application are shown in Figs. 160-10 through 160-14.

Covering the Roof

The most common roof coverings are (1) **asphalt shingles** (Fig. 160-15); (2) **wood shingles,** or **shakes** (Fig. 160-16); and (3) **built-up roof coverings.** Some principal shingle woods are western red cedar, redwood, and bald cypress. These are cut from heartwood, they are all edge grain, and they are tapered. They are highly decay resistant and are low in shrinkage. Asphalt

160-13. Special strips are nailed to studs when wood shingles are used without sheathing as underlayment.

(National Lumber Manufacturers' Association)

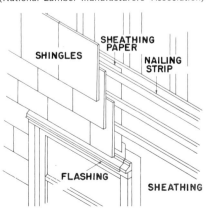

SHINGLES
SHEATHING PAPER
NAILING STRIP
FLASHING
SHEATHING

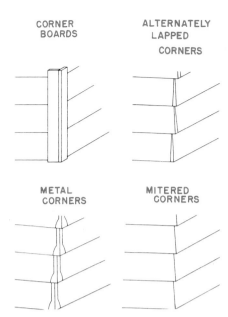

(National Lumber Manufacturers' Association)
160-14. Typical methods of covering corners on siding.

and wood shingles can be attached as shown in Figs. 160-17 and 160-18.

Built-up roofs (Fig. 160-19) are usually installed by specialized roofing companies. Special panel deck roofs and plywood decks are also used (Figs. 160-20 and 160-21).

160-15. Special staple nails or roofing nails are used to attach asphalt shingles.

(Spotnails, Inc.)

(Koppers Company, Inc.)

160-16. Treated roof shakes (shingles) make a decorative, longlasting roof covering.

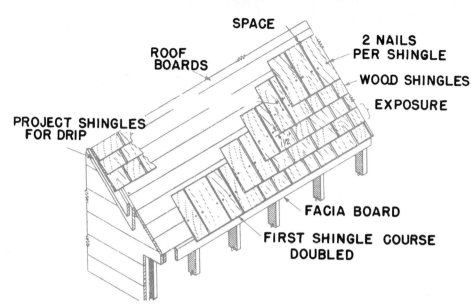

(USDA booklet 73, *Wood-frame House Construction*)

160-18. Procedure for laying wood shingles.

160-17. Procedure for laying asphalt shingles.

(USDA booklet 73, *Wood-frame House Construction*)

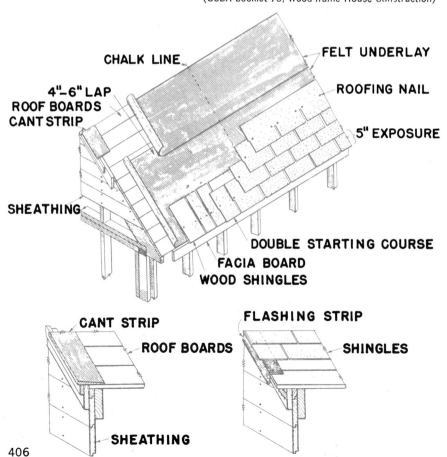

Floor Covering

Subfloors should be clean and level. They are covered with a sound-deadening felt or with building paper. See Unit 154, "Floor Framing."

Many types of materials and designs are available for finish flooring (Fig. 160-22). It is laid after the ceiling and the interior walls are completed.

Strip flooring should be laid crosswise on the floor joists, and it is usually laid lengthwise in a rectangular room.

Wood floor tile, linoleum, asphalt tile, and rubber tile floors are popular. Correct installation of these materials is important (Figs. 160-23, 160-24, and 160-25). Most manufacturers of special types of flooring materials provide instructions for doing an efficient, satisfactory job of installation. These directions should be followed.

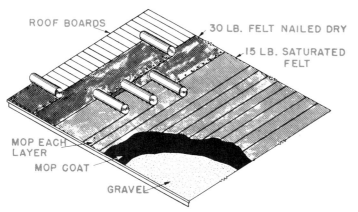

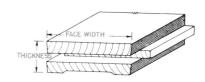

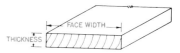

(USDA booklet 73, *Wood-frame House Construction*)

160-19. Procedure for laying a built-up roof.

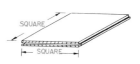

(USDA booklet 73, *Wood-frame House Construction*)

160-22. There are many types of finish flooring.

(Douglas Fir Plywood Association)

160-20. Lumber frames, covered with plywood, are used to make some roof panels. Insulation can be added inside between the plywood sheets.

(USDA booklet 73, *Wood-frame House Construction*)

160-23A. Laying and nailing strip flooring.

160-21. Wood panels are used as decks on some roofs.

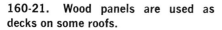

(Simpson Timber Company)

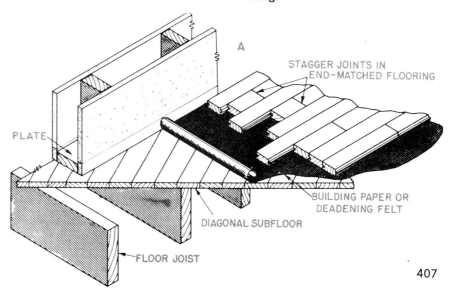

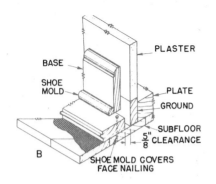

BASE

PLASTER

SHOE MOLD

PLATE

GROUND

SUBFLOOR

5/8" CLEARANCE

B

SHOE MOLD COVERS FACE NAILING

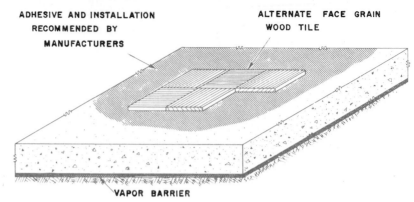

ADHESIVE AND INSTALLATION RECOMMENDED BY MANUFACTURERS

ALTERNATE FACE GRAIN WOOD TILE

VAPOR BARRIER

(USDA booklet 73, *Wood-frame House Construction*)

160-24. Follow the manufacturer's recommendations in laying special floors.

160-25. Various subfloors are used for different types of flooring.

(USDA booklet 73, *Wood-frame House Construction*)

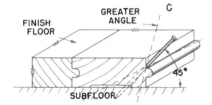

FINISH FLOOR

GREATER ANGLE

C

45°

SUBFLOOR

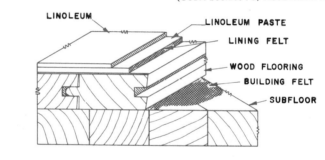

LINOLEUM

LINOLEUM PASTE

LINING FELT

WOOD FLOORING

BUILDING FELT

SUBFLOOR

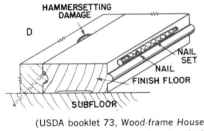

HAMMERSETTING DAMAGE

D

NAIL SET

NAIL

FINISH FLOOR

SUBFLOOR

(USDA booklet 73, *Wood-frame House Construction*)

160-23B, C, and D. (B) Laying the first strip. (C) Method of nailing. (D) Method of setting nails.

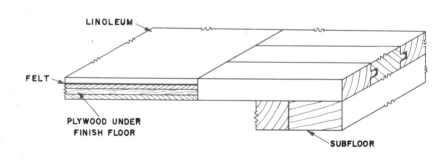

LINOLEUM

FELT

PLYWOOD UNDER FINISH FLOOR

SUBFLOOR

Unit 161 Concrete Slab Construction

Concrete slab construction is used where drainage is not a problem. Improved methods of construction reduce heating or cooling losses and in addition, they lessen former disadvantages of slab construction, such as floor sweating.

Basic Foundation and Slab Construction

The finished floor level should be above the finished ground grade for complete drainage. Topsoil and all foreign matter should be removed. All loose soil should be thoroughly packed. Sewer, water, and gas lines, as well as any other subsurface work, must be completed before the slab is poured.

Space between the soil level and the slab is filled and packed with at least 4 inches of coarse gravel or rock. This is covered with a solid plastic sheet, which serves as a **vapor barrier** (Fig. 161-1). Succeeding steps for frame construction of plates, studs, walls, and floors are also in this illustration.

The combined slab and foundation, with reinforced footing, is poured as a complete unit. This type of construction is suitable in climates where frost penetration is not a problem.

Independent Slabs and Foundation Walls

In climates where the ground freezes deeply, the foundation is poured separately from the slab. The footing and foundation walls should extend below the frost line to solid, unfilled soil.

Insulation is added to the outside of the foundation wall (Fig. 161-2), or it is put inside, and independent of, the slab (Fig. 161-3). The vapor barrier is on the warm side of the insulation and below the slab. Space is left above the insulation, and it is filled with hot tar to the top of the slab. The tar serves as a protection against termites.

Vapor Barriers and Slab Insulation

A vapor barrier should give high resistance to vapor transmission, resist damage by moisture, and withstand rough treatment before the concrete is poured. A polyethylene film four thousandths (.004") of an inch or more thick is considered to have these properties.

Slab insulation materials must be highly resistant to heat transmission and to crushing by floor loads, slab weight, and expansion forces. They must be durable when exposed to frost, dampness, and fungus or insect attack.

Materials which have these desirable properties are cellular glass, insulation board, and glass fibers with plastic binder. Special insulating concrete is made with specific aggregates (mixes) of mica, pumice, or slag. Some wood or plant fiberboards are used under certain dry-climate conditions.

Forced-air Ducts and Radiant Heating in Slabs

Ductwork for cold-air return in some forced-air heating systems is located in a slab around the exterior wall (Fig. 161-5). A vapor barrier is added to both sides of the insulation to stop soil moisture and cold weather condensation.

Different construction is used when a forced hot-water radiant heating system is used (Fig. 161-4). Copper or steel pipes are embedded in the concrete slab floor in a regular pattern.

Floors in Slab Construction

A finished concrete floor is sometimes used in slab construction, but it feels cold to the touch. Asphalt or other tiles are often laid in mastic (adhesive), according to the various manufacturer's directions.

Strip oak flooring is frequently laid over concrete slabs. Tests show that this method, which does not use wood

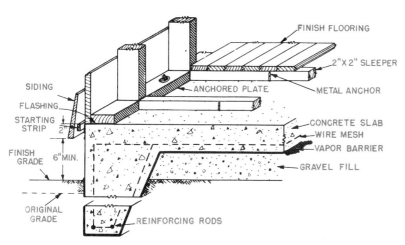

(USDA booklet 73, *Wood-frame House Construction*)

161-1. Coarse fills are covered with a special sheet to serve as a vapor barrier between the soil and the combination concrete slab and foundation.

161-2. Insulation is added to the outside of the foundation wall when the slab and foundation are separated.

(USDA booklet 73, *Wood-frame House Construction*)

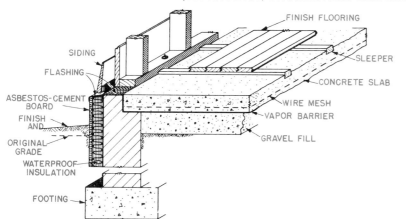

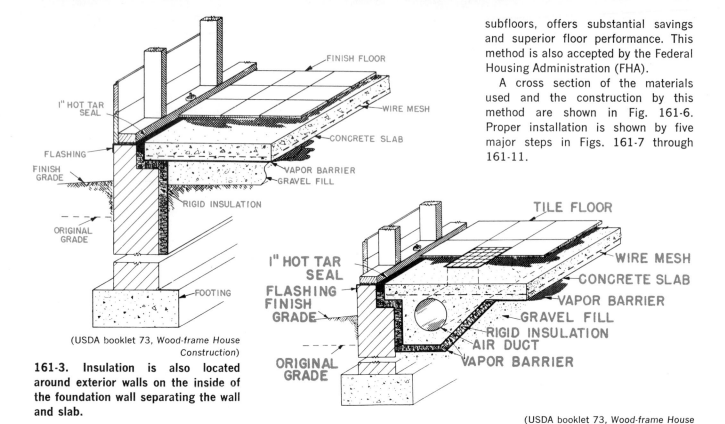

subfloors, offers substantial savings and superior floor performance. This method is also accepted by the Federal Housing Administration (FHA).

A cross section of the materials used and the construction by this method are shown in Fig. 161-6. Proper installation is shown by five major steps in Figs. 161-7 through 161-11.

(USDA booklet 73, *Wood-frame House Construction*)

161-3. Insulation is also located around exterior walls on the inside of the foundation wall separating the wall and slab.

(USDA booklet 73, *Wood-frame House Construction*)

161-5. Cold-air return ducts are located in the slab around exterior walls in some forced-air heating systems.

(USDA booklet 73, *Wood-frame House Construction*)

161-4. Radiant heating pipes are embedded in the slab for some hot-water radiant heating systems.

161-6. A cross section of an accepted method of installation of strip flooring on a concrete slab.

(National Oak Flooring Association)

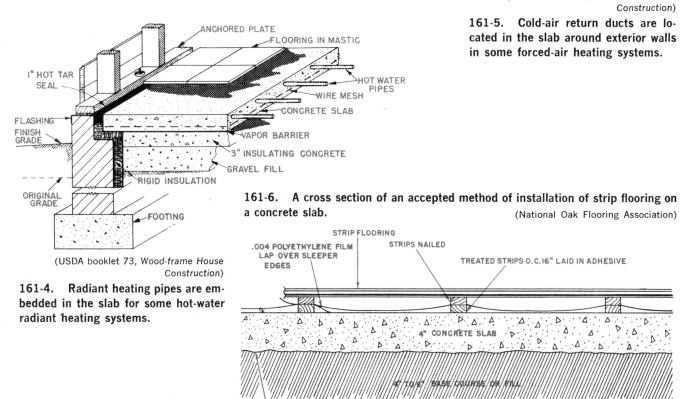

(National Oak Flooring Association)

161-7. Chalk lines, 16 inches apart, are laid on over a primer. Then wood-to-concrete asphalt mastic is applied.

(National Oak Flooring Association)

161-9. A four-thousandths-inch (.004") polyethylene sheet is laid over first layer (course) of strips (sleepers).

(National Oak Flooring Association)

161-10. A second layer of strips is placed over the sheet. They are nailed into the bottom layer.

161-8. Special concrete nails are used to imbed 1-inch by 2-inch strips (sleepers) in the adhesive.

(National Oak Flooring Association)

161-11. Strip flooring is nailed at right angles to each sleeper. One-half-inch expansion space is provided between the flooring and the wall.

(National Oak Flooring Association)

Unit 162 Prefabricated Housing

162-1. A typical prefabricated home.

(National Homes, Inc.)

Fabricate means "put together." If "pre" is added to the word, it indicates that parts are put together before they are sent to the building site.

Prefabrication is not a new idea. Almost everything in our modern economy is mass produced. Factory-finished components are used in many parts of the prefabricated home (Fig. 162-1).

The time-, motion-, and method-analysis techniques used in factory engineering and production control have been borrowed by home builders.

Automated procedures are now used in the prefabrication of all parts of the home, from foundation to roof.

Centuries of Building Prefabrication

Thousands of years ago primitive man cut and trimmed wood and tanned hides and skins to make a crude shelter. These were often carried from one place to another as he traveled.

About 3,000 years before the birth of Christ, the Great Pyramid, a monu-

411

ment to Pharaoh Khufu, was built by prefabrication of over 2 million limestone blocks. These were shaped in the quarries and then hauled to the construction site. Other great temples and buildings of biblical times were similarly erected.

Prefabrication in America

Records in the Library of Congress show that the English shipped a wood-paneled house to the Colonies in 1624. It was to be used by their fishing fleet when the men were ashore between trips.

Thousands of prefabricated homes were produced in New York during the California gold rush in the 1850s. They were shipped around Cape Horn to the West Coast to be sold to prospectors.

In 1861, some Boston and New York lumber dealers patented a system of building houses. These houses consisted of a few standardized panels and many interchangeable parts which could be assembled in a few hours.

Thomas A. Edison built panels and other prefabricated parts for two homes that were erected in the nineteenth century. They still stand.

The boyhood home of Mark Twain is a historical landmark that is still standing in Hannibal, Missouri. It was prefabricated in Cincinnati, Ohio, and shipped by boat to Hannibal.

Twentieth-century Prefabrication

The use of precut housing has increased during the twentieth century. Until World War II it was a modified "do-it-yourself" concept. Companies gradually ventured into the production of a more complete house package, which included floor panels, walls (Fig. 162-2), and ceilings.

A better, less expensive window sash could be produced in a millwork plant than could be made by hand on the job. Preassembled components followed. These included medicine and kitchen cabinets, doors and frames (Fig. 162-3), gable ends (Fig. 162-4), roof trusses (Fig. 162-5), and all other parts of the house.

The walls of small units are sometimes preassembled on the subfloor deck. These small unit walls are easily handled by a few workers (Fig. 162-6). Larger sections of precut housing are also assembled and set in place (Figs. 162-7 and 162-8).

(National Homes, Inc.)

162-2. All components of a house are produced at a prefabrication plant.

(National Homes, Inc.)

162-4. Roof trusses are laid in place, ready to be placed in position on walls.

(Andersen Corporation)

162-6. Small wall units are easily handled by two workers.

162-3. Doors are attached to the door frames before leaving the plant.

(National Homes, Inc.)

162-5. Trusses are swung in place and nailed to prefabricated walls.

(National Homes, Inc.)

162-7. Large wall sections are swung into place with overhead cranes.

(Andersen Corporation)

(Andersen Corporation)

162-8. Parts for complete walls are sometimes erected on the subfloor deck and then raised into place.

The framing is cut, and complete walls are assembled (Fig. 162-9) in some factories before shipment to the building location. Sheathing is attached with automatic nailing machines (Fig. 162-10). The frame is reversed, and insulation is glued between the studs (Fig. 162-11).

External sheathing is attached, and a quick-drying adhesive and aluminum sheets are laid on (Fig. 162-12). The unit is passed through rollers which firmly join (press) the sheathing and the aluminum (Fig. 162-13).

Special routing machines cut window and door openings in the aluminum, gypsum board, and sheathing (Fig. 162-14). Similar operations are used to produce other parts of the home.

The UNICOM Method of House Construction

The UNICOM method of house construction also permits fast planning and erection. The name "UNICOM" was chosen by the National Lumber Manufacturers Association because the use of modular coordination and dimensional standards provides a uniform basis for the manufacture of components. This system cuts builder inventory costs, offers unlimited design flexibility, and conforms to accepted legal requirements in all regions. It can

(National Homes, Inc.)

162-9. Cutting and framing walls at the plant.

(National Homes, Inc.)

162-11. Insulation is glued between studs and layers of sheathing on the inside and the outside of prefabricated walls.

162-10. Attaching sheathing with an automatic nailer. This machine can drive 22 nails in a single stroke.

(National Homes, Inc.)

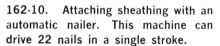

162-12. Outer walls of aluminum sheathing can be attached with an adhesive.

(National Homes, Inc.)

162-13. An aluminum wall is permanently attached to sheathing by passing the wall section through special rollers.

(National Homes, Inc.)

be used efficiently by both the large builder and the custom builder who erects only a few houses per year.

The method is applicable to either on-site or shop fabrication. It is based on standard lumber sizes. It deals with the total house: floors, walls, roof variations, partitions, and stairways. It is adaptable to one-, one-and-one-half, and two-story houses, as well as split- and multiple-level houses.

Applying the UNICOM Method

The concept of **modular coordination and design** is basic to the UNICOM method (Fig. 162-17). A **module** is a standard, or unit, of measurement. Architecturally, it is the size of some one part. Emphasis is placed on the importance of the use of a **modular planning grid** as a design control.

The wall, floor, and roof elements are not tied to any fixed panel size. A complete house is divided into basic horizontal and vertical elements at regular modular intervals (units of measurement); see Fig. 162-15. The elements are shown as planes without thickness, but allowance is made for wall thickness and tolerance variables (Fig. 162-16). These are based on fixed (not imaginary) module lines at the outside faces of the exterior wall studs.

Complete exterior walls and partitions may have overall thickness variables. This depends on load-bearing or

(National Homes, Inc.)

162-14. Routing window and door openings through sheathing and walls.

non-load-bearing use, and also on the covering materials. Floor and roof construction elements vary in thickness, depending upon their structural requirements and their types of framing and finishing.

Figure 162-18 shows how separations of exterior wall elements are made at natural division points between solid portions and door and window openings. Overall house dimensions are based on the 48-inch major module (unit) and the 24-inch minor module.

Maximum flexibility in location of door and window openings (for good proportion) is achieved by adhering to the natural 16-inch module. Location of wall openings to this 16-inch unit of measurement eliminates the extra wall framing that is commonly needed in nonmodular planning.

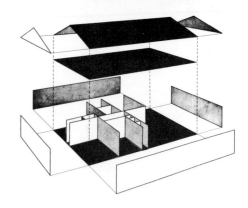

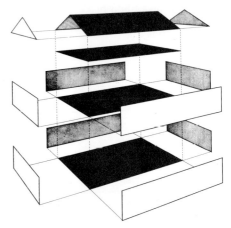

(National Lumber Manufacturers' Association)

162-16. Basic planes for modular (unit-of-measurement) study.

162-15. Plane sections with thickness and tolerance variables for a home division.

(National Lumber Manufacturers' Association)

OUTSIDE CORNER   EXTERIOR WALL AND PARTITION   INSIDE CORNER

MODULE LINES

414

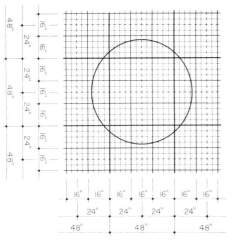

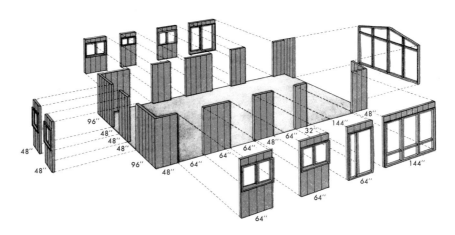

162-17. The modular planning grid shows the principle of the UNICOM method.

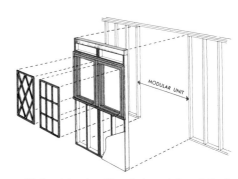

162-18. Separations are made at natural division points in modular exterior walls.

Unit 163 Mobile Homes

163-1. A typical mobile home.
(American Coach Co.)

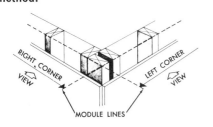

163-2. A typical travel trailer.
(Lonergran Corp.)

Mobile homes (Fig. 163-1) and travel trailers (Fig. 163-2) have become the permanent homes for thousands of persons. The units can be moved on wheels, but they often remain in one location. It is estimated that at least 10 percent of the one-family home market is in mobile homes.

Mobile-home Construction

The "foundation" of the mobile home is a steel-frame chassis (Fig. 163-3). Lumber, plywood, and many other wood products go into the completed home on wheels.

Framing is added to the steel foundation in almost the same way as for the conventional house (Fig. 163-4). To the basic frame construction are attached insulation, electrical wiring, heating and cooling ducts (Fig. 163-5), flooring, paneling (Fig. 163-6), cabinets (Fig. 163-7), plumbing, and other utilities and interior finishings.

Some mobile homes have complete living, dining, kitchen, and bedroom facilities (Fig. 163-8). Some have sanitary facilities and fireplaces. All new mobile homes must meet standard codes for construction, plumbing, heating, and electrical installation.

(Mobile Homes Manufacturers' Association)

163-3. A steel chassis is used under mobile homes and travel trailers.

163-4. Framing similar to regular house construction is used for mobile homes.

(Mobile Homes Manufacturers' Association)

(American Coach Company)

163-5. Heating and cooling ducts are placed between floor joists.

163-6. Wood paneling is a typical interior wall covering.

(American Coach Company)

(American Coach Company)

163-7. Cabinets are built in the kitchen and other areas of the mobile home.

163-8. Most facilities of modern homes are included in many mobile homes.

(Liberty Coach Company, Inc.)

Unit 164 The Production and Use of Plastic Laminates

Laminated plastic sheets bonded to plywood have become especially suitable for many residential, commercial, and institutional uses. Basically the sheets are made of several layers of strong kraft papers that have been impregnated with synthetic resins. First, special kraft papers are impregnated with phenolic resins to make core layers. Then, special cellulose papers are printed with colors and designs and saturated with melamine resins to be laid over the core (Fig. 164-1). A melamine resin sheet forms the top layer. The finished decorative sheet is extremely durable when used to cover such surfaces as furniture and furnishings in schools and banks. Some of the common trade names for this covering are Formica, Textolite, Nevamar, and Micarta.

Manufacturing Plastic Laminates

The special kraft papers (Fig. 164-2) that make up the bulk of the laminated plastic sheet are called **filler stock.** They are used for the core. The paper

164-1. Plastic laminates are made of layers of strong kraft paper, a decorative sheet, and protective top sheet.

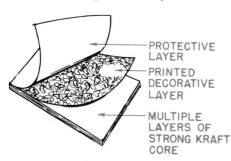

PROTECTIVE LAYER

PRINTED DECORATIVE LAYER

MULTIPLE LAYERS OF STRONG KRAFT CORE

(Formica Corporation)

164-2. Rolls of special kraft paper are used in making the core for plastic laminates.

(Formica Corporation)

164-3. Pattern paper is stored in special rooms. A one-rail "trolley car" is used to move the racks efficiently.

(Formica Corporation)

164-4. This printer will print patterns in which more than one color is required.

is impregnated with phenolic resins, such as phenol-formaldehyde, by passing it through a long treating machine. It enters the "wet end" through a container of resin, its excess resin is removed, and it travels several hundred feet through the various heat zones of a drying oven.

The amount of resin in the paper is controlled by special electronic equipment which measures the weight of the paper as it travels through metering rolls and into the oven to the "dry end." When the dry, treated paper emerges, it is cut to length and stacked.

A second major layer of the laminate, the pattern, or liner sheet, is processed in the printing, or graining, room. A high grade of alpha cellulose (specially prepared) paper (Fig. 164-3) is printed (Fig. 164-4) by the rotogravure lithographing or other graphic arts process to convert the paper into a wide range of colors and patterns. Pigments can be added to the paper to give hiding (covering) power and color. After this paper is printed, it is rerolled before it is sent to the treating machine for impregnation with melamine-formaldehyde resin. The impregnation process is essentially the same for the pattern sheets as for the core layer of kraft papers.

A thin layer of translucent (semi-clear) material about .004 inch thick, such as alpha cellulose or rayon-base paper, is heavily impregnated with melamine-formaldehyde resin, which becomes transparent during curing. This resin is used because of its clarity, lack of color, hardness, and resistance to heat, water, and stains. This overlay becomes the highly protective top sheet. Both the pattern, or liner, materials and the top overlay sheets are cut to the required size after the coating and curing treatment. They must be processed in special rooms, wrapped in a dustproof film, and stored in rooms (Fig. 164-5) where the humidity, temperature, and dust are carefully controlled until the sheets are processed under regulated conditions. The final laminated sheet is built up from these treated raw materials. Several layers of filler stock, depending on the final thickness desired, are overlayed with one layer of pattern, or liner, material and a top protective sheet. Highly polished stainless steel plates are placed between the **build-ups** next to the top lamination. These mirror-finished plates impart a high gloss to the finished sheet. The desired number of build-ups are assembled to make a **pack,** or

book. Several packs are required to fill the large presses used in curing.

The packs of laminated plastic sheets are placed between the platens of huge hydraulic presses (Fig. 164-6). Pressure (about 1,500 pounds per square inch) and heat (over 300°F) are used to cure the decorative material properly in about 1 hour. The steam in the platens is replaced by cold water, which cools the load. After the curing is completed, the packs are removed from the press and returned to the build-up rooms. The

164-5. Raw material is stored in a special humidity control room.

(Decorative Micarta Division, Westinghouse Electric Corporation)

(Formica Corporation)

164-6. Large hydraulic presses are used to cure laminated plastic sheets under heat and pressure.

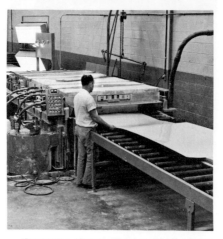

(Decorative Micarta Division, Westinghouse Electric Corporation)

164-7. Satinizer uses water, pumice, and brushes for low-glare finish.

164-8. Special wood files are laid flat on the surface to file edge strips flush with the surface.

cured plastic and stainless steel sheets are removed to prepare the next run of packs for curing.

The sides and then the ends of sheets are trimmed in special machines. After trimming, the sheet passes directly through the sander, where the back side is sanded to uniform thickness and provides the rough surface necessary for good adhesion to various surfaces. Throughout the entire manufacturing processes, the material is frequently inspected to ensure high quality.

Additional finishing operations are used to dull the high gloss finish to a satin texture which reduces glare (Fig. 164-7). Another popular finish is the semigloss surface, which looks like a hand-rubbed furniture finish. The finish is protected by tissue placed between the sheets. Packages of sheets are made up of like colors, patterns, and sizes for storage or shipment to customers.

Characteristics and Uses

This plastic surfacing material is easily cleaned with a damp cloth or sponge. It is resistant to wear, heat,

denting, scuffing, most stains, and ordinary temperature and humidity changes. Under normal use it will not chip, crack, or lose its original color and finish. However, it is not generally recommended for constant use out of doors.

The laminates are most often used on flat areas, but they can also be attached to curved surfaces. Pressure can be used to bend the sheet at normal room temperature around a radius as small as 8 inches without dies and fixtures (special forms). Radii as small as $\frac{1}{2}$ inch inside and $\frac{3}{4}$ inch outside can be formed with dies and fixtures on sheets which have been heated properly.

Plastic laminates can be sawed, drilled, punched, filed, routed, shaped, sanded, and polished. Standard woodworking tools and machines can be used. Special bits on these machines do the most satisfactory job, however. Normal cutting tools dull easily and do not make as smooth a cut.

Numerous colors and patterns are available. These range from solid and multicolors to marble and metallic effects, wood grains, and various abstract-pattern designs.

Several combinations of lengths and widths are commonly available. Some of these are 24-, 30-, 36-, 48-, and 60-inch widths and 60-, 72-, 84-, 96-, 120-, and 144-inch lengths. Practically any width and length can be made by cutting standard-size sheets.

The finish and color of plastic laminates which are properly manufactured are not visibly affected by many mild products. Some examples of these products are household soaps, washing powders, detergents, citric acid, ammonia, alcohol, gasoline, mustard, coffee, and fly spray. Soap and water usually remove stains left by tea, dye, vinegar, ink, and such common medical disinfectants as iodine.

Some products, however, react with the plastic and should not be allowed to remain on a surface. Some examples are bleach, grape juice, nonfood acids, peroxide, and lye.

Plastic laminate sheets, which are usually about $\frac{1}{16}$ inch thick, can be bonded to many surfaces, including plywood, particle board, aluminum, and asbestos, producing exceptionally durable and attractive surfaces. Plastic laminated panels are also used for desk tops and office partitions, coffee

164-9. A special roller guide and cutter are used in the router to cut edge strips flush with the top.

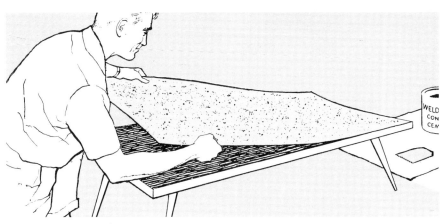

164-10. The top surface is added after plastic edges are attached.

tables and display-room fixtures, doors, store display counters, and restaurant counter, back, and bar surfaces.

Application of Plastic Laminates

Laminates are frequently bonded to plywood and high-grade particle boards before they are attached to supporting parts. Plastic laminates are also attached to tables, cabinets of various kinds, desks, walls, and many other items after the major construction has been completed. When edges are to be covered, it is recommended that this decorative strip be applied first and smoothed flush with the face surfaces (Figs. 164-8 and 164-9). Tapping the narrow edge piece with a rubber mallet helps set the strip securely in place. The face is applied and lapped over the edge on such items as tables (Fig. 164-10) and kitchen cabinets. The overlap is cut and smoothed flush with the edges.

The type of adhesive used to bond plastic laminates to various materials depends on how the final product will be used. The manufacturer's recommendations should be followed exactly to obtain the best results. Two of the

common adhesives are polyvinyl (cold set, usually under slight pressure for a brief time) and neoprene-base cement (the common contact cement). A flammable mixture of toluol and naptha is one solvent, and water is another. One main advantage of water-base adhesives is fire safety. Some disadvantages are the following: (1) Their slower drying causes possible water entrapment, which can result in blistering and separation of the core and the laminate. (2) When frozen, the adhesive becomes a solid and is unusable. (3) Water rusts or corrodes metals unless they are specially treated. (4) They have inferior heat resistance. (5) They are impractical for self-edging because they require higher pressure for a good bond. Other contact cements are nonflammable and use other bases.

Some adhesives are thinned slightly with lacquer thinner. Lacquer thinner is especially useful for cleaning tools and parts exposed to some contact cements. Paint thinner also dissolves adhesive resins and allows the remaining rubber to be rolled off some materials. In all cases, follow the manufacturer's directions for application and use of the adhesive chosen.

Hot or cold spray contact adhesives are used by some manufacturers. The equipment for this process and the procedures are not practical for smaller operations.

Decorative laminates can be worked with practically all wood- and metalworking tools and machines. Special hardened saws, drills, and other cutters are recommended for best results. Saw teeth should be fine, and a faster than normal speed of operation is recommended. In practically all situations, the cut should be *into* the decorative surface to prevent chipping.

For small operations, hand tools are most frequently used. Straight lines are cut with a fine-tooth crosscut saw (Fig. 164-11). Use a soft lead or grease pencil to lay out the size of sheet needed. Clamp wood strips to both sides of the line. Saw only on the downstroke, and use a very low angle. Allow a slight overhang for final finishing.

An awl, a special laminate cutter, or a knife resembling a floor-tile knife can also be used to cut straight lines (Figs. 164-12 and 164-13). The cut made by the jaw of the special cutter forms its own path and prevents chipping. The

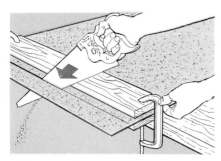

164-11.   A fine-tooth handsaw can be used to cut straight pieces of laminate.

164-14.   Bend the laminate toward the decorative surface to secure a sharp break after scoring.

164-15.   The drill and the keyhole saw are valuable in cutting internal curves.

164-12.   A special laminate cutter can be used to cut straight across large or small pieces.

164-13.   The cut should be made through both the top layer and the decorative layer when the awl or carbide-tip knife are used to score laminates before breaking.

knife has a carbide tip and is flattened slightly to form a V-shape tip. When using a knife or an awl, the cut should be made through the decorative layer. To secure a clean, sharp break, bend the laminate *toward* the decorative surface (Fig. 164-14).

Hand tools can also be used to cut internal and external curves. With the decorative side up, use a twist drill and a hand or portable electric drill to drill a series of holes around the arc in the scrap material (Fig. 164-15). Cut the curve with a keyhole saw, using vertical downward strokes. The straight cuts can be made with a crosscut handsaw.

External curves can be cut with tin snips if the laminate is not too thick (Fig. 164-16). Special care must be used to cut away most of the excess material before the final cut to prevent chipping. Cut with the face of the laminate turned up.

Procedure for Using Edge Molding

Cove and edge molding are sometimes used to cover edges and form corners after the horizontal surface has been covered with plastic laminate. The laminate is sometimes also joined. The following procedure will serve as a guide.

1. Fill all holes in the surfaces, and sand clean and smooth (Fig. 164-17). Any rotted material should be replaced.

Warped and irregular surfaces should be made level; if not, the laminate will tend to loosen where curves and low spots exist in the surface.

2. Apply contact cement to the horizontal surface with the metal spreader (Fig. 164-18). Many workers prefer a large brush or a frieze-covered roller to spread the cement (Fig. 164-19). Rollers should have a phenolic-type core, which resists attack by the solvents used in the contact cement.

3. Apply cement to the back face of the plastic laminate and let it dry until it is tacky.

4. Start at one edge, and place the laminate carefully on the surface. The cement grips instantly, and the sheet

164-16.   External curves on regular plastic laminates can be cut with sharp tin snips. Remove only small amounts on each cut to prevent chipping.

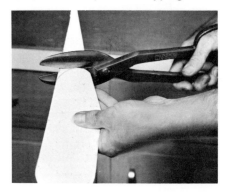

164-17. All surfaces should be very smooth and level.

164-19. Rollers and large brushes are preferred by many to apply cement on large surfaces.

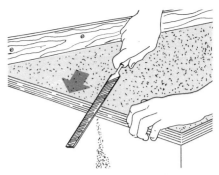

164-21. Use a flat wood file to remove overhang when an edge molding is used.

is extremely difficult to shift or remove. Roll the surface with a linoleum roller or a rolling pin to secure complete contact (Fig. 164-20). A roller not over 3 inches in width is recommended to give the best pressure for proper bonding.

5. Using downward strokes only, trim off the rough overhang with a flat wood file (Fig. 164-21). Final finishing can be done with a finer file. On furniture, the edge can be finished with a sander.

6. Attach a piece of ¾-inch-thick plywood to the wall for a backsplash. The width of the plywood is optional.

7. Use special corner or cove molding, and attach it to the plywood (Fig. 164-22).

8. Apply cement to the plywood, and laminate as in steps 2 and 3; then set the laminate in place and roll as in step 4.

9. Attach edge molding to cover the wood edges. Cut a miter (Fig. 164-23A) to form around corners.

10. Apply sealing compound inside the molding, and snap over the edge of the top (Fig. 164-23B).

11. The edges of the backsplash should be covered with cap molding in the same manner (Fig. 164-23C).

When L- or U-shape surfaces are to be installed, join the sheets as shown in Fig. 164-24. This keeps the seam away from the sink area. If a seam or butt joint is required around the sink, try to locate it at the center of the sink.

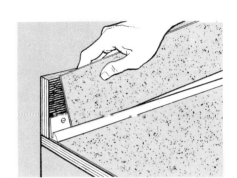

164-22. Attaching a plastic backsplash by using cove molding attached to plywood.

164-18. The metal spreader is sometimes used to apply contact cement to surfaces.

164-20. The rolling pin is used to apply light pressure for bonding.

164-23. Edge molding is attached after top surfaces are covered. (A) Miter cut in molding for corner. (B) Bending around corner. (C) Cap molding for top and edges of backsplash.

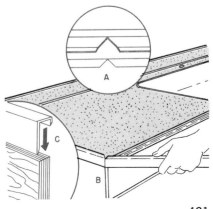

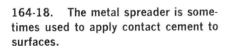

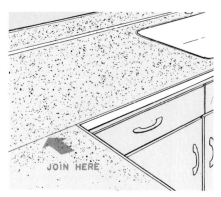

164-24. Join surface sheets as shown to keep joints as far away from the sink area as possible.

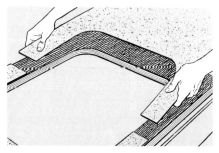

164-25. If absolutely necessary, make joints near the center of the sink to minimize fitting of pieces.

164-26. Cover edges first when laminates are used, beginning at one end and following through to the opposite end.

164-27. Common metal nippers can be used to remove excess plastic, and the edge is filed smooth.

This requires less fitting of pieces (Fig. 164-25). Joints should be carefully squared and smoothed with a block plane, a file, or sandpaper.

Procedure for Using Preformed Sheets

Covering edges and other surfaces between cabinets:

1. Cut the required decorative laminate strip; apply cement properly; let it dry; then attach the laminate to the edge of the cabinet (Fig. 164-26).

2. Smooth the edges flush with the surfaces, using the router and a file.

164-28. Scrap laminate strips prevent the top surface from bonding while the vertical back is set into place when using a complete preformed sheet.

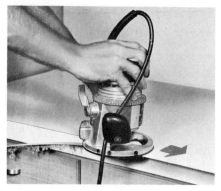

164-29. Excess overlap is easily smoothed and made flush with the edges by using the router and the special cutter.

Overlapping edges near the cabinet wall can be removed with metal nippers (Fig. 164-27) and filed smooth if a special router cutter is not available.

3. Cut the preformed laminate to the required length to fit easily but snugly between cabinets.

4. Spread cement on the vertical and horizontal surfaces of the cabinet and the back side of the laminate; let it dry.

5. Temporarily place narrow scrap strips of laminate on the horizontal (top) cabinet surface to prevent the regular laminate top from sticking (Fig. 164-28).

164-30. Holes over electrical outlets may be broken out after the laminate has been securely bonded to the backing. Otherwise it will chip and crack.

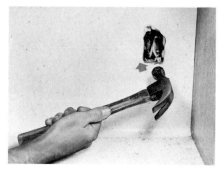

6. Set the vertical backsplash portion of the preformed laminate in place, and form it to the vertical wall.

7. Remove strips, and press laminate to the horizontal surface.

8. Use the router with the special cutter to remove the overhang, and smooth the top flush with the edge (Fig. 164-29).

9. Laminates can be laid over electrical outlet boxes, and similar holes. If the bond between the decorative plastic and the base material is firm, the plastic can be broken out safely with a hammer (Fig. 164-30). The edges of the covering can be filed smooth. Extreme care must be taken to prevent chipping and cracking the plastic laminate.

Common Bonding Failures

Some of the causes of improper bonding of laminates to core materials:

1. Coating too thinly, bonding too soon, applying insufficient pressure, and exposing the laminate to heat or direct sunlight within 3 days may cause edge lifting.

2. Bubbles in the center of laminates are caused by bonding too soon and trapping solvent or bonding edges first instead of working across or from the center outward.

3. Testing the adhesive with the fingers for dryness before it is dry may cause small circular unbonded areas.

4. Forcing a backsplash of a cabinet to fit may cause buckling.

5. Using common fir or solid lumber as a core causes the adhesive to soak into softer areas faster and to give uneven coating.

6. Vegetable and animal glues do not hold laminates properly.

7. Working adhesives and laminates when they are below normal room temperature gives poor results.

Precautions in Using Contact Cements

Several precautions are necessary when using some contact cements:

1. Some contact cement requires thorough mixing after long storage. The vulcanizing agents and rubber have separated and need to be stirred back into the mixture.

2. Frozen adhesives which have jelled should be heated to about 70°F.

3. Prevent sawdust and other particles from getting onto or into the adhesive. The presence of these particles causes improper bonding.

4. High temperatures give shorter drying times. High humidity or thick adhesive coats cause longer drying.

5. Contact cements should not be applied at temperatures below 50°F.

6. Apply adequate adhesive and bonding pressure. Most failures can be attributed to these factors.

DISCUSSION TOPICS

1. Explain the difference between a beam, a joist, and a truss.
2. What is the meaning of the expression **square of roofing?**
3. What are the lumber grades?
4. Name five checks which should be made concerning the location and the excavation of a house.
5. How much hardening time should be allowed load-bearing concrete?
6. Discuss the sizes of beams and how they are joined, built up, and placed on foundations.
7. What are the two popular types of house construction over foundation walls?
8. What is the recommended height of ceilings and spacing of studs?
9. Make a sketch to show how studs are put together to form a corner post. What are the main reasons for this construction?
10. When is it possible to eliminate wall braces?
11. Describe the construction of gable dormer, hip, and gable-and-valley and hip-and-valley roofs.
12. Name the three major types of rafters which touch both the ridge board and the wall plate.
13. Using the square, find the number of board feet (bd ft) in two pieces of lumber 2″ X 10″ X 8′.
14. What is the proper length of a brace if the run on the plate or stud is 36 inches?
15. If a building is 36 feet wide and the rise of the roof is 6 feet, what is the pitch?
16. What are the standard pitches?
17. What are the heel and the plumb cuts on rafters?
18. Which rafters have sides cut on their ends?
19. Why is construction cost increased by bay windows and dormers?
20. If the total rise is 9 feet, determine the height of each riser. Lay out a set of continuous stairs.
21. What are the four common types of wall and roof sheathing?
22. How should strip flooring be laid?
23. Discuss the problems and procedure of building on a concrete slab.
24. Why has the development of precut housing increased so rapidly since World War II?
25. What major house components can be factory assembled?
26. Define **module** and **modular.**
27. Explain the basic composition and manufacture of laminated plastic.
28. Why is the back side of laminates sanded and roughened?
29. List some of the common failures in bonding plastics and precautions for using contact cement.

SECTION
25

PATTERNMAKING

Unit 165 The Importance of Patternmaking

165-1. Wood patterns are made for many machine parts.

(American Foundrymen's Society)

Primitive man discovered that poured molten copper would take the shape of an impression in the sand. He soon realized that many intricate shapes could be obtained by making different impressions. These discoveries led to the development of the important art of patternmaking. This art has helped man make metal fit his needs better.

The Patternmaker

The patternmaker's job is to make the pattern to form a mold into which the molten metal is poured for a casting. A master patternmaker is one of the most important and skilled woodworkers in industry. His job requires that he be an expert in the use of woodworking machines and tools. He must also be proficient in reading drawings. With this knowledge he can make three-dimensional patterns (Fig. 165-1) by following the drawings of the designer.

A patternmaker must also have enough knowledge of foundry work to make the pattern so that it can be properly extracted from the molding sand. A knowledge of the shrinkage of metals and metal alloys is also necessary. The foundryman pours the molten metal into shapes made in the sand by a pattern or core mold (Fig. 165-2). In addition, a patternmaker can help eliminate the waste of time, effort, and money by knowing the problems of the machinist.

A pattern must first be made for everything that is cast in metal. Temporary patterns are made both of wood and of other materials, such as plastic. More permanent metal patterns are then made (Fig. 165-4).

Practically all motors and machines used in modern industry are dependent upon patternmaking. For this reason, the work of the foundryman and of the patternmaker are closely related.

Before a pattern can be used, the foundryman prepares the molding sand properly. It is prepared either (1) by hand, (2) by portable units (Fig. 165-5), or (3) in larger machines for more extensive foundry work (Fig. 165-3).

Patterns are placed in a **flask** in preparation for molding (Fig. 165-6). Necessary cores (Fig. 165-7) are added as needed, and sand is rammed

(packed) around the pattern (Fig. 165-8). The next step is the careful separation of the mold in order to remove the pattern from it.

The cavity, or hole, left in the sand is poured full of molten metal to produce the required casting (Fig. 165-9). The final casting would not be possible without the knowledge and ability of the patternmaker to make an accurate pattern.

165-2.   Pouring metal into core molds after melting by the induction method.

(American Foundrymen's Society)

165-4.   A wood pattern is needed to make the mold for pouring a permanent aluminum cope and drag pattern.

(American Foundrymen's Society)

165-5.   A portable sand mixer used to condition foundry sand.

(American Foundrymen's Society)

165-3.   A typical scene in a large foundry where sand is prepared and delivered from overhead to the molding area.

(American Foundrymen's Society)

165-6.   A remote-controlled sand "slinger," continuous turntable, pin-lift machines, and an automatic sand strike-off are used in high-production miscellaneous pattern molding.

(American Foundrymen's Society)

(American Foundrymen's Society)

165-7. Dry-sand core forms pouring box; it sits on four sand crankcase cores and lower section of a permanent mold.

(American Foundrymen's Society)

165-8. Use of sand slinger to fill huge molds at the rate of one ton per minute eliminates hand filling and ramming.

(American Foundrymen's Society)

165-9. Thirty to ninety huge molds are poured per hour as they travel along a continuous conveyor.

Unit 166 Patternmaking and Foundry Terms

The patternmaker works with such materials as wood, plastic, and plaster. The foundryman melts various metals and pours (casts) them into molds. Even though each craftsman uses different materials, the patternmaker must still be familiar with foundry work and its terms. When the final cast product is considered, it is easy to understand why the terminology is directly related to both areas of work.

Definition of Terms

■ **Alloy.** A combination of two or more metals.

■ **Blow hole.** A hole in a casting caused by air or gases trapped in the mold which prevent a smooth, solid casting.

■ **Bottomboard, or moldboard.** This is a platform or large board on which the flask and molded sand rest.

■ **Casting.** A metal shape resulting from pouring molten metal into a mold, and from which all gates, risers, and other extra metal have been removed (Fig. 166-1).

■ **Cheek.** The middle part of a flask, if more than the cope (top) or drag

166-1. A typical large machine-tool casting.

(bottom) portions are used for a mold.

■ **Cope.** The top portion of a flask.

■ **Core.** The portion, usually made of baked sand and binder, placed in the mold opening to create various holes or cavities in the finished casting. The core helps to eliminate the use of extra metal and machining.

■ **Core box.** A box, or mold, of wood or metal in which the core is shaped.

■ **Draft.** The small taper on patterns which allows them to be removed easily from the sand.

■ **Drag.** The bottom portion of a flask.

■ **Drawing.** Removing the pattern from the sand after it has been rapped (tapped) lightly to loosen it.

■ **Flask.** A wood or metal frame (sides) with no top or bottom, consisting of the cope, the drag, and possibly the cheek.

■ **Fillet.** A concave shape made from wood, leather, wax, or other material to round (shape) sharp internal corners when two pieces intersect.

■ **Gate.** The opening, or channel, cut in the sand through which the molten metal runs from the sprue and riser to the casting cavity left by the pattern.

■ **Green sand.** Special molding sand which has been dampened and conditioned (tempered) with water for proper foundry use.

■ **Green sand core.** An unbaked molding sand core. (See **core.**)

■ **Kiln drying.** Kiln drying is a process of drying lumber to a specific moisture content in a special enclosure under controlled heat and humidity conditions.

■ **Master pattern.** This is usually an original pattern from which permanent metal patterns are cast (Fig. 166-2).

■ **Match plate.** A special plate (Fig. 166-3) to which the pattern is attached at the parting line, or where the mold (flask) parts (separates).

■ **Model.** An exact likeness of a finished object; it may be either full size or miniature.

■ **Mold.** The molded sand or other material which contains the cavity left by the pattern to form a casting when poured full of metal.

■ **Molding sand.** A special sand which can be conditioned (tempered) uniformly. It sticks together well, but it allows air and gases to escape.

■ **Parting line.** The line, or joint, where the flask separates to allow removal of the pattern before the metal is poured.

■ **Pouring.** The actual filling of the mold cavity with molten metal (Fig. 166-4).

■ **Ramming.** Packing the sand over and around the pattern in the mold or flask.

■ **Rapping.** Jarring the pattern so that it loosens from the sand and can be more easily removed.

■ **Rechucking.** Reversing a pattern on a lathe faceplate so that the opposite side can be turned to the necessary shape.

■ **Riser.** An extra hole in the molding sand into which molten metal either can be poured or can rise from the cavity to feed (fill) the casting as it shrinks during solidification.

■ **Shrinkage.** The amount of decrease in volume when molten metal cools and solidifies.

■ **Sizing.** The process of applying watery, thin glue or a wash coat of shellac on wood; especially on end grain to seal the pores.

■ **Snap flasks.** Flasks which have hinged sides and latches so that flask parts can be removed from around the molded sand before pouring and which allow multiple molds to be made with one flask, when necessary.

■ **Split pattern.** A split pattern is a pattern made in two, or several, parts for convenience in molding and removing from sand.

■ **Spline.** A thin strip of wood, sometimes called a **feather,** or **tongue,** used to strengthen butt and miter joints.

■ **Sprue.** The hole, or opening, through which the molten metal is poured, entering the mold by way of the gate.

■ **Vent.** A small opening that is often made in sand with wire before the pattern is removed. It allows air and gases to escape when pouring molten metal into the cavity, and it helps prevent blow holes.

166-2. Skill is required to produce a master wheel pattern.

(Steelways Magazine)

166-3. A pattern match plate is attached where the molding flask parts.

(American Foundrymen's Society)

166-4. Pouring molten metal into small molds.

(American Foundrymen's Society)

Unit 167 Tools, Equipment, and Supplies for Patternmaking

Patterns are made by using a wide variety of hand tools, portable and stationary power machinery, and various supplies. Many of the items are standard woodworking tools, machines, and materials.

Special Hand Tools

Some of the particular layout and measuring tools used in patternmaking are the **straight** and **bent-point scribers,** the **center head** for the **combination square,** and various **gauges.** Special **hand planes** used are the circular, core, box, round-sole, left-side, right-side, and bullnose rabbet planes.

Shrink rules are needed to make measurements for patterns used in molds into which metal is poured. When molten metal cools, it usually shrinks a uniform amount, according to the kind of metal. Knowledge of this amount of shrinkage for each type of metal permits a decision as to which specific shrink rule to use. To allow for shrinkage, graduations on the shrink rules resemble those on the common rule, but each division is greater.

Inside and outside ground **gouges** with straight and bent shanks, and **wood carving tools** of various shapes are necessary to produce delicate pattern designs. Long and short bent **chisels** and V-shape **veining chisels** are included. All these special tools are variations and adaptations of the basic hand tools discussed in SECTION 3, "Basic Hand-tool Processes."

Special Machine Accessories

Standard woodworking machines are often used to prepare and work material for patternmaking. **Saws** for fine, smooth cutting; special **grinding wheels; sander spindles;** shaper and router **cutters;** and **bits** of various kinds are required accessories.

The only special machine that might be needed to make patterns would be the heavy-duty, variable-speed **gap-bed woodturning lathe.** However, the ordinary lathe serves for most woodturning work in patternmaking.

Special Supplies

In addition to regular woodworking supplies, special materials and supplies are needed. These include pearl, flake, and pulverized glue; fillets made of wax; materials such as leather, paper, wood, metal, and composition; and brass or other metal dowels. Layout fluids, pattern identification stencils, plaster of paris, and pattern mountings, such as letters, are additional supplies that are used.

Unit 168 Patternmaking Materials

Wood is the material that is most often selected for making patterns. Plastic resins, ordinary plaster, and various low-melting-point alloys are used in varying quantities for specific needs.

Since wood is the predominant material used, review SECTION 1, "Technology of Woods," to appreciate the structure and characteristics of wood and its growth.

Wood for Patterns

The majority of pattern lumber is obtained from the white or sugar pines in the softwoods. Redwood and Alaskan and red cedar are also used when they are easily obtained. White pine from the northern Appalachian region is considered one of the best woods. It is moderately light, uniform in texture, and easily worked. The dimensions of this species change very little when moisture conditions vary.

Some hardwood lumber is used by patternmakers. The Mexican and Central American species of mahogany are most often used commercially. Maple and hard cherry are often formed into parts of a pattern which may receive severe wear.

Seasoning Pattern Wood

Most pattern wood can be kiln-dried to a moisture content as low as 6 percent. This shrinks the material and brings out imperfections not apparent in air-dried lumber.

Many pattern craftsmen believe that water curing and then air seasoning is the best method of preparing pattern wood. Logs are cut to length and placed in water, where they remain for as long as 2 years. The soaking extracts various resins and tends to cure the log. The resulting lumber is more mellow, has fewer strains, and can be air-dried faster.

Lumber cut from the cured logs is stacked carefully in the woodyard, properly supported for even air circulation. The average drying time is 1 year per inch of thickness.

From the yard, air-dried lumber is taken to the pattern shop and again carefully stacked. The drying time necessary is from 6 months to 2 years, depending upon the thickness.

About 3 to 5 years would be necessary to prepare top quality 1-inch pattern lumber by the water-curing, air-seasoning method. This method is still used sometimes, but modern methods, materials, and production costs make the water curing, air-seasoning operation less desirable than modern drying methods.

Another form of wood and pattern is shown in Fig. 168-1. Veneer core pieces $\frac{1}{10}$ inch thick are impregnated with phenolic resin and bonded into panel form for fabrication into die molds. These molds are used as die blocks for metal forming and show practically no dimensional changes under severe use conditions.

Plasters for Patterns

Patterns, molds, and models have been made from plaster for hundreds of years. The material commonly used was plaster of paris. In recent years, numerous mixtures of gypsum cements have been formulated to meet specific pattern needs of the aircraft, spacecraft, transportation, and plastics industries.

Gypsum cements, called **hard plasters,** are gray or white natural minerals. They meet very exacting requirements of modern industrial patternmaking (Fig. 168-2). They must be ground and processed into the many mixtures they can make.

Hard plasters are very adaptable to irregular and intricate shapes, and they save time because they are simple to use. They do not shrink or warp with moisture changes.

Dental, or casting, plaster is often called **soft plaster.** It is processed and formulated for different purposes than hard plaster is. It usually requires mixing with more water before it can be poured.

168-1.   Veneer is impregnated with phenolic resin and bonded into panel form to make die molds.

(Hardwood Plywood Institute)

168-2.   A hard plaster mold and core.

(American Foundrymen's Society)

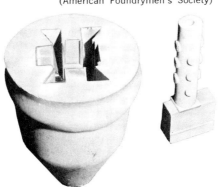

168-3.   The cope and the drag halves of a plastic pattern.

(American Foundrymen's Society)

The most uniform mix of plasters and water is obtained when the proportions are measured by weight rather than by volume. Plaster is always added *to* the water. The amount of water affects the final durability, hardness, strength, and density of gypsum patterns. Generally speaking, the more water required in the mix, the weaker the final object of gypsum will be when set.

Cast Plastic Patterns

Organic plastics are generally divided into three groups: (1) thermoplastic, (2) thermosetting, and (3) chemical setting. The **thermoplastic** types are softened by heat and become hard when they cool. These can be reworked by reheating after they have hardened. **Thermosetting** plastics may be soft or in liquid form when they are heated and formed, but then they take a permanent shape when cool and cannot be reworked (Fig. 168-3). These types are used in casting patterns. **Chemical-setting** plastics harden when the correct chemical is added.

Plastic production patterns are cheaper, they eliminate finishing and nearly all draft, and they can be made identical with master patterns. Surface wear is less, so they last for much longer. Such plastic production patterns require no special equipment except a drying oven.

Epoxy resins have excellent properties for laminating, casting, and surface coating. Proper proportions of the hardening agent and the resin are mixed in their liquid forms. A chemical reaction occurs and cures the resin into a hard material. Epoxies are versatile, strong, and very stable when they are stored under correct conditions. They adhere to most surfaces and have the lowest shrinkage of the resin types.

Wood and plaster are still used in producing the long-lasting, versatile plastic pattern.

Metal-alloy Patterns

Low-melting-point alloys are used in connection with wooden patterns. These alloys are not new, but they are receiving special use in modern production techniques. **Bismuth** is the base for the patternmaking metal alloy. Various alloys are produced by adding cadmium, tin, lead, zinc, and other low-melting-point metals to form a combination that melts at a temperature less than 212°F.

Alloys have little or no shrinkage and are not hot enough to scorch wood when they are melted. Low-melting-point alloys are an excellent material to speed production. One example of the use of alloys would be in adding fillets to wooden patterns.

DISCUSSION TOPICS

1. Of what importance is the wood patternmaker to the metalworking industry?
2. Besides being an expert woodworker, what other trades and occupations must the patternmaker know something about?
3. With what craftsman is the work of the patternmaker most closely associated?
4. Name 10 items cast in metal for which a wooden pattern was needed originally.
5. Describe each of the following: (a) moldboard, (b) cope, (c) drag, (d) cheek, (e) fillet, (f) core box, (g) master pattern, and (h) rechucking.
6. In what industries are patternmakers most likely to be employed?
7. Name several special hand planes used in patternmaking.
8. What is the name and the purpose of the special measuring rule used in patternwork? Why is it necessary?
9. Name five other special patternmaking tools.
10. List some special machine accessories which are useful in patternmaking.
11. What special supplies are needed?
12. What materials are used for patterns? What material is used the most?
13. Name the softwoods and the hardwoods which are especially adaptable for patterns.
14. Why is the northern Appalachian white pine one of the best woods for patterns?
15. Discuss the seasoning of pattern wood as it differs from ordinary lumber seasoning.
16. What benefits are derived from soaking pattern woods over long periods of time?
17. What types of plasters are used for patterns?
18. Explain the differences between the types of plasters.
19. What advantages do plastic patterns have over plaster or wood?
20. Discuss the importance of the new epoxy resins.

SECTION 26

CONDITIONING AND SHARPENING TOOLS

Unit 169 Maintaining Basic Hand Tools

169-1. A standard grinder can be used with special grinding attachments to sharpen most tools.

(Delta Power Tool Division, Rockwell Manufacturing Company)

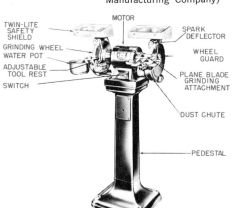

TWIN-LITE
SAFETY
SHIELD

MOTOR

SPARK
DEFLECTOR

GRINDING WHEEL
WATER POT

WHEEL
GUARD

ADJUSTABLE
TOOL REST

PLANE BLADE
GRINDING
ATTACHMENT

SWITCH

DUST CHUTE

PEDESTAL

Tools which are dull and improperly maintained cause poor workmanship, require expenditure of more energy in their use, and are unsafe. A worker must understand the proper use of tools and machines to know whether or not they are in an acceptable working condition. Tools naturally become dull in normal use. The safe, careful craftsman sharpens and conditions hand and machine tools when necessary.

Causes of Dulling

Some of the conditions leading to dull tools are improper care and use, improper adjustment, feeding too fast for cutter-head speed, and boards which bind or stick in a machine. Dust and grit on lumber also dull tools.

Dulling results from improper cutting angles on the cutting edges of tools. Cracks and chips appear when cutting edges are ground too thin and when the edges are overheated and burned during grinding or in use.

Tool Grinders

Two common grinders used in limited operations are the standard grinder (Fig. 169-1) and the small tool grinder (Fig. 169-2). Either can be mounted on a bench or on a pedestal. Many sizes and shapes of both the grinders and the grind wheels are produced for the various grinding operations. Specific recommendations should be obtained from their manufacturers when special sharpening and conditioning are required. Determine the correct speed for a particular size, shape, and type of wheel before it is mounted.

Observe the following safety precautions when operating any grinder:

1. Wear safety goggles when doing any grinding.

2. Keep all hoods and guards in place.

3. Keep the work rest adjusted close to the wheel to prevent the work from being caught between the rest and the wheel.

4. Avoid touching the moving wheel or the work being ground.

5. Tuck in all loose clothing so that it cannot be caught in the wheel.

6. Hold all work securely.

7. Occasionally cool the piece being ground. This prevents burning or annealing (softening) the metal. Water and kerosene are sometimes mixed for use as a coolant in tool grinders. This coolant does not rust the parts, and it cools the metal as the grinding operation is performed.

Determine the kind of metal being ground by the spark test. As tiny metal particles are thrown off by the abra-

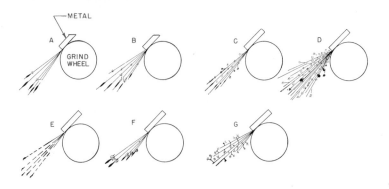

(Delta Power Tool Division, Rockwell Manufacturing Company)

169-3. The simple spark test helps determine the kind of metal. (**A**) Wrought iron: distinct torpedo spark; a few small radial sparks caused by carbon. (**B**) Mild steel: more radial sparks than wrought iron. (**C**) Tool steel: slight torpedo; good shower of radial sparks. (**D**) High-carbon steel: great number of radial sparks, igniting close to the wheel. (**E**) High-speed steel: dull, red, broken line; dewdrop at the end of line of sparks. (**F**) Cast iron: torpedo with feathery tail. (**G**) Manganese iron or steel: branching sparks from main line.

sive wheel, they combine with oxygen to form a spark. The sparks from different metals vary (Fig. 169-3). Test known kinds of metal to get a better idea of the index.

Three things should be observed when testing metals by grinding: (1) the **color** of the spark as it leaves the wheel and as it explodes, (2) the **shape** of the explosion as the metal particle ignites, and (3) the **distance** from the wheel at which the explosion occurs.

Plane Irons, Spokeshaves, and Wood Chisels

Plane irons, spokeshaves, and wood chisels should have **hollow-ground** (concave) bevels on their cutting edges. They enter the wood better and last longer. Grinders cut the steel fast and give this type of edge. These tools are sharpened with a 20- to 30-degree bevel, depending upon their use:

1. Push the tool straight into the grinding wheel lightly to remove all nicks (Fig. 169-4).

2. Adjust the tool rest, or chisel-grinding attachment, to the required angle to grind the bevel (Fig. 169-5).

3. Place the tool in the holder, and work it evenly across the wheel. See Fig. 169-1. If the attachment is not available and the tool rest does not adjust to the proper angle, hold the tool as shown in Fig. 169-6.

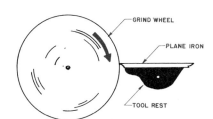

169-4. Nicks in a blade should be ground off before sharpening the blade. Push the blade straight into the wheel.

169-5. Adjust the tool rest to the proper angle for grinding blades.

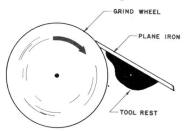

169-2. A special tool grinder helps to sharpen tools more accurately.

(Delta Power Tool Division, Rockwell Manufacturing Company)

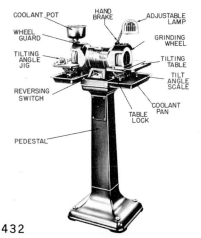

169-6. A steady hand is needed when a support is not available.

169-7. The bevel on plane irons for most cutting operations is twice as long as the plane-blade thickness.

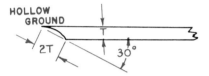

4. Continue grinding until a complete hollow-ground bevel is produced. Make the bevel twice the thickness of the blade to secure the 30-degree angle that is used for most cutting operations (Fig. 169-7). A 20-degree bevel can be used on softwood, but it crumbles when used on hardwood.

5. Grinding forms burrs on plane blades and chisels (Fig. 169-8), and they must be removed. Place the bevel on an oilstone with the heel of the bevel slightly raised (Fig. 169-9). Stroke it back and forth on the stone, pressing with both hands (Fig. 169-10). Lubricate the sharpening stone with thin oil or kerosene to float metal particles away so that they do not become embedded in the stone. Wipe the stone after using.

6. Turn the tool over and stroke the flat side lightly against the stone (Fig. 169-11). Alternate honing on the bevel and the back until the burr is removed.

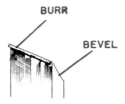

(Delta Power Tool Division, Rockwell Manufacturing Company)

169-8. A burr is formed on the cutting edges of plane irons and chisels when grinding.

169-9. Honing the bevel on an oilstone helps to remove the burr.

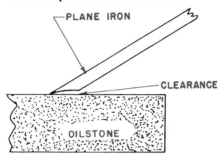

Honing produces a small second bevel on the cutting edge and gives a clean edge. As the tool becomes dull through use, additional whetting and honing are necessary. Eventually the second bevel becomes too long; the original one begins to round (Fig. 169-12) and does not cut well. The tool should then be reground.

Scrapers

Scrapers smooth a wood surface after planing. If properly sharpened, they will remove a fine shaving. They should be tilted away from the worker and pushed, or tilted toward the worker and pulled. To sharpen an edge:

1. Place the scraper in a vise, and file the edge *flat* (Fig. 169-13). Draw-filing is also used to square the edge. For fast cutting, file a bevel of about 30 degrees, similar to that on the chisel or plane iron.

(Delta Power Tool Division, Rockwell Manufacturing Company)

169-10. Hold the plane iron or chisel in both hands when honing.

2. Check the edge against a flat, smooth surface. (A concave edge causes the scraper to leave scratches on the work.)

3. Lay the scraper on an oilstone. Hone the edge, or edges (if filed flat), until the corners are absolutely square.

4. Replace the scraper in a vise. Run a burnisher firmly over the filed edge at an angle of approximately 15 degrees to press the steel out from the edge (Fig. 169-14).

169-11. Honing the flat side of blades helps to remove the burr and sharpens a keen edge.

(Delta Power Tool Division, Rockwell Manufacturing Company)

433

(Delta Power Tool Division, Rockwell Manufacturing Company)

169-12. After blades are honed several times, they must be reground to remove the long honed bevel.

5. Repeat the operations at about 5 to 8 degrees to bend the hook for the cutting edge or edges (Fig. 169-15).

Auger and Wood Bits

Auger and wood bits are sharpened with the small, half-round file (Fig. 169-16A), the auger-bit file (Fig. 169-16B), and a specially shaped honing stone. A small, square file or a triangular one can also be used.

Touch-up filing on bits is done through the throat of the bit (Fig. 169-17A). A half-round file is used if the throat is rounded; the auger-bit file is used if the throat is open. The cutting lip of the wood bit should be filed from the lower side. Maintain the original bevel.

169-13. File the edges of a hand scraper square.

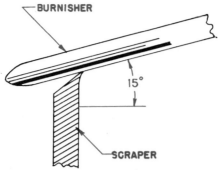

169-14. The hook is turned by beginning with the burnisher at an angle of 15 degrees to the bevel.

169-15. Turn the burr or hook on both edges of a scraper which has been filed square; turn it on one edge for bevels.

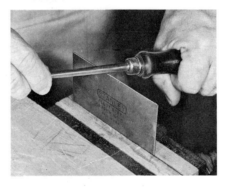

Spurs on bits are *always* sharpened on the inside (Fig. 169-17B). The top edge of the wood bit is filed as shown in Fig. 169-18. File only the upper edge on wood auger bits (Fig. 169-19).

Twist Drills

The main parts of the twist drill are the **point,** the **body,** and the **shank.** Study the diagrams in Figs. 169-20 and 169-21. The angle across the web (center) on the point (Fig. 169-20A) has a close relationship to the lip clearance (Fig. 169-20B and C). The angle of the point and the lengths of the cutting lips must be equal (Fig. 169-20D).

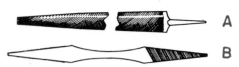

(Delta Power Tool Division, Rockwell Manufacturing Company)

169-16. Files for sharpening bits are (A) the half round, and (B) the auger bit.

169-17. (A) Touch up the cutting edge of a bit by filing through the throat; (B) spurs on wood bits are always filed on the inside.

(Delta Power Tool Division, Rockwell Manufacturing Company)

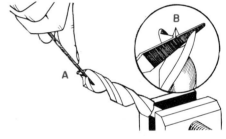

To sharpen a twist drill:

1. Square the surface of the grind wheel with a grindstone dresser. Place the tool rest close to the wheel.

2. Firmly grasp the end of the twist drill near the point with the tips of the fingers of your right hand. Lay your middle finger on the tool rest to act as a fulcrum, or pivot point.

3. Hold the shank of the drill with your left hand.

4. Move the drill shank until the cutting lip is horizontal with the tool rest and parallel with the face of the grinding wheel. The twist drill will be pointed at an angle toward the wheel.

5. Move the drill slowly toward the wheel until it touches.

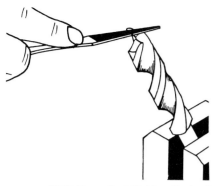

(Delta Power Tool Division, Rockwell Manufacturing Company)

169-18. The top edges of twist-drill-pattern wood bits are easily filed when they are held in a vise.

169-19. File only upper edge of auger-bit cutters (A), and inside of spurs (B).

(The Irwin Auger Bit Company)

A   B

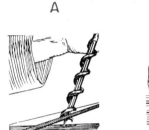

6. Use the middle finger of your right hand as a pivot. Push the shank of the drill slightly downward with your left hand. *Do not roll the drill.*

7. Continue grinding each cutting lip and clearance surface until the properly ground point is formed.

8. Check the point for accuracy with a drill-grinding gauge. If the shank of the drill is pushed downward too much, the opposite cutting-lip clearance will be ground and require regrinding.

Handsaws

The two types of handsaws are **crosscut** (for sawing across wood grain) and **rip** (for cutting with the grain). In the manufacturing process,

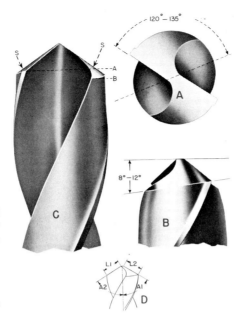

(The Cleveland Twist Drill Company)

169-20. Parts and standard angles of twist drills: (A) proper angle of web line, (B) lip-clearance angle at the circumference of the drill, (C) heel line at B is lower than the cutting-lip line at A, and (D) equal angles and equal lengths of cutting lips.

handsaws are cut to shape and toothed (Fig. 169-22), ground (Fig. 169-23), and polished (Fig. 169-24) in preparation for proper setting and sharpening.

In small industrial operations, and in some of the larger school shops, the saw is retoothed with a special machine (Fig. 169-25) and is filed in an automatic filer (Fig. 169-26). It can also be set and filed by hand.

Handsaw filing should be done with a triangular, tapered file. Saws with 4½ to 6 points per inch should be filed with a 7-inch slim taper file. Those having 7 or 8 points per inch are filed with a 6-inch taper file, and those with 10 points per inch are filed with a 5-inch slim taper file. Use a 5-inch extra-slim taper file on 11 or 12 point saws.

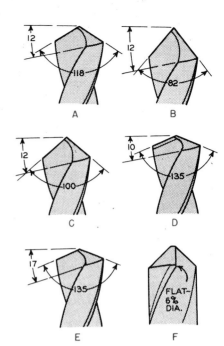

(Delta Power Tool Division, Rockwell Manufacturing Company)

169-21. Points of drills vary for drilling different materials. (A) Standard: satisfactory for all materials, specifically for soft to medium steel. (B) Sharp: for wood, thermoplastics, high-silicon aluminum; 60-degree angle also used. (C) Medium: high-silicon aluminum, hard copper, cast iron, hard rubber, and fiber. (D) Blunt: all very hard steels; lips should be ground to zero rake. (E) Blunt: all soft-to-medium aluminum alloys; good for drilling in very thin sheets. (F) Zero rake: soft-to-medium brass, copper, most plastics, and very hard steels.

A number showing the points per inch is usually stamped below the handle on the heel (left rear) of the saw. If no number is there, lay a rule along the teeth with an inch mark on one saw point. Begin counting with this point. Continue to a point nearest the next inch mark to find the number of saw points per inch. There is always one less tooth than there are points per inch.

(H. K. Porter Company)

169-22. Handsaw toothing at the factory.

(Foley Manufacturing Company)

169-25. Handsaws can be retoothed with special machines.

169-27. Jointing the teeth of a handsaw with a flat file.

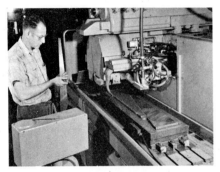

(H. K. Porter Company)

169-23. Handsaw grinding at the factory.

To sharpen a crosscut handsaw:

1. Place the saw in a special saw clamp or between two boards in a vise so that the teeth are slightly exposed.

2. Joint the teeth to make them equal in height by laying a common, fine file (an 8-inch mill file is suggested) flat on the teeth and filing lightly (Fig. 169-27).

3. File straight across the gullets if they are not equal in depth. The height of teeth, depth of gullets, and fronts and backs of teeth must have the same shape and angle to cut accurately.

4. Remove the saw carefully from the vise. Set the teeth with a saw set

(Figs. 169-28 and 169-29). The upper part of the first saw tooth is set in one direction; the next, in the opposite direction.

5. Replace the saw in the vise with the saw handle to the right.

6. The teeth should be filed as shown in Fig. 169-30A, *B*, and *C*.

Hand ripsaws are filed in the same way except that there is no bevel on the teeth. The gullets are filed straight across. See Fig. 169-30D. File every second gullet and turn the saw around. If it is filed from one side only, the saw will tend to pull to one side when ripping a line.

169-24. Handsaw polishing at the factory.

(H. K. Porter Company)

169-26. Automatic saw filers sharpen saws very accurately.

(Foley Manufacturing Company)

169-28. Typical pistol-grip handsaw set.

(Millers Falls)

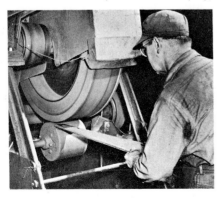

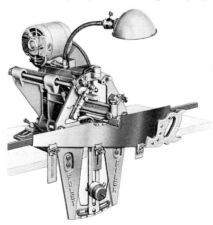

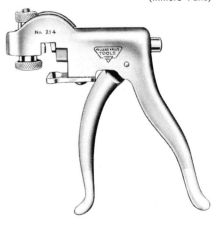

169-29.   Setting saw teeth.

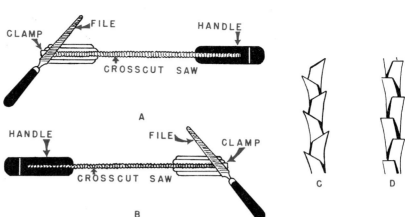

169-30.   The position of the file for sharpening, and final teeth appearance: (A) file in position, left; (B) file in position, right; (C) crosscut teeth, and (D) ripsaw teeth.

Unit 170 Sharpening Circular Saw Blades

The general classes of circular saw blades are (1) crosscut, (2) rip, and (3) combination (which is used for both purposes). Refer to Unit 31, "Circular Saw Blades and Accessories." A close view of the different shapes of teeth is also shown in Unit 31. A dado head is a combination set of saws and chippers or cutters.

Crosscut Blades

Crosscut saw blades are made for both rough and smooth cutting. Some of the various types of crosscut teeth are shown in Fig. 170-1. True rim travel, proper setting, and taper grinding give the smoothness of cut required and desired.

Side clearance helps produce smooth cuts, and coarse and fine teeth are set before grinding tapers (Fig. 170-2). More efficient cuts are made when every fifth tooth is a **raker** type. This cuts the V left by the other teeth, speeds the cutting, and reduces friction (Fig. 170-3). Some raker-tooth blades for fine, smooth crosscutting are not set.

Large and small saws are condi-

tioned (prepared) by the manufacturer on precision machines (Figs. 170-4 and 170-5). Very accurate work is required to recondition saws by hand.

Ripsaw Blades

The teeth of ripsaws are shaped like a group of small wood chisels. The saw is used to cut wood in the direction of the grain. Each ripsaw tooth must be strong and have an adequate back clearance. The swaged ripsaw tooth has a real chisel shape and cuts a flat kerf (Fig. 170-6A). The set ripsaw tooth leaves a slight V notch in the center of the kerf, or cut (Fig. 170-6B). If a rip tooth is set, it should be set on a setting stake close to the tip (Fig. 170-6C).

Combination Saw Blades

The combination saw is usually made up of sections of four cutting teeth and one raker. The raker tooth in each section is filed $\frac{1}{64}$ to $\frac{1}{32}$ inch shorter than the cutting teeth to improve cutting and to reduce the chip load in the cut.

170-1.   Various angles and shapes are used on crosscut circular saw teeth: (A) rough work; (B) fine, small work where smoothness is not essential; (C) saw drags and dulls quickly, so is used where the material passes under the saw; (D) desirable for most large-tooth saws; (E) desirable for most small-tooth saws; (F) adapted for smooth-cutting saws.

(E. C. Atkins and Company)

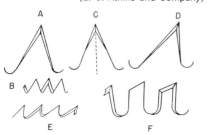

437

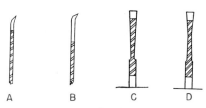

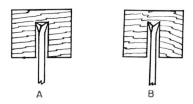

(E. C. Atkins and Company)

170-2. Proper setting and taper grinding give a smoother cutting action: (A) set for coarse teeth, (B) set for fine teeth, (C) even-taper grinding to collar for slow cutting, (D) abrupt-taper grinding for fast work.

(H. K. Porter Company)

170-4. Large circular saws are conditioned on precision machines.

(E. C. Atkins and Company)

170-6. The effect of swaged and set teeth on circular saws: (A) swaged tooth, (B) set tooth, (C) rip tooth set close to the tip.

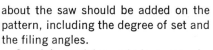

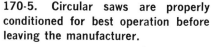

(E. C. Atkins and Company)

170-3. Saws with raker teeth (A) clean the V from the saw kerf.

The saw filer can be used to sharpen a combination saw (Fig. 170-7). The saw should be checked for proper layout of the shape and angle of the teeth. A layout for one form of combination saw is shown in Fig. 170-8.

Refitting and Conditioning Circular Saws

Proper cutting and accuracy of circular saws is assured only when the original manufactured shape of the teeth is maintained. The saw must be round, and each tooth must be even in length and sharpness and swaged or set evenly to operate properly. Some of the factors to consider in purchasing, using, and conditioning circular saw blades are (1) size, (2) gauge, (3) hole size, (4) speed of use, (5) number of teeth, (6) type of set, (7) flat or hollow grind, and (8) general classification.

An accurate pattern of the original teeth should be made immediately after a saw is purchased. All information

about the saw should be added on the pattern, including the degree of set and the filing angles.

Special precision grinders may be needed to **gum,** or **grind,** special saws with carbide-tip teeth (Fig. 170-9). The following general procedure will assist in refitting circular saws by hand:

1. Disconnect the electric power to the table saw. Reverse the saw on the arbor or mandrel. Lower the blade below the saw table.

2. Place an oilstone or a discarded fine grinding wheel flat over the saw.

170-5. Circular saws are properly conditioned for best operation before leaving the manufacturer.

(H. K. Porter Company)

Prepare for jointing by raising the saw until it touches the stone lightly (Fig. 170-10A).

3. Turn the saw by hand in its regular direction to joint (grind) the teeth. Joint them only enough to level them.

4. Hold a pencil to the saw as it is turned by hand to show the bottom of the gullets (Fig. 170-10B). File or grind (gum) to the line, and maintain the original shape of the teeth. This operation is called **gumming** and is necessary only after the saw has had several previous filings.

170-7. Bench saw filers can be used to file combination saw teeth.

(Foley Manufacturing Company)

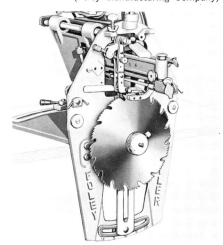

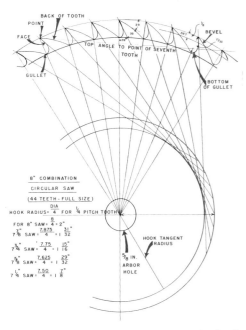

170-8.   The layout for reconditioning a combination circular saw blade.

170-9.   A precision carbide saw grinder is needed to assure accurate conditioning of carbide-tip saw teeth.

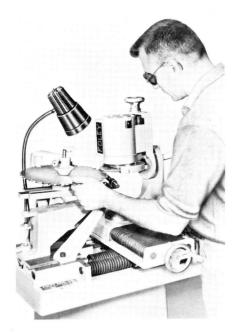

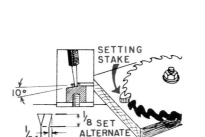

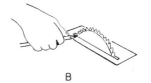

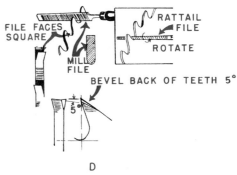

170-10.   Conditioning saw blades: (A) jointing, (B) mark for gumming (grinding gullets), (C) setting, (D) filing.

5. Set alternate teeth right and left with a hand set or with a suitable setting stake (Fig. 170-10C). Do not exceed the amount of set specified for the particular saw. Raker teeth of flat-ground combination saws should not be set. Teeth and rakers of hollow-ground combination saws should not be set.

6. Place the saw in a saw clamp, and use a mill file to file the face of the teeth straight across for the ripsaw (Fig. 170-10D). Bevels on the back of some combination saw teeth, crosscut saw teeth, and other types must be filed according to specifications.

7. Clean and smooth the gullets with a rat-tail (round) file (Fig. 170-10D). Sharp corners and nicks in gullets cause cracks to form in the saw.

Reconditioning the Dado Head

The two saws and several chippers or cutters comprising the dado head are filed several times before refitting or reconditioning is needed. Count the file strokes and use an even pressure on the file for each cutting tooth (spur) or raker. A section of the outside cutter is shown in Fig. 170-11.

Follow this suggested procedure:

1. Reverse the outside cutters on the saw arbor. Joint the cutting teeth or spurs by turning the saw arbor (Fig. 170-12A).

2. Joint rakers $\frac{1}{64}$ inch less than spurs. Use a crosswise motion of the oilstone. Wrap paper around the stone to protect the saw table. Joint inside cutters at the same setting (Fig. 170-12B).

3. Place an outside cutter on the setting stake and set the spurs only. Set all spurs in one group in one direction (Fig. 170-12C); joint outside cutters lightly on the side to equalize set.

4. Put outside cutter in a saw clamp. File spurs with a square file to original angle of the tooth (Fig. 170-12D).

5. File the rakers square across the top and face, using a mill file (Fig. 170-12E).

6. Place each inside cutter in the saw clamp. File the top of the teeth (Fig. 170-12F). Do not file the face.

When each cutter has been correctly filed, the dado cut will be smooth and even. Uneven cutters and lack of set will cause the wood edges and the cutters to burn (Fig. 170-12G).

439

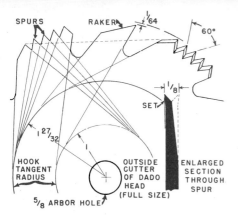

(Delta Power Tool Division, Rockwell Manufacturing Company)

170-11. A section of the dado-head saw.

170-12. Conditioning the dado head: (*A*) jointing spurs, (*B*) jointing rakers, (*C*) setting spurs, (*D*) filing spurs, (*E*) filing rakers, (*F*) filing inside cutters or chippers, (*G*) examples of even and uneven cut of cutters.

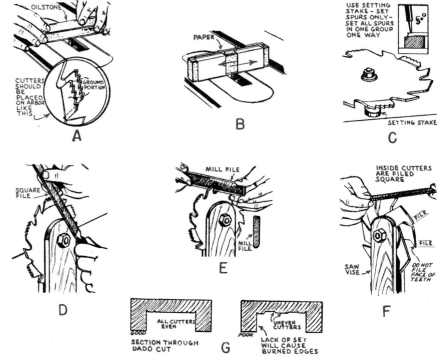

(Delta Power Tool Division, Rockwell Manufacturing Company)

Unit 171 Reconditioning Jointer and Planer Knives

171-1. Honing or whetting jointer knives.

(Delta Power Tool Division, Rockwell Manufacturing Company)

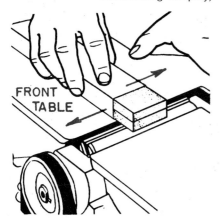

Jointer and planer knives (blades) will cut very smooth surfaces when properly sharpened and installed in the machines. Dull knives cause the jointer to chatter and make more noise.

Special grinding attachments are available to grind jointer and planer knives without removing them from the machines. The same grinding attachments, or other special accessories, are equipped for honing (whetting) and jointing knives. Detailed instructions are included with each accessory. When such equipment is not available, sharpening can be done by hand honing, jointing and honing, or grinding and honing.

Honing Jointer Knives

To hone knives:

1. Cover most of a fine oilstone with paper so that it will not mark the table.

2. Place the stone on the front (infeed) jointer table, as shown in Figs. 171-1 and 171-2.

3. Turn the cutter head until the stone is flat on the bevel of the knife. The stone will face each knife.

4. Clamp the head in place.

5. Hone (whet) the knife by stroking the stone lengthwise with the blade. Use the same number of strokes for each knife blade. Uneven honing causes blades to be different lengths.

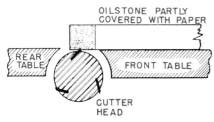

(Delta Power Tool Division, Rockwell Manufacturing Company)

171-2. Placement of the oilstone for whetting.

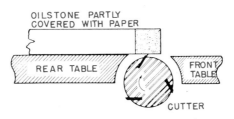

(Delta Power Tool Division, Rockwell Manufacturing Company)

171-4. Placing the oilstone for jointing.

(Delta Power Tool Division, Rockwell Manufacturing Company)

171-7. A cup wheel can be used on the drill press for sharpening jointer knives.

Jointing Jointer Knives

Knife jointing can be done with a special hand-knife jointer that contains an oilstone or with the stone held in the hand. Special care is needed in hand jointing because the cutter head is revolving. Thorough understanding of the operation and the machine is necessary:

1. Cover most of the oilstone with paper. Place it on the rear (outfeed) table (Figs. 171-3 and 171-4).

2. Lower the rear table until the stone barely touches the knives as the cutter head is turned slowly by hand.

3. Remove the jointer fence, if necessary. Attach a stop block to the front table. See Fig. 171-3. The cutters should not strike the block.

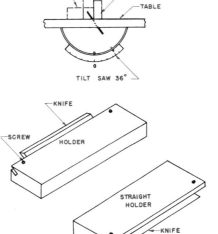

171-5. A jig can be made to hold jointer knives for sharpening.

4. Pick up the stone. Start the machine.

5. Hold the stone securely. Slowly place it on the rear table and against the stop block until it barely touches the rotating knives.

6. Move the oilstone along the stop block slowly until the full length of all the knives is competely jointed. All knives should be exactly even and level with the rear table.

7. Stop the machine. Hone the knives.

Grinding Jointer and Planer Knives

Jointer and planer knives are usually ground at an angle of 35 to 36 de-

171-3. Jointing the knives.

(Delta Power Tool Division, Rockwell Manufacturing Company)

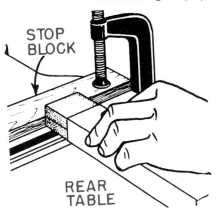

171-6. Using a hand-made jig to hold jointer knives for sharpening.

(Delta Power Tool Division, Rockwell Manufacturing Company)

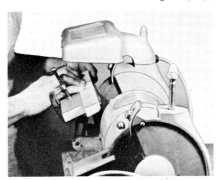

171-8. The table saw can be rigged for use as a jointer knife grinder.

(Delta Power Tool Division, Rockwell Manufacturing Company)

441

grees. The angle can be varied according to the type and size of machine, the blade thickness, and the predominant type of soft- or hardwood to be planed. When a grinding attachment is not available, the knives can be ground by hand. Grinding is always done dry.

1. Make a knife-holding block. Saw a kerf (cut) through a piece of hardwood to fit the thickness of the blade snugly (Fig. 171-5). Saw with the block in either position shown, depending upon the method used for grinding.

2. Add a flat-head wood screw at the end of the knife to hold the blade securely. The screwhead should be flush (even) with the wood surface.

3. Adjust the tool rest of the grinder to the required angle.

4. Attach a guide block squarely across the grind wheel to ensure a straight cut on the knife (Fig. 171-6).

5. Make a single, *light* cut on *each* of the knives. Heavy cuts on high-speed steel will invariably burn the knife and ruin it.

6. Paste a strip of paper along the edge of the holding block with rubber cement. The paper sets the next light cut without any change of the guide block.

7. Make several cuts to give each knife the proper cutting edge.

8. Replace the knives in the machine. Hone them.

A cup wheel mounted on a drill press (Fig. 171-7), a grind wheel on a table saw (Fig. 171-8), or a disk sander can sharpen knives.

Unit 172 Sharpening Band Saw Blades

The band saw was invented in France and patented in England around 1808. Developments have been continuous, resulting in saws of various lengths, widths, and thicknesses. They are sharpened and set by hand or with special filers (Fig. 172-1).

Types of Band Saw Teeth and Sets

There are three kinds of teeth and sets on band saws: (1) regular tooth, (2) skip tooth, and (3) hook tooth. The regular tooth is the oldest type; it is for general cutting. Teeth are set alternately right and left. Other sets are the raker and the wavy (Fig. 172-2).

The **raker set** is common on all three kinds of teeth. Two teeth are set alternately right and left, followed by a straight raker tooth which reduces the chip load and improves cutting.

Wavy-set saws reduce saw breakage, eliminate teeth stripping, and completely remove chips for faster cutting to close tolerances. Each fourth tooth is straight, and the next three are set alternately to the right and left.

Hook-tooth and skip-tooth blades (Figs. 172-3 and 172-4) are slightly different. The hook tooth has more hook and rake. Skip-tooth saws remain sharp until they are worn out.

Hand-sharpening Mounted Band Saws

Light filing and touching up are easier when the blade is reversed on the wheels of the band saw machine, with the teeth pointing upward (Fig. 172-5). A 6-inch extra-slim taper file is recommended for use on saws having eight points (seven teeth) per inch or finer; a 7-inch extra-slim taper file for saws with six and seven points per inch; a 7-inch slim taper file for a five-point saw; and 8- and 10-inch slim taper files for four- and three-point saws.

To hand-sharpen:

1. Use your left index finger as a guide. File every other tooth lightly straight across.

2. Reverse the procedure, and file alternate teeth.

3. Tilt the file slightly to obtain a hook in the teeth (Fig. 172-6).

Refitting Unmounted Band Saws by Hand

An automatic filing machine (Fig. 172-7) makes band saw sharpening easy. When one is not available, the band saw blade may be sharpened by hand:

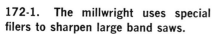

172-1. The millwright uses special filers to sharpen large band saws.

(Weyerhaeuser Timber Company)

RAKER SET

WAVY SET

172-2. Regular band saw teeth with a raker and a wavy set.

(Paxton Equipment and Supply Company)

172-6. A slight hook is obtained on band saw blades by tilting the file slightly during sharpening.

(Delta Power Tool Division, Rockwell Manufacturing Company)

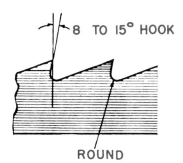

8 TO 15° HOOK

ROUND

RAKER SET

172-3. The hook-tooth band saw blade with a raker set.

(Paxton Equipment and Supply Company)

RAKER SET

172-7. An automatic filer is valuable in sharpening band and other saws.

(Foley Manufacturing Company)

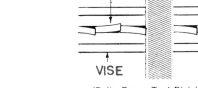

172-4. A raker set on a skip-tooth band saw blade.

(Paxton Equipment and Supply Company)

RAKER SET

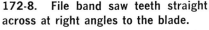

SAW   FILE

VISE

(Delta Power Tool Division, Rockwell Manufacturing Company)

172-8. File band saw teeth straight across at right angles to the blade.

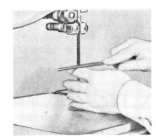

172-5. Light filing of a band saw blade is easily done by reversing the saw on the wheels.

(Delta Power Tool Division, Rockwell Manufacturing Company)

172-9. Setting a band saw is easily done with an automatic band saw setter.

(Foley Manufacturing Company)

1. Place the saw on a long bench with the entire length supported on the same level.

2. Use a vise or a clamp to hold about 40 to 50 teeth at once.

3. Joint each section of teeth. Make them uniform height; run a mill file lightly over the tops. See Fig. 169-27.

4. Select the correct file for the particular number of teeth per inch.

5. Hold the file in a horizontal position. File the teeth straight across at right angles to the blade (Fig. 172-8). Use an even pressure, and file each tooth the same. Lift the file on each back stroke.

When setting is necessary, do it before the teeth are filed. Setting can be done with an automatic band saw setter (Fig. 172-9) or with a pistol-grip saw set. See Fig. 169-28. For straight-line cutting, the least set possible is best. In curved cutting, sufficient set is needed to clear the blade in the cut.

443

Unit 173 Sharpening Shaper and Router Cutters

Two types of shaper cutters can do most work. One is the cutter that consists of two separate knives mounted between two specially grooved collars. The other type, and the safest, is the one-piece, two- or three-winged cutter. See Unit 105, "Shaper Cutters, Collars, and Spindles." The one-piece cutter is available for shapers and routers. Molding heads for the table saw or other machines are occasionally used for shaping.

Cutters can be machined and ground from solid stock, but they are usually obtained from manufacturers.

These are already formed and sharpened for use. After cutters become dull, they must be resharpened. Grinding and whetting are most successful when the correct angles and bevels are known.

Rake Angle on Cutters

The **rake angle** of a cutter determines its shape and cutting action. The length of a cutter working at an angle must be greater than if the cutter is worked straight across the wood (Fig. 173-1). Rake angles are used on all shaper cutters. They are greatest when mounted in a molding head, as compared to other types of cutters used on the shaper or router (Fig. 173-2). The greater the rake angle, the greater the difference should be between the shape of the knife and the molding it cuts.

Bevels on Cutters

Bevels on the edges of shaper cutters vary from 30 to 45 degrees. A bevel which provides clearance at one

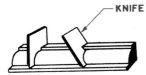

173-1. Cutters operating at an angle to the work must be longer and have more clearance on the cutting edge than cutters which operate straight across.

173-2. Rake angles of cutters used in a molding head are greater than the three-wing, or loose, cutters used on shapers.

(Delta Power Tool Division, Rockwell Manufacturing Company)

173-3. Different clearance angles are required for cutters used on different cutting circles.

(Delta Power Tool Division, Rockwell Manufacturing Company)

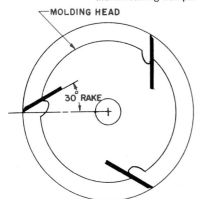

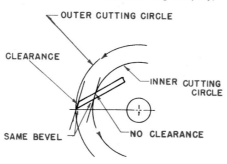

173-4. More bevel is put on inner edges of factory-sharpened cutters.

(Delta Power Tool Division, Rockwell Manufacturing Company)

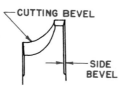

173-5. Hone only the flat side on factory-sharpened shaper cutters.

444

cutting circle may not give clearance on a smaller one (Fig. 173-3).

The factory-sharpened cutter has the most bevel at the inner edges of the knife (Fig. 173-4). This maintains the exact, even amount of clearance. Side bevels require only a minimum angle to provide necessary clearance.

Grinding Shaper Cutters

A silicon carbide stick or a diamond-wheel dresser is used to form desired shapes on the edges of grinding wheels used to grind cutters. Regular grinders are used, or the cutter can be mounted on a special spindle in the machine. It can then be ground with a shaped wheel on a tool post grinder.

Using either method, the cutter and the grind wheel are positioned so that the rake angle and the bevel on each wing of the cutter are ground exactly the same. In addition, stops, guides, and indexing pins are used to grind accurately.

Sharpening Knives

Factory-ground shaper knives should be sharpened by honing the flat side of the cutting edge (Fig. 173-5). The involute (coiled) bevel retains the same shape regardless of the amount of honing.

Straight bevels can be resharpened in the same manner, and the bevel itself can be honed. No grinding or honing should be done on cutters with involute or curved bevels.

DISCUSSION TOPICS

1. Name several conditions which cause dull tools.
2. What is the effect on a tool when its cutting edges have been ground too thin?
3. List several personal safety precautions to observe when sharpening tools on a grinder.
4. Name three tools which are sharpened with approximately the same angle on the cutting edge and in about the same way.
5. What effect does honing have on the plane-iron blade?
6. What advantage is there in sharpening a flat hand scraper straight on the edge, rather than beveling it?
7. Name two kinds of files needed to sharpen wood and auger bits.
8. List the three main parts of the twist drill.
9. If a saw is rated as an eight-point crosscut saw, how many teeth per inch does it have?
10. Where is the point number stamped on most handsaws?
11. Describe the differences between filing hand crosscut and ripsaws.
12. Name the three general classes of circular saw blades.
13. What are the purposes of raker teeth on a circular saw blade?
14. Describe the difference between a swaged tooth and a set tooth on a saw blade.
15. What is the purpose of jointing circular saw teeth? Of gumming? Of setting or swaging?
16. Why is it not necessary to set the teeth or rakers of hollow-ground combination saws?
17. What is the probable result when sharp corners are filed in the bottoms of gullets?
18. Name the two main sets or parts of the dado head.
19. What are cutting teeth called on the saw of a dado head?
20. Why are the chippers placed between saws when using the dado head?
21. How can sound indicate when planer and jointer knives are dull?
22. On which table of the jointer is the oilstone placed when honing the knives? On which table is it placed when jointing?
23. What is the purpose of the stop block when jointing jointer knives by hand?
24. At what angle are jointer and planer knives usually ground?
25. What three machines can be used to grind jointer and planer knives by hand?
26. Where was the band saw invented? Where was it patented? In about what year was it patented?
27. What are the three kinds of teeth and sets on band saw blades?
28. Of what special advantage is the wavy set in a band saw blade?
29. What type of band saw blade is used until dull and then thrown away?
30. How can a band saw blade be filed lightly while on the wheels?
31. At what angle is the file held in relation to the band saw blade when filing?
32. What are the two types of shaper cutters for ordinary use?
33. Which type of cutter is the safest? Why?
34. What is the purpose of the rake angle on a shaper or router cutter?
35. When bevels are used to give clearance to shaper-cutter edges, what is the range of angles used?
36. What kind of material or tool is used to shape grinding wheels for grinding shaper and router cutters?
37. How are factory-ground shaper and router cutters best sharpened?

SECTION PROJECT 1
27

stereo cabinet

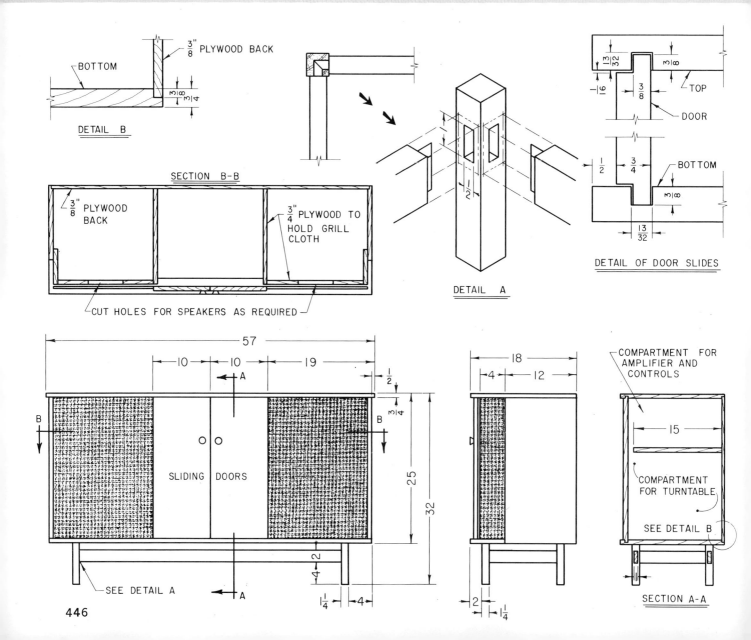

$\frac{3}{8}"$ PLYWOOD BACK

BOTTOM

$\frac{3}{8}$

$\frac{3}{4}$

DETAIL B

SECTION B-B

$\frac{3}{8}"$ PLYWOOD BACK

$\frac{3}{4}"$ PLYWOOD TO HOLD GRILL CLOTH

CUT HOLES FOR SPEAKERS AS REQUIRED

$\frac{1}{2}$

DETAIL A

$\frac{13}{32}$ $\frac{3}{8}$

$\frac{1}{16}$ $\frac{3}{8}$ TOP

DOOR

$\frac{1}{2}$ $\frac{3}{4}$ BOTTOM

$\frac{3}{8}$

$\frac{13}{32}$

DETAIL OF DOOR SLIDES

57

10   10   19 $\frac{1}{2}$

$\frac{3}{4}$

B   A   B

SLIDING DOORS

25

32

SEE DETAIL A   A

$\frac{4}{2}$

$1\frac{1}{4}$ 4

18

4   12

2
$1\frac{1}{4}$

COMPARTMENT FOR AMPLIFIER AND CONTROLS

15

COMPARTMENT FOR TURNTABLE

SEE DETAIL B

SECTION A-A

PROJECT 2

wall components

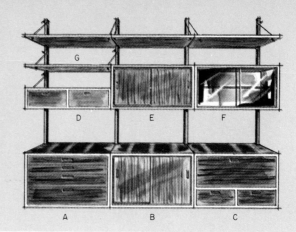

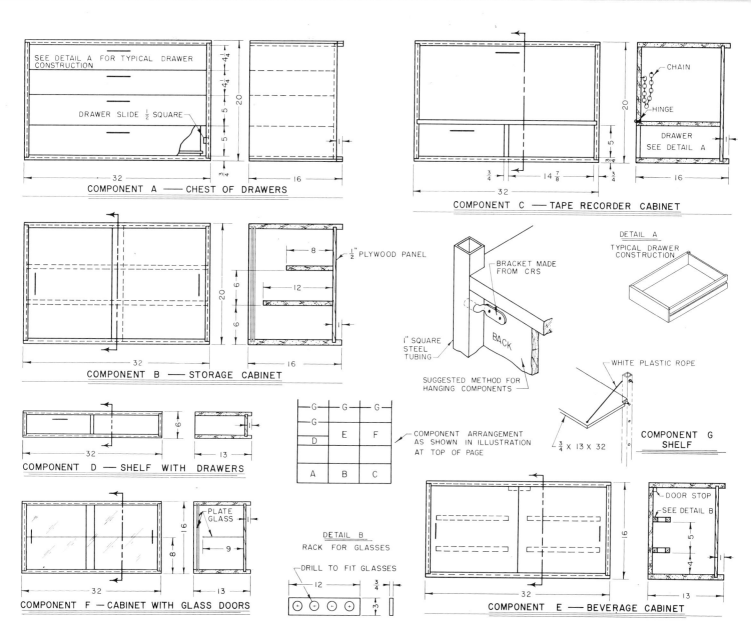

COMPONENT A — CHEST OF DRAWERS

SEE DETAIL A FOR TYPICAL DRAWER CONSTRUCTION

DRAWER SLIDE ½ SQUARE

$4\frac{1}{4}$ $4\frac{1}{4}$ 5 5 5 20 $\frac{3}{4}$ 32 16 1

COMPONENT C — TAPE RECORDER CABINET

CHAIN

HINGE

DRAWER SEE DETAIL A

20 5 $\frac{3}{4}$ $\frac{3}{4}$ $14\frac{7}{8}$ $\frac{3}{4}$ 32 16 1

COMPONENT B — STORAGE CABINET

8 ½" PLYWOOD PANEL 12 6 6 6 20 32 16 1

DETAIL A

TYPICAL DRAWER CONSTRUCTION

BRACKET MADE FROM CRS

BACK

1" SQUARE STEEL TUBING

SUGGESTED METHOD FOR HANGING COMPONENTS

WHITE PLASTIC ROPE

$\frac{3}{4}$ X 13 X 32

COMPONENT G SHELF

COMPONENT D — SHELF WITH DRAWERS

6 32 13 1

G	G	G
G		
D	E	F
A	B	C

COMPONENT ARRANGEMENT AS SHOWN IN ILLUSTRATION AT TOP OF PAGE

COMPONENT F — CABINET WITH GLASS DOORS

PLATE GLASS 16 8 9 32 13 1

DETAIL B

RACK FOR GLASSES

DRILL TO FIT GLASSES

12 $\frac{3}{4}$ 3

COMPONENT E — BEVERAGE CABINET

DOOR STOP

SEE DETAIL B

16 5 4 32 13 1

PROJECT 3

pepper mill and salt shakers

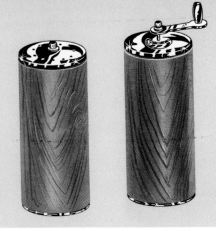

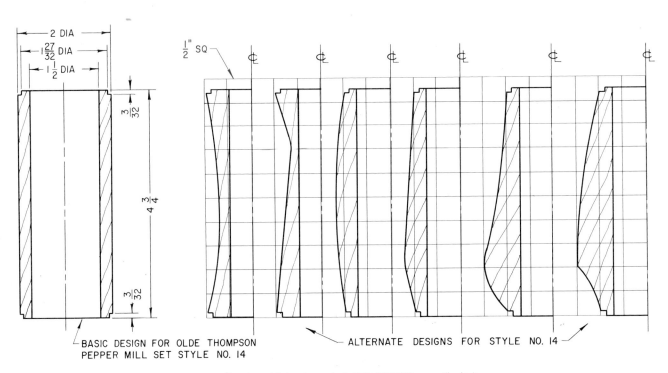

2 DIA

1 27/32 DIA

1 1/2 DIA

1/2" SQ

3/32

4 3/4

3/32

BASIC DESIGN FOR OLDE THOMPSON
PEPPER MILL SET STYLE NO. 14

ALTERNATE DESIGNS FOR STYLE NO. 14

Dimensions and designs given are for the OLDE THOMPSON pepper mill and salt
shaker parts manufactured by The George S. Thompson Corporation - 727 South
Monterey Pass Road, Monterey Park, California.

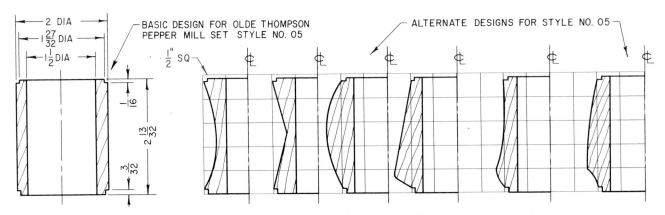

2 DIA

1 27/32 DIA

1 1/2 DIA

BASIC DESIGN FOR OLDE THOMPSON
PEPPER MILL SET STYLE NO. 05

ALTERNATE DESIGNS FOR STYLE NO. 05

1/2" SQ

1/16

2 13/32

3/32

PROJECT 4

chest

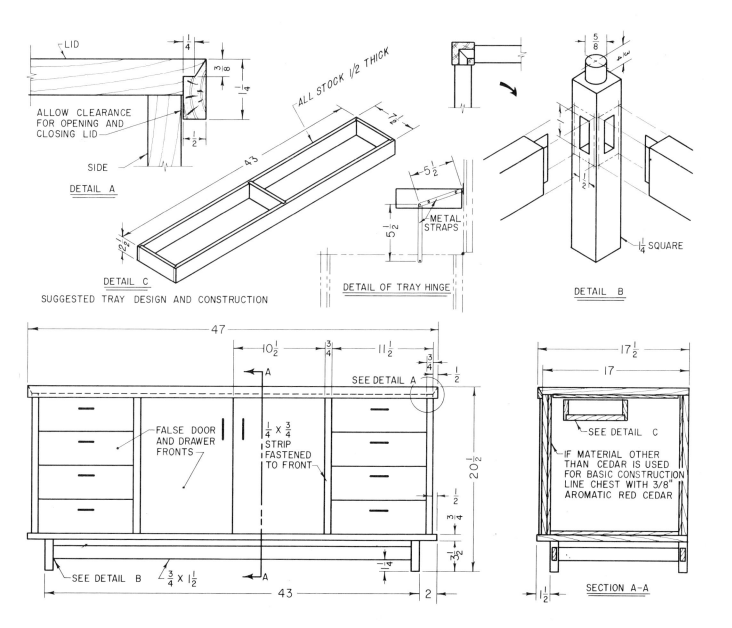

LID

ALLOW CLEARANCE
FOR OPENING AND
CLOSING LID

SIDE

$\frac{1}{4}$

$\frac{3}{8}$

$1\frac{1}{4}$

$\frac{1}{2}$

DETAIL A

ALL STOCK 1/2 THICK

43

$2\frac{1}{2}$

$2\frac{1}{2}$

DETAIL C

SUGGESTED TRAY DESIGN AND CONSTRUCTION

$5\frac{1}{2}$

$5\frac{1}{2}$

METAL
STRAPS

DETAIL OF TRAY HINGE

$\frac{5}{8}$

$\frac{3}{4}$

$\frac{1}{2}$

$\frac{1}{4}$ SQUARE

DETAIL B

47

$10\frac{1}{2}$

$\frac{3}{4}$

$11\frac{1}{2}$

$\frac{3}{4}$

$\frac{1}{2}$

A

SEE DETAIL A

FALSE DOOR
AND DRAWER
FRONTS

$\frac{1}{4} \times \frac{3}{4}$
STRIP
FASTENED
TO FRONT

$20\frac{1}{2}$

$\frac{1}{2}$

$3\frac{3}{4}$

$3\frac{1}{2}$

$\frac{1}{4}$

SEE DETAIL B

$\frac{3}{4} \times 1\frac{1}{2}$

A

43

2

$17\frac{1}{2}$

17

SEE DETAIL C

IF MATERIAL OTHER
THAN CEDAR IS USED
FOR BASIC CONSTRUCTION
LINE CHEST WITH 3/8"
AROMATIC RED CEDAR

$1\frac{1}{2}$

SECTION A-A

PROJECT 5

coffee table

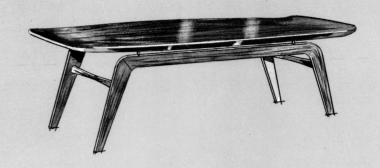

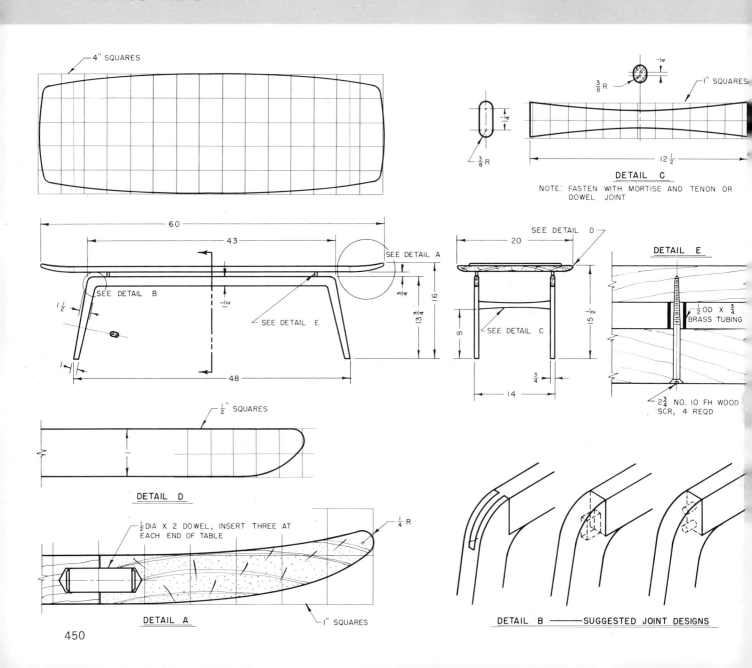

4" SQUARES

$\frac{3}{8}$R

$\frac{1}{4}$

1" SQUARES

$\frac{3}{8}$R

$\frac{1}{4}$

12 $\frac{1}{2}$

DETAIL C

NOTE: FASTEN WITH MORTISE AND TENON OR
DOWEL JOINT

60

43

SEE DETAIL A

SEE DETAIL B

$\frac{3}{4}$

16

13 $\frac{3}{4}$

1 $\frac{1}{2}$

$\frac{1}{2}$

SEE DETAIL E

1

48

SEE DETAIL D

20

DETAIL E

$\frac{1}{2}$ OD X $\frac{3}{4}$
BRASS TUBING

8

SEE DETAIL C

15 $\frac{1}{2}$

$\frac{3}{4}$

14

2 $\frac{3}{4}$ NO. 10 FH WOOD
SCR, 4 REQD

$\frac{1}{2}$" SQUARES

DETAIL D

$\frac{1}{2}$DIA X 2 DOWEL, INSERT THREE AT
EACH END OF TABLE

$\frac{1}{4}$ R

DETAIL A

1" SQUARES

DETAIL B ——— SUGGESTED JOINT DESIGNS

450

PROJECT 6

wall desk

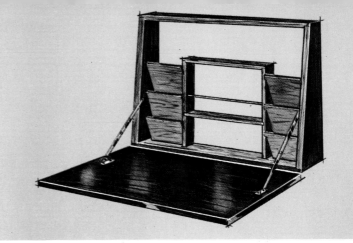

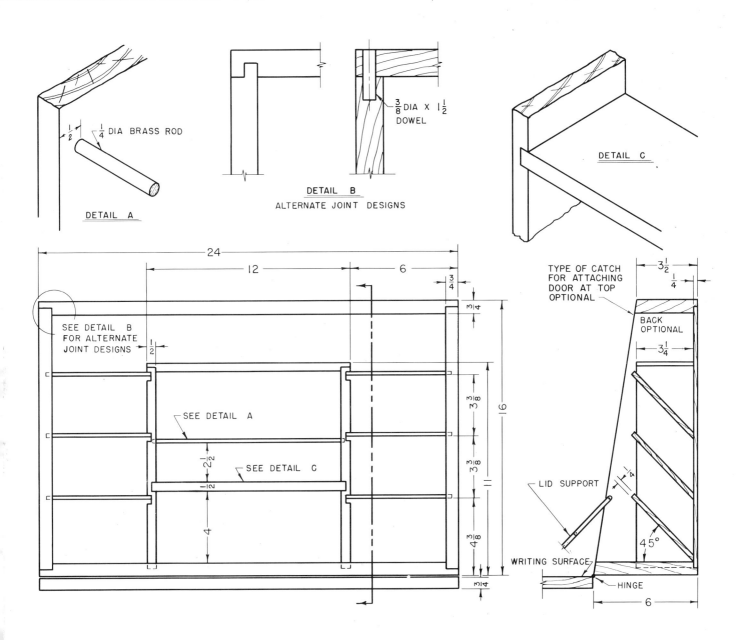

$\frac{1}{4}$ DIA BRASS ROD

$\frac{1}{2}$

DETAIL A

$\frac{3}{8}$ DIA X $1\frac{1}{2}$ DOWEL

DETAIL B
ALTERNATE JOINT DESIGNS

DETAIL C

24

12

6

$\frac{3}{4}$

$\frac{3}{4}$

SEE DETAIL B
FOR ALTERNATE
JOINT DESIGNS

$\frac{1}{2}$

$3\frac{3}{8}$

16

SEE DETAIL A

$3\frac{3}{8}$

11

$2\frac{1}{2}$

SEE DETAIL C

$\frac{1}{2}$

4

$4\frac{3}{8}$

$\frac{3}{4}$

TYPE OF CATCH
FOR ATTACHING
DOOR AT TOP
OPTIONAL

$3\frac{1}{2}$

$\frac{1}{4}$

BACK
OPTIONAL

$3\frac{1}{4}$

LID SUPPORT

$\frac{1}{4}$

45°

WRITING SURFACE

HINGE

6

PROJECT 7

tray table

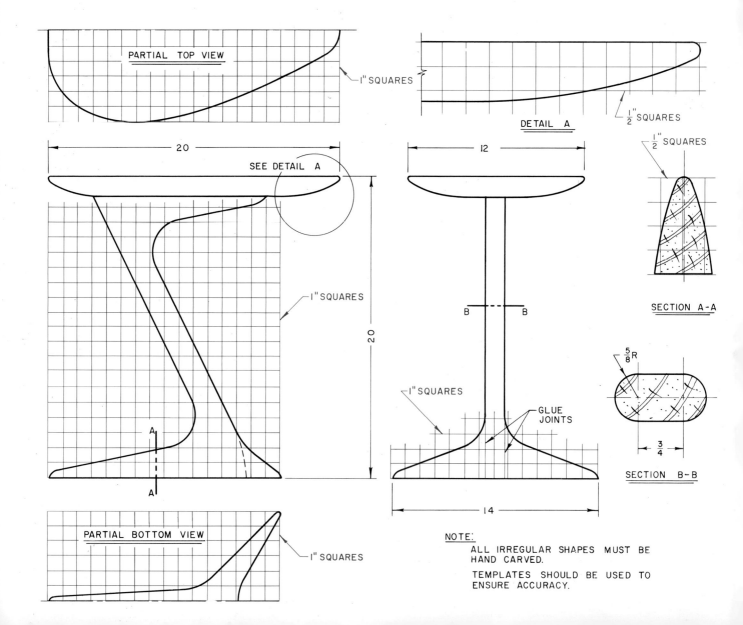

PARTIAL TOP VIEW

1" SQUARES

DETAIL A

½" SQUARES

20

SEE DETAIL A

1" SQUARES

20

½" SQUARES

SECTION A-A

12

B   B

⅝ R

1" SQUARES

¾

SECTION B-B

1" SQUARES

GLUE
JOINTS

14

A

A

PARTIAL BOTTOM VIEW

1" SQUARES

NOTE:

ALL IRREGULAR SHAPES MUST BE
HAND CARVED.

TEMPLATES SHOULD BE USED TO
ENSURE ACCURACY.

PROJECT 8

desk

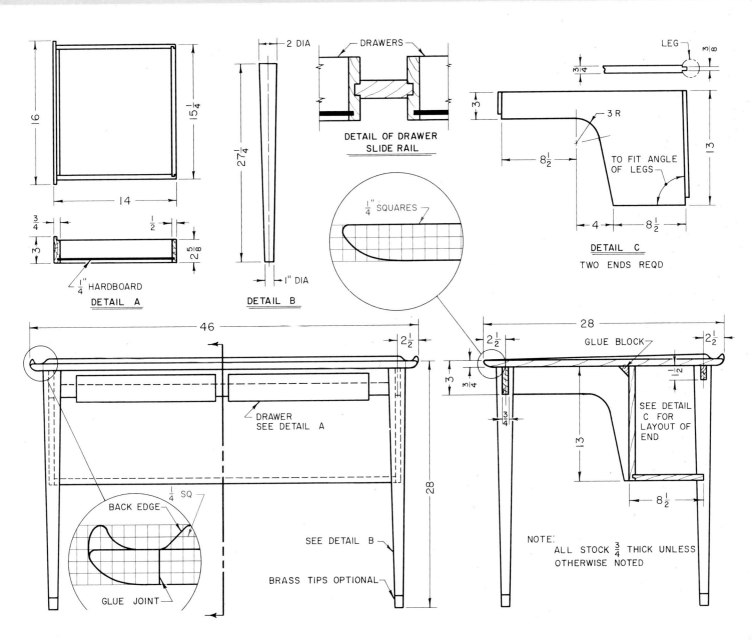

16

15 1/4

14

3/4   1/2

3

2 5/8

1/4" HARDBOARD

DETAIL A

2 DIA

27 1/4

1" DIA

DETAIL B

DRAWERS

DETAIL OF DRAWER
SLIDE RAIL

1/4" SQUARES

LEG

3/8

3/4

3

3 R

8 1/2

TO FIT ANGLE
OF LEGS

13

4   8 1/2

DETAIL C
TWO ENDS REQD

46   2 1/2

DRAWER
SEE DETAIL A

1/4 SQ

BACK EDGE

GLUE JOINT

SEE DETAIL B

BRASS TIPS OPTIONAL

28

2 1/2   2 1/2

GLUE BLOCK

3

3/4

3/4

1/2

SEE DETAIL
C FOR
LAYOUT OF
END

13

28

8 1/2

NOTE:
ALL STOCK 3/4 THICK UNLESS
OTHERWISE NOTED

PROJECT 9

lattice back chair

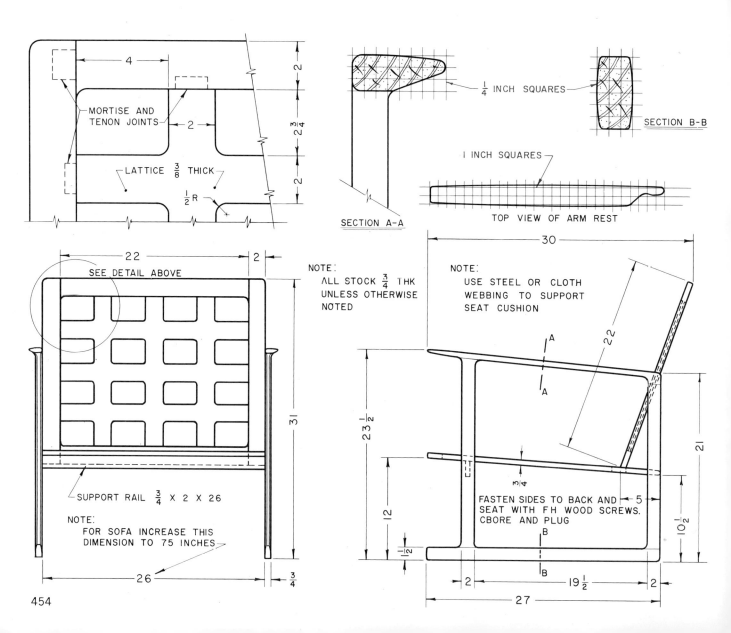

MORTISE AND TENON JOINTS

4

2

2

2 3/4

2

LATTICE 3/8 THICK

1/2 R

1/4 INCH SQUARES

SECTION B-B

1 INCH SQUARES

SECTION A-A

TOP VIEW OF ARM REST

22

2

SEE DETAIL ABOVE

31

SUPPORT RAIL 3/4 X 2 X 26

NOTE:
FOR SOFA INCREASE THIS
DIMENSION TO 75 INCHES

26

3/4

NOTE:
ALL STOCK 3/4 THK
UNLESS OTHERWISE
NOTED

NOTE:
USE STEEL OR CLOTH
WEBBING TO SUPPORT
SEAT CUSHION

30

22

A

A

23 1/2

12

1/2

3/4

21

10 1/2

5

FASTEN SIDES TO BACK AND
SEAT WITH F H WOOD SCREWS.
CBORE AND PLUG

B

B

2

19 1/2

2

27

454

PROJECT 10

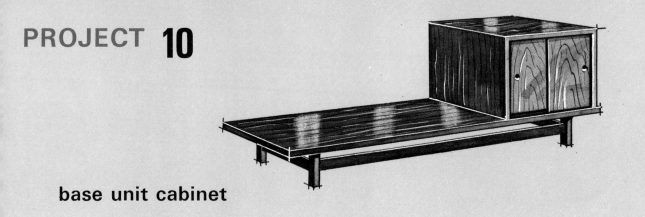

base unit cabinet

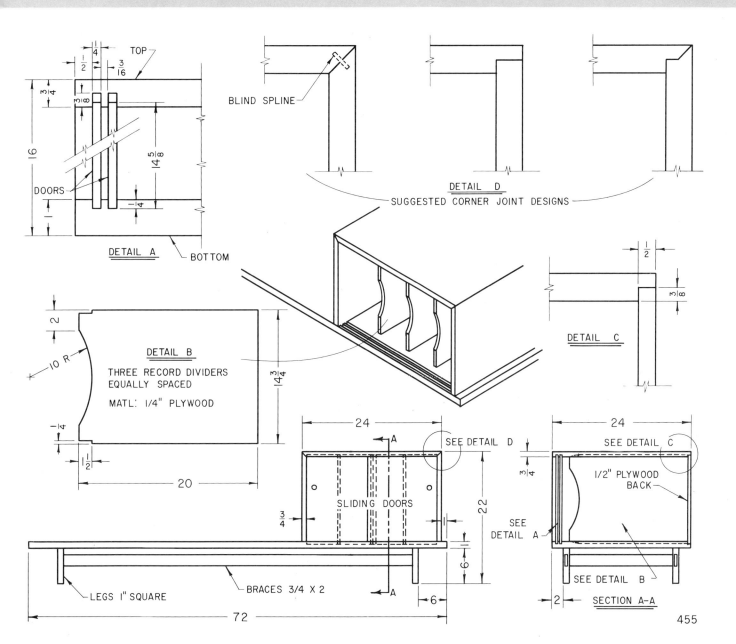

DETAIL A

TOP

DOORS

BOTTOM

16

14 5/8

3/4

1/2

1/4

3/16

3/8

1/4

BLIND SPLINE

DETAIL D
SUGGESTED CORNER JOINT DESIGNS

DETAIL B
THREE RECORD DIVIDERS
EQUALLY SPACED

MATL: 1/4" PLYWOOD

2

10 R

1/4

1 1/2

20

14 3/4

DETAIL C

1/2

3/8

24

SEE DETAIL D

3/4

SLIDING DOORS

22

6

LEGS 1" SQUARE

BRACES 3/4 X 2

72

A

A

24

SEE DETAIL C

3/4

1/2" PLYWOOD
BACK

SEE
DETAIL A

SEE DETAIL B

2

SECTION A-A

6

455

PROJECT 11

desk with file drawer

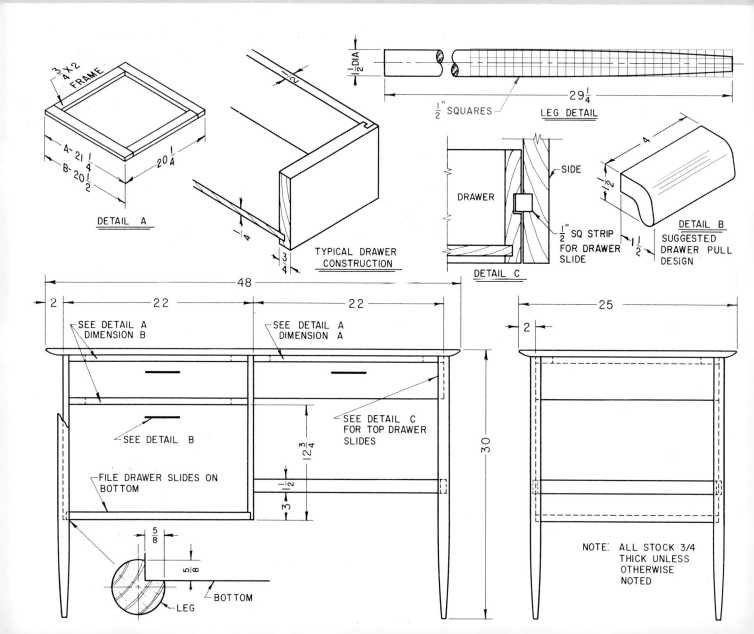

3/4 x 2 FRAME

DETAIL A

A- 21 1/4
B- 20 1/2
20 1/4

TYPICAL DRAWER CONSTRUCTION

1/2
1/4
3/4

1/2 DIA

1/2" SQUARES

29 1/4

LEG DETAIL

SIDE

DRAWER

1/2" SQ STRIP FOR DRAWER SLIDE

DETAIL C

DETAIL B
SUGGESTED DRAWER PULL DESIGN

4
1/2
1 1/2

48
2
22
22

SEE DETAIL A
DIMENSION B

SEE DETAIL A
DIMENSION A

SEE DETAIL C
FOR TOP DRAWER SLIDES

SEE DETAIL B

FILE DRAWER SLIDES ON BOTTOM

12 3/4
1 1/2
3

30

25
2

5/8
5/8

LEG

BOTTOM

NOTE: ALL STOCK 3/4 THICK UNLESS OTHERWISE NOTED

PROJECT 12

bookcase

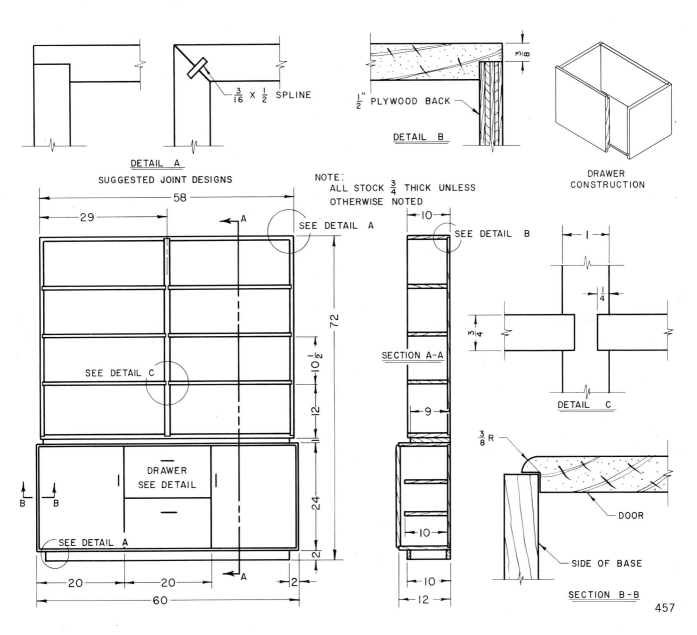

$\frac{3}{16} \times \frac{1}{2}$ SPLINE

DETAIL A

SUGGESTED JOINT DESIGNS

$\frac{1}{2}$" PLYWOOD BACK

$\frac{3}{8}$

DETAIL B

DRAWER CONSTRUCTION

NOTE:
ALL STOCK $\frac{3}{4}$ THICK UNLESS
OTHERWISE NOTED

58

29

SEE DETAIL A

A

72

SEE DETAIL C

$10\frac{1}{2}$

12

24

2

B

SEE DETAIL A

DRAWER
SEE DETAIL

20

20

2

60

10

SEE DETAIL B

SECTION A-A

9

10

10

12

1

$\frac{1}{4}$

$\frac{3}{4}$

DETAIL C

$\frac{3}{8}$ R

DOOR

SIDE OF BASE

SECTION B-B

457

PROJECT 13

table tennis table

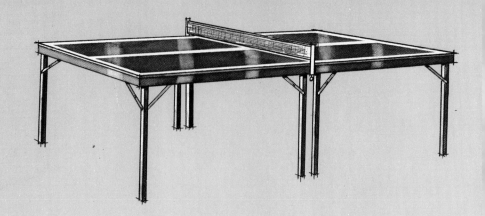

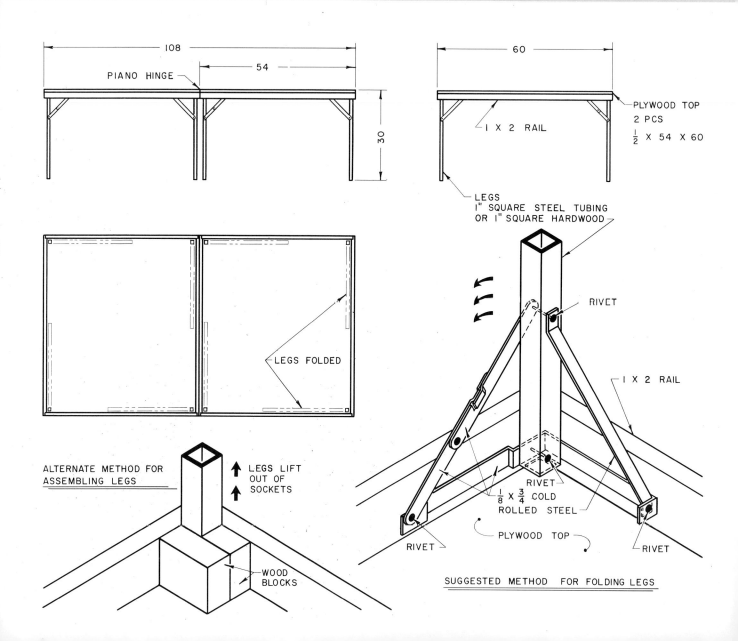

108

PIANO HINGE

54

30

60

1 X 2 RAIL

PLYWOOD TOP
2 PCS
$\frac{1}{2}$ X 54 X 60

LEGS
1" SQUARE STEEL TUBING
OR 1" SQUARE HARDWOOD

LEGS FOLDED

RIVET

1 X 2 RAIL

RIVET

$\frac{1}{8}$ X $\frac{3}{4}$ COLD
ROLLED STEEL

ALTERNATE METHOD FOR
ASSEMBLING LEGS

LEGS LIFT
OUT OF
SOCKETS

WOOD
BLOCKS

RIVET

PLYWOOD TOP

RIVET

SUGGESTED METHOD FOR FOLDING LEGS

PROJECT 14

carport—garden house

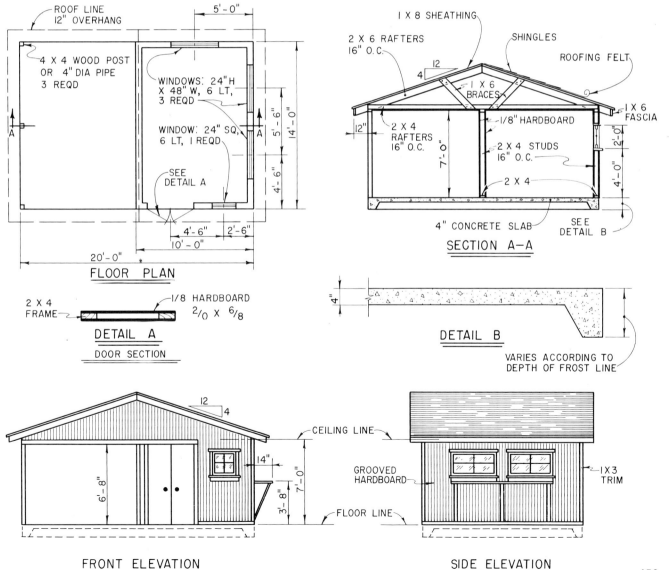

ROOF LINE
12" OVERHANG

5'-0"

4 X 4 WOOD POST
OR 4" DIA PIPE
3 REQD

WINDOWS: 24" H
X 48" W, 6 LT,
3 REQD

WINDOW: 24" SQ,
6 LT, 1 REQD

SEE
DETAIL A

5'-6"

14'-0"

4'-6"

A   A

4'-6"   2'-6"

10'-0"

20'-0"

FLOOR PLAN

2 X 4
FRAME

1/8 HARDBOARD
2/0 X 6/8

DETAIL A

DOOR SECTION

1 X 8 SHEATHING

SHINGLES

2 X 6 RAFTERS
16" O.C.

ROOFING FELT

12
4

1 X 6
BRACES

1 X 6
FASCIA

12

1/8" HARDBOARD

2 X 4
RAFTERS
16" O.C.

2 X 4 STUDS
16" O.C.

7'-0"

2'-0"

4'-0"

2 X 4

4" CONCRETE SLAB

SEE
DETAIL B

SECTION A—A

4"

DETAIL B

VARIES ACCORDING TO
DEPTH OF FROST LINE

12
4

14"

6'-8"

7'-0"

3'-8"

CEILING LINE

GROOVED
HARDBOARD

1 X 3
TRIM

FLOOR LINE

FRONT ELEVATION

SIDE ELEVATION

459

project suggestions **TURNINGS**

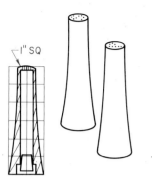

1" SQ

Salt & Pepper Shakers

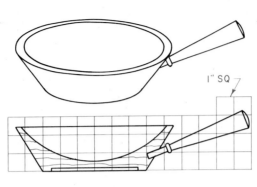

1" SQ

Chip Server

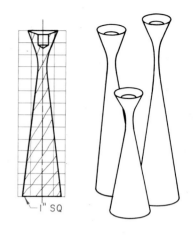

1" SQ

1" SQ

Candlesticks

Hamburger Press

Kitchen Utensil Caddy

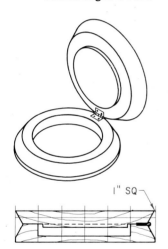

1" SQ

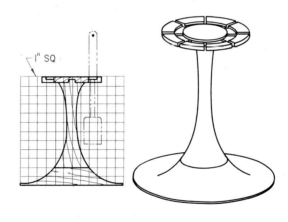

1" SQ

Hurricane Lamp

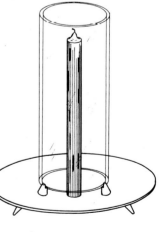

Bongo Drums

Salad Bowl

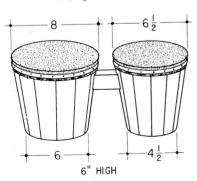

8   6 ½

6   4 ½

6" HIGH

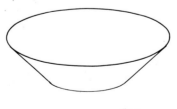

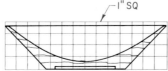

1" SQ

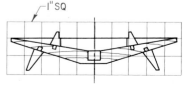

1" SQ

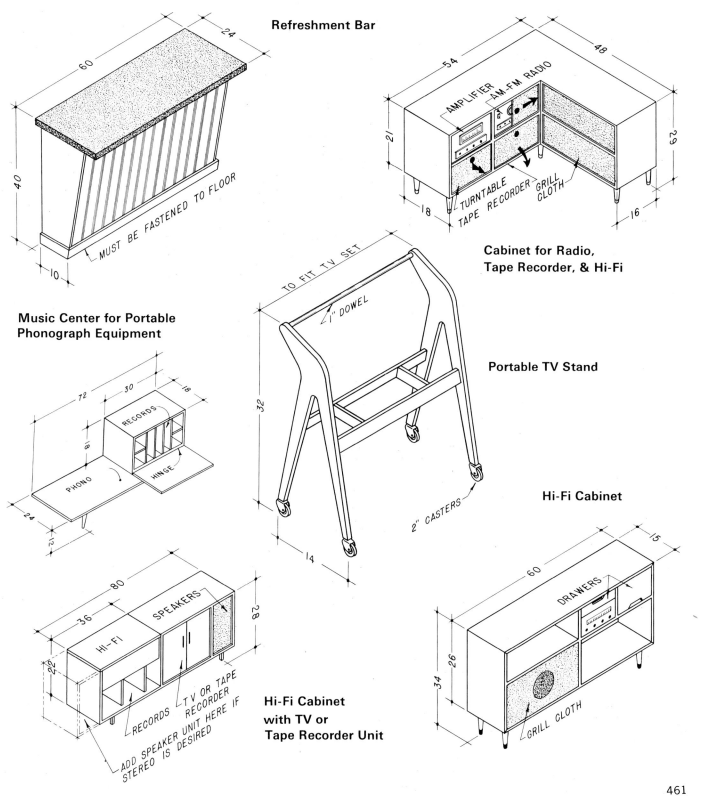

Refreshment Bar

MUST BE FASTENED TO FLOOR

Cabinet for Radio, Tape Recorder, & Hi-Fi

AMPLIFIER   AM-FM RADIO

TURNTABLE   TAPE RECORDER   GRILL CLOTH

Music Center for Portable Phonograph Equipment

RECORDS

PHONO   HINGE

TO FIT TV SET

1" DOWEL

2" CASTERS

Portable TV Stand

Hi-Fi Cabinet

DRAWERS

GRILL CLOTH

SPEAKERS

HI-FI

RECORDS   TV OR TAPE RECORDER

ADD SPEAKER UNIT HERE IF STEREO IS DESIRED

Hi-Fi Cabinet with TV or Tape Recorder Unit

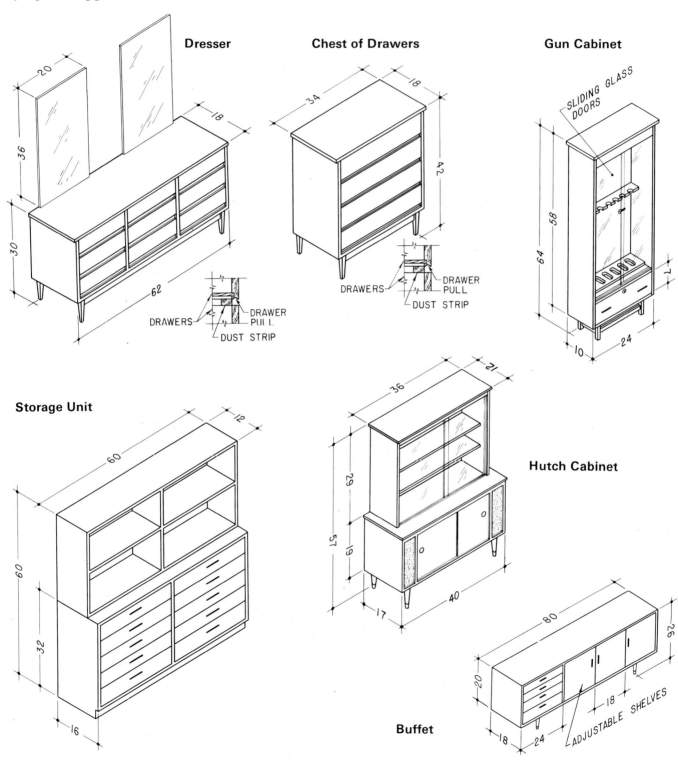

Dresser

Chest of Drawers

Gun Cabinet

20

18

36

18

42

SLIDING GLASS DOORS

58

64

30

62

DRAWERS

DRAWER PULL

DUST STRIP

DRAWERS

DRAWER PULL

DUST STRIP

7

10

24

Storage Unit

Hutch Cabinet

Buffet

12

21

60

36

60

29

57

19

32

17

40

16

80

26

20

18

24

18

ADJUSTABLE SHELVES

project suggestions **CABINETS AND CHESTS**

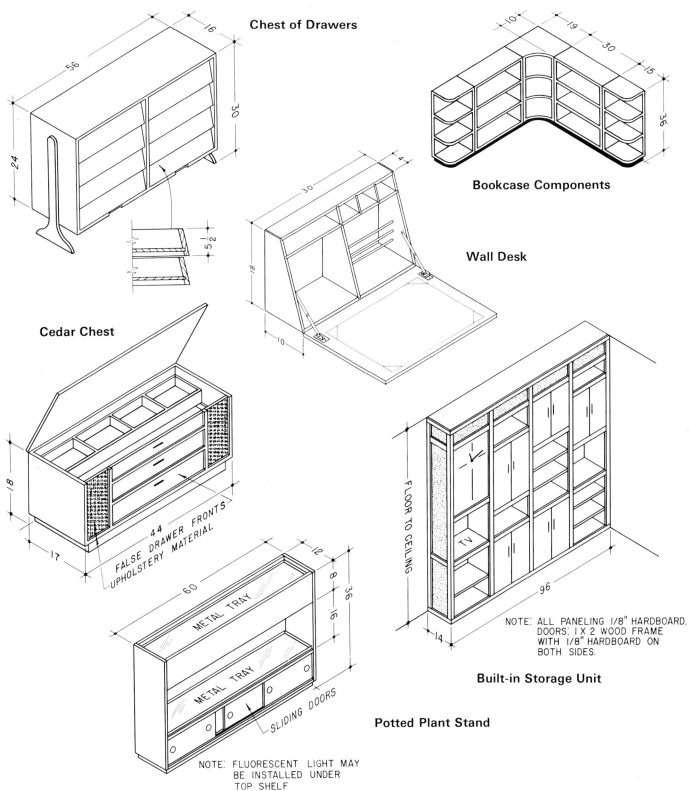

Chest of Drawers

56

16

30

24

5 $\frac{1}{2}$

Bookcase Components

10

19

30

15

36

Wall Desk

30

4

18

10

Cedar Chest

18

17

44

FALSE DRAWER FRONTS

UPHOLSTERY MATERIAL

Potted Plant Stand

METAL TRAY

METAL TRAY

60

12

8

16

36

SLIDING DOORS

NOTE: FLUORESCENT LIGHT MAY
BE INSTALLED UNDER
TOP SHELF

Built-in Storage Unit

FLOOR TO CEILING

96

14

TV

NOTE: ALL PANELING 1/8" HARDBOARD.
DOORS: 1 X 2 WOOD FRAME
WITH 1/8" HARDBOARD ON
BOTH SIDES.

463

project suggestions CHAIRS

Settee

Freeform Lounge Chair

Danish Modern Settee

Dining Room Chair

Side Chair

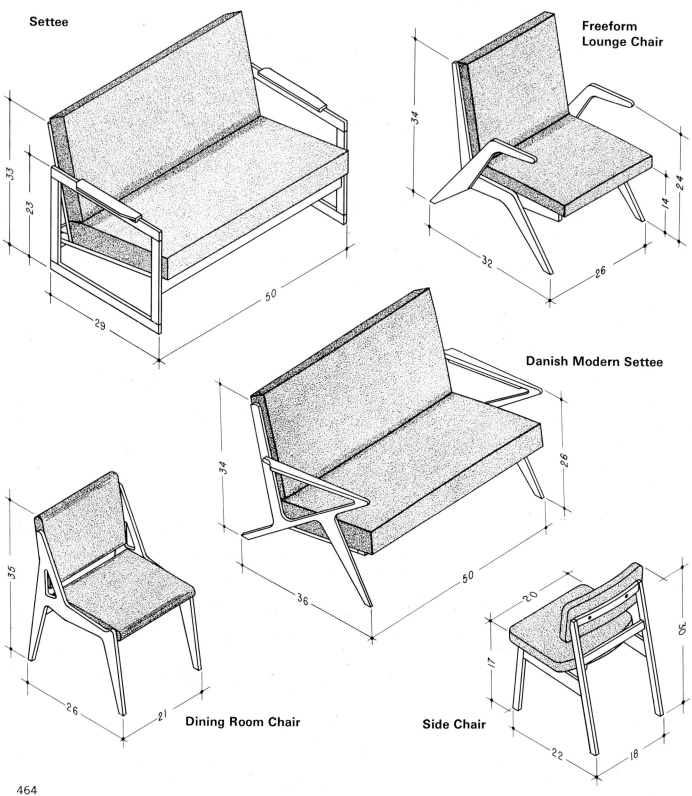

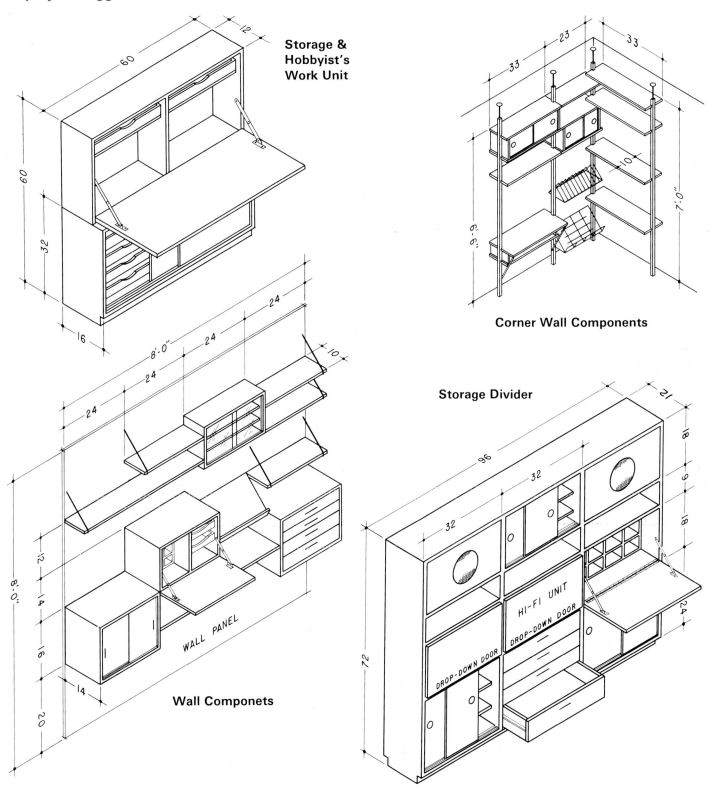

Storage &
Hobbyist's
Work Unit

60

12

60

32

16

Corner Wall Components

33

33

23

33

7'-0"

9'-6"

8'-0"

24

24

24

24

10

8'-0"

12

14

16

14

20

WALL PANEL

Wall Componets

Storage Divider

96

32

32

21

18

9

18

HI-FI UNIT

DROP-DOWN DOOR

DROP-DOWN DOOR

72

24

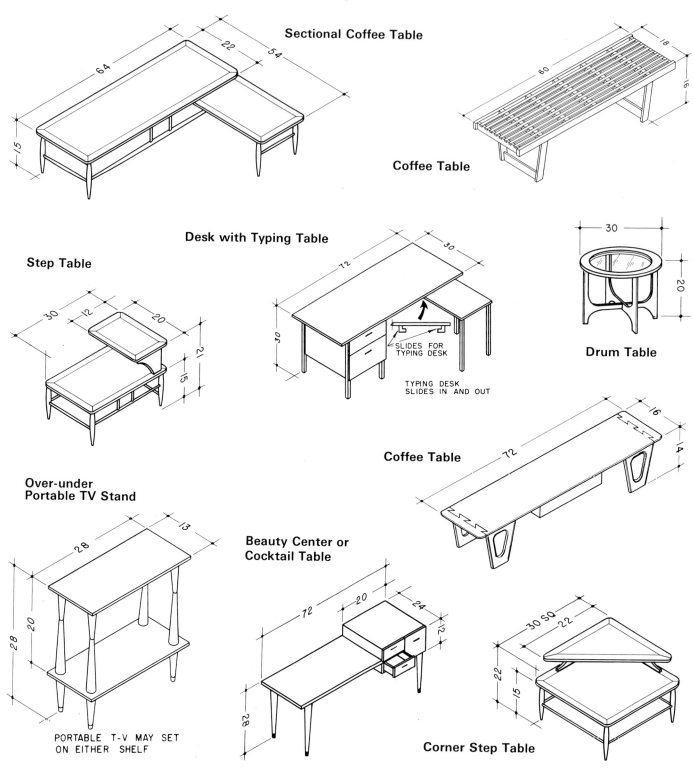

Sectional Coffee Table

Coffee Table

Desk with Typing Table

SLIDES FOR
TYPING DESK

TYPING DESK
SLIDES IN AND OUT

Step Table

Drum Table

Coffee Table

Over-under
Portable TV Stand

Beauty Center or
Cocktail Table

PORTABLE T-V MAY SET
ON EITHER SHELF

Corner Step Table

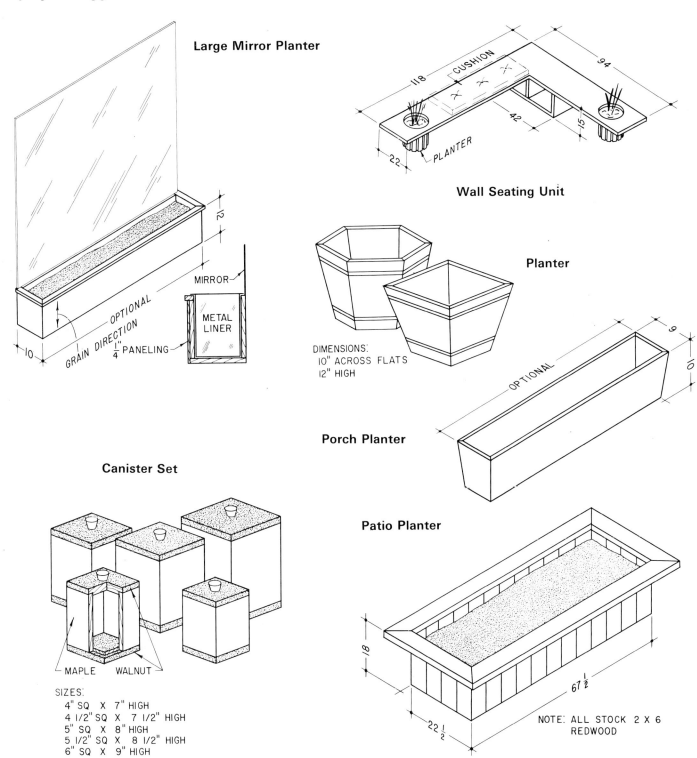

Large Mirror Planter

12

MIRROR

OPTIONAL
GRAIN DIRECTION

METAL
LINER

10   1/4" PANELING

Wall Seating Unit

118   CUSHION   94

42   15

22   PLANTER

Planter

DIMENSIONS:
10" ACROSS FLATS
12" HIGH

Porch Planter

OPTIONAL   9

10

Canister Set

MAPLE   WALNUT

SIZES:
4" SQ   X   7" HIGH
4 1/2" SQ   X   7 1/2" HIGH
5" SQ   X   8" HIGH
5 1/2" SQ   X   8 1/2" HIGH
6" SQ   X   9" HIGH

Patio Planter

18

67 1/2

22 1/2   NOTE: ALL STOCK 2 X 6
REDWOOD

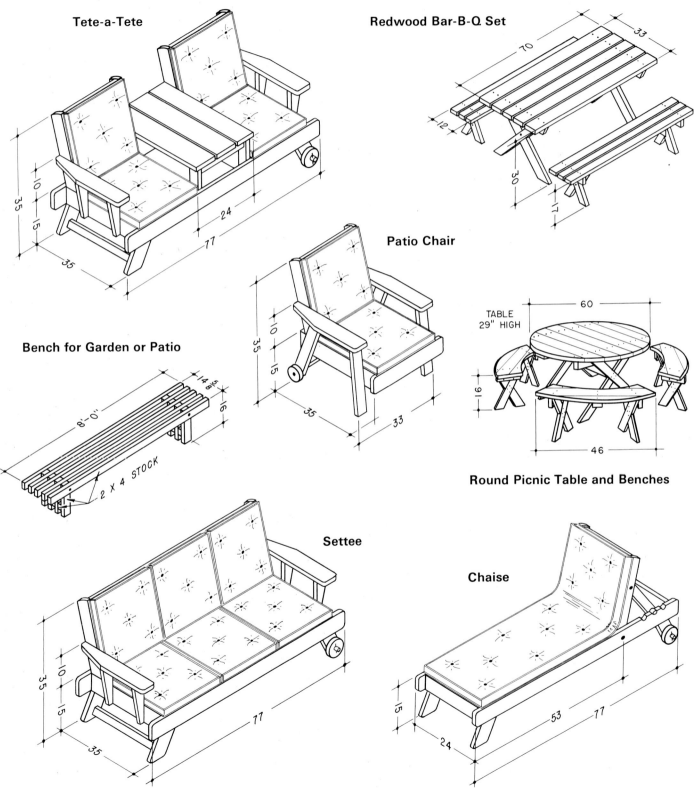

Tete-a-Tete

Redwood Bar-B-Q Set

Patio Chair

Bench for Garden or Patio

2 X 4 STOCK

Round Picnic Table and Benches

TABLE 29" HIGH

Settee

Chaise

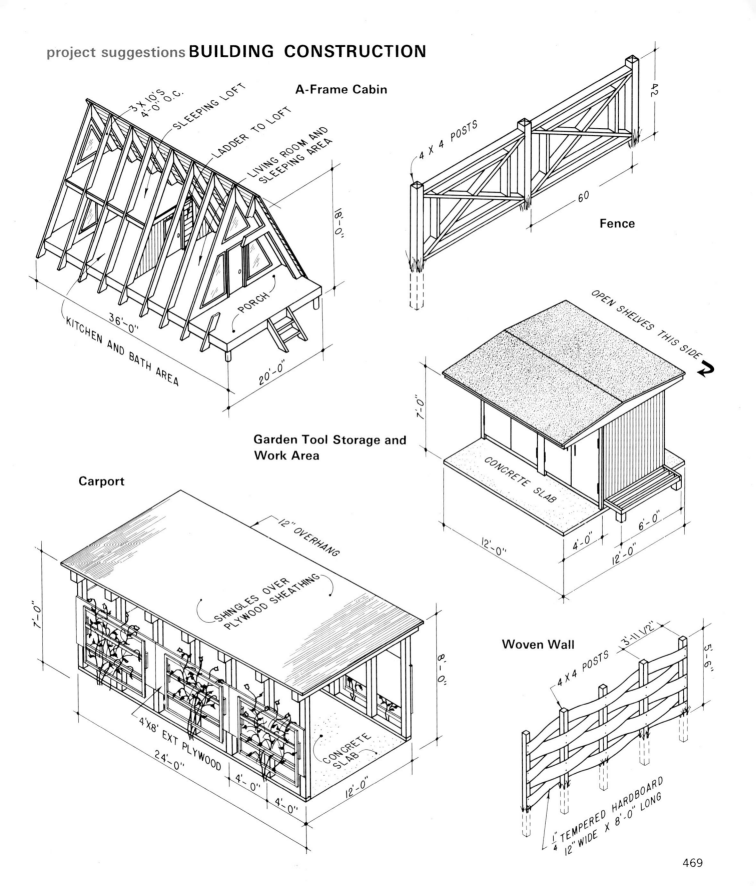

A-Frame Cabin

3 X 10'S
4'-0" O.C.
SLEEPING LOFT
LADDER TO LOFT
LIVING ROOM AND SLEEPING AREA
18'-0"
PORCH
36'-0"
KITCHEN AND BATH AREA
20'-0"

Fence

42
4 X 4 POSTS
60

Garden Tool Storage and Work Area

OPEN SHELVES THIS SIDE
7'-0"
CONCRETE SLAB
12'-0"
4'-0"
6'-0"
12'-0"

Carport

12" OVERHANG
SHINGLES OVER PLYWOOD SHEATHING
7'-0"
8'-0"
4'X8' EXT PLYWOOD
CONCRETE SLAB
24'-0"
4'-0"
4'-0"
12'-0"

Woven Wall

3'-11 1/2"
5'-6"
4 X 4 POSTS
1/4" TEMPERED HARDBOARD
12" WIDE X 8'-0" LONG

469

Bookshelf Room Divider

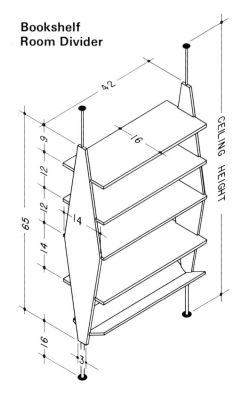

Shelf Divider

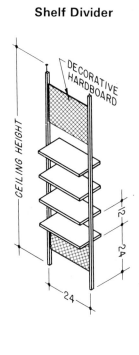

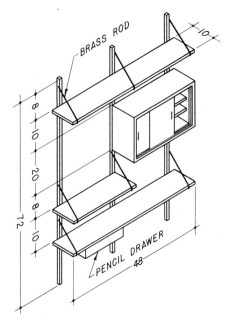

Bookshelf and Storage Divider

Entrance Planter-Divider

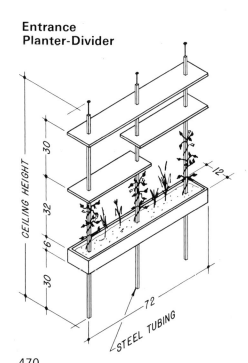

Desk Divider

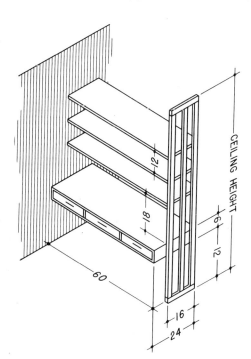

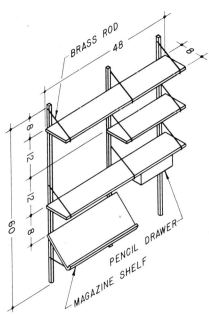

Bookshelf-Magazine Rack Divider

Index